The BIGGEST TRIVIA QUIZ BOOK in the World

The BIGGEST TRIVIA QUIZ BOOK in the World

ARCTURUS

Published by
Arcturus Publishing Limited
1-7 Shand Street
London SE1 2ES

This edition published 2001

Printed and bound by Omnia Books Limited

Cover design by Chris Smith

Compiled and designed by

ISBN1-84193-070-9

Entertainment

Your rating: ● **0-5 Buy a TV** ● **6-10 Keep at it** ● **11-15 Join a quiz team** ● **16-20 Enter a quiz show**

1. Which actress played Hannah in the sitcom *Faith in the Future*?
2. Which Geordie singer and actor released an album entitled *Big River* in 1995?
3. Which 1995 comedy film featured Bo Derek and Dan Aykroyd in cameo roles?
4. Paul and Pauline Calf were creations of which British comic actor?
5. Which U.K. vocal trio released an album entitled *Power of a Woman* in 1995?
6. Who starred as the captain of the Soviet nuclear submarine in the 1990 film *The Hunt for Red October*?
7. What was the foolish name of Squeeze's 1995 album?
8. Who played Paul Sutton in the 1995 film *A Walk in the Clouds*?
9. How many U.K. number one singles did the Rolling Stones have in the Seventies?
10. Which fellow thespian is the mother of actress Beatie Edney?
11. Which *Emmerdale* character was played by Sandra Gough?
12. Who starred as *Doctor Dolittle* in the 1967 film?
13. Who had a U.K. top ten hit in 1977 with *2-4-6-8 Motorway*?
14. Who played Stephen Biko in the 1987 film *Cry Freedom*?
15. Who sang the title track for the 1995 Bond film *GoldenEye*?
16. Which 1995 film starred Demi Moore and Gary Oldman?
17. Which veteran comedienne played Aunt Florence in the Nineties TV adaptation of *Just William*?
18. Which animated film featuring Wallace and Gromit won Nick Park his third Oscar?
19. Which former cult soccer show featured 'Phoenix from the Flames'?
20. Which 1995 film starred Leonardo DiCaprio as a sportsman turned performance poet?

ANSWERS: *1 Julia Sawalha, 2 Jimmy Nail, 3 Tommy Boy, 4 Steve Coogan, 5 Eternal, 6 Sean Connery, 7 Ridiculous, 8 Keanu Reeves, 9 None, 10 Sylvia Syms, 11 Nellie Dingle, 12 Rex Harrison, 13 The Tom Robinson Band, 14 Denzel Washington, 15 Tina Turner, 16 The Scarlet Letter, 17 Mollie Sugden, 18 A Close Shave, 19 Fantasy Football League, 20 The Basketball Diaries.*

General Knowledge

Your rating: ● 0-5 Join a library ● 6-10 Keep at it ● 11-15 Join a quiz team ● 16-20 Join Mensa

1. Which British novelist wrote *My Cousin Rachel* and *Rebecca*?
2. What name is given to the compulsory enlistment of recruits for military service?
3. Which British landscape painter painted *The White Horse* and *The Haywain*?
4. A statue of which English footballer has been placed in a Buddhist temple in Bangkok?
5. Which two Middle Eastern countries fought each other in a war that began in 1980?
6. In which European city can the Champs Élysées be found?
7. Which Brazilian footballer was born Edson Arantes do Nascimento?
8. In which country did Queen Beatrix succeed her mother Queen Juliana in 1980?
9. Which all-girl group visited the 2000 Cannes Film Festival to promote their film *Honest*?
10. In which American city was there a famous 'Tea Party' in 1773?
11. Which English explorer, who made three attempts to discover the Northwest Passage, gave his name to a bay on Baffin Island?
12. In Greek mythology, who was the legendary lover of Hero who swam across the Hellespont each night?
13. Which rugby team clinched the 2000 Allied Dunbar Premiership by beating Bristol?
14. Who wrote *The Last Days of Pompeii*?
15. Which diamond-mining city in South Africa is the capital of Northern Cape Province?
16. What name is given to trees of the genus *Larix*?
17. What is the largest island of Japan?
18. Which British tour operator was taken over by the German company Preussag?
19. Who directed the films *Doctor Mabuse the Gambler* and *Metropolis*?
20. Which British poet wrote *The Song of the Shirt*?

ANSWERS: *1 Daphne Du Maurier, 2 Conscription, 3 John Constable, 4 David Beckham, 5 Iran and Iraq, 6 Paris, 7 Pelé, 8 The Netherlands, 9 All Saints, 10 Boston, 11 Sir Martin Frobisher, 12 Leander, 13 Leicester, 14 Edward Bulwer-Lytton, 15 Kimberley, 16 Larch, 17 Honshu, 18 Thomson, 19 Fritz Lang, 20 Thomas Hood.*

General Knowledge

Your rating: ● 0-5 Join a library ● 6-10 Keep at it ● 11-15 Join a quiz team ● 16-20 Join Mensa

1. Which slow-moving South American mammal hangs upside down from branches feeding on leaves and fruit?
2. What is the traditional Chinese practice of inserting needles into selected points in the body called?
3. Which part of Chaucer's *Canterbury Tales* contains descriptions of the pilgrims?
4. What were the first names of the poet T.S. Eliot?
5. Which evergreen tree's berries are used to flavour gin?
6. In which country is the city of Tijuana?
7. Which English-born actor starred in *The Private Life of Henry VIII* and *The Hunchback of Notre Dame*?
8. Of which county is Trowbridge the administrative centre?
9. Which European city became a battleground before the 2000 UEFA Cup final between Arsenal and Galatasaray?
10. To what genus of fruit trees do orange, lemon and lime belong?
11. Which U.S. national holiday is celebrated on the fourth Thursday in November?
12. What sort of creature is a sidewinder?
13. Which ingredient of chewing gum is obtained from the latex of sapodilla trees?
14. In Irish politics, which party is the conservative rival of Fianna Fáil?
15. Which football team smashed their transfer record by signing Sergei Rebrov from Dynamo Kiev?
16. In concert pitch, to what note are orchestral instruments tuned?
17. Which American author wrote *The Red Badge of Courage*?
18. What sort of creature is a fritillary?
19. Who was the first person of Jewish ancestry to become prime minister of Britain?
20. Which Germanic people invaded England, especially Kent, along with the Angles and Saxons in the 5th century AD?

ANSWERS: *1 Sloth, 2 Acupuncture, 3 The Prologue, 4 Thomas Stearns, 5 Juniper, 6 Mexico, 7 Charles Laughton, 8 Wiltshire, 9 Copenhagen, 10 Citrus, 11 Thanksgiving Day, 12 A snake, 13 Chicle, 14 Fine Gael, 15 Tottenham Hotspur, 16 A, 17 Stephen Crane, 18 A butterfly, 19 Benjamin Disraeli, 20 Jutes.*

General Knowledge

Your rating:
- 0-5 Join a library
- 6-10 Keep at it
- 11-15 Join a quiz team
- 16-20 Join Mensa

1. Which hypothetical substance did alchemists seek for its ability to turn base metals into gold?
2. What name is given to the hunters and gatherers who inhabited Australia before European settlement?
3. Which synthetic fibre was introduced commercially in 1938?
4. The female stars of which 60s TV series received a special award at the 2000 BAFTAs?
5. Which English preacher wrote *The Pilgrim's Progress*?
6. What does the abbreviation JP stand for?
7. Apart from the cue ball, how many balls are used in a normal game of pool?
8. What is the name of the young hero of Robert Louis Stevenson's *Treasure Island*?
9. Which Italian city is known as Firenze in Italian?
10. What does CD-ROM stand for?
11. Which British novelist wrote *Jacob's Room* and *Mrs Dalloway*?
12. By what name is Beethoven's Third Symphony known?
13. Which team beat Northampton to win the 2000 Tetley Bitter Cup?
14. In which English city did the Peterloo massacre take place?
15. Which English-born monk and missionary became known as the Apostle of Germany?
16. In economics, what does GDP stand for?
17. What name is given to drugs that increase the output of urine by the kidneys?
18. Which British conductor founded the London Promenade concerts at the Queen's Hall?
19. To which African country were British troops sent in May 2000?
20. Which British writer created the flying ace *Biggles*?

ANSWERS: *1 Philosopher's stone, 2 Aborigines, 3 Nylon, 4 The Avengers, 5 John Bunyan, 6 Justice of the Peace, 7 Fifteen, 8 Jim Hawkins, 9 Florence, 10 Compact Disc - Read Only Memory, 11 Virginia Woolf, 12 Eroica, 13 Wasps, 14 Manchester, 15 St Boniface, 16 Gross Domestic Product, 17 Diuretics, 18 Sir Henry Wood, 19 Sierra Leone, 20 W E Johns.*

Entertainment

Your rating: ● 0-5 Buy a TV ● 6-10 Keep at it ● 11-15 Join a quiz team ● 16-20 Enter a quiz show

1. Which *Brookside* character was played by Philip Dowd?
2. *The Ghost of Tom Joad* was a 1995 album release by which rock star?
3. In which country is the soap opera *Shortland Street* set?
4. How many U.K. number one singles did the Rolling Stones have in the sixties?
5. Who played Billie Holiday in the 1972 film *Lady Sings the Blues*?
6. To which BBC programme did Princess Diana famously give an exclusive interview in November 1995?
7. Which soul diva had a U.K. top ten hit in 1968 with *I Say a Little Prayer*?
8. Who directed the 1995 Bond film *GoldenEye*?
9. In which year was the first televised *Children in Need* extravaganza?
10. *Fresh Horses* was a 1995 album release by which U.S. country music star?
11. Who directed the 1978 classic punk movie *Jubilee*?
12. Who played Neil in the eighties comedy series *The Young Ones*?
13. Which legendary singer/songwriter was killed on December 8th, 1980?
14. Who directed the 1962 film *Lolita*?
15. Which Irish singer reinterpreted his own material backed by an orchestra on the album *Beautiful Dreams*?
16. Which sitcom was set in Bayview Retirement Home?
17. Peter Hook (Hooky) was the bassist of which popular Manchester band?
18. Who played Dr Paul Dangerfield in the drama series *Dangerfield*?
19. Which 1995 Jean Becker film starred Gerard Depardieu and Vanessa Paradis?
20. Which barefoot sixties singer was born Sandra Goodrich?

ANSWERS: *1 Christian, 2 Bruce Springsteen, 3 New Zealand, 4 Eight, 5 Diana Ross, 6 Panorama, 7 Aretha Franklin, 8 Martin Campbell, 9 1980, 10 Garth Brooks, 11 Derek Jarman, 12 Nigel Planer, 13 John Lennon, 14 Stanley Kubrick, 15 Chris De Burgh, 16 Waiting for God, 17 New Order, 18 Nigel Le Vaillant, 19 Elisa, 20 Sandie Shaw.*

General Knowledge

Your rating:
- **0-5 Join a library**
- **6-10 Keep at it**
- **11-15 Join a quiz team**
- **16-20 Join Mensa**

1. Which fictional detective is featured in *A Study in Scarlet* and *The Hound of the Baskervilles*?
2. What name is given to a tied score after six points in a tennis game?
3. What is a mandolin?
4. What is the first name of Tony and Cherie Blair's fourth child?
5. Which metallic chemical element is also known as wolfram?
6. Of which Middle Eastern country is Amman the capital?
7. Which work by Shakespeare do superstitious actors refer to as 'the Scottish play'?
8. In Greek mythology, which handsome youth was loved by Aphrodite?
9. Which prolific romantic novelist died in the year 2000 at the age of 98?
10. What is the ancient name of the peninsula occupied by Spain and Portugal?
11. Which American author wrote *Breakfast at Tiffany's* and *In Cold Blood*?
12. Which branch of medicine deals with the diagnosis and treatment of disorders of the heart?
13. Who scored Chelsea's winning goal in the 2000 FA Cup Final?
14. Which novel by Charles Dickens features the Circumlocution Office?
15. What is the capital of Suriname?
16. Which European lake is also known as Lac Léman?
17. Which channel separates New Zealand's North Island and South Island?
18. What is the state capital of Connecticut?
19. With which sport is Susan Devoy associated?
20. Which ancient Roman festival honoured the God of agriculture?

ANSWERS: *1 Sherlock Holmes, 2 Deuce, 3 A stringed musical instrument, 4 Leo, 5 Tungsten, 6 Jordan, 7 Macbeth, 8 Adonis, 9 Dame Barbara Cartland, 10 Iberia, 11 Truman Capote, 12 Cardiology, 13 Roberto Di Matteo, 14 Little Dorrit, 15 Paramaribo, 16 Lake Geneva, 17 Cook Strait, 18 Hartford, 19 Squash, 20 Saturnalia.*

General Knowledge

Your rating: ● 0-5 Join a library ● 6-10 Keep at it ● 11-15 Join a quiz team ● 16-20 Join Mensa

1. Which Australian entertainer sang *Tie Me Kangaroo Down, Sport* and *Jake the Peg*?
2. In the Old Testament, who was the elder brother of Moses?
3. Which Icelandic pop star picked up a Best Actress award at Cannes in the year 2000?
4. What name is given to the skin of an animal prepared as a surface for writing?
5. Which tribe of Britons was led by Boadicea or Boudicca?
6. Who was the first British jockey to be knighted?
7. Which Scottish music hall star was associated with the songs *I Love a Lassie* and *Roamin' in the Gloamin'*?
8. Who was the first person to set foot on the moon?
9. How many Wimbledon singles titles did Martina Navratilova win?
10. Which animals are the subject of Richard Adams's novel Watership Down?
11. Of which African country is Mogadishu the capital?
12. Which Canadian poet, novelist and singer-songwriter wrote *Flowers for Hitler* and *Beautiful Losers*?
13. What is the Latin motto on the Great Seal of the United States?
14. Which Italian painter and architect had the surname di Bondone?
15. Who became the first woman to serve as U.S. attorney general in 1993?
16. What is the smallest unit of fluid measure in the apothecaries' system of measurement?
17. Which uniformed youth organisation was founded by William Alexander Smith in 1883?
18. With which theatrical genre are Eugene Ionesco and Samuel Beckett associated?
19. What sort of creature is a schipperke?
20. Who was the first King of the Belgians?

ANSWERS: *1 Rolf Harris, 2 Aaron, 3 Björk, 4 Parchment, 5 The Iceni, 6 Sir Gordon Richards, 7 Sir Harry Lauder, 8 Neil Armstrong, 9 Nine, 10 Rabbits, 11 Somalia, 12 Leonard Cohen, 13 E Pluribus Unum, 14 Giotto, 15 Janet Reno, 16 Minim, 17 Boys' Brigade, 18 Theatre of the Absurd, 19 A dog, 20 Leopold I.*

General Knowledge

Your rating: ● 0-5 Join a library ● 6-10 Keep at it ● 11-15 Join a quiz team ● 16-20 Join Mensa

1. Which actor starred in *Serpico*, *Scarface* and *Scent of a Woman*?
2. What sort of creature is a Lhasa apso?
3. What is the smallest British pony breed?
4. What is the name for a French castle or large country house?
5. Which South American Indian people ruled an empire centred on southern Peru?
6. What name is given to a young hare?
7. Which English author wrote *Scoop* and *The Loved One*?
8. What name is given to towns near mines that became abandoned when the mines were exhausted?
9. Coir is a coarse fibre made from the husks of which fruit?
10. Which alcoholic drink are hops used to flavour?
11. Which German composer wrote *Der Freischutz* and *Invitation to the Dance*?
12. Who succeeded Joseph Smith as leader of the Mormon church in 1844?
13. Which Romanian footballer was sent off in the 2000 UEFA Cup final?
14. Who wrote *Fahrenheit 451* and *I Sing the Body Electric*?
15. Which allergic condition is also called nettle rash and hives?
16. Who marries Katherine in Shakespeare's *The Taming of the Shrew*?
17. With what sort of films was Tom Mix associated?
18. In Greek mythology, who was the wife of Agamemnon and mother of Orestes?
19. What is the pen name of David Cornwell?
20. Which austere sect which originated in England was established by Ann Lee?

ANSWERS: *1 Al Pacino, 2 A dog, 3 Shetland pony, 4 Chateau, 5 Incas, 6 Leveret, 7 Evelyn Waugh, 8 Ghost towns, 9 Coconut, 10 Beer, 11 Carl Maria von Weber, 12 Brigham Young, 13 Gheorghe Hagi, 14 Ray Bradbury, 15 Urticaria, 16 Petruchio, 17 Westerns, 18 Clytemnestra, 19 John Le Carré, 20 Shakers.*

Sports

Your rating:	● 0-5	Wooden spoon	● 6-10	Bronze medal
	● 11-15	Silver medal	● 16-20	Gold medal

1. In which two European countries were the Euro 2000 football championships held?
2. How many players make up an ice hockey team?
3. Which country knocked Romania out of Euro 2000?
4. Which horse won the Grand National in 1983?
5. How many Formula One world championships did Jackie Stewart win as a driver?
6. Which American football team won Super Bowl XXXIV, beating the Tennessee Titans?
7. Which country does footballer Paulo Wanchope represent?
8. Which snooker player was world champion in 1985?
9. In which sport did Audley Harrison win gold at the Sydney Olympics?
10. What nationality is tennis player Marat Safin?
11. Which England bowler took 4 wickets in one over in the fourth Test against the West Indies at Headingley in August 2000?
12. How many points are awarded for a try in rugby union?
13. Which team knocked Newcastle United out of the Worthington Cup in two successive seasons?
14. How many yards long is a cricket pitch?
15. With which sport are the Harlem Globetrotters famously associated?
16. Who won his seventh men's singles title at Wimbledon in 2000?
17. Who was the first athlete to run 100 sub-four-minute miles?
18. Which boxer was known as the Dark Destroyer?
19. Which player scored the first goal of the 1999 FA Cup Final?
20. For which country does rugby league star Gorden Tallis play?

ANSWERS: *1 Belgium & Holland, 2 Six, 3 Italy, 4 Corbiere, 5 Three, 6 St Louis Rams, 7 Costa Rica, 8 Dennis Taylor, 9 Boxing, 10 Russian, 11 Andrew Caddick, 12 Five, 13 Birmingham City, 14 22, 15 Basketball, 16 Pete Sampras, 17 John Walker, 18 Nigel Benn, 19 Teddy Sheringham, 20 Australia.*

General Knowledge

Your rating: ● 0-5 Join a library ● 6-10 Keep at it ● 11-15 Join a quiz team ● 16-20 Join Mensa

1. Which U.S. city is served by O'Hare International airport?
2. What are 25th wedding anniversary gifts traditionally made of?
3. Which Irish actor played George Adamson in the film *To Walk With Lions*?
4. What name is given to a device that enables computers to send and receive information via telephone?
5. Which English poet and dramatist wrote *The Beggar's Opera*?
6. What is the largest city in Switzerland?
7. Which famous World War II fighter plane was designed by Reginald Mitchell?
8. What name is given to a word that has the same meaning as another word?
9. Which song by Travis earned Fran Healy an Ivor Novello award as Songwriter of the Year?
10. Who wrote *The Railway Children*?
11. Which actor won a posthumous Oscar for the film *Network*?
12. Which German footballer is the only man to have both captained and managed World Cup-winning teams?
13. Who founded the Académie Française to preserve the purity of the French language?
14. Which star of *Blackadder* was elected to Labour's national executive in 2000?
15. What is the capital of Malawi?
16. Which U.S. author created *Brer Rabbit* and *Brer Fox*?
17. Which U.S. dramatist wrote the plays *American Buffalo* and *Glengarry Glen Ross*?
18. What are the names of the two bones in the forearm?
19. Who was the Irish Taoiseach from December 1982 to March 1987?
20. Which Bolshevik leader was assassinated in Mexico in 1940?

ANSWERS: *1 Chicago, 2 Silver, 3 Richard Harris, 4 Modem, 5 John Gay, 6 Zurich, 7 Spitfire, 8 Synonym, 9 Why Does It Always Rain On Me?, 10 Edith Nesbit, 11 Peter Finch, 12 Franz Beckenbauer, 13 Cardinal Richelieu, 14 Tony Robinson, 15 Lilongwe, 16 Joel Chandler Harris, 17 David Mamet, 18 Radius and ulna, 19 Garret Fitzgerald, 20 Leon Trotsky.*

General Knowledge

Your rating: ● 0-5 Join a library ● 6-10 Keep at it ● 11-15 Join a quiz team ● 16-20 Join Mensa

1. Which U.S. actor starred in *A Streetcar Named Desire*, *On the Waterfront* and *The Godfather*?
2. What name is given to the body of soldiers that protects the Pope?
3. Which Spanish football team won the 2000 Champions League final?
4. Who was the leader of the Khmer Rouge who took power in Cambodia in 1975?
5. Which German tennis player won his first Wimbledon title in 1985?
6. What is the capital of Brazil?
7. Which British actor starred in *Saturday Night and Sunday Morning* ?
8. With which physicist is the formula E=MC squared associated?
9. To which playwright was Anne Hathaway married?
10. Who was the second wife of Henry VIII?
11. Which Pakistan batsman was banned for life after being found guilty of match-fixing in 2000?
12. Who wrote *How to Win Friends and Influence People*?
13. What sort of terrier gets its name from a character in Sir Walter Scott's novel *Guy Mannering*?
14. Which former Scotland captain joined Liverpool on a free transfer in 2000?
15. What nationality was the operatic soprano Kirsten Flagstad?
16. Which English physician discovered how blood circulates?
17. Who wrote the novel *To Kill a Mockingbird*?
18. Which silvery metallic element has the symbol Yb?
19. Which king of France was the husband of Catherine de' Medici?
20. How many novels are there in C.P. Snow's *Strangers and Brothers* series?

ANSWERS: *1 Marlon Brando, 2 Swiss Guard, 3 Real Madrid, 4 Pol Pot, 5 Boris Becker, 6 Brasilia, 7 Albert Finney, 8 Albert Einstein, 9 William Shakespeare, 10 Anne Boleyn, 11 Salim Malik, 12 Dale Carnegie, 13 Dandie Dinmont terrier, 14 Gary McAllister, 15 Norwegian, 16 William Harvey, 17 Harper Lee, 18 Ytterbium, 19 Henry II, 20 Eleven.*

General Knowledge

Your rating: ● 0-5 Join a library ● 6-10 Keep at it ● 11-15 Join a quiz team ● 16-20 Join Mensa

1. Which book of the Old Testament tells of Shadrach, Meshach and Abednego being cast into a fiery furnace?
2. What name is given to a condition in which the temperature of the body is abnormally low?
3. Which team won promotion to the Premiership by beating Barnsley in the 2000 play-off final?
4. What is the Latin word for lead, from which the chemical symbol Pb is derived?
5. Which U.S. actor won an Oscar for his role in *True Grit*?
6. What colour is a flag of truce?
7. In which Texas city was President John F. Kennedy assassinated in 1963?
8. Which French national holiday is celebrated on July 14?
9. Which mathematician is said to have run naked into the street shouting "Eureka"?
10. What is the second largest of the Great Lakes?
11. Which artist and typographer carved the Stations of the Cross in Westminster Cathedral?
12. In which European country is Gustav Mahler's birthplace?
13. Which actress plays an unlikely drug dealer in the film *Saving Grace*?
14. Who won an Oscar for directing *My Fair Lady*?
15. Which red giant is the fourth brightest star in the sky?
16. What have to be interpreted in a Rorschach test?
17. Which controversial film rewrote history to give the Americans credit for capturing an Enigma decoding machine?
18. In which U.S. city was Legionnaires' disease first identified?
19. Which classic yacht race begins annually on Boxing Day?
20. Which emergency first aid procedure is known by the abbreviation CPR?

ANSWERS: *1 Daniel, 2 Hypothermia, 3 Ipswich Town, 4 Plumbum, 5 John Wayne, 6 White, 7 Dallas, 8 Bastille Day, 9 Archimedes, 10 Lake Huron, 11 Eric Gill, 12 Czech Republic, 13 Brenda Blethyn, 14 George Cukor, 15 Arcturus, 16 Inkblots, 17 U-571, 18 Philadelphia, 19 Sydney-to-Hobart race, 20 Cardiopulmonary resuscitation.*

Entertainment

Your rating: ● **0-5 Buy a TV** ● **6-10 Keep at it** ● **11-15 Join a quiz team** ● **16-20 Enter a quiz show**

1. In the 1995 Bond film *GoldenEye*, which character was played by Samantha Bond?
2. Which *Brookside* character was played by Paul Usher?
3. In 1995, which band broke Michael Jackson's record for first-week sales of a double album in America?
4. Who played Jimmy Porter in the 1959 film version of *Look Back in Anger*?
5. Which *Star Trek* character was played on TV and film by DeForrest Kelley?
6. Which 1995 film starred Kevin Bacon as a convict and Christian Slater as his defence attorney?
7. How is Glasgow-born pop star James Ure better known?
8. Who directed the 1977 film *New York New York*?
9. Which former sitcom starred Jimmy Jewel and Hylda Baker, and was set in Pledge's pickle factory?
10. Who were voted Best Group and Worst Group at the 1995 *Smash Hits Poll Winners' Party*?
11. Who directed and starred in 1985's *Pale Rider*?
12. Who had a UK number one hit single in 1972 with *Take Me Bak 'Ome*?
13. *Home Improvement* star Tim Allen played a toy salesman in which 1994 Christmas movie?
14. Which presenter of the children's TV show *Blue Peter* left the show in 1995 to become an early morning host on BBC Radio 2?
15. The attempted assassination of which pop artist and film-maker was the subject of a 1996 film by Mary Harron?
16. Which *Boon* star played Billy Bones in the 1995 TV movie *Ken Russell's Treasure Island*?
17. In 1995, Kim Wilde appeared in a production of which rock musical in London's West End?
18. Who wrote and directed the 1995 film *In the Bleak Midwinter*?
19. Who had a U.K. number one hit single in 1981 with *It's My Party*?
20. Who won a Best Supporting Actress Oscar in 1984 for her performance in *A Passage to India*?

ANSWERS: *1 Miss Moneypenny, 2 Barry Grant, 3 The Beatles, 4 Richard Burton, 5 Dr McCoy, 6 Murder in the First, 7 Midge Ure, 8 Martin Scorsese, 9 Nearest and Dearest, 10 Take That, 11 Clint Eastwood, 12 Slade, 13 The Santa Clause, 14 Diane-Louise Jordan, 15 Andy Warhol (I Shot Andy Warhol), 16 Michael Elphick, 17 Tommy, 18 Kenneth Branagh, 19 Dave Stewart with Barbara Gaskin, 20 Peggy Ashcroft.*

General Knowledge

Your rating: ● 0-5 Join a library ● 6-10 Keep at it ● 11-15 Join a quiz team ● 16-20 Join Mensa

1. Which Jane Austen novel features Elizabeth Bennet and Fitzwilliam Darcy?
2. How many events are there in the modern pentathlon?
3. Of which country is Damascus the capital?
4. What was the former name of the Zimbabwean capital Harare?
5. In the Old Testament, who was the son of Saul who formed a close friendship with David?
6. Of which European country is Piraeus the chief port?
7. Which nocturnal beetle emits a greenish light from organs on its abdomen?
8. What is the first day of Lent?
9. Which major naval battle was fought on October 21 1805?
10. Which ball game of North American Indian origin is played with a stick with a net at one end?
11. Which Asian country was divided into North and South in 1954?
12. In which county is the town of Corby?
13. What name is given to a device that increases or decreases the voltage of alternating current?
14. What are the only crustaceans adapted to living on land rather than water?
15. What is the longest river of the Iberian Peninsula?
16. Which Czech author wrote *The Trial* and *The Castle*?
17. Of which metal is bauxite the chief ore?
18. What sort of creature is an addax?
19. Which playwright received the Order of Merit in May 2000?
20. Which British author edited *Household Words* and *All the Year Round*?

ANSWERS: *1 Pride and Prejudice, 2 Five, 3 Syria, 4 Salisbury, 5 Jonathan, 6 Greece, 7 Firefly, 8 Ash Wednesday, 9 The Battle of Trafalgar, 10 Lacrosse, 11 Vietnam, 12 Northamptonshire, 13 Transformer, 14 Woodlice, 15 Tagus, 16 Franz Kafka, 17 Aluminium, 18 An antelope, 19 Sir Tom Stoppard, 20 Charles Dickens.*

General Knowledge

Your rating: ● 0-5 Join a library ● 6-10 Keep at it ● 11-15 Join a quiz team ● 16-20 Join Mensa

1. Which children's author wrote about Tom Kitten and Squirrel Nutkin?
2. Who was the first black tennis player to win the men's singles title at Wimbledon?
3. Which academic discipline is the study of the individuals, groups and institutions that make up society?
4. Who directed *The Bridge on the River Kwai* and *Lawrence of Arabia*?
5. Of which country is Table Mountain a famous landmark?
6. What name is given to an optical illusion such as of an oasis in a desert?
7. What name is given to a Londoner born within the sound of Bow bells?
8. Of which Mediterranean island is Palermo the capital?
9. What is the state capital of Colorado?
10. Who was the father of Shem, Ham and Japheth?
11. Which veteran actress won a Best Actress BAFTA for her performance in *Lost For Words*?
12. In Greek mythology, who was the Muse of history?
13. What is the only wild monkey now living in Europe?
14. Which metallic element has the symbol Cd?
15. Which British composer wrote *A Child of Our Time* and *The Ice Break*?
16. What was the highest mountain climbed until Everest was conquered in 1953?
17. Which art gallery has opened in the former Bankside power station?
18. What is a honey locust?
19. Which novel by Wilkie Collins features the detective Sergeant Cuff?
20. In which country did the Sharpeville massacre take place?

ANSWERS: *1 Beatrix Potter, 2 Arthur Ashe, 3 Sociology, 4 Sir David Lean, 5 South Africa, 6 Mirage, 7 Cockney, 8 Sicily, 9 Denver, 10 Noah, 11 Dame Thora Hird, 12 Clio, 13 Barbary ape, 14 Cadmium, 15 Sir Michael Tippett, 16 Annapurna, 17 Tate Modern, 18 A tree, 19 The Moonstone, 20 South Africa.*

General Knowledge

Your rating: ● **0-5 Join a library** ● **6-10 Keep at it** ● **11-15 Join a quiz team** ● **16-20 Join Mensa**

1. Which American dancer and flautist starred in *Riverdance* and *Lord of the Dance*?
2. What name is given to the knocking down of all ten pins with the first ball in tenpin bowling?
3. Which comedian and author is the director of the film *Maybe Baby*?
4. How many zeros does a trillion have in its British definition?
5. Who became president of South Africa in 1994?
6. What is the anatomical name for the lower jawbone?
7. Which star of the film Grease won Grammy Awards in 1973, 1974 and 1982?
8. What name was given to a Japanese pilot who flew suicide missions in World War II?
9. Who won a Best Actor BAFTA for his performance in *Wives and Daughters*?
10. What is the chief seaport of Tanzania?
11. Which public school was founded by John Lyon in 1572?
12. Who won the men's 800m and 1500m at the 1964 Olympics?
13. Which vehicle takes its name from the Russian for a group of three?
14. Who is the French international goalkeeper who joined Manchester United in 2000?
15. Which Israeli prime minister shared the 1978 Nobel Peace Prize with Anwar Sadat?
16. What was the name of the first English child born in America?
17. Which black tennis player won the ladies singles at Wimbledon in 1957 and 1958?
18. In Greek mythology, which nymph was changed into a laurel tree to escape from Apollo?
19. Which classic horserace was won by Love Divine in 2000?
20. Which singer and actress starred in the film *The Next Best Thing*?

ANSWERS: *1 Michael Flatley, 2 Strike, 3 Ben Elton, 4 Eighteen, 5 Nelson Mandela, 6 Mandible, 7 Olivia Newton-John, 8 Kamikaze, 9 Michael Gambon, 10 Dar es Salaam, 11 Harrow, 12 Peter Snell, 13 Troika, 14 Fabien Barthez, 15 Menachem Begin, 16 Virginia Dare, 17 Althea Gibson, 18 Daphne, 19 The Oaks, 20 Madonna.*

Entertainment

Your rating: ● 0-5 Buy a TV ● 6-10 Keep at it ● 11-15 Join a quiz team ● 16-20 Enter a quiz show

1. At the 1995 *Smash Hits Poll Winners' Party*, who was voted Best Dressed Person, Best Haircut and Most Fanciable Male Star?
2. Which *Brookside* character was played by Andrew Fillis?
3. Which 1995 political comedy film was directed by *When Harry Met Sally* director Rob Reiner?
4. Which cult Sixties TV series starred David Janssen as Dr Richard Kimble?
5. Who had a U.K. top ten hit single in 1977 with *No More Heroes*?
6. Which popular sixties singer played the title role in the 1972 film version of *The Pied Piper*?
7. At the 1995 *Smash Hits Poll Winners' Party*, who were voted Best Indie Band?
8. Which half-Russian actor played a conniving gladiator ring operator in the 1960 film *Spartacus*?
9. Who played Jerzy Balowski, the landlord, in the Eighties sitcom *The Young Ones*?
10. Who starred as Rusty Sabich in the 1990 film *Presumed Innocent*?
11. Who had a U.K. number one hit single in 1983 with *Wherever I Lay My Hat (That's My Home)*?
12. Which *Four Weddings and a Funeral* actress starred in the 1995 film *Unstrung Heroes*?
13. Which arch-villain was played by John Shea in the TV series *The New Adventures of Superman*?
14. What was the name of Audrey Hepburn's character in the 1961 film *Breakfast at Tiffany's*?
15. Who played Richie Cunningham in the sitcom *Happy Days*?
16. Who had a U.K. number one hit in 1972 with *You Wear It Well*?
17. Which controversial former American football star played Nordberg in *The Naked Gun* movies?
18. Which 'difficult' multi-instrumentalist released a single entitled *Pumpkin* in 1995?
19. Which low-budget film about three Catholic brothers won the top prize at America's Sundance Film Festival in 1995?
20. Which comedy series written by Jimmy Perry and David Croft was set in Walmington-on-Sea?

ANSWERS: 1 Mark Owen of *Take That*, 2 Gary, 3 *The American President*, 4 *The Fugitive*, 5 The Stranglers, 6 Donovan, 7 Blur, 8 Sir Peter Ustinov, 9 Alexei Sayle, 10 Harrison Ford, 11 Paul Young, 12 Andie MacDowell, 13 Lex Luthor, 14 Holly Golightly, 15 Ron Howard, 16 Rod Stewart, 17 OJ Simpson, 18 Tricky, 19 *The Brothers McMullen*, 20 *Dad's Army*.

General Knowledge

Your rating:
- 0-5 Join a library
- 6-10 Keep at it
- 11-15 Join a quiz team
- 16-20 Join Mensa

1. Which character in Shakespeare's play *The Merchant of Venice* demands a pound of flesh?
2. By what first name was U.S. trumpet player John Birks Gillespie known?
3. Which Irish dramatist wrote *Waiting for Godot*?
4. Before David Coulthard's 2000 victory, who was the last British driver to win the Monaco Grand Prix?
5. Which indoor game is also called ping-pong?
6. What name is given to a dagger attached to the barrel of a gun?
7. What does the abbreviation AD stand for?
8. Which Greek philosopher died by drinking hemlock?
9. What sort of creature is a mallard?
10. By what nickname are Yeomen Warders of the Tower of London known?
11. What name is given to a barrier placed across a river to stop the flow of water?
12. Which Scottish surgeon was the first European to trace the course of the River Niger?
13. At which racecourse did jockeys Frankie Dettori and Ray Cochrane survive a plane crash in 2000?
14. Which American golfer won the U.S. and British Opens in 1932?
15. Of which U.S. state is Juneau the capital?
16. Which ancient city was also called Ilium?
17. Who was the most famous creation of the Australian author P.L. Travers?
18. Which British actress beat her mother Rosemary Harris to win a Tony Award as Best Actress in 2000?
19. What is the oldest title of nobility in the British peerage?
20. Which popular garden plant has the Latin name *Dianthus barbatus*?

ANSWERS: *1 Shylock, 2 Dizzy, 3 Samuel Beckett, 4 Jackie Stewart, 5 Table tennis, 6 Bayonet, 7 Anno Domini, 8 Socrates, 9 A duck, 10 Beefeaters, 11 A dam, 12 Mungo Park, 13 Newmarket, 14 Gene Sarazen, 15 Alaska, 16 Troy, 17 Mary Poppins, 18 Jennifer Ehle, 19 Earl, 20 Sweet william.*

General Knowledge

Your rating:
- 0-5 Join a library
- 6-10 Keep at it
- 11-15 Join a quiz team
- 16-20 Join Mensa

1. Which gas needed by green plants is released into the atmosphere by animals during respiration?
2. What was the largest county in Wales before April 1996?
3. Which Italian city is famous for its leaning bell tower?
4. Members of which organisation heckled and slow-handclapped Tony Blair when he addressed their conference in 2000?
5. Who was the supreme god in Greek mythology?
6. From which animals is pork obtained?
7. In law, what name is given to the unlawful entrance upon the property of another?
8. What name is given to a plane figure with eight sides?
9. Which Soviet cosmonaut was the first man in space?
10. Of which U.S. state is Trenton the capital?
11. Which Hollywood great won Best Actress Oscars for *Dangerous* and *Jezebel*?
12. Which Irish author wrote *The Old Boys* and *The Ballroom of Romance*?
13. Who directed the film *Sweet and Lowdown* starring Sean Penn?
14. Which orchestra did George Szell conduct from 1946 until his death in 1970?
15. In which country was the singer Miriam Makeba born?
16. Which member of the cat family is also called an ounce?
17. Which corrosive acid has the chemical formula HCl?
18. Which Spanish priest founded the Society of Jesus, commonly known as the Jesuits?
19. In which African country is the town of Timbuktu, or Tombouctou?
20. Which Brazilian tennis player won the men's singles at the 2000 French Open?

ANSWERS: *1 Carbon dioxide, 2 Dyfed, 3 Pisa, 4 Women's Institute, 5 Zeus, 6 Pigs, 7 Trespass, 8 Octagon, 9 Yuri Gagarin, 10 New Jersey, 11 Bette Davis, 12 William Trevor, 13 Woody Allen, 14 Cleveland Symphony Orchestra, 15 South Africa, 16 Snow leopard, 17 Hydrochloric acid, 18 St Ignatius Loyola, 19 Mali, 20 Gustavo Kuerten.*

General Knowledge

Your rating: ● **0-5** **Join a library** ● **6-10** **Keep at it** ● **11-15** **Join a quiz team** ● **16-20** **Join Mensa**

1. Which well-known portrait is Sir Thomas Gainsborough's most famous work?
2. What is the name of the largest asteroid and the first to be discovered?
3. Which popular toy is based on a weapon from the Philippines whose name means 'come come'?
4. Who scored England's first goal in Euro 2000?
5. Which ceremony on Horse Guards Parade celebrates the Queen's official birthday?
6. What is the capital of Turkey?
7. Which Saturday night TV programme was first broadcast on August 22 1964?
8. What name is given to an earthed metal rod placed at the top of a tall building?
9. Which African mammal has a name which means earth pig in Afrikaans?
10. What name is given to the region around the North Pole?
11. With which branch of social science was Bronislaw Malinowski associated?
12. Which English poet is best known for nautical ballads such as *Drake's Drum*?
13. Who won the women's singles title at the 2000 French Open?
14. Which Russian port is the eastern terminus of the Trans-Siberian railway?
15. What is the smallest of the anthropoid apes?
16. Which Roman poet is known for his 16 *Satires*?
17. Which chemical element has the symbol Zr?
18. Which many-headed monster was killed by Hercules as one of his labours?
19. Who wrote the novel *Fair Stood the Wind for France*?
20. Which county beat Glamorgan to win the 2000 Benson and Hedges Cup final?

ANSWERS: *1 The Blue Boy, 2 Ceres, 3 Yo-yo, 4 Paul Scholes, 5 Trooping the Colour, 6 Ankara, 7 Match of the Day, 8 Lightning conductor, 9 Aardvark, 10 Arctic, 11 Anthropology, 12 Sir Henry Newbolt, 13 Mary Pierce, 14 Vladivostok, 15 Gibbon, 16 Juvenal, 17 Zirconium, 18 Hydra, 19 H E Bates, 20 Gloucestershire.*

Sports

Your rating: ● 0-5 Wooden spoon ● 6-10 Bronze medal ● 11-15 Silver medal ● 16-20 Gold medal

1. Which Arsenal player was sent off twice in three days at the start of the 2000/01 Premiership season?
2. How many balls are used in a game of snooker?
3. In which sport did Australia's Ian Baker-Finch make his name?
4. Who won the women's singles at Wimbledon in 1977?
5. What was the name of the dog that found the missing World Cup trophy in 1966?
6. Which British athlete won the gold medal in the women's heptathlon event at the 2000 Sydney Olympics?
7. Where is the 2001 Ryder Cup to be held?
8. Which horse won the 2000 Guineas in 1998?
9. In which sport is the Davis Cup contested?
10. Who was Formula 1 world champion in 1992?
11. Which golf course hosted the Open Championship in 2000?
12. Who beat Stephen Hendry to win the snooker world championship in 1997?
13. What nationality is 1991 Wimbledon champion Michael Stich?
14. Which country won the cricket World Cup in 1992?
15. Which England player scored five goals against Cyprus in 1975?
16. Which Portuguese footballer became the world's most expensive player when he joined Real Madrid from Barcelona?
17. Who was the first boxer to beat Thomas Hearns in a professional bout?
18. How many gold medals did Jesse Owens win at the Berlin Olympics in 1936?
19. When was Mike Tyson born?
20. Which female tennis player won the Toyota Princess Cup in Tokyo in September 1999?

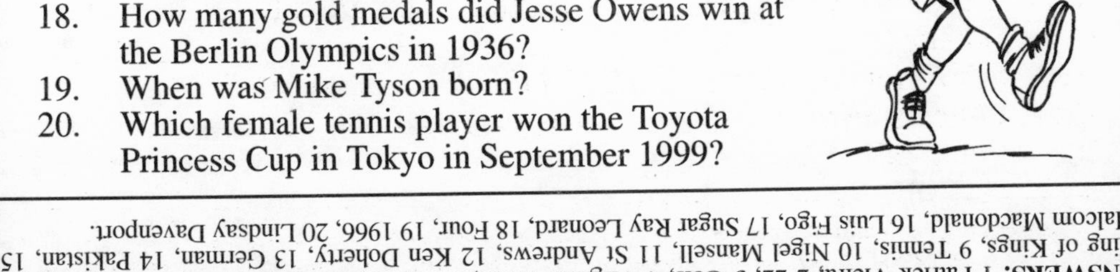

ANSWERS: 1 Patrick Vieira, 2 22, 3 Golf, 4 Virginia Wade, 5 Pickles, 6 Denise Lewis, 7 The Belfry, 8 King of Kings, 9 Tennis, 10 Nigel Mansell, 11 St Andrews, 12 Ken Doherty, 13 German, 14 Pakistan, 15 Malcolm Macdonald, 16 Luis Figo, 17 Sugar Ray Leonard, 18 Four, 19 1966, 20 Lindsay Davenport.

General Knowledge

Your rating:
- 0-5 Join a library
- 6-10 Keep at it
- 11-15 Join a quiz team
- 16-20 Join Mensa

1. Which novel by Margaret Mitchell won the Pulitzer Prize for fiction in 1937?
2. How many years of marriage does a golden wedding anniversary celebrate?
3. Which Scottish city was chosen as European City of Culture in 1990?
4. Who scored England's winning goal in their Euro 2000 victory over Germany?
5. Which organ of the body is inflamed in a case of hepatitis?
6. What was the former name of Sri Lanka?
7. Which epic poem attributed to Homer describes Odysseus's journey home after the Trojan War?
8. What colour is paprika?
9. Of which German orchestra was Herbert von Karajan musical director from 1955 to 1989?
10. What name is given to a place equipped with telescopes for studying the sky?
11. What sort of creature is a pompano?
12. Which lyricist collaborated with Richard Rodgers on the song *My Funny Valentine*?
13. To which genus does the popular houseplant mother-in-law's tongue belong?
14. Which Irish-trained horse won the 2000 Derby?
15. Who was chancellor of the Exchequer from 1979 to 1983?
16. Which French author wrote the novel *Madame Bovary*?
17. In John Milton's *Paradise Lost*, which fallen angel is ranked second to Satan in power?
18. Which actress stars in the film *28 Days*?
19. With what sort of games was Edmond Hoyle chiefly associated?
20. Which British conductor, noted for his wit, wrote *A Mingled Chime*?

***ANSWERS:** 1 Gone with the Wind, 2 Fifty, 3 Glasgow, 4 Alan Shearer, 5 The liver, 6 Ceylon, 7 The Odyssey, 8 Red, 9 Berlin Philharmonic, 10 Observatory, 11 Fish, 12 Lorenz Hart, 13 Sansevieria, 14 Sinndar, 15 Geoffrey Howe, 16 Gustave Flaubert, 17 Beelzebub, 18 Sandra Bullock, 19 Card games, 20 Sir Thomas Beecham.*

General Knowledge

Your rating: ● 0-5 Join a library ● 6-10 Keep at it ● 11-15 Join a quiz team ● 16-20 Join Mensa

1. Which former U.S. First Lady helped to found a treatment centre for addiction?
2. Of which country is the Deutsche Mark the standard unit of currency?
3. Which American golfer smashed several records in winning the 2000 U.S. Open at Pebble Beach?
4. With which sport is Jean-Claude Killy associated?
5. Which notorious murderer terrorised London in 1888?
6. Of which Baltic country is Riga the capital?
7. What is the collective name for a group of geese on land or in water?
8. Which ancient symbol was adopted by the Nazis in Germany as their emblem?
9. What sort of creature is an oriole?
10. Which American baseball great was nicknamed *The Georgia Peach*?
11. Which inlet of the Atlantic divides New Brunswick from Nova Scotia?
12. Which newspaper editor's escape from South Africa was featured in the film *Cry Freedom*?
13. Who wrote the novels *Rich Man, Poor Man* and *Beggarman, Thief*?
14. Which 60s group, whose hits include Be My Baby, were awarded £1.7m in missing royalties by a New York court in 2000?
15. Who was the first African American mayor of New York City?
16. Which U.S. city is served by Hartsfield International airport?
17. Which English composer wrote the overtures *Beckus the Dandipratt* and *Tam O'Shanter*?
18. Who was the last Stuart monarch?
19. In which film did Fred Astaire first team up with Ginger Rogers?
20. Which metallic element has the symbol Sc?

ANSWERS: *1 Betty Ford, 2 Germany, 3 Tiger Woods, 4 Skiing, 5 Jack the Ripper, 6 Latvia, 7 Gaggle, 8 Swastika, 9 A bird, 10 Ty Cobb, 11 Bay of Fundy, 12 Donald Woods, 13 Irwin Shaw, 14 The Ronettes, 15 David Dinkins, 16 Atlanta, 17 Malcolm Arnold, 18 Queen Anne, 19 Flying Down to Rio, 20 Scandium.*

General Knowledge

Your rating: ● 0-5 Join a library ● 6-10 Keep at it ● 11-15 Join a quiz team ● 16-20 Join Mensa

1. Which building material is mixed with water and materials such as sand and crushed stone to make concrete?
2. In which sport are goal shooter and goal attack positions?
3. Which country knocked England out of Euro 2000?
4. In which English county is Borstal, which gave its name to young offenders' institutions?
5. Which Spanish golfer captained the 1997 European Ryder Cup team?
6. In the Old Testament, who was the favourite wife of Jacob?
7. In the Old Testament, who was the eldest son of Adam and Eve?
8. Which Norwegian dramatist wrote Hedda Gabler?
9. With which sport is Jansher Khan associated?
10. Which Belfast-born musician became principal flautist with the Berlin Philharmonic in 1967?
11. Which Australian tennis player beat Pete Sampras in the final of the 2000 Stella Artois Championships at Queen's Club?
12. Which English philosopher was the founder of utilitarianism?
13. What is the Queen Mother's favourite song?
14. Which show-jumper and rally driver married Swedish driver Erik Carlsson in 1963?
15. Of which country was Dom Mintoff prime minister from 1955 to 1958 and from 1971 to 1984?
16. Which title of nobility is derived from the Latin word for leader?
17. Which English writer was best known for his translation of the *Rubaiyat of Omar Khayyam*?
18. With which instruments was Gene Krupa associated?
19. Who was the leader of East Germany from 1971 to 1989?
20. Which disease is caused by a deficiency of vitamin B 1 or thiamine?

***ANSWERS:** 1 Cement, 2 Netball, 3 Romania, 4 Kent, 5 Severiano Ballesteros, 6 Rachel, 7 Cain, 8 Henrik Ibsen, 9 Squash, 10 James Galway, 11 Lleyton Hewitt, 12 Jeremy Bentham, 13 A Nightingale Sang in Berkeley Square, 14 Pat Moss, 15 Malta, 16 Duke, 17 Edward Fitzgerald, 18 Drums, 19 Erich Honecker, 20 Beriberi.*

Entertainment

Your rating:
- 0-5 Buy a TV
- 6-10 Keep at it
- 11-15 Join a quiz team
- 16-20 Enter a quiz show

1. Who played Isaac Davis in the 1979 film *Manhattan*?
2. Which character in the drama series *Northern Exposure* was played by Barry Corbin?
3. Who had a U.K.. top ten hit single in 1954 with *Gilly Gilly Ossenfeffer Katzenellen Bogen by the Sea*?
4. Who played the President's girlfriend in the 1995 film *The American President*?
5. Which *Absolutely Fabulous* actress appeared as Mrs Smiling in the nineties TV adaptation of *Cold Comfort Farm*?
6. Which former *Monty Python* star appeared in the 1990 film *Nuns on the Run*?
7. Who played Rowdy Yates in the western TV series *Rawhide*?
8. Which former Olympic and World Skating Champion starred in the 1995 TV movie *The Ice Princess*?
9. Mike Flowers Pops hit the top five in early 1996 with an easy listening version of which Oasis song?
10. Who played Jean Pargetter in the sitcom *As Time Goes By*?
11. Which former *EastEnders* stars released the song *Better Believe It* in aid of the 1995 Children In Need appeal?
12. Which 1995 film starred Tim Daly as a perfume developer and Sean Young as his female alter-ego?
13. Who played Maggie Prentice in the TV series *Next of Kin*?
14. Which band hit the U.K. top ten in the winter of 1995/6 with *A Winter's Tale*?
15. Which ripping 1966 Alfred Hitchcock film starred Paul Newman and Julie Andrews?
16. Which sitcom featured the DIY show *Tool Time*?
17. Who had a U.K. top ten hit single in 1986 with *What Have You Done For Me Lately*?
18. Which *Four Weddings and a Funeral* actress starred in the 1995 British film *Angels and Insects*?
19. Who played Harold Steptoe in the classic comedy series *Steptoe and Son*?
20. Who had a U.K. top ten hit single in 1981 with *Get Down On It*?

ANSWERS: 1 Woody Allen, 2 Maurice Minnifield, 3 Max Bygraves, 4 Annette Bening, 5 Joanna Lumley, 6 Eric Idle, 7 Clint Eastwood, 8 Katarina Witt, 9 Wonderwall, 10 Judi Dench, 11 Sid Owen and Patsy Palmer, 12 Dr Jekyll and Ms Hyde, 13 Penelope Keith, 14 Queen, 15 Torn Curtain, 16 Home Improvement, 17 Janet Jackson, 18 Kristin Scott Thomas, 19 Harry H Corbett, 20 Kool and the Gang.

General Knowledge

Your rating:
- 0-5 Join a library
- 6-10 Keep at it
- 11-15 Join a quiz team
- 16-20 Join Mensa

1. Which common adolescent skin complaint is caused by inflammation of the sebaceous glands?
2. For which football club did Bobby Charlton play?
3. Which dame played a countess in the film version of Noel Coward's *Relative Values*?
4. What name is given to someone born within the sound of the bells of St Mary-le-Bow church?
5. Which precious metal has the chemical symbol Ag?
6. How many lines are there in a sonnet?
7. What was the nickname of the American frontierswoman born Martha Jane Canary?
8. Which country had a player dismissed in each of their group games in Euro 2000?
9. What is the largest country in South America?
10. Which organ of the human body produces and secretes bile?
11. With which American sport is Mickey Mantle associated?
12. Which American lyricist wrote the words to the songs *Moon River* and *That Old Black Magic*?
13. What name is given to the scientific study or exploration of caves?
14. Which singer and actress plays novelist Jacqueline Susann in the film *Isn't She Great*?
15. Broxbourne is a local government district of which English county?
16. Which American jazz singer was born Ruth Lee Jones?
17. Which organ is affected by nephritis or Bright's disease?
18. In which country was baritone Peter Dawson born?
19. Which English poet wrote *V* and *The Gaze of the Gorgon*?
20. Which 16th-century English dramatist wrote *The Spanish Tragedy*?

ANSWERS: *1 Acne, 2 Manchester United, 3 Dame Julie Andrews, 4 A Cockney, 5 Silver, 6 Fourteen, 7 Calamity Jane, 8 Yugoslavia, 9 Brazil, 10 Liver, 11 Baseball, 12 Johnny Mercer, 13 Speleology, 14 Bette Midler, 15 Hertfordshire, 16 Dinah Washington, 17 Kidney, 18 Australia, 19 Tony Harrison, 20 Thomas Kyd.*

General Knowledge

Your rating: ● 0-5 Join a library ● 6-10 Keep at it ● 11-15 Join a quiz team ● 16-20 Join Mensa

1. Which former England cricket captain made his first class debut for Cambridge University in 1987?
2. What name is given to the flesh of a mature sheep used as food?
3. Which TV chef married Juliette Norton?
4. What name is given to ice crystals formed from water vapour on windows, grass and other exposed surfaces near the ground?
5. Which well-known horror story was written by Mary Shelley?
6. In which English county is the town of Woking?
7. With which English city was Beau Nash associated?
8. Which South African golfer became the youngest winner of the British Open in 1959?
9. What was the name of the hall in Asgard where Odin feasted with heroes killed in battle?
10. Which long-serving full-back joined West Ham United from Arsenal in 2000?
11. Which Scottish engineer gave the first public demonstration of television?
12. Which American silent film comedian starred in *Safety Last* and *The Freshman*?
13. How many pounds are there in a long hundredweight?
14. Which star of *Mary Poppins* and *Bedknobs and Broomsticks* died in 2000 at the age of 83?
15. In which country is the Welland Ship Canal?
16. Which contagious disease is also called infectious parotitis?
17. What name is given to the weather conditions of a particular place over a period of time?
18. Which motoring organisation is represented by the initials AA?
19. How many successive matches had Vincent Spadea lost before he knocked Greg Rusedski out of the 2000 Wimbledon?
20. Which German field marshal was known as the Desert Fox?

ANSWERS: *1 Michael Atherton, 2 Mutton, 3 Jamie Oliver, 4 Frost, 5 Frankenstein, 6 Surrey, 7 Bath, 8 Gary Player, 9 Valhalla, 10 Nigel Winterburn, 11 John Logie Baird, 12 Harold Lloyd, 13 112, 14 David Tomlinson, 15 Canada, 16 Mumps, 17 Climate, 18 Automobile Association, 19 Twenty-two, 20 Erwin Rommel.*

General Knowledge

Your rating:
- **0-5 Join a library**
- **6-10 Keep at it**
- **11-15 Join a quiz team**
- **16-20 Join Mensa**

1. Which title was given to Prince Andrew on his wedding day in 1986?
2. With which sport are the Queensberry Rules associated?
3. Which famous duo wrote *The Pirates of Penzance* and *The Mikado*?
4. Former Metropolitan Police Commissioner Sir Paul Condon was appointed to investigate corruption in which sport?
5. What name is given to a self-propelled underwater missile?
6. In which U.S. state is the tourist centre Orlando?
7. Which former British coin was equal to twelve old pence?
8. Who provides the voice for Rocky the rooster in the film *Chicken Run*?
9. Which pilgrimage centre in southwestern France is associated with St Bernadette?
10. What name is given to connecting words such as 'and' and 'or'?
11. Which organ that develops in pregnant women provides the unborn baby with nourishment and oxygen?
12. Which ancient unit of measurement was based on the length of the forearm between the middle finger and the elbow?
13. Who scored a hat trick in Holland's 6-1 demolition of Yugoslavia at Euro 2000?
14. Which American author wrote *I Know Why The Caged Bird Sings*?
15. Who directed the films *Mr Deeds Goes To Town* and *It Happened One Night*?
16. What name is given to inflammation of the mucous membrane of the nose?
17. What was the name of the project that revealed the first drafts of the human genetic code?
18. Which sea is between the Gulf of Genoa and Corsica?
19. What is the capital of Uzbekistan?
20. Which English author wrote the novel *Under the Volcano*?

ANSWERS: *1 Duke of York, 2 Boxing, 3 Gilbert and Sullivan, 4 Cricket, 5 Torpedo, 6 Florida, 7 Shilling, 8 Mel Gibson, 9 Lourdes, 10 Conjunctions, 11 Placenta, 12 Cubit, 13 Patrick Kluivert, 14 Maya Angelou, 15 Frank Capra, 16 Rhinitis, 17 Human Genome Project, 18 Ligurian Sea, 19 Tashkent, 20 Malcolm Lowry.*

Entertainment

Your rating: ● 0-5 Buy a TV ● 6-10 Keep at it ● 11-15 Join a quiz team ● 16-20 Enter a quiz show

1. Who played Christine Keeler in the 1989 film *Scandal*?
2. Which character in the drama series *Casualty* was played by Patrick Robinson?
3. Which British TV personality released a single in late 1995 entitled *Too Much For One Heart*?
4. Who starred as *Lawrence of Arabia* in David Lean's 1962 film of that name?
5. Which group had a U.K. top five hit single in 1970 with *Lola*?
6. Which Royal wrote and narrated the animated film *The Legend of Lochnagar*?
7. On which children's TV show could Trevor and Simon be seen setting sail on the Video Galleon in the Nineties?
8. Which *Educating Rita* actress played the siblings' hard-hearted employer in the 1994 film *Sister, My Sister*?
9. Which character in the Australian soap *Neighbours* was played by Anne Haddy?
10. Which soul star released an album in 1995 entitled *This is Christmas*?
11. Which U.S. medical drama series formerly starred George Clooney as Dr Doug Ross?
12. Which *Monty Python* star played Sheriff Langston in the 1985 film *Silverado*?
13. Which British comedy actress said in 1996, "I've finished with Hyacinth. It's over as far as I'm concerned"?
14. Who had a U.K. number one hit single in 1960 with *Only the Lonely*?
15. Which 1995 film starred Keith Carradine and Daryl Hannah as psychotic parents?
16. Which Irish singer/songwriter released an album in 1996 entitled *How Long Has This Been Going On*?
17. Which actress played the title role in the 1983 film *Silkwood*?
18. Who had a U.K. number one hit single in 1977 with *Yes Sir, I Can Boogie*?
19. In 1996 a Swiss museum paid £44,750 for a bowler hat and cane belonging to which silent film star?
20. Which British comic actor played MP Alan Beresford B'Stard in the U.K. sitcom *The New Statesman*?

ANSWERS: 1 Joanne Whalley-Kilmer, 2 Martin Ashford (Ash), 3 Michael Barrymore, 4 Peter O'Toole, 5 The Kinks, 6 The Prince of Wales, 7 Live & Kicking, 8 Julie Walters, 9 Helen Daniels, 10 Luther Vandross, 11 ER, 12 John Cleese, 13 Patricia Routledge, 14 Roy Orbison, 15 The Tie That Binds, 16 Van Morrison, 17 Meryl Streep, 18 Baccara, 19 Charlie Chaplin, 20 Rik Mayall.

General Knowledge

Your rating: ● 0-5 Join a library ● 6-10 Keep at it ● 11-15 Join a quiz team ● 16-20 Join Mensa

1. Which French composer wrote *The Carnival of the Animals*?
2. On what date is St David's Day celebrated?
3. Which former model played Mrs Robinson in the 2000 West End production of *The Graduate*?
4. By what name was U.S. frontier marshal James Butler Hickok known?
5. Which star of the former TV soap *Dallas* is the son of American musical comedy star Mary Martin?
6. What is the capital of the Republic of Ireland?
7. Of which arts institution was Sir Joshua Reynolds the first president?
8. Which famous public school was founded by King Henry VI in 1440?
9. What name is given to a device that measures atmospheric pressure?
10. Which actor best known for his films with Jack Lemmon died in 2000 at the age of 79?
11. Which acid is found in milk and other dairy products that have turned sour?
12. Which famous chapel in the Vatican was built by Pope Sixtus IV?
13. What is the legislative capital of South Africa?
14. Which Everton player gave away the penalty that led to France's Golden Goal victory over Portugal at Euro 2000?
15. What name is given to the mass in a unit volume of any substance?
16. Which German composer wrote the opera *Hansel and Gretel*?
17. Which sport was invented by Canadian teacher James Naismith?
18. What was the pen name of French playwright Jean Baptiste Poquelin?
19. Who was General Secretary of the TUC from 1969 to 1973?
20. Which rare-earth metal has the chemical symbol Lu?

ANSWERS: *1 Camille Saint-Saëns, 2 March 1, 3 Jerry Hall, 4 Wild Bill Hickok, 5 Larry Hagman, 6 Dublin, 7 Royal Academy of Arts, 8 Eton College, 9 Barometer, 10 Walter Matthau, 11 Lactic acid, 12 Sistine Chapel, 13 Cape Town, 14 Abel Xavier, 15 Density, 16 Engelbert Humperdinck, 17 Basketball, 18 Molière, 19 Vic Feather, 20 Lutetium.*

General Knowledge

Your rating: ● 0-5 Join a library ● 6-10 Keep at it ● 11-15 Join a quiz team ● 16-20 Join Mensa

1. Which British-born comic actor starred in the films *The Gold Rush* and *Modern Times*?
2. What did USSR stand for?
3. What does V-E Day stand for?
4. What name is given to five babies born to the same mother at one time?
5. Which Scottish castle was bought for the Royal family by Prince Albert?
6. On which continent did the Ebola virus originate?
7. Which of the Marx Brothers was famous for his cigars and bushy moustache and eyebrows?
8. For which novel was Russian author Boris Pasternak best known?
9. What was the pen name of novelist Eric Blair?
10. Which American actor starred in the TV series *Columbo*?
11. On which animal would you find fetlocks and withers?
12. Which friend of Jesus was the sister of Mary and Lazarus of Bethany?
13. Who illustrated Lewis Carroll's *Alice's Adventures in Wonderland* and *Through the Looking Glass*?
14. Which wildlife park and casino owner died in 2000 at the age of 74?
15. Who wrote *Oranges are Not the Only Fruit* and *Sexing the Cherry*?
16. Which Mongol ruler of Samarkand sacked Delhi in 1398?
17. Which former Indian prime minister was assassinated in 1991?
18. Which American poet and humorist wrote *You Can't Get There From Here*?
19. How old was Prince Charles when his mother became Queen?
20. Which English artist was the subject of the film *A Bigger Splash*?

ANSWERS: *1 Charlie Chaplin, 2 Union of Soviet Socialist Republics, 3 Victory in Europe Day, 4 Quintuplets, 5 Balmoral, 6 Africa, 7 Groucho, 8 Dr Zhivago, 9 George Orwell, 10 Peter Falk, 11 A horse, 12 Martha, 13 Sir John Tenniel, 14 John Aspinall, 15 Jeanette Winterson, 16 Tamerlane, 17 Rajiv Gandhi, 18 Ogden Nash, 19 Three, 20 David Hockney.*

General Knowledge

Your rating: ● 0-5 Join a library ● 6-10 Keep at it ● 11-15 Join a quiz team ● 16-20 Join Mensa

1. Which popular children's story was written by Johann Wyss?
2. Who was elected vice president of the United States in 1992?
3. Which actor performed his own stunts in the film *Mission: Impossible 2*?
4. What is the third longest river in England and the principal river of the Midlands?
5. Which British dramatist wrote the series of TV monologues *Talking Heads*?
6. Who became British foreign secretary in 1997?
7. Which actor and comedian starred in *Good Morning, Vietnam* and *Dead Poet's Society*?
8. What does *Robinson Crusoe* call the man who becomes his friend and servant in Defoe's novel?
9. Which country beat Italy in the final to win Euro 2000?
10. What is the largest desert in the world?
11. Which left-handed batsman captained England from 1984 to 1986?
12. Which Maltese-born psychologist originated the term 'lateral thinking'?
13. In computing, what does ISP stand for?
14. Which former Tourist Trophy Formula 1 world motorcycling champion died after crashing in a road race in Estonia in 2000?
15. Who was president of the European Commission from 1985 to 1994?
16. Which former lord chancellor was born Quintin McGarel Hogg?
17. In which African country is the city of Entebbe?
18. Which petroleum product is known as kerosene in the United States?
19. What name is given to the watering of land by artificial methods?
20. Which golfer won 83 tournaments from 1935 to 1964 including the first U.S. Women's Open?

ANSWERS: *1 The Swiss Family Robinson, 2 Al Gore, 3 Tom Cruise, 4 River Trent, 5 Alan Bennett, 6 Robin Cook, 7 Robin Williams, 8 Friday, 9 France, 10 The Sahara, 11 David Gower, 12 Edward de Bono, 13 Internet service provider, 14 Joey Dunlop, 15 Jacques Delors, 16 Lord Hailsham, 17 Uganda, 18 Paraffin, 19 Irrigation, 20 Patty Berg.*

Sports

Your rating: ● 0-5 Wooden spoon ● 6-10 Bronze medal ● 11-15 Silver medal ● 16-20 Gold medal

1. Who knocked Stephen Hendry out of the 1998 world professional snooker championship at The Crucible?
2. Which British driver won the 1958 Argentine Grand Prix?
3. Which former England international became manager of Middlesbrough in 1973?
4. In which sport do teams play on a diamond?
5. In which rowing event has Steve Redgrave won three consecutive Olympic gold medals?
6. Which boxing promoter was Terry Marsh acquitted of attempting to murder in 1990?
7. In which year did Chris Boardman become the first Briton since Tommy Simpson to wear the yellow jersey in cycling's Tour de France?
8. Which nation did Scotland play against in the first match of football's 1998 World Cup?
9. Which eccentric US tennis player claims to eat only jelly on Wednesdays?
10. In which Olympic event was athlete Bruce Jenner the 1976 champion?
11. Which city hosted the 1997 World Athletics Championships?
12. Which England player scored after 27 seconds against France in the 1982 World Cup?
13. Which county cricket side play at Headingley?
14. In which year did Debbie Meyer become the first swimmer to win three Olympic gold medals in individual events?
15. In which event did gymnast Annika Reeder retain her individual Commonwealth title at the 1998 Games?
16. In which year was football's World Cup held in Sweden?
17. Who was Willie Thorne beaten by in the final of the 1985 UK Open in snooker?
18. Which London Scottish rugby player suffered a serious ear injury in a match against Bath in 1998?
19. In which year were the summer Olympic Games held in Montreal, Canada?

***ANSWERS:** 1 Jimmy White, 2 Stirling Moss, 3 Jack Charlton, 4 Baseball, 5 Coxless pairs, 6 Frank Warren, 7 1994, 8 Brazil, 9 Venus Williams, 10 Decathlon, 11 Athens, 12 Bryan Robson, 13 Yorkshire, 14 1968, 15 The floor, 16 1958, 17 Steve Davis, 18 Simon Fenn, 19 1976, 20 Nottingham Forest.*

General Knowledge

Your rating:
- 0-5 Join a library
- 6-10 Keep at it
- 11-15 Join a quiz team
- 16-20 Join Mensa

1. Which extinct early Stone Age man is represented by skeletal remains found in China?
2. What was the name of the British royal house before it was changed to Windsor in 1917?
3. In which century was William Shakespeare born?
4. Of which island country is Port Louis the capital?
5. In which Asian country is the city of Srinagar?
6. Which face of the Eiger is one of the most difficult climbs in the Alps?
7. Which nut is an important ingredient of marzipan?
8. Which tree's leaves and bark do koalas feed on?
9. In which year was the construction of The Eiffel Tower completed?
10. In 1666, what disaster originated in a bakery in Pudding Lane, London?
11. Which U.S. president authorised the use of the atom bomb against Japan?
12. Which Shakespeare tragedy is subtitled The Prince of Denmark?
13. Which insect transmits sleeping sickness to humans?
14. Who had a number one hit in 1998 with her debut single, *Because We Want To*?
15. In which African country do the Berber people known as the Rif live?
16. What sort of creature is a frogmouth?
17. In which year did poet laureate Ted Hughes die?
18. In which country did goulash originate?
19. Which is bigger, the African or Indian elephant?
20. In which year did Queen Victoria succeed to the throne?

ANSWERS: *1 Peking man, 2 Saxe-Coburg-Gotha, 3 The 16th century, 4 Mauritius, 5 India, 6 North face, 7 Almond, 8 Eucalyptus, 9 1889, 10 The Great Fire of London, 11 Harry S Truman, 12 Hamlet, 13 Tsetse fly, 14 Billie , 15 Morocco, 16 A bird, 17 1998, 18 Hungary, 19 African, 20 1837.*

General Knowledge

Your rating:
- **0-5 Join a library**
- **6-10 Keep at it**
- **11-15 Join a quiz team**
- **16-20 Join Mensa**

1. What is the outermost layer of the Earth called?
2. Who wrote the famous trilogy *The Lord of the Rings*?
3. Which of the three armed services was founded in the 9th century by Alfred the Great?
4. What is an instrument for measuring atmospheric pressure called?
5. Whom did Mrs Anna Anderson claim to be from 1920 until her death in 1984?
6. Which Old Testament prophet was born at Ur in Chaldaea in c. 2000 BC?
7. In which field was British physicist William Henry Fox Talbot a pioneer?
8. Which flap of cartilage at the root of the tongue prevents food, etc., from entering the windpipe?
9. Who was the Greek god of wine?
10. Whom did Mark David Chapman shoot and kill on 8th December, 1980?
11. Which American state separates the Atlantic Ocean and the Gulf of Mexico?
12. Which river has Vienna, Bratislava, Budapest and Belgrade along its course?
13. Which famous composer had an affair with French novelist George Sand?
14. Which is the northernmost American state?
15. Which war lasted from 1936-1939?
16. Which building is to be found at 1600 Pennsylvania Avenue, Washington DC?
17. On which island are citizens elected to the House of Keys?
18. Who is the Czechoslovakian-born British writer of the play *The Real Thing*?
19. Which clubfooted poet died while training troops at Missolonghi in Greece?
20. Which Gorgon was so ugly that all who saw her face were turned to stone?

ANSWERS: *1 The crust, 2 J.R.R. Tolkien, 3 The Royal Navy, 4 A barometer, 5 Princess Anastasia of Russia, 6 Abraham, 7 Photography, 8 The epiglottis, 9 Dionysus, 10 John Lennon, 11 Florida, 12 The Danube, 13 Frédéric Chopin, 14 Alaska, 15 The Spanish Civil War, 16 The White House, 17 The Isle of Man, 18 Tom Stoppard, 19 Lord Byron, 20 Medusa.*

General Knowledge

Your rating:
- 0-5 Join a library
- 6-10 Keep at it
- 11-15 Join a quiz team
- 16-20 Join Mensa

1. Which famous opera company is based at the Lincoln Center for the Performing Arts in New York?
2. What was Frank Sinatra's middle name?
3. Which crop was affected by blight in 1846, leading to the Irish famine?
4. What form of arthritis commonly affects the big toe?
5. Which famous Roman statesman joined Pompey and Crassus in the first Triumvirate?
6. Of which country was Francisco Franco dictator until his death in 1975?
7. Which nomadic peoples originating in Mongolia were led by Attila?
8. Which Scottish heroine smuggled the Young Pretender to Skye after the Battle of Culloden?
9. Which small device is used to regulate the speed at which music is played?
10. Who scored a hat trick in the 1966 World Cup final?
11. Which French astronomer is famous for his catalogue of nonstellar objects?
12. By what name are members of the Society of Jesus better known?
13. Which British environmental pressure group was formed in 1971?
14. Which French diplomat supervised the building of the Suez Canal?
15. Who set up the Kelmscott Press in 1890?
16. What is the longest river in Russia?
17. What is the third longest river in Africa?
18. How many bones are there in the human hand?
19. What was the score by which the England Rugby Union team suffered their record defeat against Australia in 1998?
20. Which Canadian province was colonised by Scottish poet Sir William Alexander?

ANSWERS: *1 Metropolitan Opera, 2 Albert, 3 Potato, 4 Gout, 5 Julius Caesar, 6 Spain, 7 The Huns, 8 Flora MacDonald, 9 Metronome, 10 Geoff Hurst, 11 Charles Messier, 12 Jesuits, 13 Friends of the Earth, 14 Ferdinand de Lesseps, 15 William Morris, 16 River Lena, 17 River Niger, 18 27, 19 76-0, 20 Nova Scotia.*

Entertainment

Your rating: ● **0-5** Buy a TV ● **6-10** Keep at it ● **11-15** Join a quiz team ● **16-20** Enter a quiz show

1. Which American playwright created *The Twilight Zone* and *The Night Gallery*?
2. Which rap group had a top ten hit in 1991 with *Set Adrift On Memory Bliss*?
3. Who directed the film *Casino*?
4. Which sport was the subject of the Channel 4 series *Board Stupid*?
5. What was the title of Take That's last single?
6. Which *Birds of a Feather* actress starred in the TV drama *The Sculptress*?
7. Who played the title role in the film *Johnny Mnemonic*?
8. Who played Manuel in the TV comedy series *Fawlty Towers*?
9. Who had a top ten hit in 1992 with *Ruff in the Jungle Bizness*?
10. Which English actress and model starred in the 1997 film *Austin Powers: International Man of Mystery*?
11. Who was voted best male singer at the 1996 Brit Awards?
12. Which 1988 Alan Parker film starred Gene Hackman and Willem Dafoe as FBI agents?
13. Who played Iago in Oliver Parker's film version of *Othello*?
14. Which *Our Friends in the North* star played DCI Bilborough in TV's *Cracker*?
15. Which former choreographer had a top ten hit in 1991 with *Rush Rush*?
16. Who played Aunty, mistress of Bartertown, in *Mad Max Beyond Thunderdome*?
17. Which comedy series was set in Whitbury Leisure Centre?
18. Who was voted best female singer at the 1996 Brit Awards?
19. Which 1996 film starred Robin Williams and a host of jungle creatures?
20. Which *Dallas* star played *The Man From Atlantis*?

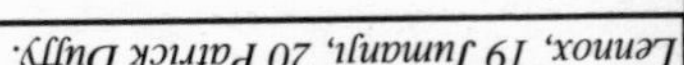

ANSWERS: *1 Rod Serling, 2 PM Dawn, 3 Martin Scorsese, 4 Snowboarding, 5 How Deep Is Your Love, 6 Pauline Quirke, 7 Keanu Reeves, 8 Andrew Sachs, 9 Prodigy, 10 Elizabeth Hurley, 11 Paul Weller, 12 Mississippi Burning, 13 Kenneth Branagh, 14 Christopher Eccleston, 15 Paula Abdul, 16 Tina Turner, 17 The Brittas Empire, 18 Annie Lennox, 19 Jumanji, 20 Patrick Duffy.*

General Knowledge

Your rating: ● **0-5** **Join a library** ● **6-10** **Keep at it** ● **11-15** **Join a quiz team** ● **16-20** **Join Mensa**

1. What name is commonly given to an injection into the space around the spinal cord during childbirth?
2. Which archbishop signs the word Ebor after his Christian name?
3. From which country's government did President Suharto resign in 1998 after more than 30 years in power?
4. How old was Boris Becker when he first won the men's singles title at Wimbledon?
5. Which British skater won the Olympic men's figure-skating title in 1976?
6. Which German composer wrote the operas *Parsifal* and *The Flying Dutchman*?
7. Which figure personifying England first appeared in pamphlets written by John Arbuthnot?
8. What name is given to the Hindu custom of self-immolation of widows on their husbands' funeral pyres?
9. Which Russian composer wrote the unfinished opera *Prince Igor*?
10. What is the fluid that remains after blood has clotted called?
11. Which London borough was created from the former municipal boroughs of Wembley and Willesden?
12. What name is given to proteins that act as biological catalysts?
13. Which U.S. novelist wrote *Something Happened*?
14. With which psychological complex is Alfred Adler chiefly associated?
15. Which city on the river Danube is the capital of Upper Austria?
16. Who founded the Society of Friends, also known as the Quakers?
17. Which unit of energy is abbreviated to btu?
18. Against which emperor did the Roman poet Lucan conspire?
19. What is the southernmost of the four main islands of Japan?
20. In which county is the resort of Cromer?

ANSWERS: *1 Epidural, 2 Archbishop of York, 3 Indonesia, 4 17, 5 John Curry, 6 Richard Wagner, 7 John Bull, 8 Suttee, 9 Aleksandr Borodin, 10 Serum, 11 Brent, 12 Enzymes, 13 Joseph Heller, 14 Inferiority complex, 15 Linz, 16 George Fox, 17 British thermal unit, 18 Nero, 19 Kyushu, 20 Norfolk*

General Knowledge

Your rating:
- **0-5 Join a library**
- **6-10 Keep at it**
- **11-15 Join a quiz team**
- **16-20 Join Mensa**

1. Who was the escaped slave who removed a thorn from a lion's paw in an ancient Roman story?
2. In which U.S. state is the city of Yonkers?
3. In which British city was the G8 summit held in May 1998?
4. Which British king was known as Silly Billy?
5. In what year did Prince Andrew marry Sarah Ferguson?
6. Which ceremonial arch stands in the centre of l'Etoile in Paris?
7. Which large island is divided between Malaysia, Indonesia and Brunei?
8. Which superstar singer and film star died in May 1998 at the age of 82?
9. What does the abbreviation YWCA stand for?
10. Which supernatural beings rank immediately above angels in the celestial hierarchy?
11. Which English poet wrote *The Borough*, on which Benjamin Britten's *Peter Grimes* is based?
12. In Greek mythology, who was the wife of Orpheus who died from a snake bite?
13. What name is given to the hydrated crystalline form of sodium carbonate?
14. Who was the king of France at the time of the Seven Years' War?
15. Which 17th century British historian wrote *The History of the Worthies of England*?
16. Of which country was Sir Robert Menzies prime minister?
17. Which Indian Muslim dynasty was established by Babur in the 16th century?
18. Which simplified form of the English language has a vocabulary of 850 words?
19. In which U.S. state is the city and port of Mobile?
20. Who succeeded Joseph Smith as leader of the Mormons and led the migration to Salt Lake City?

***ANSWERS:** 1 Androcles, 2 New York, 3 Birmingham, 4 William IV, 5 1986, 6 Arc de Triomphe, 7 Borneo, 8 Frank Sinatra, 9 Young Women's Christian Organisation, 10 Archangels, 11 George Crabbe, 12 Eurydice, 13 Washing soda, 14 Louis XV, 15 Thomas Fuller, 16 Australia, 17 Moguls, 18 Basic English, 19 Alabama, 20 Brigham Young.*

General Knowledge

Your rating: ● 0-5 Join a library ● 6-10 Keep at it ● 11-15 Join a quiz team ● 16-20 Join Mensa

1. According to legend, which sacred object was brought to Glastonbury by Joseph of Arimathea?
2. Which optical toy using multiple reflections to create patterns was invented by Sir David Brewster?
3. What name is given to the property of a body that causes it to remain at rest or in uniform motion until external force is applied?
4. Which football team won the 1997-98 Scottish Premiership, ending Rangers' hopes of winning ten titles in a row?
5. What is sometimes called the 'change of life'?
6. Which broadcasting company celebrated its 75th anniversary in 1997?
7. In which county is the new town of Basildon?
8. Which Christian sect is named after Dutch Anabaptist leader Menno Simons?
9. Who are the two sons of John Lennon who released albums on the same day in 1998?
10. In which European country is the city of Brescia?
11. Which parasitic fungus affects cereal grasses such as rye and can cause gangrene in humans?
12. What is the Celtic language of Brittany called?
13. Which monarch's government was attacked in the Letters of Junius?
14. Who stepped down as chief executive of the Body Shop in 1998?
15. Which crystalline solid is responsible for the characteristic smell of the mint plant?
16. By what name was the English nun Elizabeth Barton known?
17. Which faction of the Russian Social Democratic Party was finally suppressed by the Bolsheviks in 1922?
18. By what name is the European meadow plant *Primula veris* better known?
19. Which great popular journalist who edited the *Daily Mirror* died in 1998 at the age of 84?
20. How many masts does a brig have?

ANSWERS: *1 The Holy Grail, 2 Kaleidoscope, 3 Inertia, 4 Celtic, 5 Menopause, 6 The BBC, 7 Essex, 8 Mennonites, 9 Julian and Sean Lennon, 10 Italy, 11 Ergot, 12 Breton, 13 George III, 14 Anita Roddick, 15 Menthol, 16 Maid of Kent, 17 Mensheviks, 18 Cowslip, 19 Lord (Hugh) Cudlipp, 20 Two.*

Entertainment

Your rating: ● 0-5 Buy a TV ● 6-10 Keep at it ● 11-15 Join a quiz team ● 16-20 Enter a quiz show

1. Who was the star of the 1970s chat show *Shut That Door!*?
2. Who had a number one single in 1992 with *Sleeping Satellite*?
3. Who played J. Edgar Hoover in the film *Nixon*?
4. In which city was TV's *And the Beat Goes On* set?
5. Which British actor played Mr. Orange in the 1992 film *Reservoir Dogs*?
6. Which *Peak Practice* character was played on TV by Gary Mavers?
7. Which Antipodean heart-throb had a number one hit in 1989 with *Sealed With A Kiss*?
8. Which educational programme began in 1969 and spawned *The Muppet Show* in 1976?
9. Who starred opposite Mary Stuart Masterson in the romantic comedy film *Bed Of Roses*?
10. Which former *Blue Peter* presenter has hosted television coverage of *Crufts*?
11. Which ageing rock band sued the BBC in 1996 after Radio One banned them from their playlist?
12. Which British film-maker won Oscars in the Animated Film category in 1990, 1993 and 1995?
13. Which Canadian actor starred on TV as *T. J. Hooker*?
14. What was Blur's first top ten single in the UK?
15. Who starred as Lenny Nero in the film *Strange Days*?
16. Who played wife-beater Ian Armstrong in the TV drama *Trip Trap*?
17. Which soul combo released an album entitled *Ocean Drive* in 1996?
18. Which film starred Sean Bean as a Sheffield United footballer?
19. Who had a top ten hit in 1966 with *Sha La La La Lee*?
20. Who played the lead role in the sitcom *Shelley*?

ANSWERS: *1 Larry Grayson, 2 Tasmin Archer, 3 Bob Hoskins, 4 Liverpool, 5 Tim Roth, 6 Dr Andrew Attwood, 7 Jason Donovan, 8 Sesame Street, 9 Christian Slater, 10 Peter Purves, 11 Status Quo, 12 Nick Park, 13 William Shatner, 14 There's No Other Way, 15 Ralph Fiennes, 16 Kevin Whately, 17 Lighthouse Family, 18 When Saturday Comes, 19 Small Faces, 20 Hywel Bennett.*

General Knowledge

Your rating:
- 0-5 Join a library
- 6-10 Keep at it
- 11-15 Join a quiz team
- 16-20 Join Mensa

1. What sort of creature is a burbot?
2. Which Italian soldier and patriot won Sicily and Naples for the new kingdom of Italy?
3. Who won the Embassy world snooker championship in 1998?
4. In which war were the Battles of Bull Run fought?
5. Who wrote the songs *Mad Dogs and Englishmen* and *Mad about the Boy*?
6. How many pairs of limbs does a crab have?
7. What sort of creature is a crake?
8. Which British novelist wrote *Earthly Powers*?
9. What name is given to an inflamed swelling on the first joint of the big toe?
10. Who was the first English printer?
11. By what name was Theodore Kaczynski, jailed for life for a series of terrorist attacks, known?
12. Which Nobel prize-winning novelist wrote *Humboldt's Gift* and *The Dean's December*?
13. What nationality was the painter and sculptor Alberto Giacometti?
14. What has been the capital of Belize since 1970?
15. What sort of creature is a garganey?
16. Who wrote the musicals *Careless Rapture* and *The Dancing Years*?
17. What nationality was the conductor Karl Böhm?
18. What collective name is given to the poets Thomas Carew, Robert Herrick, Richard Lovelace and Sir John Suckling?
19. Which semiprecious stone is the birthstone for January?
20. What form of jazz is chiefly associated with John Coltrane and Ornette Coleman?

ANSWERS: *1 A fish, 2 Giuseppe Garibaldi, 3 John Higgins, 4 The American Civil War, 5 Sir Noël Coward, 6 Five, 7 A bird, 8 Anthony Burgess, 9 Bunion, 10 William Caxton, 11 The Unabomber, 12 Saul Bellow, 13 Swiss, 14 Belmopan, 15 A duck, 16 Ivor Novello, 17 Austrian, 18 Cavalier Poets, 19 Garnet, 20 Free-form or free jazz.*

General Knowledge

Your rating: ● 0-5 Join a library ● 6-10 Keep at it ● 11-15 Join a quiz team ● 16-20 Join Mensa

1. What name is given to the hunters and gatherers who inhabited Australia before European settlement?
2. Which Scottish music hall star was associated with the songs *I Love a Lassie* and *Roamin' in the Gloamin'*?
3. In which European city can the Champs Élysées be found?
4. In Scottish law, which verdict other than not guilty can accompany an acquittal?
5. In Greek mythology, by which part of Achilles's body did his mother hold him when she dipped him into the river Styx?
6. Which king of Scotland, subject of a Shakespeare play, killed Duncan I?
7. What is the name for a French castle or large country house?
8. Which movement in painting is associated with Van Gogh, Cézanne and Gauguin?
9. Against which team did Arsenal secure the 1997-'98 Premiership title?
10. By what name is the tree *Cedrus libani* better known?
11. Which English composer and lutenist wrote the famous *Lachrymae*?
12. What name is given to the French-speaking inhabitants of Louisiana, whose ancestors were driven there from Acadia (Nova Scotia)?
13. Which English poet published poems purporting to be the work of a 15th century monk, Thomas Rowley?
14. Of which Canadian province is Fredericton the capital?
15. Which Austrian monk discovered the fundamental principles of genetics?
16. In what year did the first Boer War begin?
17. Of which Caribbean island is Castries the capital?
18. Which German sociologist wrote *The Protestant Ethic and the Spirit of Capitalism*?
19. In economics, what does PSBR stand for?
20. Which British novelist wrote *The Fat Woman's Joke*?

ANSWERS: *1 Aborigines, 2 Sir Harry Lauder, 3 Paris, 4 Not proven, 5 His heel, 6 Macbeth, 7 Chateau, 8 Postimpressionism, 9 Everton, 10 Cedar of Lebanon, 11 John Dowland, 12 Cajuns, 13 Thomas Chatterton, 14 New Brunswick, 15 Gregor Mendel, 16 1880, 17 St Lucia, 18 Max Weber, 19 Public Sector Borrowing Requirement, 20 Fay Weldon.*

General Knowledge

Your rating: ● **0-5** **Join a library** ● **6-10** **Keep at it**
● **11-15** **Join a quiz team** ● **16-20** **Join Mensa**

1. Which British author wrote *The Lost World*?
2. The Fastnet race is part of which sailing cup series?
3. What name is given to the skin of an animal treated for writing on, but untanned?
4. What was the language of ancient Rome?
5. Which artist and typographer carved the Stations of the Cross in Westminster Cathedral?
6. With whose comic operas is Richard D'Oyly Carte associated?
7. What name is given to a dome-shaped Eskimo dwelling made of blocks of hard snow?
8. Which ancient Chinese martial art was popularised in the west by Bruce Lee?
9. What sort of creature is a gila monster?
10. What is the traditional London address of the Chancellor of the Exchequer?
11. What name is given to the series of radioactive elements with atomic numbers from 89 to 103?
12. What were the wealthy peasants of late imperial and early Soviet Russia called?
13. Which British movement for political reform centred on the London Working Men's Association?
14. What is the official language of Andorra?
15. Which Italian composer wrote *The Pines of Rome* and *The Fountains of Rome*?
16. What is the name of the faith healer who worked with the England soccer team under Glenn Hoddle?
17. For which country did Colin Meads play rugby?
18. What name is given to the pumping of fuel in the form of a spray directly into the cylinders of an internal-combustion engine?
19. Which Nobel prize-winning Mexican poet died in 1998 at the age of 84?
20. Which German composer wrote *Italian* and *Scottish* symphonies?

***ANSWERS:** 1 Sir Arthur Conan Doyle, 2 Admiral's Cup, 3 Parchment, 4 Latin, 5 Eric Gill, 6 Gilbert and Sullivan, 7 Igloo, 8 Kung Fu, 9 A lizard, 10 No 11 Downing Street, 11 Actinides, 12 Kulaks, 13 Chartism, 14 Catalan, 15 Ottorino Respighi, 16 Eileen Drewery, 17 New Zealand, 18 Fuel injection, 19 Octavio Paz, 20 Felix Mendelssohn.*

Entertainment

Your rating: ● 0-5 Buy a TV ● 6-10 Keep at it ● 11-15 Join a quiz team ● 16-20 Enter a quiz show

1. Which daily weekday Channel 4 series set children's tales to mime?
2. Which knighted pop star said in 1996, "I'm aware of the rumours, but I am not gay."?
3. Which writer and former milkman created the character of Alf Garnett in *Till Death Us Do Part* and its sequels?
4. Which indie-pop band released an album entitled *Lovelife* in 1996?
5. What was the title of the BBC 1 John MacUre medical drama series?
6. Who starred as the brash Brooklyn housewife in the film *For Pete's Sake*?
7. Who had a top ten UK hit single in 1988 with *Ship of Fools*?
8. Who was the writer of the drama series *The Governor*?
9. Which Sex Pistol said in 1996, "Sid was a coathanger to fill in an empty space on stage"?
10. Which actress won an Academy Award nomination for her portrayal of a teenage prostitute in the 1976 film *Taxi Driver*?
11. Who was the original manipulator of the glove puppet Sooty?
12. Who provided the voice for Woody the cowboy in the film *Toy Story*?
13. Which *EastEnders* character became a grandmother on her birthday in 1996?
14. Which actor played *Othello* in the 1995 film version?
15. Who had a UK top ten single in 1991 with *Shiny Happy People*?
16. Who directed the 1948 film *Fort Apache*?
17. Who played Hutch in *Starsky and Hutch*?
18. Which *Alien* star played a New Age guru in the film *Jeffrey*?
19. Which Dire Straits member released a solo album entitled *Golden Heart* in 1996?
20. Which 1982 film starred Eddie Murphy as a small-time crook, and Nick Nolte as a San Francisco cop?

ANSWERS: *1 A Box Full of Stories, 2 Cliff Richard, 3 Johnny Speight, 4 Lush, 5 Cardiac Arrest, 6 Barbra Streisand, 7 Erasure, 8 Lynda La Plante, 9 Johnny Rotten/Lydon, 10 Jodie Foster, 11 Harry Corbett, 12 Tom Hanks, 13 Peggy Mitchell, 14 Laurence Fishburne, 15 R.E.M., 16 John Ford, 17 David Soul, 18 Sigourney Weaver, 19 Mark Knopfler, 20 48 Hrs.*

General Knowledge

Your rating:
- 0-5 Join a library
- 6-10 Keep at it
- 11-15 Join a quiz team
- 16-20 Join Mensa

1. Which U.S. state comprises the former Sandwich Islands?
2. What is the largest and most massive planet orbiting the sun?
3. On which ill-fated Transatlantic liner was William Murdoch first officer?
4. In horticulture, what name is given to the propagation method in which part of one plant is transferred to another?
5. To which playwright was Anne Hathaway married?
6. According to legend, which twins were the founders of Rome?
7. Which English physicist wrote *A Brief History of Time*?
8. What name is given to radioactive particles deposited from the atmosphere after a nuclear explosion?
9. What name was given to the re-establishment of the monarchy in England following the fall of the Protectorate?
10. Which annual cereal grass is grown in paddy fields?
11. By what name is the plant lords-and-ladies better known?
12. Which intellectual circle included Virginia Woolf, John Maynard Keynes, Lytton Strachey and Roger Fry?
13. What was the stage name of actress, singer and dancer Virginia McMath?
14. Which veins in the neck return blood from the head to the vena cava?
15. In what year did the English Civil War begin?
16. Which plant is also known as a belladonna lily?
17. Which Scottish loch contains the ruins of a castle on one of its islands in which Mary, Queen of Scots, was imprisoned?
18. In Arthurian legend, which knight of the Round Table was the son of King Lot?
19. What sort of number is the ratio of the focal length to the size of the aperture in a camera?
20. Which German composer wrote the Mass in D, *Missa Solemnis*?

ANSWERS: *1 Hawaii, 2 Jupiter, 3 The Titanic, 4 Grafting, 5 William Shakespeare, 6 Romulus and Remus, 7 Stephen Hawking, 8 Fallout, 9 Restoration, 10 Rice, 11 Cuckoopint, 12 Bloomsbury group, 13 Ginger Rogers, 14 Jugular veins, 15 1642, 16 Amaryllis, 17 Loch Leven, 18 Gawain, 19 F-number, 20 Ludwig van Beethoven.*

General Knowledge

Your rating: ● 0-5 Join a library ● 6-10 Keep at it ● 11-15 Join a quiz team ● 16-20 Join Mensa

1. What name is given to the annual sum provided from public funds to meet the official expenses of the Queen?
2. Which French town associated with Saint Bernadette is a major pilgrimage centre for Roman Catholics?
3. What is the highest adult male singing voice, also known as countertenor?
4. What name was given to outlaws in the Australian outback such as Ned Kelly?
5. To what genus of fruits do oranges, lemons and limes belong?
6. Which Conservative politician married Jennie Jerome in 1874?
7. In which European country is the city of Foggia?
8. Which Scottish city provided a retirement home for the former Royal Yacht Britannia?
9. By what name was Arthur Wellesley known?
10. In which country is the black swan found?
11. Coeliac disease is caused by an intolerance to gliadin, a component of which protein found in wheat?
12. Who directed the films *The Magnificent Ambersons* and *Chimes at Midnight*?
13. The pods of which plant, also called lady's fingers, are used to make gumbo?
14. What was the language of the troubadours?
15. Which former world heavyweight boxing champion was nicknamed the Brown Bomber?
16. What does an apiculturist keep?
17. Which French city is the capital of the Somme department?
18. Of which planet did Percival Lowell predict the existence?
19. Which crime writer created Paul Temple?
20. Which nonvenomous European snake has the Latin name *Natrix natrix*?

ANSWERS: *1 Civil list, 2 Lourdes, 3 Alto, 4 Bushrangers, 5 Citrus, 6 Randolph Churchill, 7 Italy, 8 Edinburgh, 9 1st Duke of Wellington, 10 Australia, 11 Gluten, 12 Orson Welles, 13 Okra, 14 Provençal, 15 Joe Louis, 16 Bees, 17 Amiens, 18 Pluto, 19 Francis Durbridge, 20 Grass snake.*

General Knowledge

Your rating: • 0-5 Join a library • 6-10 Keep at it • 11-15 Join a quiz team • 16-20 Join Mensa

1. In which county is the fishing port of Lowestoft?
2. What name is given to a device that converts an alternating current from one voltage to another?
3. On which day of Holy Week was the 1998 Ulster peace deal agreed?
4. Which instrument used in aircraft measures height above sea level?
5. What name is given to a wheel turned by foot power, used in prisons in the 19th century?
6. To which king of Israel is the Old Testament book Proverbs ascribed?
7. What is the fruit of the blackthorn called?
8. In which county is the cathedral city of Wells?
9. Which comedian was injured in a quad bike accident on his country estate in 1998?
10. Which Irish adventurer attempted to steal the crown jewels from the Tower of London in 1671?
11. Which poison is also known as prussic acid?
12. From which country did the United States make the Louisiana Purchase?
13. Which golfer won the 1998 U.S. Masters at Augusta?
14. In which country is the Althing, the oldest parliament in the world?
15. By what collective name are the three Hindu gods Brahma, Vishnu and Siva known?
16. Which purple or violet variety of quartz is the birthstone for February?
17. What is the common name for the plant *Amaranthus caudatus*, which has drooping spikes of small red flowers?
18. Which English prison reformer was high sheriff of Bedfordshire?
19. Which Roman road ran from London to Wroxeter?
20. Who wrote *The Treasure of the Sierra Madre*?

ANSWERS: *1 Suffolk, 2 Transformer, 3 Good Friday, 4 Altimeter, 5 Treadmill, 6 Solomon, 7 Sloe, 8 Somerset, 9 Rik Mayall, 10 Colonel Blood, 11 Hydrocyanic acid, 12 France, 13 Mark O'Meara, 14 Iceland, 15 Trimurti, 16 Amethyst, 17 Love-lies-bleeding, 18 John Howard, 19 Watling Street, 20 B. Traven.*

Entertainment

Your rating:
- **0-5 Buy a TV**
- **6-10 Keep at it**
- **11-15 Join a quiz team**
- **16-20 Enter a quiz show**

1. Which Supremes song did Phil Collins take to the U.K. number one spot in 1982?
2. Who starred as the athlete fighting for his free will in the 1975 film *Rollerball*?
3. Which ethereal singer released an album in 1996 entitled *The Memory of Trees*?
4. What sort of animal was the star of the 1995 film *Babe*?
5. Which police drama series starred Reece Dinsdale as Detective Inspector Charlie Scott?
6. Which London pop band released an album in 1995 entitled *Up All Night*?
7. Who starred as the eponymous investigator in the Seventies detective drama series *Banacek*?
8. Who starred as the mysterious vagrant in the 1995 film *Three Wishes*?
9. With which instrument was the jazz musician John Coltrane associated?
10. Who played Tinkerbell in Steven Spielberg's 1991 film *Hook*?
11. What was the name of Noel Edmonds's nostalgic quiz show of the mid-Nineties?
12. Which soul singer had a U.K. number one hit in 1974 with *You're the First the Last My Everything*?
13. Which *Monty Python* star provided the voice of a frog in the 1994 film *The Swan Princess*?
14. What does *ER* stand for in the title of the U.S. drama series?
15. Leather trousers belonging to which rock star were sold for £28,000 at Sotheby's in 1996?
16. Which British actor played General Douglas MacArthur in the 1981 film *Inchon*?
17. What was Angus Loughran's alter-ego in the cult series *Fantasy Football League*?
18. Who had a U.K. top ten hit single in 1972 with *You're So Vain*?
19. Which 1995 thriller starred Brad Pitt as a cop on the trail of a serial killer?
20. 39-year-old Robert Hoskins received a ten-year jail sentence in 1996 after being found guilty of stalking which pop star?

ANSWERS: *1 You Can't Hurry Love, 2 James Caan, 3 Enya, 4 A pig, 5 Thief Takers, 6 East 17, 7 George Peppard, 8 Patrick Swayze, 9 Saxophone, 10 Julia Roberts, 11 Noel's Telly Years, 12 Barry White, 13 John Cleese, 14 Emergency Room, 15 Jim Morrison, 16 Laurence Olivier, 17 Statto, 18 Carly Simon, 19 Seven, 20 Madonna.*

General Knowledge

Your rating:
- 0-5 Join a library
- 6-10 Keep at it
- 11-15 Join a quiz team
- 16-20 Join Mensa

1. Which sign of the zodiac is symbolised by a ram?
2. What is the largest planet in our solar system?
3. Which England footballer won a Champions League winners medal in 2000?
4. In which country did the Boxer rebellion take place in 1900?
5. Which unit of mass is equal to one thousandth of a kilogram?
6. In which English county is the seaside resort of Eastbourne?
7. Which British singer recorded the albums *Aladdin Sane* and *Scary Monsters*?
8. Who is the spiritual leader of the Tibetan people?
9. Which Scottish team appointed the former Leicester City boss Martin O'Neill as manager?
10. What name is given to the scientific study of plants?
11. Which U.S. composer wrote *Star Dust* and *In the Cool, Cool, Cool of the Evening*?
12. What collective name is given to the Gospels of Matthew, Mark and Luke?
13. Of which U.S. state is Raleigh the capital?
14. Who was the god of war in Greek mythology?
15. Which poisonous gas has a distinctive smell like rotten eggs?
16. Which is the second largest island of the Philippines?
17. Which Australian novelist wrote *Illywhacker* and *Oscar and Lucinda*?
18. In which Irish county is the resort of Cobh?
19. Which English artist illustrated the published edition of Oscar Wilde's play *Salome*?
20. Who is the director of the film *The Ninth Gate*?

ANSWERS: *1 Aries, 2 Jupiter, 3 Steve McManaman, 4 China, 5 Gram, 6 East Sussex, 7 David Bowie, 8 Dalai Lama, 9 Celtic, 10 Botany, 11 Hoagy Carmichael, 12 The Synoptic Gospels, 13 North Carolina, 14 Ares, 15 Hydrogen sulphide, 16 Mindanao, 17 Peter Carey, 18 County Cork, 19 Aubrey Beardsley, 20 Roman Polanski.*

General Knowledge

Your rating:
- 0-5 Join a library
- 6-10 Keep at it
- 11-15 Join a quiz team
- 16-20 Join Mensa

1. Which nurse was nicknamed *The Lady with the Lamp* by her patients?
2. In which sport do women's teams compete for the Federation Cup?
3. Which British author wrote *The Woman in White*?
4. Of which country was Hafez al-Assad president?
5. Which disease of the central nervous system is represented by the abbreviation MS?
6. On which Greek island was Prince Philip born?
7. Cheltenham is at the foot of which hills?
8. Which Portuguese explorer discovered the sea route to India?
9. What is the main metallic element in the alloy brass?
10. Which British author wrote *The Small Back Room*?
11. Which French philosopher and author wrote *Memoirs of a Dutiful Daughter* and *The Second Sex*?
12. What is the capital of Bahrain?
13. Which geographical term literally means 'chief sea'?
14. What is a hygrometer used to measure?
15. Which British portrait photographer designed the costumes for *My Fair Lady* and *Gigi*?
16. In which European country are the Arlberg tunnels?
17. Of which country was Carol II king from 1930 to 1940?
18. Which Scottish cyclist claimed the yellow jersey after the first stage of the 2000 Tour de France?
19. By what name is the United Nations Children's Fund commonly known?
20. What is the capital of Liechtenstein?

ANSWERS: *1 Florence Nightingale, 2 Tennis, 3 Wilkie Collins, 4 Syria, 5 Multiple sclerosis, 6 Corfu, 7 The Cotswolds, 8 Vasco da Gama, 9 Copper, 10 Nigel Balchin, 11 Simone de Beauvoir, 12 Manama, 13 Archipelago, 14 Humidity, 15 Cecil Beaton, 16 Austria, 17 Romania, 18 David Millar, 19 UNICEF, 20 Vaduz.*

General Knowledge

Your rating: • 0-5 Join a library • 6-10 Keep at it • 11-15 Join a quiz team • 16-20 Join Mensa

1. Which equestrian discipline is the first part of a three-day event?
2. What was the title of Jeffrey Archer's first novel?
3. Which black American baptist minister won the 1964 Nobel Peace Prize?
4. What sort of apple was originally cultivated by Maria Ann Smith?
5. Which valuable gems are formed by nacre in oysters?
6. What name is given to the declarer's partner in a hand of bridge?
7. What nationality was the composer Franz Liszt?
8. Which metal has the chemical symbol Zn?
9. Of which country was Gough Whitlam the prime minister?
10 What sort of police officer takes his name from the Latin term *comes stabuli*?
11. Which U.S. author wrote *Lust for Life* and *The Agony and the Ecstasy*?
12. What name is given to the First and Second Epistles to Timothy and the Epistle to Titus?
13. Which shrub of the genus *Philadelphus* is also called syringa?
14. Of which sporting body is Gerhard Aigner the general secretary?
15. Which letter of the English alphabet is derived from the sixth letter of the Greek alphabet?
16. In which English county is Silbury Hill?
17. Which substance used in treating malaria is taken from the bark of the cinchona tree?
18. Of which mineral is the gemstone aquamarine a variety?
19. What was the pen name of the Scottish poet Christopher Murray Grieve?
20. Which visual defect is also called hyperopia or hypermetropia?

ANSWERS: *1 Dressage, 2 Not a Penny More, Not a Penny Less, 3 Martin Luther King Jr, 4 Granny Smith, 5 Pearls, 6 Dummy, 7 Hungarian, 8 Zinc, 9 Australia, 10 Constable, 11 Irving Stone, 12 Pastoral Epistles, 13 Mock orange, 14 UEFA, 15 Z, 16 Wiltshire, 17 Quinine, 18 Beryl, 19 Hugh MacDiarmid, 20 Longsightedness.*

Sports

Your rating: ● 0-5 Wooden spoon ● 6-10 Bronze medal ● 11-15 Silver medal ● 16-20 Gold medal

1. Who won the women's singles title at the 2000 French Open?
2. Which golfer won the U.S. PGA in 1995?
3. Which Argentinian scored two goals in the final of the 1978 World Cup?
4. Who was the world snooker champion in 1986?
5. Which city hosted the 1980 Olympic Games?
6. Which England bowler returned figures of 5 for 15 on the first day of the first Test against Zimbabwe in May 2000?
7. Which English football team won the European Cup in 1979?
8. A chinaman is a term from which sport?
9. Who won the 10,000 metres at the 1976 Olympics?
10. Which boxer was the European heavyweight champion in 1964 and 1968-71?
11. Who scored Chelsea's winning goal in the 2000 FA Cup Final?
12. How many golf majors has Jack Nicklaus won?
13. Which country does the cricketer Wavell Hinds play for?
14. Which team won the FA Cup in 1973?
15. Which darts player is nick-named The Power?
16. Which British Formula 1 racing driver survived a Learjet crash in May 2000?
17. Who won the U.S. Masters in golf in 2000?
18. In which sport did Felix Savon win gold at the Sydney Olympics?

19. Which number lies between 19 and 17 on a dartboard?
20. For which Premiership football team does Titus Bramble play?

ANSWERS: *1 Mary Pierce, 2 Steve Elkington, 3 Mario Kempes, 4 Joe Johnson, 5 Moscow, 6 Ed Giddins, 7 Nottingham Forest, 8 Cricket, 9 Lasse Viren, 10 Henry Cooper, 11 Roberto Di Matteo, 12 18, 13 West Indies, 14 Sunderland, 15 Phil Taylor, 16 David Coulthard, 17 Vijay Singh, 18 Boxing, 19 3, 20 Ipswich Town.*

General Knowledge

Your rating: ● **0-5** Join a library ● **6-10** Keep at it ● **11-15** Join a quiz team ● **16-20** Join Mensa

1. Which tennis player was stabbed by a spectator in 1993?
2. In which country did the Flying Doctor Service originate?
3. Which *Absolutely Fabulous* star provides the voice for Ginger in the film *Chicken Run*?
4. What was the name of Dick Turpin's horse?
5. Which infectious disease is also called TB?
6. What is the largest city in the state of Washington?
7. Which British rower won his fourth Olympic gold medal in 1996?
8. What name is given to a line on a map joining places of equal atmospheric pressure?
9. Which country has been awarded the 2006 FIFA World Cup?
10. Of which pop group did Ringo Starr replace Pete Best as the drummer in 1962?
11. What is the capital of Croatia?
12. Which British novelist wrote *My Son, My Son*, *Shabby Tiger* and *Fame is the Spur*?
13. Cocker spaniels were originally to hunt which birds?
14. Which qualifier reached the men's singles semi-finals at Wimbledon in 2000?
15. What is the capital of New York state?
16. Which cruel sport was prohibited by Parliament in 1835?
17. Which U.S. reporter was the anchorman of the CBS evening news from 1962 to 1981?
18. Who wrote the children's novel *Little Lord Fauntleroy*?
19. What is the oldest order of knighthood still in existence in Britain?
20. Which British chemist formulated the law of partial pressures in gases?

***ANSWERS:** 1 Monica Seles, 2 Australia, 3 Julia Sawalha, 4 Black Bess, 5 Tuberculosis, 6 Seattle, 7 Steven Redgrave, 8 Isobar, 9 Germany, 10 The Beatles, 11 Zagreb, 12 Howard Spring, 13 Woodcock, 14 Vladimir Voltchkov, 15 Albany, 16 Bearbaiting, 17 Walter Cronkite, 18 Frances Hodgson Burnett, 19 Order of the Garter, 20 John Dalton.*

General Knowledge

Your rating:
- **0-5 Join a library**
- **6-10 Keep at it**
- **11-15 Join a quiz team**
- **16-20 Join Mensa**

1. Which U.S. gangster is thought to have been responsible for the St Valentine's Day Massacre?
2. The Marseillaise is the national anthem of which European country?
3. Which American actress starred in the films *I'm No Angel* and *She Done Him Wrong*?
4. Who won his seventh men's singles title at Wimbledon in 2000?
5. Which mountain chain forms a natural barrier between France and Spain?
6. In which English county is Lowestoft?
7. Which stimulant is found in coffee, tea and kola nuts?
8. Which reclusive American tycoon designed the wooden flying boat known as the *Spruce Goose*?
9. Who was the prime minister of the United Kingdom from 1964 to 1970 and from 1974 to 1976?
10. Which Scottish actor won an Oscar for his performance in *The Untouchables*?
11. In which East Sussex town did Simon de Montfort defeat the forces of Henry III in 1264?
12. Which leading German World War II rocket engineer worked for the U.S. Army and NASA after the war?
13. Who was the first U.S. vice president to succeed to the presidency?
14. What name is given to the liquid part of blood?
15. What is the capital of Costa Rica?
16. Which British novelist wrote *The Magic Toyshop* and *Wise Children*?
17. Which pointillist artist painted *Sunday Afternoon on the Island of La Grande Jatte*?
18. What title is held by noblemen of the lowest rank in the British peerage?
19. What is the highest mountain in Greece?
20. Which Oscar-winning actor plays Benjamin Martin in the film *The Patriot*?

ANSWERS: *1 Al Capone, 2 France, 3 Mae West, 4 Pete Sampras, 5 The Pyrenees, 6 Suffolk, 7 Caffeine, 8 Howard Hughes, 9 Harold Wilson, 10 Sean Connery, 11 Lewes, 12 Wernher von Braun, 13 John Tyler, 14 Plasma, 15 San José, 16 Angela Carter, 17 Georges Seurat, 18 Baron, 19 Olympus, 20 Mel Gibson.*

General Knowledge

Your rating:
- 0-5 Join a library
- 6-10 Keep at it
- 11-15 Join a quiz team
- 16-20 Join Mensa

1. Which Argentinian footballer used his hand to score against England in the 1986 World Cup Finals?
2. What was the nickname of the U.S. Confederate general Thomas Jackson?
3. Which country occupies the western part of the island of Hispaniola?
4. What is the title of the fourth *Harry Potter* novel?
5. Which arm of the Mediterranean Sea lies between Greece and Turkey?
6. In which U.S. city is the Guggenheim Museum?
7. Which British heavyweight boxer was the first to win three Lonsdale Belts?
8. What name is given to the stiff, flat hat with a tassel worn by graduating students?
9. Which Russian author wrote *War and Peace* and *Anna Karenina*?
10. With which musical instrument was Django Reinhardt associated?
11. How many ounces are there in a pound avoirdupois?
12. Which American heavyweight boxer retired in 1956 after winning all of his 49 professional fights?
13. Who wrote and illustrated the children's story *Where the Wild Things Are*?
14. What name is given to the act of depriving a person of membership of a church?
15. Who headed the syndicate that owned the first non-American yacht to win the America's Cup?
16. By what name was Lyndon B Johnson's wife known?
17. Which Puccini opera was unfinished at his death?
18. What is the name of the corporation that operates intercity passenger trains in the United States?
19. Who won the women's singles title at Wimbledon in 2000?
20. Who was the deputy leader of the Labour Party from 1983 to 1992?

ANSWERS: *1 Diego Maradona, 2 Stonewall, 3 Haiti, 4 Harry Potter and the Goblet of Fire, 5 Aegean Sea, 6 New York City, 7 Henry Cooper, 8 Mortarboard, 9 Leo Tolstoy, 10 Guitar, 11 Sixteen, 12 Rocky Marciano, 13 Maurice Sendak, 14 Excommunication, 15 Alan Bond, 16 Lady Bird, 17 Turandot, 18 Amtrak, 19 Venus Williams, 20 Roy Hattersley.*

Entertainment

Your rating: ● 0-5 Buy a TV ● 6-10 Keep at it ● 11-15 Join a quiz team ● 16-20 Enter a quiz show

1. Who starred as the adopted American Indian Jack Crabb in the 1970 film *Little Big Man*?
2. Which *Coronation Street* character was played by Peter Baldwin?
3. Which husband and wife vocal duo had a U.K. top ten hit in 1985 with *Solid*?
4. Who played Chief Inspector Wexford in *The Ruth Rendell Mysteries* on TV?
5. Which 1995 French film starred Juliette Binoche and Olivier Martinez as aristocrats fleeing a cholera epidemic?
6. Which of the McGann brothers played the eighth incarnation of *Doctor Who* in a 1996 TV movie?
7. What was the uplifting title of Yoko Ono's 1996 album release?
8. What was the third film to feature the character Dirty Harry?
9. Which comedienne could be seen *Through the Cakehole* on TV in the Nineties?
10. Which member of Crosby, Stills, Nash & Young was previously a member of The Hollies?
11. On which Nineties panel game show were Eddie Large and Phill Jupitus team captains?
12. Who is the lead singer with Everything but the Girl?
13. Who starred as the psychiatrist in the 1992 film *Final Analysis*?
14. Which monarch did Dame Peggy Ashcroft play in the Seventies TV drama *Edward and Mrs Simpson*?
15. Which father and daughter had a U.K. number one hit single in 1967 with *Somethin' Stupid*?
16. Which Hollywood star directed the 1987 film version of *The Glass Menagerie*?
17. Which ex-*Blue Peter* presenter was the host of the TV series *Backdate*?
18. Who hit the U.K. number one spot in 1996 with *Jesus to a Child*?
19. Which singer played Anita in the drama series *Band of Gold*?
20. Which 1995 film starred Julia Roberts and Dennis Quaid as husband and wife?

ANSWERS: *1 Dustin Hoffman, 2 Derek Wilton, 3 Ashford and Simpson, 4 George Baker, 5 The Horseman on the Roof, 6 Paul, 7 Rising, 8 The Enforcer, 9 Jo Brand, 10 Graham Nash, 11 Gag Tag, 12 Tracey Thorn, 13 Richard Gere, 14 Queen Mary, 15 Nancy and Frank Sinatra, 16 Paul Newman, 17 Valerie Singleton, 18 George Michael, 19 Barbara Dickson, 20 Something to Talk About.*

General Knowledge

Your rating: ● **0-5** Join a library ● **6-10** Keep at it ● **11-15** Join a quiz team ● **16-20** Join Mensa

1. Which American author wrote *The Naked and the Dead* and *Tough Guys Don't Dance*?
2. Who played the title role in the film *Lawrence of Arabia*?
3. Which Christian organisation was founded by William Booth in 1865?
4. Whose handbag was sold for £100,000 in a charity auction in 2000?
5. Which children's author wrote adventure stories about the *Famous Five* and the *Secret Seven*?
6. What is the second largest city in the Netherlands?
7. How many events are there in a decathlon?
8. Which American actor starred in *Men in Black* and *The Fugitive*?
9. *Welcome to Dead House* was the first book in which best-selling series of horror stories for children by R L Stine?
10. Which island in the Tyrrhenian Sea is famous for its active volcano?
11. Who retired as the House of Commons Speaker in 2000?
12. Which important gland is attached to the hypothalamus by a stalk?
13. What is the world's smallest bird?
14. Which Argentinian footballer briefly became the world's most expensive player when he joined Lazio from Parma?
15. What name is given to a tree of the genus *Fraxinus*?
16. Which U.S. composer wrote the music for the ballets *Billy the Kid* and *Rodeo*?
17. Which U.S. president was responsible for the Louisiana Purchase?
18. Who played Norman Bates in Alfred Hitchcock's film *Psycho*?
19. Which strait between the Aegean Sea and the Sea of Marmara was once known as the Hellespont?
20. Followers of which Celtic religion regarded the oak tree as sacred?

ANSWERS: *1 Norman Mailer, 2 Peter O'Toole, 3 Salvation Army, 4 Baroness Thatcher's, 5 Enid Blyton, 6 Rotterdam, 7 Ten, 8 Tommy Lee Jones, 9 Goosebumps, 10 Stromboli, 11 Betty Boothroyd, 12 Pituitary gland, 13 Bee hummingbird, 14 Hernan Crespo, 15 Ash, 16 Aaron Copland, 17 Thomas Jefferson, 18 Anthony Perkins, 19 Dardanelles, 20 Druidism.*

General Knowledge

Your rating: ● 0-5 Join a library ● 6-10 Keep at it ● 11-15 Join a quiz team ● 16-20 Join Mensa

1. Which actress starred in *Mary Poppins* and *The Sound of Music*?
2. With what sort of entertainment were the Ringling Brothers and Barnum and Bailey associated?
3. Which English author wrote *The History of Tom Jones, a Foundling*?
4. What is the title of Thomas the Tank Engine's big-screen debut?
5. Which German missile used in World War II was also called a doodlebug or buzz bomb?
6. In Greek mythology, who was the leader of the Argonauts?
7. Which metal has the chemical symbol Cu?
8. Who wrote *The Strange Case of Dr Jekyll and Mr Hyde*?
9. Which former Beatle had a hit with the single *My Sweet Lord*?
10. What sort of creature was *Tarka* in Henry Williamson's novel?
11. Who was the commander in chief of RAF Bomber Command from 1942 to 1945?
12. Which member of Dave Brubeck's quartet wrote *Take Five*?
13. What is the capital of Slovenia?
14. Which French author, who included Chopin among her lovers, wrote the novel *Indiana*?
15. What name for a tidal wave comes from the Japanese for harbour wave?
16. Which radioactive element has the symbol Th?
17. Which form of unarmed combat takes its name from the Japanese for empty hand?
18. Which South American country knocked Great Britain out of the Davis Cup world group in 2000?
19. What is the English name for Wagner's opera *Der Fliegende Hollander*?
20. Which vegetable's name means cabbage turnip?

ANSWERS: *1 Julie Andrews, 2 Circus, 3 Henry Fielding, 4 Thomas and the Magic Railroad, 5 V1, 6 Jason, 7 Copper, 8 Robert Louis Stevenson, 9 George Harrison, 10 An otter, 11 Sir Arthur Harris, 12 Paul Desmond, 13 Ljubljana, 14 George Sand, 15 Tsunami, 16 Thorium, 17 Karate, 18 Ecuador, 19 The Flying Dutchman, 20 Kohlrabi.*

General Knowledge

Your rating: ● 0-5 Join a library ● 6-10 Keep at it ● 11-15 Join a quiz team ● 16-20 Join Mensa

1. Which semicircular device is used to measure angles?
2. In which English county is Glastonbury?
3. Which former England footballer joined Everton from Middlesbrough in 2000?
4. Of which country was Brian Mulroney the prime minister from 1984 to 1993?
5. With which sport was Gareth Edwards associated?
6. Of which U.S. state is Little Rock the capital?
7. Who played *Roseanne*'s husband in the American TV series?
8. To which Italian city does the adjective Neapolitan relate?
9. Which U.S. president was assassinated by John Wilkes Booth?
10. What is the capital of the Czech Republic?
11. Which member of the Royal Family graduated from Exeter University in 2000?
12. Which Australian tennis player won three of the Majors, but lost in his four Wimbledon finals?
13. What name is given to a common weed of the genus *Convolvulus*?
14. Which country did Britain's men beat by half a point to win the European Cup at Gateshead in 2000?
15. Who was the first Christian martyr in England?
16. Which Egyptian president was assassinated in 1981?
17. Which jockey won the Grand National on Sundew in 1957 and Kilmore in 1962?
18. Who wrote *The History of the Decline and Fall of the Roman Empire*?
19. Which actress played a nanny in the Queen Mother's 100th birthday pageant at Horse Guards Parade?
20. Which U.S. author wrote *Presumed Innocent* and *Burden of Proof*?

ANSWERS: *1 Protractor, 2 Somerset, 3 Paul Gascoigne, 4 Canada, 5 Rugby Union, 6 Arkansas, 7 John Goodman, 8 Naples, 9 Abraham Lincoln, 10 Prague, 11 Peter Phillips 12 Ken Rosewall, 13 Bindweed, 14 Germany, 15 Saint Alban, 16 Anwar Sadat, 17 Fred Winter, 18 Edward Gibbon, 19 Wendy Craig, 20 Scott Turow.*

Entertainment

Your rating:
- 0-5 Buy a TV
- 6-10 Keep at it
- 11-15 Join a quiz team
- 16-20 Enter a quiz show

1. Which *Have I Got News For You* star appeared in a series of eight comedies in the Nineties based on scripts by Ray Galton and Alan Simpson?
2. Who directed the last segment of the 1995 film *Four Rooms*?
3. Who played Larry Sanders in TV's *The Larry Sanders Show*?
4. Which German-born singer released an album entitled *Deadline For My Memories* in 1996?
5. Which *Brookside* character was played by Susan Twist?
6. Which *Twin Peaks* star played a casino entertainment boss in the 1995 film *Showgirls*?
7. Which phrase, meaning 'faithful friend' or 'trusty scout', did Tonto often greet *The Lone Ranger* with in the western series?
8. Which jazz trumpeter had Dewey as a middle name?
9. Who starred as the hard-drinking cattle baron in the 1963 film *McLintock!*?
10. In the Nineties drama series *Our Friends in the North*, which actor played Soho porn baron Bennie Barratt?
11. In which city is the grave of the Doors singer Jim Morrison?
12. Who played Easy Rawlins in the 1995 film *Devil in a Blue Dress*?
13. Which ex-Pixies singer/guitarist released an album in 1996 entitled *The Cult of Ray*?
14. Which Italian city was the scene of the heist in the 1969 film *The Italian Job*?
15. Which action-packed Sunday tea-time drama series of the Nineties starred Celia Imrie and Ronald Pickup?
16. What was the title of the 1996 album release by Tori Amos?
17. Which *Waterworld* star played a traumatised war-hero in the 1994 film *The War*?
18. Which actor played Mr Swindley in *Coronation Street* before starring in the comedy series *Dad's Army*?
19. Which singer had a U.K. number one in 1960 with *Please Don't Tease*?
20. Which *Four Weddings and a Funeral* star played Clive Durham in the 1987 film *Maurice*?

ANSWERS: *1 Paul Merton, 2 Quentin Tarantino, 3 Garry Shandling, 4 Billie Ray Martin, 5 Rosie Banks, 6 Kyle Maclachlan, 7 'Kemo Sabe', 8 Miles Davis, 9 John Wayne, 10 Malcolm McDowell, 11 Paris, 12 Denzel Washington, 13 Frank Black, 14 Turin, 15 Black Hearts in Battersea, 16 Boys For Pele, 17 Kevin Costner, 18 Arthur Lowe, 19 Cliff Richard, 20 Hugh Grant.*

General Knowledge

Your rating:
- **0-5 Join a library**
- **6-10 Keep at it**
- **11-15 Join a quiz team**
- **16-20 Join Mensa**

1. Which American general famously pledged “I shall return”?
2. What name is given to a place where coins are made?
3. What name is given to an aircraft without an engine?
4. In which European country is the city of Granada?
5. Which Siberian peasant and mystic exerted harmful influence over Nicholas II of Russia?
6. What is the longest and largest artery in the body?
7. Which winged horse in Greek mythology sprang from the blood of Medusa?
8. Of which country is Yangtze Kiang or Chang Jiang the longest river?
9. Which metallic element has the chemical symbol Mn?
10. What is the fastest animal over short distances?
11. By what name is the popular houseplant *Monstera deliciosa* better known?
12. Which athlete featured in *Chariots of Fire* held the English long jump record for over thirty years?
13. What is the capital of Gabon?
14. Which actress won Oscars for *Norma Rae* and *Places in the Heart*?
15. In what year was the Spanish-American War?
16. Which American author wrote *Charlotte’s Web* and *Stuart Little*?
17. Who was the U.S. secretary of state from 1993 to 1997?
18. Which golf course hosted the Open Championship in 2000?
19. Which artist’s best-known painting is *Nude Descending a Staircase No 2*?
20. Who directed the films *Midnight Cowboy*, *Marathon Man* and *Yanks*?

ANSWERS: *1 Douglas MacArthur, 2 Mint, 3 Glider, 4 Spain, 5 Rasputin, 6 Aorta, 7 Pegasus, 8 China, 9 Manganese, 10 Cheetah, 11 Swiss cheese plant, 12 Harold Abrahams, 13 Libreville, 14 Sally Field, 15 1898, 16 E B White, 17 Warren Christopher, 18 St Andrews, 19 Marcel Duchamp, 20 John Schlesinger.*

General Knowledge

Your rating:
- **0-5 Join a library**
- **6-10 Keep at it**
- **11-15 Join a quiz team**
- **16-20 Join Mensa**

1. Which Hungarian-born actor played *Dracula* in a 1931 film?
2. In law, what name is given to money a court orders one person to pay to another as compensation?
3. Which American actor plays record store owner Rob in the film version of Nick Hornby's *High Fidelity*?
4. With which sport are the Harlem Globetrotters associated?
5. How many degrees are there in a right angle?
6. Who was the official propagandist of Nazi Germany?
7. Which Roman general and statesman did Marcus Junius Brutus help to assassinate?
8. What name is given to the shaping of something so that it meets the least resistance when travelling through water or air?
9. Which instrument of the violin family is held between the knees?
10. What name is given to a score of one under par for a hole in golf?
11. Which *Spitting Image* puppet attracted the highest bid in an Internet auction?
12. Which English scientist discovered the principle of electromagnetic induction in 1831?
13. What was the first name of the ballet dancer Nijinsky?
14. What sort of creature is a babbler?
15. For which country did the fast bowler Ray Lindwall play?
16. Which Spanish artist painted *Las Meninas*?
17. Which archbishop of Canterbury was beheaded in 1645?
18. Which law officer combines the roles of public prosecutor and coroner in Scotland?
19. Of which Middle Eastern country is Latakia the main seaport?
20. Which chemical element has the symbol Rb?

ANSWERS: *1 Bela Lugosi, 2 Damages, 3 John Cusack, 4 Basketball, 5 Ninety, 6 Joseph Goebbels, 7 Julius Caesar, 8 Streamlining, 9 Cello, 10 Birdie, 11 Baroness Thatcher, 12 Michael Faraday, 13 Vaslav, 14 A bird, 15 Australia, 16 Diego Velazquez, 17 William Laud, 18 Procurator fiscal, 19 Syria, 20 Rubidium.*

General Knowledge

Your rating: ● 0-5 Join a library ● 6-10 Keep at it ● 11-15 Join a quiz team ● 16-20 Join Mensa

1. Which British artist and ornithologist founded the Wildfowl Trust at Slimbridge?
2. What was the name of King Arthur's sword?
3. Which Ford model rolled off the production line for the last time in 2000 after a 32-year run?
4. With which Italian city is the Medici family associated?
5. Which British colonial administrator founded Singapore and the Zoological Society?
6. By what name is the trachea commonly known?
7. Of which country is the island of Bali a part?
8. Which long fracture in the earth's crust runs through California?
9. What sort of creature is a gar?
10. In which European country is the city of Charleroi?
11. Who was the Greek god of sleep, called Somnus by the Romans?
12. Which American conductor commissioned George Gershwin's *Rhapsody in Blue*?
13. What name is given to the clear fluid part of blood left after a clot forms?
14. Which cyclist won his second successive Tour de France in 2000?
15. What name is given to the study of human populations?
16. Of which ocean is the White Sea a part?
17. What was the pen name of the novelist and literary critic Cicely Isabel Fairfield?
18. On which Japanese island was the G8 Summit held in July 2000?
19. Which Shakespeare play features Prospero, Miranda and Caliban?
20. By what name is the Collegiate Church of St Peter in London better known?

ANSWERS: 1 *Sir Peter Scott*, 2 *Excalibur*, 3 *Escort*, 4 *Florence*, 5 *Thomas Stamford Raffles*, 6 *Windpipe*, 7 *Indonesia*, 8 *San Andreas Fault*, 9 *A fish*, 10 *Belgium*, 11 *Hypnos*, 12 *Paul Whiteman*, 13 *Serum*, 14 *Lance Armstrong*, 15 *Demography*, 16 *Arctic*, 17 *Rebecca West*, 18 *Okinawa*, 19 *The Tempest*, 20 *Westminster Abbey*.

Entertainment

Your rating: ● **0-5** Buy a TV ● **6-10** Keep at it ● **11-15** Join a quiz team ● **16-20** Enter a quiz show

1. What was the nickname of Melvyn Hayes' character in the sitcom *It Ain't Half Hot Mum*?
2. Which Mike and the Mechanics singer released an album entitled *Blue Views* in 1996?
3. Which 1970 Ken Loach film starred David Bradley as a boy who becomes obsessed with a bird of prey?
4. Which Birmingham comedian was born Robert Davies?
5. Which singer/songwriter won an Oscar for his score for the 1971 film *Shaft*?
6. Which saxophonist released an album in 1996 entitled *Modern Day Jazz Stories*?
7. Which 1995 film starred Nicolas Cage as an alcoholic failed Hollywood screenwriter?
8. Who starred in the title role of the TV series *Wonder Woman*?
9. Which *Carry On* film regular starred in Disney's 1977 film *Pete's Dragon*?
10. Which Antipodean vocalist wanted to get *Physical* in 1981?
11. Which 1995 Forest Whitaker film starred Whitney Houston and Angela Bassett?
12. In which year did the reggae artist Bob Marley die?
13. In which 1995 film did Cindy Crawford star as Kate McQueen?
14. Who played the formidable Ena Sharples in *Coronation Street*?
15. Which Haircut 100 singer released an album entitled *Tangled* in 1996?
16. Who directed the 1948 film *Key Largo*?
17. Which *Men Behaving Badly* star could be heard on *The Morph Files* in the Nineties?
18. Which singer had a hit in 1979 with *Is She Really Going Out With Him?*?
19. Which *Hamish Macbeth* star played the crazed skinhead Albie in a memorable episode of *Cracker*?
20. Which Hollywood heart-throb was the guitarist of the rock group P?

ANSWERS: *1 Gloria, 2 Paul Carrack, 3 Kes, 4 Jasper Carrott, 5 Isaac Hayes, 6 Courtney Pine, 7 Leaving Las Vegas, 8 Lynda Carter, 9 Jim Dale, 10 Olivia Newton-John, 11 Waiting To Exhale, 12 1981, 13 Fair Game, 14 Violet Carson, 15 Nick Heyward, 16 John Huston, 17 Neil Morrissey, 18 Joe Jackson, 19 Robert Carlyle, 20 Johnny Depp.*

General Knowledge

Your rating:
- 0-5 Join a library
- 6-10 Keep at it
- 11-15 Join a quiz team
- 16-20 Join Mensa

1. Which British naval officer was the captain of the *Bounty* when the crew mutinied in 1789?
2. What was the popular name for the gallows which stood close to the present-day site of Marble Arch?
3. Which former star of *ER* appeared in the film *The Perfect Storm*?
4. Who does *Hiawatha* marry in Longfellow's famous poem?
5. Which U.S. president was known as Ike?
6. Are stalagmites formed on the roof or the floor of a cave?
7. Which American actor won Oscars for his performances in *Philadelphia* and *Forrest Gump*?
8. What name is given to the duplication of banknotes with the intention to defraud?
9. Which English comedian sang *When I'm Cleaning Windows*?
10. Which animals are called 'ships of the desert'?
11. Who is the youngest man to have won all four of golf's major championships?
12. Which Roman historian wrote a history of Rome in 142 volumes?
13. What name is given to members of the United Society of Believers in Christ's Second Appearing?
14. Which former Defence Secretary did George W Bush choose as his running-mate?
15. In computing, what does GUI stand for?
16. Which English novelist wrote *The Four Feathers*?
17. Of which French king was Madame Du Barry mistress?
18. Which Portuguese footballer became the world's most expensive player when he joined Real Madrid from Barcelona?
19. What is the second largest mountain system in North America?
20. Which veteran singer was born Annie Mae Bullock in 1939?

***ANSWERS:** 1 William Bligh, 2 Tyburn Tree, 3 George Clooney, 4 Minnehaha, 5 Dwight D Eisenhower, 6 Floor, 7 Tom Hanks, 8 Counterfeiting, 9 George Formby, 10 Camels, 11 Tiger Woods, 12 Livy, 13 Shakers, 14 Richard Cheney, 15 Graphical user interface, 16 A E W Mason, 17 Louis XV, 18 Luis Figo, 19 Appalachian Mountains, 20 Tina Turner.*

General Knowledge

Your rating: ● 0-5 Join a library ● 6-10 Keep at it ● 11-15 Join a quiz team ● 16-20 Join Mensa

1. Which waterway linking the Atlantic and Pacific oceans was completed in 1914?
2. What name is given to a score of one over par for a hole in golf?
3. Which country knocked the Netherlands out of Euro 2000 on penalties?
4. What name is given to a space devoid of matter?
5. Which British author wrote *Three Men in a Boat*?
6. What is the capital of Tunisia?
7. Which French author wrote *Les Miserables* and *The Hunchback of Notre Dame*?
8. What nationality is the film director Ingmar Bergman?
9. What name is given to a sweet plum that has been dried?
10. Which former Conservative MP broke the world 5000m record in 1954?
11. Which Canadian novelist wrote *The Apprenticeship of Duddy Kravitz*?
12. Who became emperor of Japan in 1989?
13. Which Australian tennis player knocked Tim Henman out of the Wimbledon championships in 2000?
14. What did the G stand for in the film company MGM?
15. Which British poet wrote *The Whitsun Weddings* and *High Windows*?
16. What sort of creature is a kuvasz?
17. What does A.E. stand for in the sci-fi film *Titan A.E.*?
18. Which British dramatist wrote *The Churchill Play* and *The Romans in Britain*?
19. How many ounces are there in an apothecary's pound?
20. Which country's deputy prime minister is known as the tanaiste?

ANSWERS: *1 Panama Canal, 2 Bogey, 3 Italy, 4 Vacuum, 5 Jerome K Jerome, 6 Tunis, 7 Victor Hugo, 8 Swedish, 9 Prune, 10 Chris Chataway, 11 Mordecai Richler, 12 Akihito, 13 Mark Philippoussis, 14 Goldwyn, 15 Philip Larkin, 16 A dog, 17 After earth, 18 Howard Brenton, 19 Twelve, 20 Republic of Ireland.*

General Knowledge

Your rating:
- **0-5 Join a library**
- **6-10 Keep at it**
- **11-15 Join a quiz team**
- **16-20 Join Mensa**

1. Which form of partly dehydrated gypsum is used for making casts and moulds?
2. Of which country is the shekel the basic monetary unit?
3. Which Australian tennis player won the men's singles title at Wimbledon in 1987?
4. What is the first name of Tony Blair's eldest son?
5. Which Canadian city is the capital of Ontario?
6. What is the largest living bird?
7. Which Jewish festival celebrates the flight of the Israelites from Egyptian slavery?
8. Who is credited with the authorship of the fable *The Tortoise and the Hare*?
9. Which Shakespeare play is subtitled *The Moor of Venice*?
10. Which bird of prey has bald and golden varieties?
11. Which West Indian-born poet and playwright won the 1992 Nobel Prize for literature?
12. Who sang *Stormy Weather* in the 1943 film of the same name?
13. Which British novelist wrote *Changing Places*, *Small World* and *Nice Work*?
14. Who directed the film *Mission: Impossible 2*?
15. Which country takes its name from the Latin word for southern?
16. What is the general name for any hoofed mammal?
17. Which Roman highway was named after Appius Claudius Caecus?
18. Who directed the films *Double Indemnity*, *The Lost Weekend* and *The Apartment*?
19. Which feature of the Spencer coat of arms has been incorporated into Prince William's coat of arms?
20. For which old Spanish coin was a piece of eight another name?

ANSWERS: *1 Plaster of Paris, 2 Israel, 3 Pat Cash, 4 Euan, 5 Toronto, 6 Ostrich, 7 Passover, 8 Aesop, 9 Othello, 10 Eagle, 11 Derek Walcott, 12 Lena Horne, 13 David Lodge, 14 John Woo, 15 Australia (australis), 16 Ungulate, 17 Appian Way, 18 Billy Wilder, 19 Red scallop shell, 20 Peso.*

Entertainment

Your rating:
- **0-5 Buy a TV**
- **6-10 Keep at it**
- **11-15 Join a quiz team**
- **16-20 Enter a quiz show**

1. Who played Neville Hope in the Eighties comedy drama series *Auf Wiedersehen, Pet*?
2. Which 1995 film starred Al Pacino as a cop in pursuit of a criminal played by Robert De Niro?
3. Who starred as *Kavanagh QC* in the drama series of that name?
4. Of which British band is Alex James the bass guitarist?
5. Who played Gordon Brittas in the sitcom *The Brittas Empire*?
6. Who wrote, directed, produced and acted in the 1990 film *Mo' Better Blues*?
7. Which actress starred in the TV series *And Mother Makes Three*, *Butterflies* and *Nanny*?
8. Who originally had a hit with *Blue Suede Shoes*?
9. Which actress played the title role in the 1995 film *Sabrina*?
10. Who plays Jimmy Corkhill in TV's *Brookside*?
11. Which US singer/songwriter released an album in 1996 entitled *Tennessee Moon*?
12. Who played Bill Sikes in the 1968 film version of *Oliver!*?
13. What are the surnames of *The Two Ronnies*?
14. What was the first U.K. number one single for the Kinks?
15. Who starred as an ex-Marine teacher in the 1995 film *Dangerous Minds*?
16. Which wartime entertainer was portrayed in the sitcom *Goodnight Sweetheart* by Phil Nice?
17. Who played Sid Vicious in the 1986 film *Sid and Nancy*?
18. Who presented the series on moral and ethical issues *Heart of the Matter*?
19. Which director made a cameo appearance in every one of his films from 1926's *The Lodger* onwards?
20. Which young pop/rock band released an album entitled *This World and Body* in 1996?

ANSWERS: 1 Kevin Whately, 2 Heat, 3 John Thaw, 4 Blur, 5 Chris Barrie, 6 Spike Lee, 7 Wendy Craig, 8 Carl Perkins, 9 Julia Ormond, 10 Dean Sullivan, 11 Neil Diamond, 12 Oliver Reed, 13 Corbett and Barker, 14 You Really Got Me, 15 Michelle Pfeiffer, 16 George Formby, 17 Gary Oldman, 18 Joan Bakewell, 19 Alfred Hitchcock, 20 Marion.

General Knowledge

Your rating: ● **0-5** Join a library ● **6-10** Keep at it ● **11-15** Join a quiz team ● **16-20** Join Mensa

1. Which English actor starred in *A Kind of Loving*, *Far from the Madding Crowd* and *Women in Love*?
2. What name was given to the bubonic plague epidemic that ravaged Europe in the 14th century?
3. What is the name of Don Quixote's squire in Cervantes' novel?
4. What is the first name of Agatha Christie's Miss Marple?
5. Which Test cricket side was captained by Clive Lloyd?
6. What did The A Team's B A Baracus' initials stand for?
7. Which German driver crashed out of his home Grand Prix at the first bend in 2000?
8. What name is given to the stomach tissue of cattle used as food?
9. Which Welsh composer wrote *Keep the Home Fires Burning*?
10. With which sport is Dennis Rodman associated?
11. What was Rick's surname in Casablanca?
12. What is the capital of Azerbaijan?
13. Which South African boxer did Lennox Lewis defeat at the London Arena in 2000?
14. Of which country was Milton Obote the president from 1966 to 1971 and from 1980 to 1985?
15. Which English conspirator fabricated the Popish Plot?
16. What sort of creature is a lammergeier?
17. Which German author wrote the short novel Death in Venice?
18. What was the official newspaper of the Communist Party of the Soviet Union called?
19. Who was the archbishop of Canterbury at the time of Edward VIII's abdication?
20. Which Spanish cubist artist was born José Victoriano Gonzalez?

ANSWERS: *1 Alan Bates, 2 Black Death, 3 Sancho Panza, 4 Jane, 5 West Indies, 6 Bad Attitude, 7 Michael Schumacher, 8 Tripe, 9 Ivor Novello, 10 Basketball, 11 Blaine, 12 Baku, 13 Francois Botha, 14 Uganda, 15 Titus Oates, 16 A vulture, 17 Thomas Mann, 18 Pravda, 19 Cosmo Gordon Lang, 20 Juan Gris.*

General Knowledge

Your rating: ● 0-5 Join a library ● 6-10 Keep at it ● 11-15 Join a quiz team ● 16-20 Join Mensa

1. Which former England cricket captain played for Somerset, Worcestershire and Durham?
2. Which is the only Western country not to have film censorship?
3. Which French footballer joined Aston Villa from Tottenham Hotspur in 2000?
4. What does AC stand for in physics?
5. Which English Romantic poet wrote *Tintern Abbey* and *The Prelude*?
6. What name is given to an American five-cent piece?
7. Where did Fawlty Towers' Manuel come from?
8. What does Descartes' famous Latin phrase 'cogito, ergo sum' mean?
9. Which English dramatist wrote *The Two Gentlemen of Verona*?
10. In which country did the game of shinty originate?
11. Whose was the first Royal wedding to be televised in colour?
12. In what year did beach volleyball become an Olympic sport?
13. What were the surnames of the animators who created *Tom and Jerry*, *The Flintstones* and *Scooby-Doo*?
14. In which country is the city of Abadan?
15. Who was the 15th U.S. president and the only one who never married?
16. Which Australian author wrote *My Brilliant Career*?
17. Which jazz pianist and composer won an Oscar for his score for the film *Round Midnight*?
18. In which sport is the Caulfield Cup contested?
19. Which former world footballer of the year joined Manchester City on a free transfer in 2000?
20. What was Mickey Mouse's original name?

ANSWERS: *1 Ian Botham, 2 Belgium, 3 David Ginola, 4 Alternating current, 5 William Wordsworth, 6 Nickel, 7 Barcelona, 8 I think, therefore I am, 9 William Shakespeare, 10 Scotland, 11 Princess Anne, 12 1996, 13 Hanna and Barbera, 14 Iran, 15 James Buchanan, 16 Miles Franklin, 17 Herbie Hancock, 18 Horseracing, 19 George Weah, 20 Mortimer Mouse.*

General Knowledge

Your rating:
- **0-5 Join a library**
- **6-10 Keep at it**
- **11-15 Join a quiz team**
- **16-20 Join Mensa**

1. Which sport involves the snatch and the clean and jerk?
2. What name is given to radioactive material that settles on the earth's surface following a nuclear explosion?
3. Who wrote the horror novel Dracula?
4. Staten Island is a borough of which U.S. city?
5. Which member of Whistler's family features in his most famous painting?
6. What is the popular name for members of the Society of Friends?
7. Which Labour MP won Oscars for *Women in Love* and *A Touch of Class*?
8. What was the name of the character played by Telly Savalas' brother George in Kojak?
9 Which British golfer was removed from his position as the Ryder Cup vice-captain in 2000?
10. Who was the first English printer?
11. Who was the BBC Sports Personality Of The Year 2000?
12. Which American union leader disappeared in 1975?
13. Ieuan Wyn Jones is the president of which political party?
14. Which controversial British artist is best known for works such as *Mother and Child, Divided*?
15. What is the highest navigable lake in the world?
16. Who was the first director to refuse an Oscar?
17. Which World War II battle is also known as the Ardennes Offensive?
18. What is the largest city in New Mexico?
19. Of which country is New Britain a part?
20. Which Latin legal term means 'you should have the body'?

***ANSWERS:** 1 Weightlifting, 2 Fallout, 3 Bram Stoker, 4 New York City, 5 His mother, 6 Quakers, 7 Glenda Jackson, 8 Stavros, 9 Mark James, 10 William Caxton, 11 Steve Redgrave, 12 Jimmy Hoffa, 13 Plaid Cymru, 14 Damien Hirst, 15 Lake Titicaca, 16 Walter Wanger, 17 Battle of the Bulge, 18 Albuquerque, 19 Papua New Guinea, 20 Habeas corpus.*

Sports

Your rating:	● 0-5	Wooden spoon	● 6-10	Bronze medal
	● 11-15	Silver medal	● 16-20	Gold medal

1. Which German footballer set a new world record when he won his 144th international cap in February 2000?
2. Which female tennis player was singles champion at the 1976 French Open?
3. Which bowler took most the wickets for England in the 2000 Test series against Pakistan?
4. From which club did Aston Villa sign Juan Pablo Angel?
5. Which country did Abdelatif Benazzi represent at the 1999 rugby union World Cup?
6. Who resigned as captain of the West Indies cricket team in February 2000?
7. Who was the European Footballer of the Year in 1968?
8. Who did Frank Bruno beat in 1995 to become the WBC world heavyweight champion?
9. Which tennis player won the 1990 Australian Open?
10. Which team beat Leeds United in the 1975 European Cup Final?
11. Which snooker player was the World Championship runner-up from 1990-94?
12. Which West Indian scored centuries in both innings of his debut versus New Zealand in 1972?
13. Which country lost 29-9 to New Zealand in the final of the 1987 rugby union World Cup?
14. How many times did golfer Severiano Ballesteros win the British Open?
15. What is the meaning of the word karate?
16. Who won the all-Welsh final at snooker's 2000 World Championship?
17. In which year did Newcastle United sign Alan Shearer?
18. What is the nickname of the darts player Ted Hankey?
19. Who did Mohammed Ali beat in May 1975 to retain his world heavyweight crown?
20. Catch-as-catch-can is a style of which sport?

ANSWERS: *1 Lothar Matthäus, 2 Sue Barker, 3 Ashley Giles, 4 River Plate, 5 France, 6 Brian Lara, 7 George Best, 8 Oliver McCall, 9 Ivan Lendl, 10 Bayern Munich, 11 Jimmy White, 12 Lawrence Rowe, 13 France, 14 Three, 15 Empty hand, 16 Mark Williams, 17 1996, 18 The Count, 19 Ron Lyle, 20 Wrestling.*

General Knowledge

Your rating:
- 0-5 Join a library
- 6-10 Keep at it
- 11-15 Join a quiz team
- 16-20 Join Mensa

1. Which symphonic fairy tale by Prokofiev uses different instruments to represent characters in the story?
2. What name is given to a court order that forbids a person from doing something?
3. For which TV show did Rossini's William Tell Overture provide the theme tune?
4. Who married his long-time girlfriend Sarah Macaulay in 2000?
5. Which fruit is the main ingredient of the Mexican dish guacamole?
6. What is the 17th letter of the alphabet?
7. Which U.S. 'Beat movement' author wrote *On The Road* and *Big Sur*?
8. What was Chewbacca in Star Wars?
9. Which two former England captains celebrated 100 Test appearances in the Third Test against the West Indies in 2000?
10. What is Pakistan's largest city and chief port?
11. Which Spanish football team bought Marc Overmars and Emmanuel Petit from Arsenal in 2000?
12. Which French author wrote Les Enfants terribles?
13. Which Northern Ireland Presbyterian minister became an MEP in 1979?
14. Which Canadian academic wrote *The Gutenberg Galaxy* and *The Medium is the Massage*?
15. With which branch of the arts was Dame Elisabeth Frink associated?
16. Which European country was ruled by Janos Kadar from 1956?
17. Which soldier and statesman was the President of France from 1958 to 1969?
18. Who played Trapper John in the film M*A*S*H?
19. Of which country is Brno the second largest city?
20. Which German airship exploded in New Jersey in 1937?

ANSWERS: *1 Peter and the Wolf, 2 Injunction, 3 The Lone Ranger, 4 Gordon Brown, 5 Avocado, 6 Q, 7 Jack Kerouac, 8 Wookie, 9 Michael Atherton and Alec Stewart, 10 Karachi, 11 Barcelona, 12 Jean Cocteau, 13 Ian Paisley, 14 Marshall McLuhan, 15 Sculpture, 16 Hungary, 17 Charles de Gaulle, 18 Elliott Gould, 19 Czech Republic, 20 The Hindenburg.*

General Knowledge

Your rating: ● 0-5 Join a library ● 6-10 Keep at it ● 11-15 Join a quiz team ● 16-20 Join Mensa

1. Which medical treatment is known by the initials HRT?
2. Of which former Soviet state is Tallinn the capital?
3. Which veteran political broadcaster and interviewer died in 2000 at the age of 76?
4. Which novel by Peter Carey won the Booker Prize?
5. In which cathedral was Saint Thomas à Becket murdered in 1170?
6. What is the largest of the Channel Islands?
7. What was the subject of the first British TV advertisement?
8. What is the Roman numeral for ten?
9. What is the capital of South Korea?
10. Who wrote the novel *Kidnapped*?
11. Which Italian neorealist film director was married to the actress Ingrid Bergman?
12. Which German author wrote *Death in Venice*?
13. What was Dynasty's original title?
14. Which West Indies batsman hit his 14th Test century in the Third Test against England in 2000?
15. Of which South American country was Pedro I the first emperor?
16. Which West Yorkshire town is noted for its Choral Society?
17. Which former Master of the Queen's Musick wrote the music for the 1935 film *Things to Come*?
18. What was the first name of the American Civil War general Custer?
19. From which Shakespeare play does Aldous Huxley's novel Brave New World get its name?
20. Which shrub is also called hypericum and rose of Sharon?

ANSWERS: *1 Hormone replacement therapy, 2 Estonia, 3 Sir Robin Day, 4 Oscar and Lucinda, 5 Canterbury Cathedral, 6 Jersey, 7 Gibbs SR toothpaste, 8 X, 9 Seoul, 10 Robert Louis Stevenson, 11 Roberto Rossellini, 12 Thomas Mann, 13 Oil, 14 Brian Lara, 15 Brazil, 16 Huddersfield, 17 Sir Arthur Bliss, 18 George, 19 The Tempest, 20 Saint-John's-wort.*

General Knowledge

Your rating:
- 0-5 Join a library
- 6-10 Keep at it
- 11-15 Join a quiz team
- 16-20 Join Mensa

1. Which star of *Friends* married actor Brad Pitt in 2000?
2. How many players make up an ice hockey team?
3. Which branch of mathematics is one of the Three Rs?
4. What name is given to the seat of the Lord Chancellor in the House of Lords?
5. Which former footballer plays The Sphinx in the film *Gone in 60 Seconds*?
6. What is the official mapping organisation of the United Kingdom called?
7. To which Robert Louis Stevenson novel is Catriona the sequel?
8. Betelgeuse is one of the brightest stars in which constellation?
9. Which reading disability is popularly known as word blindness?
10. What sort of creature is a painted lady?
11. Which horse won the Grand National in 1983?
12. Which English metaphysical poet wrote the sonnet that begins "Death be not proud"?
13. Which trio of singing sisters had the first names Patty, Maxine and Laverne?
14. What is the capital of Belarus?
15. Which British doctor edited *The Family Shakespeare*, published in 1818?
16. Which country knocked Romania out of Euro 2000?
17. Which French author wrote the story on which Bizet based his opera *Carmen*?
18. What name is given to a part of speech used in place of a noun?
19. Which U.S. statesman served as the secretary of state from 1973 to 1977?
20. What name is given to plants of the genus *Vinca*?

ANSWERS: *1 Jennifer Aniston, 2 Six, 3 Arithmetic, 4 The woolsack, 5 Vinnie Jones, 6 Ordnance Survey, 7 Kidnapped, 8 Orion, 9 Dyslexia, 10 A butterfly, 11 Corbière, 12 John Donne, 13 The Andrews Sisters, 14 Minsk, 15 Thomas Bowdler, 16 Italy, 17 Prosper Merimee, 18 Pronoun, 19 Henry Kissinger, 20 Periwinkle.*

Entertainment

Your rating: ● **0-5** **Buy a TV** ● **6-10** **Keep at it** ● **11-15** **Join a quiz team** ● **16-20** **Enter a quiz show**

1. Which actress played Lizzie Kavanagh in *Kavanagh QC*?
2. Which Disney film won a special Academy Award in 1938 for significant screen innovation?
3. What was the title of Chris Evans's live Friday night TV show?
4. Who sang the lead vocal on the Crusaders' 1979 U.K. top ten hit single *Streetlife*?
5. Which Claude Lelouch cinematic epic won a Golden Globe award in 1996 for Best Foreign Film?
6. Who played Pam Ewing in the U.S. soap *Dallas*?
7. Which former Lone Justice vocalist released an album entitled Life is Sweet in 1996?
8. Who directed the 1988 film *Talk Radio*?
9. In which two English cities was the Nineties drama series *Our Friends in the North* set?
10. Which founder member of Roxy Music co-wrote the Talking Heads hit *Once in a Lifetime*?
11. Which cult 1987 film, set in the Sixties and starring Richard E. Grant, was re-released in 1996?
12. Which pioneering singer/songwriter was backed by the Crickets?
13. What was the name of Dick Dastardly's canine companion in the cartoon series *Wacky Races*?
14. What was the title of the debut album by The Bluetones?
15. Which Monty Python star played Robin Hood in the 1981 film *Time Bandits*?
16. Which German model sang on the Velvet Underground's first album?
17. Who starred as the father/grandfather in the 1995 film *Father of the Bride Part II*?
18. Which actress appeared as a landlady both in the sitcom *Goodnight Sweetheart* and in the drama series *Ballykissangel*?
19. With which instrument was the jazz musician Buddy Rich associated?
20. Which *Emmerdale* character was played by Tonicha Jeronimo?

ANSWERS: *1 Lisa Harrow, 2 Snow White and the Seven Dwarfs, 3 TFI Friday, 4 Randy Crawford, 5 Les Miserables, 6 Victoria Principal, 7 Maria McKee, 8 Oliver Stone, 9 London and Newcastle, 10 Brian Eno, 11 Withnail and I, 12 Buddy Holly, 13 Muttley, 14 Expecting to Fly, 15 John Cleese, 16 Nico, 17 Steve Martin, 18 Dervla Kirwan, 19 The drums, 20 Linda Glover.*

General Knowledge

Your rating:
- **0-5 Join a library**
- **6-10 Keep at it**
- **11-15 Join a quiz team**
- **16-20 Join Mensa**

1. Which bridge over the River Thames has a central section that can be raised to allow ships to pass?
2. How many Von Trapp children are there in The Sound Of Music?
3. Which Manchester United player was sent off in the 2000 Charity Shield?
4. After which French novelist is sadism named?
5. Which famous rock festival took place in New York state in August 1969?
6. What is the 24th letter of the alphabet?
7. Of which U.S. state is Lincoln the capital?
8. What were the names of the policemen in the TV series *Chips*?
9. Which U.S. government agency is known by the initials CIA?
10. What name is given to a thin sheet of wood applied to the surface of furniture made of a cheaper material?
11. In which country is the River Suir?
12. How many Formula One world championships did Jackie Stewart win as a driver?
13. What nationality was the philosopher Benedict Spinoza?
14. Which U.S. presidential candidate selected Senator Joseph Lieberman as his running-mate?
15. In which country was the Nazi war criminal Adolf Eichmann seized by Israeli agents in 1960?
16. Which Australian golfer won the British Open in 1991?
17. Who was born Allan Stewart Konigsberg?
18. What nationality was the 1979 Formula 1 world champion Jody Scheckter?
19. Who founded Virgin as a mail-order company in 1969?
20. In which sea did the Russian submarine the *Kursk* sink in 2000?

ANSWERS: *1 Tower Bridge, 2 7, 3 Roy Keane, 4 Marquis de Sade, 5 Woodstock, 6 X, 7 Nebraska, 8 Baker and Ponch, 9 Central Intelligence Agency, 10 Veneer, 11 Republic of Ireland, 12 Three, 13 Dutch, 14 Al Gore, 15 Argentina, 16 Ian Baker-Finch, 17 Woody Allen, 18 South African, 19 Richard Branson, 20 Barents Sea.*

General Knowledge

Your rating: ● **0-5** Join a library ● **6-10** Keep at it ● **11-15** Join a quiz team ● **16-20** Join Mensa

1. Which planet is named after the Roman god of the sea?
2. To which English king did Hans Holbein the Younger become court painter?
3. In which sport did Audley Harrison win gold at the Sydney Olympics?
4. Who is the traditional author of the third Gospel?
5. Which American actor played Andy Hardy in a series of films beginning in 1937?
6. What is the capital of Poland?
7. Which pop programme was the predecessor of Top Of The Pops?
8. What nationality was the operatic tenor Beniamino Gigli?
9. Which star of *Great Expectations* and *Star Wars* died in 2000 at the age of 86?
10. Which former British coin was worth four old pence?
11. Who wrote The Godfather?
12. Which New Zealand director made the films *The Piano* and *An Angel at my Table*?
13. What name is given to the practice of rearranging constituency boundaries to favour the party in power?
14. Which Croatian footballer joined Middlesbrough from Lazio in 2000?
15. Who wrote *The Compleat Angler*?
16. Which optical toy was invented by Sir David Brewster in 1816?
17. Which British conductor was the Musical Director of the Royal Opera House from 1971 to 1986?
18. For which country does the rugby league star Gorden Tallis play?
19. Which British dramatist wrote *The Winslow Boy* and *The Browning Version*?
20. What is the capital of Puerto Rico?

ANSWERS: *1 Neptune, 2 Henry VIII, 3 Boxing, 4 Luke, 5 Mickey Rooney, 6 Warsaw, 7 Teen And Twenty Record Club, 8 Italian, 9 Sir Alec Guinness, 10 Groat, 11 Mario Puzo, 12 Jane Campion, 13 Gerrymandering, 14 Alen Boksic, 15 Izaak Walton, 16 Kaleidoscope, 17 Sir Colin Davis, 18 Australia, 19 Sir Terence Rattigan 20 San Juan.*

General Knowledge

Your rating: ● 0-5 Join a library ● 6-10 Keep at it ● 11-15 Join a quiz team ● 16-20 Join Mensa

1. Which American singer and actor starred in the films *Carmen Jones* and *Island in the Sun*?
2. Who was elected president of the United States in 1988?
3. Who won the women's singles at Wimbledon in 1977?
4. Who was said to have ridden naked through the streets of Coventry in the 11th century?
5. Which comic actor played Basil Fawlty in *Fawlty Towers*?
6. For which country did the fast bowler Jeff Thomson play?
7. An outbreak of which disease of pigs led to a ban on exports from the U.K. in 2000?
8. In the film, where do Butch Cassidy And The Sundance Kid meet their end?
9. Which American country singer had hits with *I Walk the Line* and *A Boy Named Sue*?
10. What is the holiest city of Islam?
11. Which actor failed his first screen test because his ears were too big?
12. Which American tennis player won three Grand Slam tournaments in 1974, including Wimbledon?
13. For which film did Loretta Young win a Best Actress Oscar in 1947?
14. Which Irish poet won the 1995 Nobel Prize for literature?
15. Of which African country is Bujumbura the capital?
16. Which soft metallic element has the chemical symbol Cs?
17. With which sport are the Harlem Globetrotters famously associated?
18. Which Irish dramatist wrote *The Rivals* and *The School for Scandal*?
19. What name is given to a device that measures high temperatures beyond the range of a thermometer?
20. Which 2000 film starred Samuel L Jackson and Tommy Lee Jones?

ANSWERS: *1 Harry Belafonte, 2 George Bush, 3 Virginia Wade, 4 Lady Godiva, 5 John Cleese, 6 Australia, 7 Swine fever, 8 Bolivia, 9 Johnny Cash, 10 Mecca, 11 Clarke Gable, 12 Jimmy Connors, 13 The Farmer's Daughter, 14 Seamus Heaney, 15 Burundi, 16 Caesium, 17 Basketball, 18 Richard Brinsley Sheridan, 19 Pyrometer, 20 Rules of Engagement.*

Entertainment

Your rating: ● **0-5** Buy a TV ● **6-10** Keep at it ● **11-15** Join a quiz team ● **16-20** Enter a quiz show

1. Which soul queen had a top ten hit in 1967 with *Respect*?
2. Who played the mysterious and malevolent *High Plains Drifter*?
3. Who presented the final Saturday night *Match of the Day* programme to feature Premiership highlights in May 2001?
4. Which band played to crowds of up to 40,000 on its *Voodoo Lounge* tour?
5. Who played Jimmy Porter in the 1959 film version of *Look Back In Anger*?
6. Which record producer presented *The Hit Man and Her*?
7. *The Prince and the Pauper* was about life under which British king?
8. Which hospital comedy featured Sheila Sabatini and Joyce Watson?
9. Which heavyweight boxer has played Juliet to Lenny Henry's Romeo?
10. Which sitcom actress played Phillippa Troy in *Law and Disorder*?
11. Who had a top ten hit in 1982 with *Senses Working Overtime*?
12. What type of creature was *Dumbo*?
13. Who had number ones with *I'm Not in Love* and *Dreadlock Holiday*?
14. Hitchcock's *Strangers on a Train* was based on a novel by which British author?
15. Which charity fund-raiser was the lead singer of the Boomtown Rats?
16. Which barber-shop comedy series was set in Peckham?
17. Which pop singer played *Buster*?
18. Who made the disco favourites *Everybody Dance* and *Le Freak*?
19. Who was *The Prisoner*?
20. What was the Ewings' ranch called in *Dallas*?

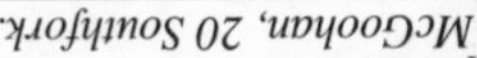

***ANSWERS:** 1 Aretha Franklin, 2 Clint Eastwood, 3 Gary Lineker, 4 The Rolling Stones, 5 Richard Burton, 6 Pete Waterman, 7 Henry VIII, 8 Surgical Spirit, 9 Frank Bruno, 10 Penelope Keith, 11 XTC, 12 An elephant, 13 10CC, 14 Patricia Highsmith, 15 Bob Geldof, 16 Desmond's, 17 Phil Collins, 18 Chic, 19 Patrick McGoohan, 20 Southfork.*

General Knowledge

Your rating: ● 0-5 Join a library ● 6-10 Keep at it ● 11-15 Join a quiz team ● 16-20 Join Mensa

1. What name is given to the state of being insensitive to pain, as induced artificially before operations?
2. Which branch of physics is concerned with light and vision?
3. What name is given to a native Eskimo canoe?
4. Which former Middlesbrough and Newcastle United footballer was controversially left out of England's 1998 World Cup squad?
5. In which Japanese martial art do combatants fence with bamboo sticks?
6. The Colosseum in Rome is a famous example of what sort of building?
7. Which American film star retired from acting after marrying Prince Rainier III of Monaco in 1956?
8. Against which country did Michael Owen find the net to become the youngest player ever to score for England?
9. Which British jockey retired in 1985 having ridden over 1000 National Hunt winners?
10. Which South American country is named after Venice?
11. Which U.S. physicist was put in charge of the development of the atom bomb at Los Alamos in 1943?
12. Jimmu is the legendary first leader of which Asian country?
13. Which town in Warwickshire has a castle which gives its name to a Walter Scott novel?
14. Ammonia is a chemical compound of which two gases?
15. What name is given to a force exerted at the boundary between two solids or fluids that retards motion between them?
16. Which Sicilian port was originally called Zancle?
17. To which country do the Andaman and Nicobar Islands belong?
18. What name is given to the removal for examination of fluid surrounding an unborn baby in the mother's womb?
19. Which weapon is represented by the initials S.L.C.M.?
20. Which former European Footballer of the Year played for Liverpool, Hamburg, Southampton and Newcastle United?

ANSWERS: *1 Anaesthesia, 2 Optics, 3 Kayak, 4 Paul Gascoigne, 5 Kendo, 6 Amphitheatre, 7 Grace Kelly, 8 Morocco, 9 John Francome, 10 Venezuela, 11 J Robert Oppenheimer, 12 Japan, 13 Kenilworth, 14 Nitrogen and hydrogen, 15 Friction, 16 Messina, 17 India, 18 Amniocentesis, 19 Sea-launched cruise missile, 20 Kevin Keegan*

General Knowledge

Your rating:
- ● 0-5 Join a library
- ● 6-10 Keep at it
- ● 11-15 Join a quiz team
- ● 16-20 Join Mensa

1. Which brass musical instrument has the lowest pitch?
2. What was the surname of the Angevin, Lancastrian and Yorkist Kings of England?
3. What is Willy Messerschmitt famous for designing?
4. Which member of the Spice Girls quit the group in 1998?
5. Which British novelist wrote *Our Man in Havana*?
6. What name is given to the seventh day of the week in Judaism?
7. What name is given to the deterioration of metal caused by repeated stresses?
8. In which county is the spa town of Buxton?
9. What relation is painter Lucian Freud to psychoanalysis pioneer Sigmund Freud?
10. Which town in Cumbria is famous for its mint cake?
11. Which Labour foreign secretary was awarded the Nobel peace prize in 1934?
12. What is the name of the cathedral in Red Square, Moscow?
13. Which joint rulers of Castile were the parents of Joanna the Mad and patrons of Christopher Columbus?
14. Who won the best director award at the 1998 Cannes Film Festival for *The General*?
15. Which Malaysian state was formerly known as North Borneo?
16. What sort of creature is a dragonet?
17. After which saint is the massacre of Huguenots that began in Paris on August 24 1572 named?
18. Which Spanish football team won the European Cup for the first time in 32 years in 1998?
19. What name is given to the speed of an object in a specified direction?
20. Who invented the flying shuttle that contributed to the mechanisation of weaving?

ANSWERS: *1 Tuba, 2 Plantagenet, 3 Aircraft, 4 Ginger Spice, Geri Halliwell, 5 Graham Greene, 6 The Sabbath, 7 Metal fatigue, 8 Derbyshire, 9 Grandson, 10 Kendal, 11 Arthur Henderson, 12 St Basil's, 13 Ferdinand V and Isabella I, 14 John Boorman, 15 Sabah, 16 A fish, 17 Saint Bartholomew, 18 Real Madrid, 19 Velocity, 20 John Kay.*

General Knowledge

Your rating: ● **0-5** **Join a library** ● **6-10** **Keep at it** ● **11-15** **Join a quiz team** ● **16-20** **Join Mensa**

1. What name is given to any device used to moor a vessel to the bottom of a body of water?
2. Which French city and wine centre on the river Garonne is the capital of the Gironde department?
3. In which country did ice hockey originate?
4. Which two nurses were pardoned by King Fahd of Saudi Arabia in 1998?
5. Which major ocean current flows from the polar seas past Newfoundland?
6. In which country was the painter Marc Chagall born?
7. Which Australian operatic soprano married the conductor Richard Bonynge?
8. In which village in South Vietnam were civilians massacred by U.S. soldiers in March 1968?
9. Whom did Valery Giscard d'Estaing succeed as French president?
10. What is the name of the Japanese emperor?
11. In Greek mythology, who was Hector's wife who was taken as a concubine by Achilles's son?
12. Who invented the spinning mule?
13. Which German Expressionist painter of the Blaue Reiter movement painted Blue Horses?
14. What is both the genus to which the lilac belongs and another name for the mock orange?
15. Which Methodist bishop and politician was succeeded by Robert Mugabe as prime minister of Zimbabwe?
16. What name is given to a strip of paper with only one side and one edge?
17. Which Scottish novelist wrote *Juan in America* and *Judas*?
18. Who directed Greta Garbo in the film *Ninotchka*?
19. In Greek mythology, which nymph was changed into a laurel tree to escape from Apollo?
20. What sort of creature is an indri?

ANSWERS: *1 Anchor, 2 Bordeaux, 3 Canada, 4 Lucille McLauchlan and Deborah Parry, 5 Labrador current, 6 Russia, 7 Dame Joan Sutherland, 8 My Lai, 9 Georges Pompidou, 10 Akihito, 11 Andromache, 12 Samuel Crompton, 13 Franz Marc, 14 Syringa, 15 Abel Muzorewa, 16 Möbius strip, 17 Eric Linklater, 18 Ernst Lubitsch, 19 Daphne, 20 A lemur.*

Entertainment

Your rating: ● **0-5** **Buy a TV** ● **6-10** **Keep at it** ● **11-15** **Join a quiz team** ● **16-20** **Enter a quiz show**

1. Until *Titanic*'s success at the 1998 Academy Awards, which film held the record for winning the most Oscars?
2. What is the title of Sting's 1996 album?
3. Who is the only person to have been nominated for an Oscar as producer, director, actor and screenwriter in the same year?
4. Who presented the show about coincidences, *One In A Million*?
5. Which actor played the serial murderer in the 1995 film *Seven*?
6. Which 1996 series attracted 10,000 engaged couples who applied to get married on TV?
7. Who were voted best British newcomers at the 1996 Brit Awards?
8. Which *EastEnders* character is played by Steve McFadden?
9. Who directed the 1977 film *Jabberwocky*?
10. Who starred as Terry in TV's *Terry and June*?
11. Who had a top ten hit in 1972 with *Rocket Man*?
12. Which British actor played Colonel Brandon in the film *Sense And Sensibility*?
13. Who replaced Diane-Louise Jordan as a presenter of *Blue Peter*?
14. Which US godfather of punk released an album in 1996 entitled *Naughty Little Doggy*?
15. Who starred as baseball player Roy Hobbs in the film *The Natural*?
16. What was Madonna's first top ten single in the UK?
17. Which 1996 film starred Ewan McGregor as fast-talking heroin addict Renton?
18. Which sitcom screened a special edition in 1996 entitled *The Chigwell Years*?
19. Which soul veteran released an album in 1996 entitled *Strong Love Affair*?
20. Who starred as Ben Richards in the 1987 film *The Running Man*?

***ANSWERS:** 1 Ben Hur, 2 Mercury Falling, 3 Orson Welles, 4 Phillip Schofield, 5 Kevin Spacey, 6 The Shane Richie Experience, 7 Supergrass, 8 Phil Mitchell, 9 Terry Gilliam, 10 Terry Scott, 11 Elton John, 12 Alan Rickman, 13 Romana D'Annunzio, 14 Iggy Pop, 15 Robert Redford, 16 Holiday, 17 Trainspotting, 18 Birds of a Feather, 19 Ray Charles, 20 Arnold Schwarzenegger.*

General Knowledge

Your rating: ● 0-5 Join a library ● 6-10 Keep at it ● 11-15 Join a quiz team ● 16-20 Join Mensa

1. Which British prime minister introduced old-age pensions in 1908?
2. What name is given to the counties that surround London?
3. Which transsexual Israeli singer won the 1998 Eurovision Song Contest?
4. Who is the patron saint of travellers?
5. Which unpaid World War II British defence force was formerly known as the Local Defence Volunteers?
6. Which area of lakes in Norfolk and Suffolk was created by digging out peat deposits?
7. Which English actor and director who died in 1989 was the first director of the National Theatre?
8. Which island off the Northumberland coast is also known as Lindisfarne?
9. What name is given to the amount of money owed by the government of a country?
10. Who was the father of the apostles James and John?
11. Which violinist was frequently partnered in recitals by his pianist sister Hephzibah?
12. What was Cyrano de Bergerac's first name?
13. To which African country did Sandline International supply arms in breach of a United Nations embargo?
14. Who is the patron saint of hunters?
15. Which cold dry northerly wind is funnelled down the Rhône Valley to the Mediterranean?
16. What was the pen name of Scottish playwright Osborne Henry Mavor?
17. Which American mountain range contains the Yosemite National Park?
18. What name is given to the threadlike structures in the nuclei of cells that carry genetic information?
19. What is the capital of the Australian state of Queensland?
20. Which American river is the chief tributary of the Mississippi?

ANSWERS: *1 David Lloyd George, 2 Home Counties, 3 Dana International, 4 Saint Christopher, 5 Home Guard, 6 The Broads, 7 Laurence Olivier, 8 Holy Island, 9 National debt, 10 Zebedee, 11 Yehudi Menuhin, 12 Savinien, 13 Sierra Leone, 14 Saint Eustace, 15 The Mistral, 16 James Bridie, 17 Sierra Nevada, 18 Chromosomes, 19 Brisbane, 20 Missouri.*

General Knowledge

Your rating: ● 0-5 Join a library ● 6-10 Keep at it ● 11-15 Join a quiz team ● 16-20 Join Mensa

1. Which archbishop of Canterbury was tried as a heretic under Queen Mary and burned at the stake after initially recanting?
2. How many furlongs are there in a mile?
3. Which British film starring Gwyneth Paltrow marked the directorial debut of former *Bread* star Peter Howitt?
4. *Narcissus pseudonarcissus* is the Latin name for which popular yellow-flowered garden bulb?
5. Which nonmetallic element isolated by Sir Humphry Davy has the symbol B?
6. How many legs does a mite have?
7. Which famous London art gallery had only 38 pictures when it opened in 1824?
8. Against which team did Arsenal clinch the Double by winning the 1998 F.A. Cup Final?
9. Which government department is responsible for immigration, prisons and the police?
10. Which metallic element has the symbol Cr?
11. Which character from Germanic legend is the hero of the last two operas in Wagner's Ring cycle?
12. What name is given to the ceremonial distribution of gifts practised by American Indians of the NW Pacific coast region?
13. Which British poet wrote the epic narrative poems *The Torchbearers* and *Drake*?
14. What is the name of the world's largest passenger liner which was launched in Italy in 1998?
15. For which Shakespearean role was actress Sarah Siddons most famous?
16. What is the governing body of freemasonry in England called?
17. Of which country is the Sierra Madre the main mountain system?
18. Which viral disease of cattle was used in Edward Jenner's smallpox vaccine?
19. What was the stage name of French music hall star Jeanne-Marie Bourgeois who often appeared with Maurice Chevalier?
20. Which Irish king was murdered after the battle of Clontarf?

ANSWERS: *1 Thomas Cranmer, 2 Eight, 3 Sliding Doors, 4 Daffodil, 5 Boron, 6 Eight, 7 The National Gallery, 8 Newcastle United, 9 Home Office, 10 Chromium, 11 Siegfried, 12 Potlatch, 13 Alfred Noyes, 14 Grand Princess, 15 Lady Macbeth, 16 The Grand Lodge, 17 Mexico, 18 Cowpox, 19 Mistinguett, 20 Brian Boru.*

General Knowledge

Your rating:
- 0-5 Join a library
- 6-10 Keep at it
- 11-15 Join a quiz team
- 16-20 Join Mensa

1. What name is given to a water spout in the shape of a grotesque person or animal, associated with gothic architecture?
2. Which German breed of dog is informally known as a sausage dog?
3. What is the staple food of the Chinese silkworm?
4. Which region and former duchy of France is famous for wines such as Chablis?
5. Which gothic Paris cathedral is famous for its flying buttresses and great rose windows?
6. Which wild dog of Central and North America is also known as a prairie wolf?
7. What name is given to a force of mounted soldiers?
8. Which American actor was born Marion Michael Morrison?
9. For which county did former England cricket captain Colin Cowdrey play?
10. Which large American frog can jump up to two metres?
11. What name was given to the forces organised in London by General de Gaulle during the Second World War?
12. Which English chemist and physicist discovered hydrogen?
13. What is the longest and deepest fjord in Norway?
14. Which 16th century Florentine sculptor and goldsmith is best known for his autobiography?
15. By what name is sodium hydroxide commonly known?
16. In which U.S. state is the city of Gary?
17. What is the SI unit of conductance, named after a German electrical engineer?
18. Which Roman soldier and politician was a member of the First Triumvirate with Julius Caesar and Crassus?
19. What name is given to poetry without regular metre or form?
20 Who wrote the music for *The Threepenny Opera*?

ANSWERS: *1 Gargoyle, 2 Dachshund, 3 Mulberry leaves, 4 Burgundy, 5 Notre-Dame de Paris, 6 Coyote, 7 Cavalry, 8 John Wayne, 9 Kent, 10 Bullfrog, 11 Free French, 12 Henry Cavendish, 13 Sogne Fjord, 14 Benvenuto Cellini, 15 Caustic soda, 16 Indiana, 17 Siemens, 18 Pompey the Great, 19 Free verse, 20 Kurt Weill.*

Entertainment

Your rating:	● 0-5	Buy a TV	● 6-10	Keep at it
	● 11-15	Join a quiz team	● 16-20	Enter a quiz show

1. Which Australian actor played 'Scissors' Smedley in the TV drama *Cardiac Arrest*?
2. Which cockney duo had a UK top ten single in 1986 with *Snooker Loopy*?
3. Which gameshow and talk show host was the BBC's *Our Man In ...* in the TV series?
4. Who provided the voice for Buzz Lightyear in the film *Toy Story*?
5. Who wrote the World War II TV comedy drama *Over Here*?
6. Which outlaw was played by Robert Redford in the 1969 film *Butch Cassidy and the Sundance Kid*?
7. Which *Changing Rooms* star co-presented TV's *Hearts of Gold* with Esther Rantzen?
8. Which Canadian vocalist released an album in 1996 entitled *Falling Into You*?
9. Which five-year-old was awarded an honorary Oscar in 1934?
10. Who starred as investigative reporter *Shoestring* on TV?
11. With which Italian vocalist did Paul Young sing the 1991 top ten hit *Senza Una Donna (Without A Woman)*?
12. Who played physician Robert Merivel in the film *Restoration*?
13. Which band released an album entitled *Regular Urban Survivors* in 1996?
14. Which musical won five Academy Awards in 1966?
15. Which BBC police detective series starred Warren Clarke and Colin Buchanan?
16. Which Manchester band had a top ten hit in 1990 with *Elephant Stone*?
17. Who played Chili Palmer in the film *Get Shorty*?
18. Which *Taggart* character was played on TV by Blythe Duff?
19. Which dancer and wife of (The Artist Formerly Known As) Prince released an album in 1996 entitled *Child Of The Sun*?
20. Who won a Best Actor Oscar posthumously in 1976?

ANSWERS: *1 Peter O'Brien, 2 Chas and Dave, 3 Clive Anderson, 4 Tim Allen, 5 John Sullivan, 6 The Sundance Kid, 7 Carol Smillie, 8 Celine Dion, 9 Shirley Temple, 10 Trevor Eve, 11 Zucchero, 12 Robert Downey Jr, 13 Terrorvision, 14 The Sound of Music, 15 Dalziel and Pascoe, 16 Stone Roses, 17 John Travolta, 18 Jackie Reid, 19 Mayte, 20 Peter Finch.*

General Knowledge

Your rating: ● **0-5** **Join a library** ● **6-10** **Keep at it** ● **11-15** **Join a quiz team** ● **16-20** **Join Mensa**

1. Which large water bird has a pouch underneath its long bill in which it stores fish?
2. 'Oswiecim' is the Polish name for which notorious German World War II extermination and concentration camp?
3. What name is given to tissue damage caused by exposure to extreme cold?
4. Who was the director of the film *Midnight in the Garden of Good and Evil*?
5. Which West Sussex resort owes its royal title to a convalescent visit by King George V?
6. What is the light-sensitive area at the back of the eye called?
7. In Greek mythology, which handsome youth was loved by Aphrodite?
8. What are the main respiratory organs of fishes and many aquatic animals?
9. Who was James Earl Ray convicted of killing?
10. Which British crown colony occupies a tiny peninsula at the southern tip of Spain?
11. Which French director made the films *Hiroshima mon amour* and *Last Year at Marienbad*?
12. What was the first name of Sherlock Holmes's friend Dr Watson?
13. Which glands are affected by Addison's disease?
14. In which country is the port of Abadan?
15. To which continent is the guanaco native?
16. Which British film actor wrote *Snakes and Ladders* and *A Gentle Occupation*?
17. Which ancient unit of length is based on the distance from the elbow to the tip of the middle finger?
18. What were the Guarneri family famous for making?
19. Which humorous American writer wrote poems collected in *Not So Deep as a Well*?
20. Which twin heroes of classical mythology are also known as the Dioscuri?

ANSWERS: *1 Pelican, 2 Auschwitz, 3 Frostbite, 4 Clint Eastwood, 5 Bognor Regis, 6 Retina, 7 Adonis, 8 Gills, 9 Martin Luther King, 10 Gibraltar, 11 Alain Resnais, 12 John, 13 Adrenal glands, 14 Iran, 15 South America, 16 Dirk Bogarde, 17 Cubit, 18 Violins, 19 Dorothy Parker, 20 Castor and Pollux.*

General Knowledge

Your rating:
- 0-5 Join a library
- 6-10 Keep at it
- 11-15 Join a quiz team
- 16-20 Join Mensa

1. Whey is a by-product of the manufacture of which dairy product?
2. Which unit of mass is equal to one thousandth of a kilogram?
3. Who was the leader of the Khmer Rouge whose death was announced in April 1998?
4. Which basin-like structure in the body is composed of the hip bones and lower part of the spine?
5. In which part of a football pitch can the goalkeeper handle the ball?
6. Which famous U.S. evangelist was born in 1918?
7. Which famous Spanish surrealist painter made the film *Un Chien Andalou* with Luis Buñuel?
8. Which former world snooker champion died in 1998 at the age of 84?
9 What name is given to the inability of a person or company to pay their debts?
10. Of which salad plant are cos and iceberg examples?
11. Which Scottish scientist, after whom a law on the diffusion of gases is named, coined the term osmosis?
12. What was the adopted name of Joseph de Veuster, the Belgian missionary who worked at a leper colony at Molokai from 1873?
13. In which war was the Battle of Blenheim fought?
14. Which constellation contains Tycho's star?
15. In which U.S. state is the city of Fargo?
16. Which silvery-white metallic element has the symbol Pd?
17. Which book of the Old Testament describes the history of the Israelites from the death of Joshua to shortly before the reign of Saul?
18. What name is given to the official liturgical plainchant of the Roman Catholic Church codified under the papacy of Gregory I?
19. Which group of expressionist painters included Franz Marc, Wassily Kandinsky and Paul Klee?
20. Of what is cholecystectomy the surgical removal?

ANSWERS: *1 Cheese, 2 Gram, 3 Pol Pot, 4 Pelvis, 5 The penalty area, 6 Billy Graham, 7 Salvador Dali, 8 Fred Davis, 9 Insolvency, 10 Lettuce, 11 Thomas Graham, 12 Father Damien, 13 War of the Spanish Succession, 14 Cassiopeia, 15 North Dakota, 16 Palladium, 17 Judges, 18 Gregorian Chant, 19 Der Blaue Reiter, 20 Gall bladder.*

General Knowledge

Your rating: ● 0-5 Join a library ● 6-10 Keep at it ● 11-15 Join a quiz team ● 16-20 Join Mensa

1. Which Roman goddess was the wife of Jupiter?
2. Baron Haussmann was responsible for the rebuilding of which major European city in the 19th century?
3. Which British film was Best Film, but not Best British Film, at the 1998 BAFTAs?
4. In which English county is the resort of Exmouth?
5. Which river joins the River Trent to form the Humber estuary?
6. Whom did Neil Kinnock replace as leader of the Labour Party?
7. What name is given to the fossilised resin of coniferous trees which is used for jewellery?
8. Of which U.S. state is Providence the capital?
9. Which former Olympic swimming champion became the first Tarzan in sound films?
10. By what name is the bluebottle also known?
11. What sort of blood cells are also called leucocytes?
12. Which German engineer founded a motor car company in 1890 which later merged with the Benz Company?
13. In which county is the market town of Bedworth?
14. Which Prussian general who fought at Waterloo was known as Marshal Forward?
15. What is the capital of Azerbaijan?
16. Which breed of short-haired cat was previously known as Chestnut Brown Foreign?
17. Which Spanish composer wrote *The Three-Cornered Hat* and *Nights in the Gardens of Spain*?
18. Who succeeded to the U.S. presidency when Zachary Taylor died?
19. Which large plain in Argentina, Paraguay and Bolivia was the cause of a war in the 1930s?
20. Who wrote *The Way of All Flesh* and *Erewhon*?

ANSWERS: *1 Juno, 2 Paris, 3 The Full Monty, 4 Devon, 5 River Ouse, 6 Michael Foot, 7 Amber, 8 Rhode Island, 9 Johnny Weissmuller, 10 Blowfly, 11 White blood cells, 12 Gottlieb Daimler, 13 Warwickshire, 14 Gebhard von Blücher, 15 Baku, 16 Havana cat, 17 Manuel de Falla, 18 Millard Fillmore, 19 Gran Chaco, 20 Samuel Butler.*

Sports

Your rating: ● **0-5 Wooden spoon** ● **6-10 Bronze medal** ● **11-15 Silver medal** ● **16-20 Gold medal**

1. Which popular grey steeplechaser died at Aintree on the eve of the 1998 Grand National?
2. Between 1986 and 1995, which Scottish rugby union player scored 140 penalty goals for his country?
3. What is the name of the Paris-based controlling body of world motor racing?
4. In which year did Ronnie O'Sullivan win his first UK Open snooker championship?
5. Which team were knocked out of the 1998 World Cup despite winning their final group game 6-1?
6. What is the name given to the start or restart of an ice hockey match?
7. From which Olympic Games did 22 African countries withdraw because of the participation of New Zealand?
8. In which sport are the foil and epee used?
9. Which Chilean tennis star became world number one after beating Andre Agassi in the final of the 1998 Lipton Championship in Florida?
10. By winning which 1992 track event did Paraskevi Patoulidou become the first Greek woman to win an Olympic gold medal?
11. Who outpointed Oliver McCall in 1995 to win the WBC world heavyweight title?
12. Who won the FA Cup in 1969?
13. In which sport has David Bryant been both indoor and outdoor world champion?
14. What was the venue for the 1998 Winter Olympics?
15. In 1998, which Dutch player equalled his country's all-time scoring record of 35 goals?
16. Which Olympic double did Ethiopian Miruts Yifter achieve in 1980?
17. Holland lost to Scotland in the 1978 World Cup - true or false?
18. Which British sprinter won gold in the 100m at the 1982 Commonwealth Games?
19. Which former British Lions captain became a team captain on the TV show *A Question of Sport*?
20. Which German football team lost the 1977 European Cup Final?

***ANSWERS:** 1 One Man, 2 Gavin Hastings, 3 FIA, 4 1993, 5 Spain, 6 Face off, 7 1972, 8 Fencing, 9 Marcelo Rios, 10 100m hurdles, 11 Frank Bruno, 12 Manchester City, 13 Bowls, 14 Nagano, Japan, 15 Dennis Bergkamp, 16 He won the 5,000m & 10,000m, 17 True, 18 Allan Wells, 19 Bill Beaumont, 20 Borussia Moenchengladbach.*

General Knowledge

Your rating: • **0-5** Join a library • **6-10** Keep at it • **11-15** Join a quiz team • **16-20** Join Mensa

1. Which British artist painted *Rain, Steam and Speed*?
2. What are louse eggs called?
3. Which British pop singer was arrested in the toilets of a public park in America in 1998?
4. In what year was the Battle of Trafalgar?
5. Which small parrots get their name from the great affection they show to their mates?
6. Which academic discipline is concerned with the study of society?
7. Which former coalmining village in South Wales was the scene of a 1966 disaster that killed 116 children?
8. For what is radar an acronym?
9. Which highly venomous snake has ‘king’ and ‘spitting’ varieties?
10. By what abbreviation is polyvinyl chloride better known?
11. Which English king was the son of John of Gaunt?
12. What name is given to a semiconductor device with three or more electrodes?
13. Which Italian composer wrote *Stabat Mater* at the end of his very short life?
14. In which U.S. state is the city of Grand Rapids?
15. Which musical term, literally meaning in chapel style, indicates that a work is to be sung without accompaniment?
16. What sort of creature is a cockchafer?
17. Which British politician co-founded the Anti-Corn Law League with John Bright?
18. In which Italian city were the Amati family of violin makers based?
19. Who was the first president of Israel?
20. Which English composer was granted a monopoly in the printing and selling of music with his teacher Thomas Tallis?

ANSWERS: *1 J. M. W. Turner, 2 Nits, 3 George Michael, 4 1805, 5 Lovebirds, 6 Sociology, 7 Aberfan, 8 Radio detection (or detecting) and ranging, 9 Cobra, 10 PVC, 11 Henry IV, 12 Transistor, 13 Giovanni Pergolesi, 14 Michigan, 15 A cappella, 16 A beetle, 17 Richard Cobden, 18 Cremona, 19 Chaim Weizmann, 20 William Byrd.*

General Knowledge

Your rating:
- **0-5 Join a library**
- **6-10 Keep at it**
- **11-15 Join a quiz team**
- **16-20 Join Mensa**

1. Which disease of adults caused by the herpes zoster virus is closely associated with chickenpox?
2. What is the official map-making body of the U.K. called?
3. Which termite-eating nocturnal mammal has a name which means earth pig in Afrikaans?
4. With what sort of alcoholic drink is the town of Cognac associated?
5. Who won a Best Supporting Actor Oscar for his role in *Good Will Hunting*?
6. Which style of jazz originated in New Orleans in 1912?
7. Which horse won the Grand National in 1998?
8. What was the stage name of French-born film actress Lily Claudette Chauchoin?
9. Which ancient calculating device consists of a frame of wires on which beads are strung?
10. Which famous Irish theatre opened in Dublin in 1904?
11. Which U.S. president succeeded to the presidency after the death of Warren Harding?
12. What is the SI unit of frequency, named after a German physicist?
13. Which country singer died at her home in Nashville, Tennessee in 1998 at the age of 55?
14. What name is given to a swelling in the neck caused by enlargement of the thyroid gland?
15. Which American composer wrote the ballets *Billy the Kid* and *Rodeo*?
16. Which American humorist's pieces are contained in *Crazy Like a Fox* and *Baby, It's Cold Inside*?
17. Which king of France was the husband of Catherine de' Medici?
18. How many books are there in the Christian version of the Old Testament?
19. Which female boxer is known as the Fleetwood Assassin?
20. What was the pen name of American short-story writer William Sidney Porter?

***ANSWERS:** 1 Shingles, 2 Ordnance Survey, 3 Aardvark, 4 Brandy, 5 Robin Williams, 6 Dixieland, 7 Earth Summit, 8 Claudette Colbert, 9 Abacus, 10 Abbey Theatre, 11 Calvin Coolidge, 12 Hertz, 13 Tammy Wynette, 14 Goitre, 15 Aaron Copland, 16 S J Perelman, 17 Henry II, 18 339, 19 Jane Couch, 20 O. Henry.*

General Knowledge

Your rating: ● 0-5 Join a library ● 6-10 Keep at it ● 11-15 Join a quiz team ● 16-20 Join Mensa

1. Which French noblewoman assassinated Jean-Paul Marat in his bath?
2. What name is shared by a contagious disease affecting dogs and a method of painting?
3. Who won a Best Supporting Actress Oscar for her role in *L.A. Confidential*?
4. Which condiment is derived from the climbing plant *Piper nigrum*?
5. What are the leaves of ferns called?
6. Of which ocean is the Coral Sea a section?
7. Who wrote *The Executioner's Song*?
8. What is the name of the organ in mammals that produces eggs?
9. Which British travel agent organised his first excursion, a train journey from Leicester to Loughborough, in 1841?
10. By what acronym is soccer's world governing body known?
11. Which Egyptian village near Luxor is the site of the huge temple of Amon?
12. What was the name of the pupil Peter Abelard married in secret?
13. Which sculptor was jailed in 1998 for stealing body parts?
14. In which African country did the Coptic Church originate?
15. Which hoofed African mammal of the giraffe family was unknown to Europeans until 1901?
16. Who founded the Académie Française to preserve the purity of the French language?
17. What is the French name for the German city of Aachen?
18. Which British sculptor was married to the painter Ben Nicholson?
19. Which character in Greek mythology avenged his father's death by killing his mother, Clytemnestra?
20. In which U.S. state is the city of Peoria?

ANSWERS: *1 Charlotte Corday, 2 Distemper, 3 Kim Basinger, 4 Pepper, 5 Fronds, 6 Pacific, 7 Norman Mailer, 8 Ovary, 9 Thomas Cook, 10 FIFA, 11 Karnak, 12 Heloise, 13 Anthony-Noel Kelly, 14 Egypt, 15 Okapi, 16 Cardinal Richelieu, 17 Aix-la-Chapelle, 18 Barbara Hepworth, 19 Orestes, 20 Illinois.*

Entertainment

Your rating: ● 0-5 Buy a TV ● 6-10 Keep at it ● 11-15 Join a quiz team ● 16-20 Enter a quiz show

1. Who hosted the long-running TV quiz show *Double Your Money*?
2. Who starred as the American monster-hunter Dempsey in the 1995 film *Loch Ness*?
3. Which saucy late night quiz was presented by Maria McErlane and Graham Norton?
4. Which veteran rock group released an album in 1996 entitled *Don't Stop*?
5. Who directed the 1986 movie *She's Gotta Have It*?
6. Who played Dave Briggs in the sitcom *The Detectives*?
7. Who was the lead vocalist of the Undertones?
8. Which 1995 Robert Rodriguez film starred Antonio Banderas?
9. Which Knotty Ash comedian created the Diddymen?
10. Which former Wilson Phillips member released an album entitled *Naked and Sacred* in 1996?
11. What was the title of Kylie Minogue's first U.K. number one single?
12. Which Stanley Kubrick film was based on a Stephen King novel and starred Jack Nicholson?
13. Who played Vince Pinner in the Eighties sitcom *Just Good Friends*?
14. Who duetted with Shakin' Stevens on the 1984 hit *A Rockin' Good Way*?
15. Which Frances Hodgson Burnett story was adapted into a 1995 Hollywood film?
16. Which British cop show starring Jack Warner ran from 1955 to 1976?
17. Which U.S. rock group was fronted by sisters Ann and Nancy Wilson?
18. Who played movie queen Joan Crawford in the 1981 film *Mommie Dearest*?
19. Which U.S. boy band released their second album, *This Time Around*, in 2000?
20. Which 1999 *Star Trek* send-up starred Sigourney Weaver as blonde communications officer Lieutenant Tawny Madison?

ANSWERS: *1 Hughie Green, 2 Ted Danson, 3 Carnal Knowledge, 4 Status Quo, 5 Spike Lee, 6 Robert Powell, 7 Feargal Sharkey, 8 Desperado, 9 Ken Dodd, 10 Chynna Phillips, 11 I Should Be So Lucky, 12 The Shining, 13 Paul Nicholas, 14 Bonnie Tyler, 15 A Little Princess, 16 Dixon of Dock Green, 17 Heart, 18 Faye Dunaway, 19 Hanson, 20 Galaxy Quest.*

General Knowledge

Your rating:
- **0-5 Join a library**
- **6-10 Keep at it**
- **11-15 Join a quiz team**
- **16-20 Join Mensa**

1. Which British actor starred in *Henry V*, *Peter's Friends* and *Dead Again*?
2. What colour does blue litmus turn in the presence of acid?
3. TV series London's Burning follows the adventures of a fire crew called what?
4. By what name are secretions of the lacrimal glands commonly known?
5. Which Australian golfer is known as the Great White Shark?
6. Of which African country is Kigali the capital?
7. Which *Big Brother* contestant was asked to leave the show for breaking the rules in 2000?
8. Which university did Tom Brown go to after his School Days?
9. Which astronomical phenomena are also called shooting stars or falling stars?
10. What date is Saint Patrick's Day?
11. In which of his films did River Pheonix play an American marine?
12. In Greek mythology, who was the goddess of warfare, wisdom and arts and crafts?
13. What was the pen name of the American author William Sydney Porter?
14. Which West Indies bowler took his 400th Test wicket in the fourth Test against England in 2000?
15. In which city was the actor Michael Gambon born?
16. Which port is the capital of South Australia?
17. What was the real name of the novelist who used the pen name George Eliot?
18. In computing, what does the abbreviation DBMS stand for?
19. Which organ is inflamed in a case of encephalitis?
20. Which 2000 film based on a comic starred Patrick Stewart and Ian McKellen?

ANSWERS: *1 Kenneth Branagh, 2 Red, 3 Blue Watch, 4 Tears, 5 Greg Norman, 6 Rwanda, 7 'Nasty' Nick Bateman, 8 Oxford, 9 Meteors, 10 March 17, 11 Dogfight, 12 Athena, 13 O Henry, 14 Curtly Ambrose, 15 Dublin, 16 Adelaide, 17 Mary Ann Evans, 18 Database management system, 19 The brain, 20 X-Men.*

General Knowledge

Your rating:
- **0-5 Join a library**
- **6-10 Keep at it**
- **11-15 Join a quiz team**
- **16-20 Join Mensa**

1. Which horse race run annually at Aintree is the most famous steeplechase in the world?
2. What name is given to a butterfly or moth in its larval stage?
3. Who is the housekeeper in the TV series Father Ted?
4. Who wrote *The Three Musketeers*?
5. Which country was invaded by Iraq in 1990, leading to the Gulf War?
6. How many noughts are there in an English billion?
7. Which snooker player was the world champion in 1985?
8. In which country did the Doberman pinscher originate?
9. Which British dependency did Sir George Rooke capture from Spain in 1704?
10. What nationality is the former skier Franz Klammer?
11. Who created the fictional hypnotist Svengali?
12. Which fabric is named after the Iraqi city of Mosul?
13. What name is given to the science of the physical laws according to which projectiles move in flight?
14. Which newly-promoted team topped the English Premiership after the first Saturday of the 2000-01 season?
15. What does the abbreviation ISBN stand for?
16. Which Old Testament book is the shortest in the Bible?
17. How many yards long is a cricket pitch?
18. Which Egyptian diplomat was the secretary-general of the United Nations from 1992 to 1996?
19. In which country was the philosopher Sir Isaiah Berlin born?
20. What sort of creature is a pratincole?

ANSWERS: *1 Grand National, 2 Caterpillar, 3 Mrs Doyle, 4 Alexandre Dumas, 5 Kuwait, 6 Twelve, 7 Dennis Taylor, 8 Germany, 9 Gibraltar, 10 Austrian, 11 George du Maurier, 12 Muslin, 13 Ballistics, 14 Charlton Athletic, 15 International standard book number, 16 Obadiah, 17 22, 18 Boutros Boutros-Ghali, 19 Latvia, 20 A bird.*

General Knowledge

Your rating:
- 0-5 Join a library
- 6-10 Keep at it
- 11-15 Join a quiz team
- 16-20 Join Mensa

1. Which building designed by Joseph Paxton for the Great Exhibition of 1851 burned down in 1936?
2. What name is given to a score of two under par for a hole in golf?
3. Which football team was owned by the former steel magnate Jack Walker?
4. Who was the first actress from the stage to win an academy award?
5. Which Scottish poet wrote *To a Mouse* and *To a Louse*?
6. In which country is the city of Chihuahua?
7. What name for a place of wild disorder and confusion is derived from the hospital of St Mary of Bethlehem?
8. Where did Lord Peter Wimsey live?
9. Which title did Tiger Woods win at Valhalla in 2000, his third major of the year?
10. In which English county were the artists Thomas Gainsborough and John Constable born?
11. Which term describes the amount of water vapour in the air?
12. What name is given to a court that tries offences against military discipline?
13. What nationality is tennis player Marat Safin?
14. Which Irish dramatist wrote *The Playboy of the Western World*?
15. Of which South American country was Bernardo O'Higgins the chief liberator?
16. Which Austrian-born philosopher wrote *Philosophical Investigations*?
17. Which island at the entrance to the Bristol Channel is a bird sanctuary owned by the National Trust?
18. Who wrote *Mr Norris Changes Trains* and *Goodbye to Berlin*?
19. How many points are awarded for a try in rugby union?
20. In which German city were the trials of the main Nazi war criminals held after World War II?

ANSWERS: *1 Crystal Palace, 2 Eagle, 3 Blackburn Rovers, 4 Helen Hayes, 5 Robert Burns, 6 Mexico, 7 Bedlam, 8 Piccadilly, 9 U.S. PGA Championship, 10 Suffolk, 11 Humidity, 12 Court-martial, 13 Russian, 14 J M Synge, 15 Chile, 16 Ludwig Wittgenstein, 17 Lundy, 18 Christopher Isherwood, 19 Five, 20 Nuremberg.*

Entertainment

Your rating: ● 0-5 Buy a TV ● 6-10 Keep at it ● 11-15 Join a quiz team ● 16-20 Enter a quiz show

1. What was the name of Stephen Tompkinson's reporter character in the topical comedy series *Drop the Dead Donkey*?
2. Which U.S. punk/ska band released their sixth studio album, *Pay Attention*, in 2000?
3. Which legendary actress played a school teacher in a Welsh mining community in the 1945 film *The Corn is Green*?
4. Which comedy panel game show hosted by Nick Hancock embarked on its ninth series on BBC 1 in 2000?
5. Which 2000 horror sequel saw Courteney Cox Arquette reprising her role as a TV reporter and her husband David Arquette his as a small town cop?
6. Which lowlife *Coronation Street* character, suspected of killing Natalie's son Tony, lent Steve McDonald the money to set up a taxi firm in 2000?
7. Which pop duo collaborated with the stars of the TV comedy series on the 1994 U.K. top ten hit *Absolutely Fabulous*?
8. Which actor starred as an ex-rodeo champion in the 1979 film *The Electric Horseman*?
9. Which *EastEnders* character made his exit from Walford in 2000, hitching a lift in a long-distance lorry?
10. Which 2000 British film starred the likes of John Hannah, Brian Conley and Eddie Izzard?
11. What was the title of the 1977 U.K. top five hit for the Tom Robinson Band?
12. Which actor played an FBI agent investigating a death in a rundown LA hotel in the 2000 film *The Million Dollar Hotel*?
13. Which Eighties sitcom starred William Gaunt and Patricia Garwood as Arthur and Beryl Crabtree?
14. Which U.S. singer just couldn't help having a U.K. number one single with *Oops! I Did It Again!* in 2000?
15. Which 1977 film starred Henry Winkler and Sally Field as a young couple dealing with the emotional aftermath of the Vietnam War?
16. Which celebrity imitator made a *Big Impression* with his BBC 1 series?
17. Which singer/songwriter released an album entitled *Living in the Present Future* in 2000, a follow-up to his 1998 debut album, *Desireless*?
18. Which actor played blacksmith Quint Asper in the classic western series *Gunsmoke*?
19. What is the title of Tom Jones' 2000 top five collaboration with Mousse T?
20. Which 1970 film starred Elliott Gould and Candice Bergen as college sweethearts?

ANSWERS: *1 Damien Day, 2 The Mighty Mighty Bosstones, 3 Bette Davis, 4 They Think It's All Over, 5 Scream 3, 6 Jez Quigley, 7 Pet Shop Boys, 8 Robert Redford, 9 Ricky Butcher, 10 Circus, 11 2-4-6-8 Motorway, 12 Mel Gibson, 13 No Place Like Home, 14 Britney Spears, 15 Heroes, 16 Alistair McGowan, 17 Eagle-Eye Cherry, 18 Burt Reynolds, 19 Sex Bomb, 20 Getting Straight.*

General Knowledge

Your rating: ● 0-5 Join a library ● 6-10 Keep at it ● 11-15 Join a quiz team ● 16-20 Join Mensa

1. Which American tennis player won her first Wimbledon singles title in 1974?
2. What substance do bees collect from flowers and turn into honey?
3. How many balls are used in a game of snooker?
4. What is the lower house of the British Parliament?
5. Which fabric used for jeans takes its name from the French city of Nimes?
6. In which English county is the New Forest?
7. Who was the first athlete to run 100 sub-four-minute miles?
8. What name is given to the process of exterminating pests using smoke or gases?
9. Which unit of length is equal to 12 inches?
10. What nationality is the fashion designer Giorgio Armani?
11. Which Arsenal player was sent off twice in three days at the start of the 2000-01 Premiership season?
12. Which country extends farther north than any other country in Africa?
13. Who directed the films Hope and Glory, Deliverance and The Emerald Forest?
14. Which country does footballer Paulo Wanchope represent?
15. What is the brightest star in the constellation Virgo?
16. Which British conductor founded the BBC Symphony Orchestra in 1930?
17. Which Frankish ruler was the grandfather of Charlemagne?
18. Which British author wrote a series of medical novels including *Doctor in the House*?
19. Which boxer was known as the Dark Destroyer?
20. What became the official instrument of execution in France during the French Revolution?

***ANSWERS:** 1 Chris Evert, 2 Nectar, 3 22, 4 House of Commons, 5 Denim, 6 Hampshire, 7 John Walker, 8 Fumigation, 9 Foot, 10 Italian, 11 Patrick Vieira, 12 Tunisia, 13 John Boorman, 14 Costa Rica, 15 Spica, 16 Sir Adrian Boult, 17 Charles Martel, 18 Richard Gordon, 19 Nigel Benn, 20 Guillotine.*

General Knowledge

Your rating:
- 0-5 Join a library
- 6-10 Keep at it
- 11-15 Join a quiz team
- 16-20 Join Mensa

1. Which American aviator crossed the Atlantic in *The Spirit of St Louis*?
2. To which British poet was Sylvia Plath married?
3. Which player scored the first goal of the 1999 FA Cup Final?
4. What sort of creature is *Stuart Little* in the film of the same name?
5. How many noughts are there in an American billion?
6. What name is given to the official reports of proceedings in the British parliament?
7. Which city is the administrative centre of Norfolk?
8. Which team has knocked Newcastle United out of the Worthington Cup in two successive seasons?
9. Which 2000 comedy western featured martial arts star Jackie Chan?
10. What is the second largest country in South America?
11. Which American married couple were executed for spying in 1953?
12. What is the state capital of South Dakota?
13. Which king of Lydia was famous for his immense wealth?
14. In which sport did Australia's Ian Baker-Finch make his name?
15. Which U.S. president was assassinated in 1901?
16. What was Hillary Clinton's maiden name?
17. What nationality was the scientist Robert Boyle?
18. Which fish related to the carp has the scientific name *Tinca tinca*?
19. What was the name of the dog that found the missing World Cup trophy in 1966?
20. Which unstable radioactive element has the symbol At?

ANSWERS: *1 Charles Lindbergh, 2 Ted Hughes, 3 Teddy Sheringham, 4 A mouse, 5 Nine, 6 Hansard, 7 Norwich, 8 Birmingham City, 9 Shanghai Noon, 10 Argentina, 11 Julius and Ethel Rosenberg, 12 Pierre, 13 Croesus, 14 Golf, 15 William McKinley, 16 Rodham, 17 Irish, 18 Tench, 19 Pickles, 20 Astatine.*

General Knowledge

Your rating:
- 0-5 Join a library
- 6-10 Keep at it
- 11-15 Join a quiz team
- 16-20 Join Mensa

1. Which Bizet opera is about a gypsy girl who works in a cigarette factory?
2. In the New Testament, how many apostles did Jesus choose?
3. Who rode Red Marauder to victory in the 2001 Grand National?
4. Of which war was the Battle of Gettysburg a decisive conflict?
5. Which country was ruled by Enver Hoxha from 1944 to 1985?
6. Of which country is Prince Edward Island a province?
7. What is the minimum depth in inches of a golf hole?
8. In the Old Testament, which two ancient cities were destroyed by fire and brimstone?
9. Who was the last British tennis player to win the men's singles at Wimbledon?
10. Of which European country is the Cote d'Azur a part?
11. Which Shakespeare plays features Tamora and Aaron the Moor?
12. What is the chief protein in milk and cheese?
13. In which city did Roberto Duran famously defeat Sugar Ray Leonard in June 1980?
14. Permalloy is an alloy of which two metals?
15. Which 17th-century French mathematician was famous for his last theorem?
16. What is the capital of Trinidad and Tobago?
17. Which star of *The Full Monty* played Fred Flintstone in *The Flintstones in Viva Rock Vegas*?
18. Jai alai is a version of which game?
19. Which administrative divisions of Anglo-Saxon England were subdivided into hundreds?
20. What nationality was the writer and environmental activist Ken Saro-Wiwa?

ANSWERS: *1 Carmen, 2 Twelve, 3 Richard Guest, 4 American Civil War, 5 Albania, 6 Canada, 7 4, 8 Sodom and Gomorrah, 9 Fred Perry, 10 France, 11 Titus Andronicus, 12 Casein, 13 Montreal, 14 Nickel and iron, 15 Pierre de Fermat, 16 Port-of-Spain, 17 Mark Addy, 18 Pelota, 19 Shires, 20 Nigerian.*

Entertainment

Your rating: ● **0-5** **Buy a TV** ● **6-10** **Keep at it**
● **11-15** **Join a quiz team** ● **16-20** **Enter a quiz show**

1. Which U.S. girl group had a 1963 top five hit with *Da Doo Ron Ron*?
2. Which comic actor played the late stand-up comedian Andy Kaufman in the 1999 film *Man on the Moon*?
3. Which BBC 1 documentary series followed the progress of the inhabitants of the remote island of Taransay during 2000?
4. Which legendary U.S. vocalist had a top five single in 1969 with *Lay Lady Lay*?
5. Which giant actor played the title role in the 1983 film *Hercules*?
6. Which Everly Brother, along with Cliff Richard, had a 1983 top ten hit with *She Means Nothing to Me*?
7. In which 1999 film did Patsy Kensit appear as an Essex girl office worker?
8. Which comic actor, who later starred in *Terry and June*, played his own namesake in the Sixties sitcom *Hugh and I*?
9. Who had a number one hit in 2000 with *Don't Call Me Baby*?
10. Which actor played the title role in the 1972 film *Jeremiah Johnson*?
11. Which veteran entertainer was the host of the ITV show *Tonight at the London Palladium*?
12. Who played Maximus Decimus Meridius in the 2000 film epic *Gladiator*?
13. Which BBC 1 series starred Dervla Kirwan as Emma Rose, a woman in love with her husband's brother?
14. What was the title of Britney Spears' second album release?
15. Which actress played Sister Anna Kirkwall in ITV's drama series *Where the Heart Is*?
16. Which U.S. teen singer released an album in 2000 entitled *I Wanna Be With You*, featuring the hit single *Candy*?
17. Which actress played Freddie's wife in the Sixties sitcom *Meet the Wife*?
18. Which former Hollywood couple appeared in the 1967 film version of *Doctor Faustus*?
19. Which ITV drama series featured James Fox as the billionaire Milton Friedkin?
20. Who had *Lovesick Blues* at number one in 1962?

ANSWERS: 1 *The Crystals*, 2 *Jim Carrey*, 3 *Castaway 2000*, 4 *Bob Dylan*, 5 *Lou Ferrigno*, 6 *Phil Everly*, 7 *Janice Beard: 45wpm*, 8 *Terry Scott*, 9 *Madison Avenue*, 10 *Robert Redford*, 11 *Bruce Forsyth*, 12 *Russell Crowe*, 13 *Hearts and Bones*, 14 *Oops!...I Did It Again*, 15 *Lesley Dunlop*, 16 *Mandy Moore*, 17 *Thora Hird*, 18 *Richard Burton & Elizabeth Taylor*, 19 *Metropolis*, 20 *Frank Ifield*.

General Knowledge

Your rating: ● 0-5 Join a library ● 6-10 Keep at it ● 11-15 Join a quiz team ● 16-20 Join Mensa

1. Which actor starred in the films *Guess Who's Coming To Dinner* and *In the Heat of the Night*?
2. By what first name is rock and roll singer Charles Edward Anderson Berry known?
3. Which author created the British intelligence officer George Smiley?
4. When was Wisden Cricketers Almanack first published?
5. Which 14th century rebellion was led by Wat Tyler?
6. What name is given to a bird's entire covering of feathers?
7. The term ippon is used in which sport?
8. How many lines were there in *Picture This*, Andrew Motion's poem to celebrate the Queen Mother's 100th birthday?
9. Which London street is synonymous with the newspaper industry?
10. Who wrote the long-running play *The Mousetrap*?
11. Which American novelist wrote *Goodbye, Columbus* and *Portnoy's Complaint*?
12. What name is given to a party or dance at which masks are worn?
13. Which British dramatist wrote the companion plays *House* and *Garden*?
14. Who is the all-time highest points scorer in rugby union Test matches for England?
15. Which French statesman became the premier for the second time in 1917 at the age of 76?
16. What sort of creature is a caracara?
17. Who created the cartoon character *Colonel Blimp*?
18. How many players make up a Gaelic football team?
19. Which Spanish Jesuit missionary was known as the Apostle of the Indies?
20. What is the southernmost cape of Africa?

ANSWERS: *1 Sidney Poitier, 2 Chuck, 3 John le Carré, 4 1864, 5 Peasants' Revolt, 6 Plumage, 7 Judo, 8 100, 9 Fleet Street, 10 Agatha Christie, 11 Philip Roth, 12 Masquerade, 13 Alan Ayckbourn, 14 Jonny Wilkinson, 15 Georges Clemenceau, 16 A bird, 17 Sir David Low, 18 15, 19 Saint Francis Xavier, 20 Cape Agulhas.*

General Knowledge

Your rating:
- 0-5 Join a library
- 6-10 Keep at it
- 11-15 Join a quiz team
- 16-20 Join Mensa

1. Which English poet wrote *The Rape of the Lock*?
2. With what sort of buildings was Conrad Hilton associated?
3. Which relief agency was founded in 1864 to assist the wounded in wars?
4. In which English city is Edgbaston Test cricket ground?
5. Which official summons MPs to the House of Lords to hear the Queen's Speech?
6. In which continent might one see an alpaca?
7. Who wrote Portrait of the Artist as a Young Dog?
8. Who was emperor of Rome at the time of the fire that destroyed much of the city in 64 AD?
9. With which musical instrument is Benny Goodman associated?
10. What name is given to a creature that lacks a backbone?
11. Who holds the world record for the most weight gained for a film?
12. Which rock and roll star wrote *Blue Suede Shoes*?
13. Who was the first American tennis player to win the men's singles at Wimbledon?
14. Which driver achieved his first victory in 123 races at the 2000 German Grand Prix?
15. What nationality was the composer Anton Bruckner?
16. Lake Taupo is the largest lake in which country?
17. Who created Hannibal Lecter?
18. In which country was the basketball star Patrick Ewing born?
19. In what year was the Berlin Wall built?

ANSWERS: *1 Alexander Pope, 2 Hotels, 3 International Red Cross, 4 Birmingham, 5 Black Rod, 6 South America, 7 Dylan Thomas, 8 Nero, 9 Clarinet, 10 Invertebrate, 11 Robert de Niro, 12 Carl Perkins, 13 Bill Tilden, 14 Rubens Barrichello, 15 Austrian, 16 New Zealand, 17 Thomas Harris, 18 Jamaica, 19 1961, 20 Bangalore.*

General Knowledge

Your rating: ● **0-5** Join a library ● **6-10** Keep at it ● **11-15** Join a quiz team ● **16-20** Join Mensa

1. Which knight of the Round Table had an affair with Queen Guinevere?
2. On which date in 2001 did the General Election take place?
3. Which bespectacled young wizard does Daniel Radcliffe play in a 2001 film?
4. What is the largest city in the United States?
5. Queen Victoria is buried in the Home Park adjoining which Royal residence?
6. Is a chimpanzee a monkey or an ape?
7. Who did Nick Faldo beat in a play-off to win the U.S. Masters in 1990?
8. What name is given to the ancient calculating device consisting of a frame containing rows of beads?
9. Which U.S. tennis player won the men's singles at Wimbledon in 1981, 1983 and 1984?
10. What is the capital of Thailand?
11. Who did the West Indies beat by 92 runs to win the cricket World Cup final in 1979?
12. Which surface with one side and one edge is named after the German mathematician who discovered it?
13. Who wrote the musicals *Company*, *Follies* and *A Little Night Music*?
14. Which county won the 20th and last NatWest Trophy final at Lord's?
15. Galena is the chief ore of which metal?
16. According to legend, who cut the Gordian knot?
17. Who was the only U.S. boxer to win gold at the 1992 Olympics?
18. Which book of the Old Testament tells the story of Samson and Delilah?
19. Who succeeded Warren G. Harding as the president of the United States in 1923?
20. Which British tennis player was the last to reach the men's final at Wimbledon?

ANSWERS: *1 Sir Lancelot, 2 June 7th, 3 Harry Potter, 4 New York City, 5 Windsor Castle, 6 An ape, 7 Ray Floyd, 8 Abacus, 9 John McEnroe, 10 Bangkok, 11 England, 12 Mobius strip, 13 Stephen Sondheim, 14 Gloucestershire, 15 Lead, 16 Alexander the Great, 17 Oscar De La Hoya, 18 Judges, 19 Calvin Coolidge, 20 Bunny Austin.*

Sports

Your rating:
- **0-5 Wooden spoon**
- **6-10 Bronze medal**
- **11-15 Silver medal**
- **16-20 Gold medal**

1. In which field event did Jonathan Edwards claim Olympic gold in Sydney?
2. Who won the cricket World Cup in 1996?
3. What nationality is tennis player Lleyton Hewitt?
4. Who lost to Manchester United in the final of the European Cup Winners Cup in 1991?
5. How many majors did golfer Tony Jacklin win?
6. The actor Sean Bean is a fan of which football team?
7. In which country was heavyweight boxer Joe Bugner born?
8. How many players make up a baseball team?
9. In which sport is the Ryder Cup contested?
10. What is the name of the small usually white ball in bowls?
11. In which city was Maurice Green born?
12. A scrum half in rugby union would traditionally wear which number on his back?
13. Which country hosted the 1968 Olympic Games?
14. Who was the Formula One world champion in 1996?
15. Which country won the rugby union World Cup in 1991?
16. Which horse won the 2000 Grand National at Aintree?
17. Which boxer was known as the Brown Bomber?
18. What nationality is cricketer Shaun Pollock?
19. Who won the F.A. Cup in 1979?
20. With which sport is the Queensberry rules associated?

ANSWERS: *1 The triple jump, 2 Sri Lanka, 3 Australian, 4 Barcelona, 5 Two, 6 Sheffield United, 7 Hungary, 8 9, 9 Golf, 10 Jack, 11 Kansas City, 12 Nine, 13 Mexico, 14 Damon Hill, 15 Australia, 16 Papillon, 17 Joe Louis, 18 South African, 19 Arsenal, 20 Boxing.*

General Knowledge

Your rating:
- **0-5 Join a library**
- **6-10 Keep at it**
- **11-15 Join a quiz team**
- **16-20 Join Mensa**

1. Henry Steinway is chiefly associated with the manufacture of which musical instruments?
2. Alex Hay and Peter Alliss are commentators on which sport?
3. Which American actor plays an Irish gypsy in Guy Ritchie's film *Snatch*?
4. What type of fertiliser is made from partly decayed plant material?
5. Which U.S. film director won Oscars for four films, including *The Grapes of Wrath* and *The Quiet Man*?
6. What is the capital of Afghanistan?
7. Who captained Fulham in the 1975 FA Cup final?
8. What name is given to the announcement to Mary that she was to be the mother of Jesus?
9. What is the second largest planet?
10. In which ocean is the island of Mauritius?
11. In what year was the boxer Naseem Hamed born?
12. Which Irish author and poet wrote the autobiography *My Left Foot*?
13. In which South American country is the active volcano Cotopaxi?
14. Which 2000 film adaptation of a Shakespeare play featured Anthony Hopkins and Jessica Lange?
15. What is the family name of the Dukes of Devonshire?
16. Which metallic element has the symbol Pd?
17. Which football team won the 2001 F.A. Cup Final at the Millennium Stadium, Cardiff?
18. Which U.S. author wrote *Another Country* and *The Fire Next Time*?
19. Where would you find a caldera?
20. In which U.S. state is the Painted Desert?

ANSWERS: *1 Pianos, 2 Golf, 3 Brad Pitt, 4 Compost, 5 John Ford, 6 Kabul, 7 Bobby Moore, 8 The Annunciation 9 Saturn, 10 Indian Ocean, 11 1974, 12 Christy Brown, 3 Ecuador, 4 Titus, 5 Cavendish, 6 Palladium, 17 Liverpool, 18 James Baldwin, 19 At the top of a volcano, 20 Arizona.*

General Knowledge

Your rating:
- 0-5 Join a library
- 6-10 Keep at it
- 11-15 Join a quiz team
- 16-20 Join Mensa

1. Which British actress won an Oscar for her performance in *A Passage to India*?
2. What is the highest mountain in the world?
3. How many majors has golfer Lee Trevino won?
4. What name is given to the poisonous substance produced by snakes and scorpions?
5. In which U.S. state is the city of San Antonio?
6. With which musical instrument is Mstislav Rostropovich associated?
7. Who won the FA Cup in 1981?
8. Which well-known song concerns a swagman who camped by a billabong?
9. In Greek mythology, who was the goddess of love and beauty?
10. Which famous American sharpshooter was the subject of the musical *Annie Get Your Gun*?
11. How old was Jack Nicklaus when he won the U.S. Masters in 1986?
12. Which French composer wrote the *Symphonie fantastique* and *Harold in Italy*?
13. Before their 2000 triumph, in which year did England last beat the West Indies in a Test match series?
14. Which island in New York Harbor was a reception centre for immigrants from 1892 to 1943?
15. On which river does the city of Lincoln stand?
16. Who was the first Protestant archbishop of Canterbury?
17. What nationality is footballer Jean-Marc Bosman?
18. Which American golfer retired from tournament play in 1930 at the age of 28 after winning 13 major titles?
19. What is the name of the militia that kidnapped 11 British soldiers in Sierra Leone in August 2000?
20. Which heavy metal group recorded the album *Paranoid*?

ANSWERS: *1 Dame Peggy Ashcroft, 2 Mount Everest, 3 6, 4 Venom, 5 Texas, 6 Cello, 7 Spurs, 8 Waltzing Matilda, 9 Aphrodite, 10 Annie Oakley, 11 46, 12 Hector Berlioz, 13 1969, 14 Ellis Island, 15 Witham, 16 Thomas Cranmer, 17 Belgian, 18 Bobby Jones, 19 West Side Boys, 20 Black Sabbath.*

General Knowledge

Your rating: ● **0-5** Join a library ● **6-10** Keep at it ● **11-15** Join a quiz team ● **16-20** Join Mensa

1. Which Irish novelist wrote *The Commitments*, *The Snapper* and *The Van*?
2. Tonie Carroll and Brett Mullins are top names from which sport?
3. Which Ford model was nicknamed the Tin Lizzie?
4. Who was the most famous new girl at St George's School in Ascot in 2000?
5. Which hormone regulates the level of sugar in the blood?
6. Of which African country is Mogadishu the capital?
7. How many dismissals did wicketkeeper Rodney Marsh take for Australia in Test matches?
8. In which English university city is the Ashmolean Museum?
9. Which novel by Charles Dickens features Bill Sikes and Fagin?
10. With which invention is Alexander Graham Bell associated?
11. Which painter is the subject of the novel *The Agony and the Ecstasy* by Irving Stone?
12. In which U.S. state is the area of high-technology industries known as Silicon Valley?
13. What is the name of Hamlet's mother in Shakespeare's play?
14. Which Russian tennis player beat Pete Sampras to win the men's singles at the 2000 U.S. Open?
15. What sort of creature is a Bombay duck?
16. Into which vitamin does the liver convert carotene?
17. Who was the first British golfer to win the US Open?
18. Which English composer wrote the song *Jerusalem* to words from William Blake's poem *Milton*?
19. What sort of wheat is used to make pasta?
20. Which producer of TV documentaries was married to Esther Rantzen?

ANSWERS: *1 Roddy Doyle, 2 Rugby league, 3 Model T, 4 Princess Beatrice, 5 Insulin, 6 Somalia, 7 355, 8 Oxford, 9 Oliver Twist, 10 Telephone, 11 Michelangelo, 12 California, 13 Gertrude, 14 Marat Safin, 15 A fish, 16 Vitamin A, 17 Harry Vardon, 18 Sir Hubert Parry, 19 Durum wheat, 20 Desmond Wilcox.*

Entertainment

Your rating: ● **0-5 Buy a TV** ● **6-10 Keep at it** ● **11-15 Join a quiz team** ● **16-20 Enter a quiz show**

1. Which TV comedienne/celebrity interviewer returned to her native U.S. for a slice of *American Pie* in 1999?
2. What do the Righteous Brothers, Cilla Black, and Telly Savalas have in common?
3. Which writing partnership were behind the comedy series *Steptoe and Son*?
4. Who won the Oscar for Best Director at the 1996 Academy Awards ceremony?
5. Which Gaelic group released an album entitled *Lore* in 1996?
6. What was the name of *Dennis the Menace*'s dog in the cartoon series?
7. Who won the Oscar for Best Actor at the 1996 Academy Awards ceremony?
8. Who had a top ten hit single in 1976 with *Silly Love Songs*?
9. Which *Prime Suspect* star played DS Nolan in TV's *Deep Secrets*?
10. Which film won five Oscars at the 1996 Academy Awards ceremony?
11. Which former *Eldorado* star played Beckett in TV's *Bugs*?
12. Which band was sued by former drummer Tony McCarroll for a six-figure royalty share?
13. Who played the title role in the 1944 film *Cover Girl*?
14. Who starred on TV as *Madson*?
15. What do Bing Crosby, Sinead O'Connor, and Bros have in common?
16. Which Channel 4 quiz show was presented by William G. Stewart?
17. Who directed the 1989 film *Crimes and Misdemeanors*?
18. Who had a top ten hit single in 1991 with *Smells Like Teen Spirit*?
19. Who was the host of TV's *That's Showbusiness*?
20. Who won the Oscar for Best Actress at the 1996 Academy Awards ceremony?

ANSWERS: *1 Ruby Wax, 2 They have all released versions of You've Lost That Lovin' Feeling, 3 Ray Galton and Alan Simpson, 4 Mel Gibson, 5 Clannad, 6 Gnasher, 7 Nicolas Cage, 8 Paul McCartney, 9 Colin Salmon, 10 Braveheart, 11 Jesse Birdsall, 12 Oasis, 13 Rita Hayworth, 14 Ian McShane, 15 They have all released versions of Silent Night, 16 Fifteen to One, 17 Woody Allen, 18 Nirvana, 19 Mike Smith, 20 Susan Sarandon.*

General Knowledge

Your rating:
- 0-5 Join a library
- 6-10 Keep at it
- 11-15 Join a quiz team
- 16-20 Join Mensa

1. What is the largest county of the Republic of Ireland?
2. Which nocturnal beetle emits a greenish light from organs on its abdomen?
3. Which French city in the Côte d'Or department is famous for its mustard?
4. In which athletics field event does a man have to throw something that weighs 2 kg?
5. Which British naval explorer claimed New South Wales for Britain?
6. Who won a Best Actress Oscar for her role in *As Good As It Gets*?
7. Who won a Best Actor Oscar for his role in *As Good As It Gets*?
8. What are the organs of locomotion and balance in fishes called?
9. How many events are there in the modern pentathlon?
10. What name is given to the domesticated form of polecat used to hunt rabbits and rats?
11. Which African country was formerly known as the French Territory of the Afars and Issas?
12. In Irish politics, which party is the conservative rival of Fianna Fáil?
13. Which Greek god was also known as Bacchus?
14. In music, what name is given to a combination of notes that sounds harsh to the ear?
15. Which British dramatist wrote *A Patriot For Me* and *West of Suez*?
16. The island Martha's Vineyard is off the coast of which U.S. state?
17. What name was given to the circular towers built as a defence against the potential invasion of Britain by Napoleon?
18. Who wrote *Other Voices, Other Rooms* and *In Cold Blood*?
19. Who won the ladies' singles title at the 1999 Wimbledon championships?
20. Which political doctrine claims that monarchs are accountable only to God for their actions?

ANSWERS: *1 Cork, 2 Firefly, 3 Dijon, 4 Discus, 5 Captain James Cook, 6 Helen Hunt, 7 Jack Nicholson, 8 Fins, 9 Five, 10 Ferret, 11 Djibouti, 12 Fine Gael, 13 Dionysus, 14 Dissonance, 15 John Osborne, 16 Massachusetts, 17 Martello towers, 18 Truman Capote, 19 Lindsay Davenport, 20 Divine right of kings.*

General Knowledge

Your rating: ● **0-5 Join a library** ● **6-10 Keep at it** ● **11-15 Join a quiz team** ● **16-20 Join Mensa**

1. Which legendary Greek poet and musician attempted to rescue his wife Eurydice from Hades?
2. Which Welsh port has a ferry connection with Rosslare in the Republic of Ireland?
3. With which branch of the arts was Sergei Diaghilev chiefly associated?
4. Who resigned the captaincy of the England cricket team in 1998?
5. Which common complaint is also known as dyspepsia?
6. What were G. K. Chesterton's Christian names?
7. Which chesspiece is also called a castle?
8. What title used by German emperors derives from the Latin word Caesar?
9. Which wife of Henry VIII was the mother of Mary I?
10. Which American film star won Oscars for his roles in *High Noon* and *Sergeant York*?
11. Of which U.S. state is Annapolis the capital?
12. Which Scottish historian and essayist wrote *The French Revolution*?
13. In which country was the Latin poet Martial born?
14. Which actress provided the voice of *Anastasia* in the feature-length cartoon?
15. Of what is the sensitivity or speed usually quoted as an ASA rating?
16. Which New Zealand-born short-story writer wrote *Bliss* and *The Garden Party*?
17. Which resin, also known as colophony, is applied to the hairs of violin bows?
18. Which Italian word describes the overall pattern of light and shade in a picture?
19. What name is given to the burrowing crab with an enlarged claw that it holds like a violin?
20. What name is given to drugs that increase the output of urine by the kidneys?

ANSWERS: *1 Orpheus, 2 Fishguard, 3 Ballet, 4 Michael Atherton, 5 Indigestion, 6 Gilbert Keith, 7 Rook, 8 Kaiser, 9 Catherine of Aragon, 10 Gary Cooper, 11 Maryland, 12 Thomas Carlyle, 13 Spain, 14 Meg Ryan, 15 Photographic film, 16 Katherine Mansfield, 17 Rosin, 18 Chiaroscuro, 19 Fiddler crab, 20 Diuretics.*

General Knowledge

Your rating: ● 0-5 Join a library ● 6-10 Keep at it ● 11-15 Join a quiz team ● 16-20 Join Mensa

1. What was the pen name of British author Eric Blair?
2. On which river does Bedford stand?
3. In what country was chewing gum first patented?
4. Which North American rodent is also known as a musquash?
5. Which naturalist and wildlife painter, son of a famous explorer, founded the Wildfowl Trust at Slimbridge in Gloucestershire?
6. With which musical instrument is Mstislav Rostropovich chiefly associated?
7. What name is given to the branch of zoology that involves the study of birds?
8. By what abbreviation is deoxyribonucleic acid usually known?
9. Which London street is synonymous with the bespoke tailoring trade?
10. How many Oscars did *Titanic* win, equalling the record set by *Ben-Hur*?
11. Who wrote *V*, *Gravity's Rainbow* and *The Crying of Lot 49*?
12. What name is given to the branch of biology involving the study of fungi?
13. Who was the autocratic director-general of New Netherland who surrendered the colony to British forces in 1664?
14. What is the common name for pyrite or iron pyrites?
15. Which late eighteenth century literary movement's name means 'storm and stress' in German?
16. Who was the god of the dead in Egyptian mythology?
17. Which English painter and poet was a founder member of the Pre-Raphaelite Brotherhood?
18. Who wrote *The Song of the Shirt*?
19. Which genus of plants includes the Eurasian bindweed?
20. Which American novelist wrote *The Red Badge of Courage*?

ANSWERS: *1 George Orwell, 2 River Ouse, 3 The United States, 4 Muskrat, 5 Sir Peter Scott, 6 Cello, 7 Ornithology, 8 DNA, 9 Savile Row, 10 Eleven, 11 Thomas Pynchon, 12 Mycology, 13 Peter Stuyvesant, 14 Fool's gold, 15 Sturm und Drang, 16 Osiris, 17 Dante Gabriel Rossetti, 18 Thomas Hood, 19 Convolvulus, 20 Stephen Crane.*

Entertainment

Your rating:	● 0-5	Buy a TV	● 6-10	Keep at it
	● 11-15	Join a quiz team	● 16-20	Enter a quiz show

1. Which *Professionals* star played Hudson the butler in TV's *Upstairs, Downstairs*?
2. Which female vocalist was *Running Up That Hill* in 1985?
3. Which British rock star played the Goblin King in the film *Labyrinth*?
4. Which teen drama series was based on the best-selling novels by Francine Pascal?
5. Which Seattle band released an album in 1996 entitled *Devil's Road*?
6. Which British actress played Lenny Weinribb's wife in the Woody Allen film *Mighty Aphrodite*?
7. Which British character actor won a BAFTA award for his performance in the title role of TV's *I, Claudius*?
8. Which actress won an Academy Award nomination for her performance in the 1988 film *Working Girl*?
9. Who played Alf in TV's *Home and Away*?
10. Who had a number one hit single in 1984 with *You Spin Me Round (Like A Record)*?
11. Who was the writer/director of the film *Dead Man Walking*?
12. Which BBC sitcom was set in the Porter household?
13. Which band released an album entitled *Moseley Shoals* in 1996?
14. Which 1950s rock'n'roller was the subject of the 1987 film *La Bamba*?
15. Who played Eric Sykes's sister in numerous comedy shows from the '50s to the '70s?
16. Who had a top ten hit single in 1968 with *Yummy Yummy Yummy*?
17. Who starred in the 1996 film version of *Sergeant Bilko*?
18. What was the title of Lionel Richie's 1996 album?
19. Who starred as blacklisted director David Merrill in the film *Guilty By Suspicion*?
20. Who is the lead singer of The Cure?

ANSWERS: *1 Gordon Jackson, 2 Kate Bush, 3 David Bowie, 4 Sweet Valley High, 5 The Walkabouts, 6 Helena Bonham Carter, 7 Derek Jacobi, 8 Melanie Griffith, 9 Ray Meagher, 10 Dead Or Alive, 11 Tim Robbins, 12 2point4 Children, 13 Ocean Colour Scene, 14 Ritchie Valens, 15 Hattie Jacques, 16 Ohio Express, 17 Steve Martin, 18 Louder Than Words, 19 Robert De Niro, 20 Robert Smith.*

General Knowledge

Your rating:
- **0-5 Join a library**
- **6-10 Keep at it**
- **11-15 Join a quiz team**
- **16-20 Join Mensa**

1. In which athletics field event do men throw a heavy sphere attached to a chain with a handle?
2. Which American outlaw was killed by gang member Robert Ford for a $10,000 reward?
3. What name is given to the treatment of injuries and disabilities by massage, exercise or heat?
4. Of which country was Henry Pu-Yi the last emperor?
5. What name is given to an abscess at the root of an eyelash?
6. Of which revolution was the Reign of Terror a feature?
7. Which actor, whose films included *High Noon* and *Airplane*, founded an acting dynasty?
8. In the New Testament, what was the occupation of St Joseph, husband of the Virgin Mary?
9. What are Pontefract (or Pomfret) cakes made of?
10. What sort of buns are traditionally eaten on Good Friday?
11. What is the oldest U.S. military decoration?
12. Which British conductor was principal conductor of the Hallé Orchestra until his death in 1970?
13. What sort of projectiles were pioneered by U.S. physicist Robert Hutchings Goddard?
14. Which plant was the source of the poison by which Socrates killed himself?
15. In what year was Prince Andrew born?
16. Which Italian town is said to contain the home of the Virgin Mary, carried by angels from Nazareth?
17. With which musical instrument is Heinz Holliger chiefly associated?
18. In which U.S. state is Los Alamos, where the first atom bombs were made?
19. Which Austrian theatre director founded the Salzburg Festival in 1920?
20. Which Scottish fishing port is famous as the birthplace of Ramsay MacDonald?

ANSWERS: *1 Hammer, 2 Jesse James, 3 Physiotherapy, 4 China, 5 Stye, 6 French Revolution, 7 Lloyd Bridges, 8 Carpenter, 9 Liquorice, 10 Hot cross buns, 11 The Purple Heart, 12 Sir John Barbirolli, 13 Rockets, 14 Hemlock, 15 1960, 16 Loreto, 17 Oboe, 18 New Mexico, 19 Max Reinhardt, 20 Lossiemouth.*

General Knowledge

Your rating:
- **0-5 Join a library**
- **6-10 Keep at it**
- **11-15 Join a quiz team**
- **16-20 Join Mensa**

1. Which famous painting by Leonardo Da Vinci can be seen in Sta Maria delle Grazie in Milan?
2. Of which form of surgery are skin grafting and facelifts examples?
3. Who won the first Formula 1 grand prix of the 1998 season after team-mate David Coulthard gave way to him?
4. Which British aviators made the first nonstop flight across the Atlantic in 1919?
5. What is the English name for the Swedish city of Göteborg?
6. Which style of music is associated with the Jamaican cult of Rastafarianism?
7. From which card game did bridge evolve?
8. In Greek mythology, what creatures formed the hair of the Gorgons?
9. Which spiny shrub is also called furze or whin?
10. Which Russian jeweller was noted especially for his jewelled Easter eggs?
11. What remedy against unlawful imprisonment is in the form of a writ requiring a detained person to be brought before a court?
12. Which category in the biological classification of animals can be divided into classes?
13. From which country do the 13th century books known as the Eddas come?
14. Which two young actors starred in and co-wrote the film *Good Will Hunting*?
15. Who wrote the novels *Castle Rackrent* and *Ormond*?
16. Which Asian plant yields marijuana and a tough fibre used for rope?
17. What is the name of the space probe that discovered water on the moon in 1998?
18. Which Italian composer is wrongly credited with the composition of a popular *Adagio*, actually composed by his biographer?
19. Who was the wife of the Emperor Augustus and mother of the Emperor Tiberius?
20. In which constellation is the red giant Aldebaran?

ANSWERS: *1 The Last Supper, 2 Plastic surgery, 3 Mika Hakkinen, 4 Alcock and Brown, 5 Gothenburg, 6 Reggae, 7 Whist, 8 Snakes, 9 Gorse, 10 Peter Carl Fabergé, 11 Habeas corpus, 12 Phylum, 13 Iceland, 14 Matt Damon and Ben Affleck, 15 Maria Edgeworth, 16 Hemp, 17 Lunar Prospector, 18 Tomaso Albinoni, 19 Livia Drusilla, 20 Taurus.*

General Knowledge

Your rating: ● 0-5 Join a library ● 6-10 Keep at it ● 11-15 Join a quiz team ● 16-20 Join Mensa

1. What name is given to the process by which green plants exposed to sunlight produce carbohydrates?
2. Which zodiac sign is between Aquarius and Aries?
3. What name is given to the form of calcium sulphate used to make casts for broken limbs?
4. Which East Sussex resort is famous for its Royal Pavilion?
5. From which country does Gorgonzola cheese come?
6. Which aquatic bird has Canada, barnacle and greylag varieties?
7. Which fish gets its name from its long whisker-like barbels?
8. Of which science are quantum mechanics and thermodynamics branches?
9. What is the liquid constituent of blood called?
10. Which flowering plant is sometimes called the Michaelmas daisy?
11. What collective name is given to the Gospels of Matthew, Mark and Luke?
12. In which country was Alexandra, Queen consort of Edward VII born?
13. Which chemical element has the symbol P?
14. Who was the butler to the Princess of Wales who received £50,000 in her will?
15. Which Italian novelist wrote The Woman of Rome and Two Women?
16. Of which Canadian province is Regina the capital?
17. According to the New Testament, which condemned robber was released at the Passover instead of Jesus?
18. What is the more common name for metempsychosis in which the soul is born again in another body?
19. Which German composer wrote the operas *Les Huguenots* and *Robert le Diable*?
20. What sort of macaques are the apes on Gibraltar?

ANSWERS: *1 Photosynthesis, 2 Pisces, 3 Plaster of Paris, 4 Brighton, 5 Italy, 6 Goose, 7 Catfish, 8 Physics, 9 Plasma, 10 Aster, 11 The Synoptic Gospels, 12 Denmark, 13 Phosphorus, 14 Paul Burrell, 15 Alberto Moravia, 16 Saskatchewan, 17 Barabbas, 18 Reincarnation, 19 Giacomo Meyerbeer, 20 Barbary apes.*

Entertainment

Your rating: ● 0-5 Buy a TV ● 6-10 Keep at it ● 11-15 Join a quiz team ● 16-20 Enter a quiz show

1. What was the title of the 1996 album by The Cure?
2. Who directed the 1985 film version of *A Chorus Line*?
3. Which singer/songwriter released the albums *Astral Weeks* and *Moondance*?
4. Who played the Duchess of York in the 1996 film version of *Richard III*?
5. Which former Bros star released an album entitled *The Key* in 1996?
6. Who starred as the private detective in Roman Polanski's film *Chinatown*?
7. Who played Dorothea Grant in TV's *No Bananas*?
8. Which actor was the Riddler in the 1995 film *Batman Forever*?
9. Who played Sandra's mother in the TV series *The Liver Birds*?
10. Who were the two team captains in the first series of *Call My Bluff* hosted by Bob Holness?
11. Which Bristol "trip-hop" artist released an album entitled *Nearly God* in 1996?
12. Which 1996 John Woo film starred John Travolta and Christian Slater?
13. Who starred as writer Daniel Feeld in the TV drama *Karaoke*?
14. Who had a number one hit single in 1972 with *School's Out*?
15. Who directed the 1972 film *Last Tango In Paris*?
16. Which *Only Fools and Horses* star also appeared in TV's *A Sharp Intake of Breath*?
17. Who had a number one hit in 1982 with *Seven Tears*?
18. Who played the Mayor in the 1996 film *City Hall*?
19. Which ex-popstar co-presented the BBC's coverage of the 2001 RHS Chelsea Flower Show?
20. Who was the lead singer of Dexy's Midnight Runners?

ANSWERS: *1 Wild Mood Swings, 2 Richard Attenborough, 3 Van Morrison, 4 Maggie Smith, 5 Matt Goss, 6 Jack Nicholson, 7 Stephanie Beacham, 8 Jim Carrey, 9 Mollie Sugden, 10 Sandi Toksvig and Alan Coren, 11 Tricky, 12 Broken Arrow, 13 Albert Finney, 14 Alice Cooper, 15 Bernardo Bertolucci, 16 David Jason, 17 Goombay Dance Band, 18 Al Pacino, 19 Kim Wilde, 20 Kevin Rowland.*

General Knowledge

Your rating: ● 0-5 Join a library ● 6-10 Keep at it ● 11-15 Join a quiz team ● 16-20 Join Mensa

1. Which administrative region of Scotland was formed from the counties of Aberdeen, Kincardine, Banff and Moray?
2. Who was the Roman goddess of the hearth, whose shrine was attended by six virgin priestesses?
3. What relation was William of Orange to Charles I?
4. Who wrote *Saturday Night and Sunday Morning*?
5. On which hill, also known as Golgotha, was Christ crucified?
6. Which British writer created *Dixon of Dock Green*?
7. Which veteran rock singer won a Grammy for Album of the Year for his album *Time out of Mind*?
8. Which Chilean island in the South Pacific, also called Rapa Nui, is noted for its gigantic stone figures?
9. In which European country is Salzburg, where an Easter festival is held annually?
10. Which star of the TV series *Father Ted* died in 1998 at the age of 45?
11. With which composer's songs is German baritone Dietrich Fischer-Dieskau chiefly associated?
12. What name is given to the opposition in an electrical circuit to the flow of an alternating current, which has the symbol Z?
13. Which Scottish tourist town on the River Tummel is noted for its Festival Theatre?
14. To which genus of plants do the guelder rose and wayfaring tree belong?
15. Which British naval commander founded New South Wales?
16. Which British novelist wrote *Memento Mori*?
17. Which Scottish football team plays at Easter Road?
18. In which county is the village of Walsingham?
19. What was the name of the decree that granted religious freedom to the Huguenots in 1598?
20. Which pH number indicates neither acidity nor alkalinity?

ANSWERS: *1 Grampian Region, 2 Vesta, 3 Grandson, 4 Alan Sillitoe, 5 Calvary, 6 Lord Ted Willis, 7 Bob Dylan, 8 Easter Island, 9 Austria, 10 Dermot Morgan, 11 Franz Schubert, 12 Impedance, 13 Pitlochry, 14 Viburnum, 15 Arthur Phillip, 16 Muriel Spark, 17 Hibernian, 18 Norfolk, 19 Edict of Nantes, 20 Seven.*

General Knowledge

Your rating: ● **0-5** Join a library ● **6-10** Keep at it ● **11-15** Join a quiz team ● **16-20** Join Mensa

1. What name is given to the Thursday before Good Friday?
2. Of which Australian state is Melbourne the capital?
3. In which event did Britain win its only medal at the 1998 Winter Olympics?
4. What was the name of the Roman procurator who condemned Christ to death?
5. Which British author wrote a series of novels set in Barsetshire?
6. After which Italian navigator was America named?
7. Which British novelist wrote *Salar the Salmon*?
8. What is the longest river in Italy?
9. On which Pacific islands are Darwin's finches found?
10. Which tragic hero of medieval romances fell in love with Isolde or Iseult?
11. Which vivid blue pigment was formerly obtained by grinding up lapis lazuli?
12. What name was given to the followers of the Greek moral philosopher Diogenes of Sinope?
13. Which winged goddess was the personification of victory in Greek mythology?
14. Of what are the Perseids and Geminids examples?
15. Which Hertfordshire town founded by Ebenezer Howard was designated a new town in 1948?
16. What name is given to abnormal accumulation of fluid in body tissues, leading to swelling?
17. Which English poet wrote *L'Allegro* and *Il Penseroso*?
18. Which Roman poet, exiled under the emperor Domitian, is best known for his 16 *Satires*?
19. What is the major endocrine gland of vertebrates?
20. Which chemical element has the symbol Mn?

ANSWERS: *1 Maundy Thursday, 2 Victoria, 3 Four-man bobsleigh, 4 Pontius Pilate, 5 Anthony Trollope, 6 Amerigo Vespucci, 7 Henry Williamson, 8 River Po, 9 Galapagos Islands, 10 Tristan, 11 Ultramarine, 12 Cynics, 13 Nike, 14 Meteor showers, 15 Welwyn Garden City, 16 Oedema, 17 John Milton, 18 Juvenal, 19 Pituitary gland, 20 Manganese.*

General Knowledge

Your rating: • 0-5 Join a library • 6-10 Keep at it • 11-15 Join a quiz team • 16-20 Join Mensa

1. To which continent is the plant poison ivy native?
2. Which U.S. poet and short-story writer wrote *The Raven*?
3. Who starred in and directed the 1997 film *The Postman*?
4. To which Italian city does the adjective Neapolitan relate?
5. Who wrote *The History of Mr Polly* and *The Shape of Things* to Come?
6. On which English river is the port of Immingham?
7. On which New York island are Broadway, Wall Street, Central Park and Greenwich Village?
8. In which country is the Nubian Desert?
9. Which French writer and dramatist was noted for his long nose and for fighting duels?
10. What is the name of the petrol-thickening jelly used extensively by the U.S. in incendiary bombs in the Vietnam War?
11. Which French city on the River Deule is the capital of the Nord department?
12. What sort of creature is a finfoot?
13. Which French artist painted *Olympia* and *A Bar at the Folies-Bergère*?
14. Of which sea is the Gulf of Tonkin an inlet?
15. In Greek mythology, which golden fruit grew on a tree guarded by the Hesperides?
16. Which British philosopher wrote *On Liberty* and *Principles of Political Economy*?
17. Which musical instrument is associated with David and Igor Oistrakh?
18. What is the second largest of the Great Lakes?
19. By what name are rare earth metals also known?
20. What was the third part of Arnold Wesker's trilogy that began with *Chicken Soup with Barley*?

ANSWERS: *1 North America, 2 Edgar Allan Poe, 3 Kevin Costner, 4 Naples, 5 H G Wells, 6 Humber, 7 Manhattan, 8 Sudan, 9 Cyrano de Bergerac, 10 Napalm, 11 Lille, 12 A bird, 13 Edouard Manet, 14 South China Sea, 15 Apples, 16 John Stuart Mill, 17 Violin, 18 Lake Huron, 19 Lanthanides, 20 I'm Talking About Jerusalem.*

Entertainment

Your rating: ● **0-5** Buy a TV ● **6-10** Keep at it ● **11-15** Join a quiz team ● **16-20** Enter a quiz show

1. Which 1996 film starred Geena Davis as a pirate?
2. Which husband and wife band released an album entitled *X* in 1996?
3. Who starred as the aging football star prematurely summoned to judgement in the film *Heaven Can Wait*?
4. Who had a top ten hit single in 1982 with *Zoom*?
5. Which controversial talk show host was formally the mayor of Cincinnati?
6. Who won the Oscar for Best Supporting Actor at the 1996 Academy Awards ceremony?
7. Which *Doctor Finlay* character was played on TV by Jessica Turner?
8. Who left the rock group Genesis in 1996 after more than 20 years?
9. Who played the title role in the 1961 film *El Cid*?
10. Which TV series starred Caroline Lee Johnson as customs chief Diane Ralton?
11. Which Bradford singer released an album in 1996 entitled *Bloom*?
12. Which dry-witted Antipodean was joined regularly in one of his TV series by Cuban singer Margarita Pracatan?
13. Who played Otto in the film *A Fish Called Wanda*?
14. Which Australian actor originally played Ed in the TV series *Bugs*?
15. Who had a top ten hit in 1982 with *Young Guns (Go For It)*?
16. Who won the Oscar for Best Supporting Actress at the 1996 Academy Awards ceremony?
17. Who originally played Alf Garnett's daughter in *Till Death Us Do Part*?
18. What was the title of Tina Turner's 1996 album?
19. Who played Group Captain Cyril Barker in TV's *Over Here*?
20. Who played Sergeant Milton Warden in the film *From Here to Eternity*?

ANSWERS: *1 Cutthroat Island, 2 The Beloved, 3 Warren Beatty, 4 Fat Larry's Band, 5 Jerry Springer, 6 Kevin Spacey, 7 Dr Napier, 8 Phil Collins, 9 Charlton Heston, 10 The Knock, 11 Tasmin Archer, 12 Clive James, 13 Kevin Kline, 14 Craig McLachlan, 15 Wham!, 16 Mira Sorvino, 17 Una Stubbs, 18 Wildest Dreams, 19 Martin Clunes, 20 Burt Lancaster.*

General Knowledge

Your rating: ● **0-5** Join a library ● **6-10** Keep at it ● **11-15** Join a quiz team ● **16-20** Join Mensa

1. Which common plant gets its name from the French for lion's tooth?
2. By what name were the Parliamentarian opponents of the Cavaliers known in the English Civil War?
3. By what name is the flesh-eating insect *Mantis religiosa* better known?
4. What is the chief port of the Netherlands?
5. Which English theologian and historian was known as the Venerable?
6. For which drink is the town of Darjeeling famous?
7. Which Greek philosopher founded the Academy in Athens in about 387 BC?
8. Of which zodiacal constellation is Pollux the brightest star?
9. Which Italian operatic composer wrote *The Thieving Magpie*?
10. What is the motto of the Scouts?
11. In which U.S. state is the town of Fairbanks?
12. Who was the King of England when the second millennium AD began?
13. In which god's honour were the Pythian Games celebrated every four years in ancient Greece?
14. Which European river is crossed by the Vasco da Gama bridge?
15. What is the most famous composition by Claude Joseph Rouget de Lisle?
16. Which cotton fabric gets its name from the Iraqi city of Mosul?
17. Who is said to have hanged himself from the tree *Cercis siliquastrum*?
18. Which organ of the body is affected by pyelitis?
19. What term, attributed to Gertrude Stein, is applied to a group of disillusioned expatriate American writers in the 1920s?
20. On which river does the town of Rotherham stand?

ANSWERS: *1 Dandelion, 2 Roundheads, 3 Praying mantis, 4 Rotterdam, 5 St Bede, 6 Tea, 7 Plato, 8 Gemini, 9 Gioacchino Rossini, 10 Be Prepared, 11 Alaska, 12 Ethelred the Unready, 13 Apollo, 14 River Tagus, 15 La Marseillaise, 16 Muslin, 17 Judas Iscariot (Judas tree), 18 The kidney, 19 The Lost Generation, 20 River Don.*

General Knowledge

Your rating: ● 0-5 Join a library ● 6-10 Keep at it ● 11-15 Join a quiz team ● 16-20 Join Mensa

1. A red variety of which flower is used as a symbol of remembrance for the dead of the World Wars?
2. What name is given to the flight of Chinese communists to Yan'an, led by Mao Tse-tung?
3. Of which Asian country is the BJP one of the main political parties?
4. Which famous Italian actress was married to film producer Carlo Ponti?
5. According to legend, at whom did Peeping Tom peep?
6. Which fairly large rodent has spines or quills with which it defends itself?
7. Which abbreviated inscription, which stands for Jesus of Nazareth, king of the Jews, often appears in paintings of the crucifixion?
8. Which London street is synonymous with private medicine?
9. Which star of *Titanic* played two roles in *The Man in the Iron Mask*?
10. What is the hardest known mineral?
11. Which German composer wrote *Seven Words of Christ on the Cross*?
12. Which metallic element was named by Sir Humphry Davy after a place in Scotland?
13. The Turtle, designed by David Bushnell, was an early example of what sort of vessel?
14. Which British field marshal commanded the 14th Army in Burma and became governor general of Australia in 1953?
15. What name was given to the American equivalent of British Music Hall?
16. Which state of Austria has the German name Steiermark?
17. What name was shared by a 19th century American physician and writer and his jurist son?
18. On which river does the German city of Magdeburg stand?
19. What name is given to Mahler's Second Symphony?
20. Which guns were superseded by rifles in the mid-19th century?

ANSWERS: *1 Poppy, 2 The Long March, 3 India, 4 Sophia Loren, 5 Lady Godiva, 6 Porcupine, 7 INRI, 8 Harley Street, 9 Leonardo DiCaprio, 10 Diamond, 11 Heinrich Schütz, 12 Strontium, 13 Submarine, 14 William Joseph Slim, 15 Vaudeville, 16 Styria, 17 Oliver Wendell Holmes, 18 Elbe, 19 Resurrection Symphony, 20 Muskets.*

General Knowledge

Your rating: ● **0-5** **Join a library** ● **6-10** **Keep at it** ● **11-15** **Join a quiz team** ● **16-20** **Join Mensa**

1. Which country house in Wiltshire is owned by the Marquess of Bath?
2. Of which country has Juan Carlos been king since 1975?
3. Which Italian island in the Tyrrhenian Sea is noted for its active volcano?
4. Including the cue ball, how many balls are used in a game of snooker?
5. Which Swiss resort on Lake Geneva hosts an annual television festival which awards a Golden Rose?
6. Who wrote *The Rape of the Lock* and *The Dunciad*?
7. Which country did Britain fight in the Opium War of 1839-42?
8. What name is given to the mixture of boiled linseed oil and whiting used for fastening glass in windows?
9. Which England cricketer made his maiden Test century in the 5th Test against the West Indies in 1998?
10. In Roman Catholic doctrine, what is the name of the state in which souls are purified after death to make them fit for heaven?
11. In the hierarchy of the English judicial system, which judge is second to the Lord Chancellor?
12. Which city associated with the Champagne industry was the scene of the coronations of most French kings?
13. In what year did the MV Derbyshire sink off the Japanese coast?
14. Which Czech composer wrote the opera the *Glagolithic Mass*?
15. Who asked for the body of Christ after the Crucifixion and buried it in his own tomb?
16. Which translucent ceramic material did Johann Böttger succeed in making in the early eighteenth century?
17. In what year was Nelson Mandela sentenced to life imprisonment?
18. Which large venomous African viper is noted for inflating its body when alarmed?
19. Which Irish poet and dramatist wrote the poem *Easter 1916*?
20. What name is given to the many-seeded fruit of the tree *Punica granatum*?

ANSWERS: 1 Longleat, 2 Spain, 3 Stromboli, 4 22, 5 Montreux, 6 Alexander Pope, 7 China, 8 Putty, 9 Mark Ramprakash, 10 Purgatory, 11 Lord Chief Justice, 12 Reims, 13 1980, 14 Leos Janacek, 15 St Joseph of Arimathea, 16 Porcelain, 17 1964, 18 Puff adder, 19 W B Yeats, 20 Pomegranate.

Sports

Your rating: ● **0-5** **Wooden spoon** ● **6-10** **Bronze medal**
● **11-15** **Silver medal** ● **16-20** **Gold medal**

1. Which Manchester United player was named Footballer of the Year and PFA Player of the Year in 2000?
2. Who knocked Gustavo Kuerten out of the Australian Open in January 2001?
3. What is the value of the yellow ball in snooker?
4. Which Briton won the silver medal in the final of the 1500m at the 1988 Seoul Olympics?
5. Which country knocked England out of the 1999 rugby union World Cup?
6. Which country's cricket team was captained by Hansie Cronje until his sacking in 2000 over match-fixing allegations?
7. Karrie Webb and Laura Davies are top female players in which sport?
8. Which British boxer won a light-middleweight bronze medal at the 1972 Olympics?
9. A Boston crab is a term from which sport?
10. Which number lies between 20 and 18 on a dartboard?
11. Which rugby team clinched the Allied Dunbar Premiership by beating Bristol in May 2000?
12. Who won the snooker world championship in 1972?
13. Bobby Fischer was the world champion from 1972-75 in what?
14. Which Brazilian footballer was awarded an honourary knighthood in 1997?
15. What is another name for skittles?
16. Who scored England's winning goal in their Euro 2000 victory over Germany?
17. Which Belgian international announced his retirement from football in January 2001?
18. What nationality is motor-racing great Niki Lauda?
19. Who scored a hole-in-one albatross at the par four 17th at the Phoenix Open in January 2001?
20. What is the surname of the two brothers who won boxing gold medals at the 1976 Olympics?

***ANSWERS:** 1 Roy Keane, 2 Greg Rusedski, 3 Two, 4 Peter Elliott, 5 South Africa, 6 South Africa, 7 Golf, 8 Alan Minter, 9 Wrestling, 10 1, 11 Leicester, 12 Alex Higgins, 13 Chess, 14 Pele, 15 Ninepins, 16 Alan Shearer, 17 Luc Nilis, 18 Austrian, 19 David Magee, 20 Spinks.*

General Knowledge

Your rating:
- 0-5 Join a library
- 6-10 Keep at it
- 11-15 Join a quiz team
- 16-20 Join Mensa

1. Which French Impressionist artist was famous for his many paintings of water-lilies?
2. What sort of creature is a bittern?
3. Which Bond actor provided the voice for *The Magic Snowman*?
4. Who beat Lindsay Davenport to win the women's singles at the 2000 U.S. Open?
5. Which element has the chemical symbol I?
6. In which English county is Launceston?
7. Which English football club won the UEFA Cup in 1981?
8. Which eccentric creation of Hugh Lofting can talk to animals?
9. Which founder of a TV dynasty was the BBC's first war correspondent?
10. What is the fourth planet from the sun?
11. Which American author created the Hardy Boys and Nancy Drew?
12. In which island group is Bishop Rock, famous for its lighthouse?
13. What sort of peas are used to make the dish hummus?
14. Which classic horse race was won by Millenary at Doncaster in 2000?
15. By what name was the Swiss clown Charles Adrien Wettach known?
16. Which Irish author wrote *Uncle Silas* and *In a Glass Darkly*?
17. Where was the film Rebeccas Daughters set?
18. Which racing driver wept after winning the 2000 Italian Grand Prix at Monza?
19. Who wrote the novels *Campbell's Kingdom* and *The Wreck of the Mary Deare*?
20. Which tree is also called a Chile pine?

ANSWERS: *1 Claude Monet, 2 A bird, 3 Roger Moore, 4 Venus Williams, 5 Iodine, 6 Cornwall, 7 Ipswich, 8 Dr Dolittle, 9 Richard Dimbleby, 10 Mars, 11 Edward Stratemeyer, 12 Scilly Isles, 13 Chick-peas, 14 St Leger, 15 Grock, 16 Sheridan Le Fanu, 17 Wales, 18 Michael Schumacher, 19 Hammond Innes, 20 Monkey puzzle tree.*

General Knowledge

Your rating: ● 0-5 Join a library ● 6-10 Keep at it ● 11-15 Join a quiz team ● 16-20 Join Mensa

1. Of which U.S. state is Boston the capital?
2. Who wrote *The Pilgrim's Progress*?
3. A table tennis ball must have a diameter of how many inches?
4. Who became the first managerial casualty of the 2000-01 Premiership season when he was sacked by Chelsea?
5. In which English county is Barnsley?
6. By what name are the edible tubers of the plant *Solanum tuberosum* better known?
7. Which American author won the 1962 Nobel Prize for Literature?
8. Which fish market was the oldest in London until its closure in 1982?
9. What was James Dean's last film?
10. In which London Park is Speakers' Corner?
11. Nathan Robertson and Donna Kellogg are internationals in which sport?
12. Which Hungarian author wrote the play *Liliom* and the novel *The Paul Street Boys*?
13. Of which planet is Amalthea a satellite?
14. Which British comedian won two Emmys for his show *Dress To Kill*?
15. What sort of creature is an argali?
16. Which English title of nobility ranks immediately below an earl?
17. Which football team plays at Ewood Park?
18. Which British metaphysical poet wrote the religious works collected in *The Temple*?
19. Woolloomooloo is a suburb of which Australian city?
20. Which English royal house was also called the Angevin Dynasty?

ANSWERS: *1 Massachusetts, 2 John Bunyan, 3 1 and a half, 4 Gianluca Vialli, 5 South Yorkshire, 6 Potatoes, 7 John Steinbeck, 8 Billingsgate, 9 Giant, 10 Hyde Park, 11 Badminton, 12 Ferenc Molnar, 13 Jupiter, 14 Eddie Izzard, 15 A wild sheep, 16 Viscount, 17 Blackburn Rovers, 18 George Herbert, 19 Sydney, 20 Plantagenet.*

General Knowledge

Your rating:
- **0-5 Join a library**
- **6-10 Keep at it**
- **11-15 Join a quiz team**
- **16-20 Join Mensa**

1. Which English actress and orange-seller was a mistress of King Charles II?
2. Which novel by Charles Dickens features the character Sidney Carton?
3. Which star of the film *The King and I* was born Taidje Khan?
4. The 60th anniversary of which battle was commemorated at Biggin Hill in 2000?
5. Which British dramatist wrote *Hay Fever* and *Bitter Sweet*?
6. What does the abbreviation IQ stand for?
7. How many books of the New Testament are epistles?
8. In which equestrian event do horses perform complex manoeuvres in response to their rider's body signals?
9. Which English naval administrator is famous for his Diary which gives an account of the Great Fire of London?
10. What name is given to precipitation containing high levels of sulphuric and nitric acids?
11. Which team won the F.A. Cup in 1993?
12. Which British author wrote *The Hitchhiker's Guide to the Galaxy*?
13. *Kol Nidre* is a prayer chanted in synagogues on the eve of which Jewish holiday?
14. Which county won cricket's County Championship in 2000?
15. What sort of gemstone is the Star of India?
16. Which Nazi leader was known as the Butcher of Lyon?
17. How many gold medals did the USA win at the Moscow Olympics in 1980?
18. Which alloy was first mass-produced by using the Bessemer process?
19. Who played the title role in the 2000 film version of *Shaft*?
20. Which American actor played Chopin in the film *A Song to Remember*?

ANSWERS: *1 Nell Gwyn, 2 A Tale of Two Cities, 3 Yul Brynner, 4 The Battle of Britain, 5 Sir Noël Coward, 6 Intelligence quotient, 7 21, 8 Dressage, 9 Samuel Pepys, 10 Acid rain, 11 Arsenal, 12 Douglas Adams, 13 Yom Kippur, 14 Surrey, 15 Sapphire, 16 Klaus Barbie, 17 0, 18 Steel, 19 Samuel L Jackson, 20 Cornel Wilde.*

Entertainment

Your rating: ● 0-5 Buy a TV ● 6-10 Keep at it ● 11-15 Join a quiz team ● 16-20 Enter a quiz show

1. In which 2000 film did Meg Ryan, Diane Keaton and Lisa Kudrow star as the daughters of a dying father, played by Walter Matthau?
2. Who were the two contestants on the first celebrity edition of the quiz show *Who Wants to Be a Millionaire*?
3. Which U.K. group had a 1973 top ten hit with *Pyjamarama*?
4. Which actor directed the 1987 version of the film *The Glass Menagerie*?
5. Which McGann played Jonathan Vishnevski in the BBC 1 drama series *Fish*?
6. Which U.S. vocalist had a top five hit in 1972 with *I Can See Clearly Now*?
7. Which footballing legend was the subject of a 2000 film about his life, in which he was played by John Lynch?
8. Who played the hero in the Seventies TV series *The Return of the Saint*?
9. Which 2000 album featured the greatest songs of Paul Simon's solo career?
10. Which Bond girl also appeared in the 1970 film *Perfect Friday*?
11. Which historian presented the Channel 4 documentary series *Elizabeth*?
12. Which Swindon teenager had a number one hit in 2000 with *Day & Night*?
13. Which showbiz stalwart became the first celebrity to be inducted into the BBC's *Hall of Fame*?
14. Which *Friends* actor starred as a dentist in the 2000 film comedy *The Whole Nine Yards*?
15. Which actor played Vince Pinner in the Eighties sitcom *Just Good Friends*?
16. Which pop group told us to *Reach* in the top five in 2000?
17. Who played Marcus in the 1971 film *Jennifer on My Mind*?
18. Which former BBC foreign correspondent introduced us to his *Forgotten Britain* on BBC 1?
19. Which U.S. vocalist had a 1976 U.K. top ten hit with *This is It*?
20. In which 2000 film did Ewan McGregor star as the writer James Joyce?

ANSWERS: *1 Hanging Up, 2 Carol Vorderman & Kirsty Young, 3 Roxy Music, 4 Paul Newman, 5 Paul McGann, 6 Johnny Nash, 7 George Best (Best), 8 Ian Ogilvy, 9 Shining Like a National Guitar, 10 Ursula Andress, 11 David Starkey, 12 Billie Piper, 13 Barbara Windsor, 14 Matthew Perry, 15 Paul Nicholas, 16 S Club 7, 17 Michael Brandon, 18 Fergal Keane, 19 Melba Moore, 20 Nora.*

General Knowledge

Your rating: ● **0-5** Join a library ● **6-10** Keep at it ● **11-15** Join a quiz team ● **16-20** Join Mensa

1. Which English artist was famous for his bleak industrial landscapes featuring matchstick figures?
2. In Indian philosophy, what term is used for the sum of a person's actions, carried forward into his next life?
3. Which flamboyant Russian-born ballet dancer died in Paris in 1993?
4. Who scored a world record 26 runs from a single Test match over in March 2001?
5. The Hindenburg Line was a defensive barrier built by the Germans in which war?
6. What sort of animal is a Saluki?
7. Which English novelist wrote *Lucky Jim* and *The Old Devils*?
8. Which was the first club to beat Manchester United at Old Trafford in a European Cup or Champions League tie?
9. Which famous comic character appears in four of Shakespeare's plays?
10. In which 1690 battle did William III defeat the exiled King James II?
11. In which sport is the term hookcheck often used?
12. *The Man of Property* is the first book in which sequence of novels by John Galsworthy?
13. Cardinal Richelieu was the chief minister of which French monarch?
14. Which cyclist won Great Britain's first gold medal at the Sydney Olympics?
15. In the Old Testament, who was the mother of Ishmael?
16. Which U.S. rock band features Bob Dylan's son Jakob?
17. Who won the 2000 Mercury Music Prize for his album *The Hour of the Bewilderbeast*?
18. What is the middle name of basketball legend Michael Jordan?
19. Which French artist painted *Olympia* and *Le Déjeuner sur l'herbe*?
20. What sort of creatures transmit Lyme disease?

ANSWERS: *1 L S Lowry, 2 Karma, 3 Rudolf Nureyev, 4 Craig MacMillan, 5 World War I, 6 A dog, 7 Kingsley Amis, 8 Fenerbache, 9 Sir John Falstaff, 10 Battle of the Boyne, 11 Ice hockey, 12 The Forsyte Saga, 13 Louis XIII, 14 Jason Queally, 15 Hagar, 16 The Wallflowers, 17 Badly Drawn Boy, 18 Jeffrey, 19 Edouard Manet, 20 Ticks.*

General Knowledge

Your rating: ● 0-5 Join a library ● 6-10 Keep at it ● 11-15 Join a quiz team ● 16-20 Join Mensa

1. Which branch of mathematics takes its name from the Greek for 'earth measurement'?
2. Who wrote *The Adventures of Tom Sawyer* and *The Adventures of Huckleberry Finn*?
3. Where is the Sabina Park cricket ground?
4. In which film did Pierce Brosnan first play James Bond?
5. Which horse won the Grand National in 1973, 1974 and 1977?
6. In the Old Testament, who was the wife of King Ahab whose name has come to mean a wicked woman?
7. Which Spanish author wrote *The Three-Cornered Hat*?
8. Which Australian swimmer is nicknamed The Thorpedo?
9. Which play by J.M. Barrie is subtitled *The Boy Who Wouldn't Grow Up*?
10. What sort of gemstone is the Koh-i-noor?
11. By how many shots did Tiger Woods win the U.S. Masters in 1997?
12. Which U.S. comedian and pianist was known as Schnozzola or The Schnoz?
13. Who was the first British woman to win an Olympic cycling medal?
14. Which Australian marsupial is also called a banded anteater?
15. With which branch of the arts was Robert Mapplethorpe chiefly associated?
16. Which U.S. rapper and actor was murdered in a drive-by shooting in 1996?
17. The 11th hole on which golf course is called White Dogwood?
18. By what name was the American striptease artiste Rose Louise Hovick better known?
19. Which Canadian singer recorded the album *Jagged Little Pill*?
20. Which three sports are included in the Triathlon?

ANSWERS: *1 Geometry, 2 Mark Twain, 3 Jamaica, 4 GoldenEye, 5 Red Rum, 6 Jezebel, 7 Pedro Antonio de Alarcon, 8 Ian Thorpe, 9 Peter Pan, 10 A diamond, 11 12, 12 Jimmy Durante, 13 Yvonne McGregor, 14 Numbat, 15 Photography, 16 Tupac Shakur, 17 Augusta, 18 Gypsy Rose Lee, 19 Alanis Morissette, 20 Swimming, cycling and running.*

General Knowledge

Your rating:
- **0-5 Join a library**
- **6-10 Keep at it**
- **11-15 Join a quiz team**
- **16-20 Join Mensa**

1. Which American actor starred in *Twelve Angry Men* and *On Golden Pond*?
2. How many goals were scored in the first international football match between England and Scotland?
3. Which Australian runner lit the Olympic cauldron in the opening ceremony of the Sydney Olympics?
4. By what name was singer and comedian Asa Yoelson better known?
5. Which large cat is also called a cougar?
6. Who was the fourth wife of Henry VIII?
7. Which jazz musician wrote the autobiography *Good Morning Blues*?
8. To which Hebridean island did Flora Macdonald help Bonnie Prince Charlie to escape?
9. What is a group of lions called?
10. Is a cobra venomous or nonvenomous?
11. Which country hosted the rugby union World Cup in 1995?
12. Which British actress starred in *The Lady Vanishes* and *The Wicked Lady*?
13. Who won the 200m freestyle at the Sydney Olympics to become the first Dutchman to win an Olympic swimming gold medal?
14. Which Italian dramatist wrote *Accidental Death of an Anarchist*?
15. By what name is Beethoven's Sixth Symphony known?
16. Who is generally regarded as the first British prime minister?
17. What number wood in golf was formerly known as a spoon?
18. What name is given to the deliberate and systematic destruction of a racial, religious or ethnic group?
19. What is the title of the novel Jane Austen left unfinished at her death?
20. Which country beat the British men's hockey team 8-1 at the Sydney Olympics?

ANSWERS: *1 Henry Fonda, 2 0, 3 Cathy Freeman, 4 Al Jolson, 5 Puma, 6 Anne of Cleves, 7 Count Basie, 8 Skye, 9 A pride, 10 Venomous, 11 South Africa, 12 Margaret Lockwood, 13 Pieter van den Hoogenband, 14 Dario Fo, 15 Pastoral Symphony, 16 Robert Walpole, 17 3, 18 Genocide, 19 Sanditon, 20 Pakistan.*

Entertainment

Your rating:
- 0-5 Buy a TV
- 6-10 Keep at it
- 11-15 Join a quiz team
- 16-20 Enter a quiz show

1. What was the title of the O'Jays' 1973 top ten hit?
2. Which 1977 film set in the world of car racing starred Richard Pryor and Beau Bridges?
3. Which actress played the title role in the Channel 4 adaptation of Tolstoy's *Anna Karenina*?
4. What was Debbie Reynolds' only U.K. top five hit?
5. Which actress played Grace in the 2000 British film *Saving Grace*?
6. Which actress played Jill Munroe in the U.S. drama series *Charlie's Angels*?
7. Which DJ and singer hit the U.K. number one spot in 2000 with *It Feels So Good*?
8. Who directed the 1979 film *1941*?
9. Which BBC 2 sitcom starred *This Life*'s Jack Davenport as Steve?
10. Which U.S. rock band returned to the U.K. top ten in 2000 with the hit single *It's My Life*?
11. Who presented us with *The Awful Truth* about Americans on Channel 4?
12. Three members of which girl group appeared as sisters in the 2000 film *Honest*?
13. Which sports presenter hosted the *BAFTA Television Awards* on ITV in 2000?
14. Which British R&B singer/songwriter released his second album, *The Other Side*, in 2000?
15. Which Seventies comedy series starred Michael Crawford and Michael Gambon as warring neighbours?
16. In which country is Elvis Presley's character stationed in the 1960 film *G.I. Blues*?
17. Who represented the U.K. in the 2000 *Eurovision Song Contest*, with an entry entitled *Don't Play That Song Again*?
18. Which boy band collaborated with Queen on the 2000 number one hit *We Will Rock You*?
19. Which 2000 film starred Kevin Bacon as a reluctant psychic?
20. Which *EastEnders* character informed the police about the bent cars being

ANSWERS: *1 Love Train, 2 Greased Lightning, 3 Helen McCrory, 4 Tammy, 5 Brenda Blethyn, 6 Farrah Fawcett-Majors, 7 Sonique, 8 Steven Spielberg, 9 Coupling, 10 Bon Jovi, 11 Michael Moore, 12 All Saints, 13 Des Lynam, 14 Lynden David Hall, 15 Chalk and Cheese, 16 Germany, 17 Nicki French, 18 Five, 19 Stir of Echoes, 20 Dan Sullivan.*

General Knowledge

Your rating: • 0-5 Join a library • 6-10 Keep at it • 11-15 Join a quiz team • 16-20 Join Mensa

1. What is the English name for what the French call La Manche?
2. Which Indian novelist wrote *Journey to Ithaca* and *Village by the Sea*?
3. What was the first of C.S. Lewis's books about the kingdom of Narnia?
4. In which event did Steve Backley win a silver medal at the Sydney Olympics?
5. How many lines are there in a limerick?
6. What sort of institution did London bookseller Thomas Guy found in the 1720s?
7. Which golfer won the U.S. Masters in 1999?
8. Which American singer and actress starred in the films *Calamity Jane* and *Pillow Talk*?
9. Which mischievous elf in Irish folklore is supposed to have a hidden store of gold?
10. What name is given to an inflamed swelling of the first joint of the big toe?
11. Whose comedy sketch show was entitled *Attention Scum*?
12. Which American singer had hits with *Papa's Got a Brand New Bag* and *It's a Man's, Man's World*?
13. Who won Britain's only medal for judo at the Sydney Olympics?
14. Which Yiddish word, meaning fit or proper, is applied to food that meets the requirements of Jewish dietary laws?
15. What were the first names of the pioneer film director D W Griffith?
16. *Raging Bull* was the autobiography of which American boxer?
17. Who wrote the books on which the TV series *Follyfoot Farm* was based?
18. Which comic actor starred in the film *Me, Myself and Irene*?
19. In which sport is Doggett's Coat and Badge contested?
20. Who directed the films *To Have and Have Not*, *The Big Sleep* and *Rio Bravo*?

ANSWERS: *1 The English Channel, 2 Anita Desai, 3 The Lion, the Witch and the Wardrobe, 4 Javelin, 5 Five, 6 A hospital, 7 Jose-Maria Olazabal, 8 Doris Day, 9 Leprechaun, 10 Bunion, 11 Simon Munnery, 12 James Brown, 13 Kate Howey, 14 Kosher, 15 David Ward, 16 Jake La Motta, 17 Monica Dickens, 18 Jim Carrey, 19 Rowing, 20 Howard Hawks.*

General Knowledge

Your rating:
- 0-5 Join a library
- 6-10 Keep at it
- 11-15 Join a quiz team
- 16-20 Join Mensa

1. Which food item takes its name from the French for 'twice cooked'?
2. In what year was *The Magic Roundabout* first shown on television?
3. Which singer and actress starred in the films *The Wizard of Oz* and *Meet Me in St Louis*?
4. How many rowing gold medals did Great Britain win at the Sydney Olympics?
5. Who wrote *The Call of the Wild* and *White Fang*?
6. What name is given to the oath taken by doctors?
7. The novel *Captain Corelli's Mandolin* was set on which Greek island?
8. What name is given to a situation in which employers of a company have to belong to a trade union?
9. By what name was the former system of racial segregation in South Africa known?
10. What colour is the eight-ball in pool?
11. Which rock star was born Marvin Lee Aday?
12. Which book by Gavin Maxwell describes his life with two pet otters in the Scottish Highlands?
13. What does the legal term 'caveat emptor' mean?
14. Which 2000 film starred veteran actors Clint Eastwood, Tommy Lee Jones, Donald Sutherland and James Garner?
15. Of which planet is Phoebe a satellite?
16. Which public school was founded by Bishop William of Wykeham in 1382?
17. Who wrote *The Thorn Birds*?
18. Which film actress and wartime pin-up girl married bandleader Harry James in 1943?
19. How many counters does each player have in a game of backgammon?
20. Which group won the 1994 Mercury Music Prize for their album *Elegant Slumming*?

ANSWERS: *1 Biscuit, 2 1965, 3 Judy Garland, 4 Two, 5 Jack London, 6 Hippocratic oath, 7 Cephalonia, 8 Closed shop, 9 Apartheid, 10 Black, 11 Meat Loaf, 12 Ring of Bright Water, 13 Let the buyer beware, 14 Space Cowboys, 15 Saturn, 16 Winchester College, 17 Colleen McCullough, 18 Betty Grable, 19 Fifteen, 20 M People.*

General Knowledge

Your rating:
- 0-5 Join a library
- 6-10 Keep at it
- 11-15 Join a quiz team
- 16-20 Join Mensa

1. In which European country did the dish goulash originate?
2. A luge is a type of what?
3. Which British physicist wrote *A Brief History of Time*?
4. In which event did Denis Lewis win a gold medal at the Sydney Olympics?
5. Which sign of the zodiac is also called the Water Bearer?
6. Who became president of Iraq in 1979?
7. Who was the world chess champion from 1969-72?
8. Who played Detective Chief Inspector Jane Tennison in the *Prime Suspect* TV series?
9. On which sport does Richie Benaud commentate?
10. What sort of creature is a gazelle?
11. Who wrote *The Good Soldier*?
12. Which former Olympic swimming champion played *Flash Gordon* and *Buck Rogers* in films?
13. What is the name of Olivia's ambitious steward in Shakespeare's *Twelfth Night*?
14. Which four-time world superbike champion announced his retirement in 2000?
15. In what year was the Great Train Robbery in Britain?
16. What is basketball player Magic Johnson's real first name?
17. Against which country did David Beckham score his first senior international goal for England?
18. By what name were the Nazi police force the Geheime Staatspolizei known?
19. Which common childhood illness related to shingles is also called varicella?
20. In Christianity, what name is given to the cup used in the celebration of the Eucharist?

ANSWERS: *1 Hungary, 2 Racing toboggan, 3 Stephen Hawking, 4 Heptathlon, 5 Aquarius, 6 Saddam Hussein, 7 Boris Spassky, 8 Helen Mirren, 9 Cricket, 10 An antelope, 11 Ford Madox Ford, 12 Buster Crabbe, 13 Malvolio, 14 Carl Fogarty, 15 1963, 16 Earvin, 17 Colombia, 18 Gestapo, 19 Chicken pox, 20 Chalice.*

Entertainment

Your rating: ● **0-5** Buy a TV ● **6-10** Keep at it ● **11-15** Join a quiz team ● **16-20** Enter a quiz show

1. Which U.S. group had a 1977 U.K. top five smash with *Native New Yorker*?
2. Which 1966 film starred Warren Beatty and Susannah York?
3. Which former children's presenter played vet Adam Forrester in ITV's *Emmerdale*?
4. What was the title of the song that was a U.K. top ten hit for both Stacy Lattisaw in 1980, and Dannii Minogue in 1991?
5. Which actor starred as *Deuce Bigalow: Male Gigolo* in the 1999 film?
6. Who starred as *Charles Endell Esquire* in the Seventies TV series?
7. Which Latino pop diva released an album entitled *Alma Caribena* in 2000?
8. Who played John Morlar in the 1978 film *The Medusa Touch*?
9. Which husband and wife team presented *The British Soap Awards 2000* on ITV?
10. Which former M People vocalist released her debut solo album, *Proud*, in 2000?
11. In which 2000 film did John Travolta star as the head of security of a race called Psychlos?
12. Which Welsh TV actress played Sandra Hutchinson in *The Liver Birds* and Megan Roberts in *The District Nurse*?
13. What was the title of the fourth album by the Glasgow group Belle & Sebastian?
14. Which hit British film, directed by Guy Ritchie, was adapted for a Channel 4 series in 2000?
15. Which 1969 film set in the Philippines starred David Niven, Faye Dunaway and Alan Alda?
16. Who presented his view of *Car Years* on BBC 2?
17. What was the title of Billy Ray Cyrus' 1992 top five hit?
18. Which 2000 film set in a World War II submarine starred Matthew McConaughey and Harvey Keitel?
19. Which former *This Life* actress starred as Lieutenant Eve Turner in the 2000 ITV drama *Rough Treatment*?
20. What was the title of Whitney Houston's first U.K. number one hit?

***ANSWERS:** 1 Odyssey, 2 Kaleidoscope, 3 Tim Vincent, 4 Jump to the Beat, 5 Rob Schneider, 6 Iain Cuthbertson, 7 Gloria Estefan, 8 Richard Burton, 9 Richard Madeley and Judy Finnigan, 10 Heather Small, 11 Battlefield Earth, 12 Nerys Hughes, 13 Fold Your Hands Child, You Walk Like a Peasant, 14 Lock, Stock and Two Smoking Barrels, 15 The Extraordinary Seaman, 16 Jeremy Clarkson, 17 Achy Breaky Heart, 18 U-571, 19 Daniela Nardini, 20 Saving All My Love For You.*

General Knowledge

Your rating: ● **0-5 Join a library** ● **6-10 Keep at it** ● **11-15 Join a quiz team** ● **16-20 Join Mensa**

1. Which U.S. novelist wrote *The Sun Also Rises* and *A Farewell to Arms*?
2. What was the name of the character played by Gene Hackman in *The French Connection*?
3. Which French actress and animal rights activist starred in the film *And God Created Woman*?
4. Who won the gold medal in the men's triple jump at the Sydney Olympics?
5. Which horror film actor was born William Henry Pratt?
6. What is the medical term for loss of memory?
7. Steve Collins and Pat Clinton are both former world champions in which sport?
8. Of which country was Albert Reynolds the prime minister from 1992 to 1994?
9. Which horror author wrote *Carrie*, *Salem's Lot* and *The Tommyknockers*?
10. By what name is the constellation *Ursa Major* also known?
11. How many squares does a chessboard have?
12. What name was adopted by Goldie Myerson when she became Israel's foreign minister in 1956?
13. In which African country was cricket's ICC Knockout Trophy held in 2000?
14. Which British dramatist wrote *Entertaining Mr Sloane* and *Loot*?
15. Who created the voices of Porky Pig, Daffy Duck, Sylvester, Tweety Pie and Bugs Bunny?
16. Which feature of chronic alcoholism is known as the DTs?
17. What is the points value of a drop goal in rugby union?
18. Which author wrote the screenplays for *Chitty Chitty Bang Bang* and *You Only Live Twice*?
19. Who might be given an Apgar score?
20. By what name was the U.S.-sponsored postwar European Recovery Program known?

***ANSWERS:** 1 Ernest Hemingway, 2 Popeye Doyle, 3 Brigitte Bardot, 4 Jonathan Edwards, 5 Boris Karloff, 6 Amnesia, 7 Boxing, 8 Republic of Ireland, 9 Stephen King, 10 The Great Bear, 11 64, 12 Golda Meir, 13 Kenya, 14 Joe Orton, 15 Mel Blanc, 16 Delirium tremens, 17 3, 18 Roald Dahl, 19 A newborn baby, 20 Marshall Plan.*

General Knowledge

Your rating: ● **0-5** **Join a library** ● **6-10** **Keep at it** ● **11-15** **Join a quiz team** ● **16-20** **Join Mensa**

1. Which Dutch Post-Impressionist painter cut off part of his left ear?
2. To which king is the Book of Proverbs in the Old Testament traditionally ascribed?
3. Which 2000 British film was about an 11-year-old boy who takes up ballet?
4. What nationality was the actress Sarah Bernhardt?
5. Which sign of the zodiac governs the period from July 23 to August 22?
6. What is the SI unit of electric current?
7. The 1947 film Forever Amber was set during which century?
8. With which musical instrument is Jascha Heifetz associated?
9. What fruit is hollowed out to make jack-o'-lantern decorations for Halloween?
10. Who won the men's 100m at the Sydney Olympics?
11. Who connects TV dramas Blott on the Landscape and Poirot?
12. Which U.S. novelist wrote *The Ballad of the Sad Cafe* and *The Heart is a Lonely Hunter*?
13. What was the name of the only horse ever to beat Brigadier Gerard in his three-year racing career?
14. Which chemical element is represented by the symbol Sr?
15. Of which planet is Phobos a satellite?
16. Which country lost in the final of the rugby union World Cup in 1999?
17. What was the title of A A Milne's second collection of stories about Winnie-the-Pooh?
18. What name is given to the dried excrement of fish-eating birds used as a fertiliser?
19. Which American actress starred in *You Can't Take It With You* and *Shane*?
20. Of which Shakespeare play is Imogen the heroine?

ANSWERS: *1 Vincent van Gogh, 2 Solomon, 3 Billy Elliot, 4 French, 5 Leo, 6 Ampere, 7 17th, 8 Violin, 9 Pumpkin, 10 Maurice Greene, 11 David Suchet, 12 Carson McCullers, 13 Roberto, 14 Strontium, 15 Mars, 16 France, 17 The House at Pooh Corner, 18 Guano, 19 Jean Arthur, 20 Cymbeline.*

General Knowledge

Your rating: ● 0-5 Join a library ● 6-10 Keep at it ● 11-15 Join a quiz team ● 16-20 Join Mensa

1. Which Venetian merchant is famous for his accounts of his travels to Asia in the late 13th century?
2. Who played the title role in the 1952 film *Hans Christian Andersen*?
3. Which race was won by Golden Fleece in 1982 and Teenoso in 1983?
4. By what first name was Nelson Mandela's second wife known?
5. Which English poet wrote *Paradise Lost*?
6. What name is given to the fruit of the tree *Citrus limon*?
7. In which Roald Dahl story does Willy Wonka appear?
8. How many medals did Great Britain's swimmers win at the Sydney Olympics?
9. What name is given to a group of witches?
10. Which left-handed American rock guitarist died in 1970 at the age of 27?
11. Which member of the Royal Family joined Cheltenham Ladies' Hockey Club in 2000?
12. Which former silent film star is best known for her portrayal of Norma Desmond in the 1950 film *Sunset Boulevard*?
13. Of which constellation is Deneb the brightest star?
14. What is the minimum number of points needed to win a tie-break in tennis?
15. What sort of creature is a bichon frise?
16. Which English novelist wrote *The Cruel Sea*?
17. Which unconventional director made the films *M*A*S*H*, *Nashville*, and *The Player*?
18. To which novel by Anthony Hope is *Rupert of Hentzau* a sequel?
19. When was the London Marathon first held?
20. Which British actor who died in 1995 starred in the *Halloween* series of films?

ANSWERS: *1 Marco Polo, 2 Danny Kaye, 3 The Derby, 4 Winnie, 5 John Milton, 6 Lemon, 7 Charlie and the Chocolate Factory, 8 None, 9 Coven, 10 Jimi Hendrix, 11 Zara Phillips, 12 Gloria Swanson, 13 Cygnus, 14 7, 15 A dog, 16 Nicholas Monsarrat, 17 Robert Altman, 18 The Prisoner of Zenda, 19 1981, 20 Donald Pleasence.*

Entertainment

Your rating: ● 0-5 Buy a TV ● 6-10 Keep at it ● 11-15 Join a quiz team ● 16-20 Enter a quiz show

1. Who starred in the title role of the 1931 film *Little Caesar*?
2. Who starred as Jesus in the Franco Zeffirelli TV series *Jesus of Nazareth*?
3. Who had a top ten hit single in 1982 with *Save a Prayer*?
4. Who directed the film *Twelve Monkeys*?
5. Which *Red Dwarf* star played a prisoner in TV's *The Governor*?
6. Which Nicholas Parsons TV show shares its name with a Sleeper hit single?
7. Who starred as the blonde chased by the 50-foot ape in the original *King Kong* movie?
8. Which U.S. president was the subject of a 1996 BBC2 documentary?
9. Who was the lead singer of The Damned?
10. Which *Neighbours* character was played on TV by Tom Oliver?
11. In which film does Kevin Spacey play movie executive Buddy Ackerman?
12. Which band led by Elizabeth Fraser released an album in 1996 entitled *Milk and Kisses*?
13. Which U.S. comedy series features Courteney Cox Arquette as Monica and David Schwimmer as Ross?
14. Who played the title role in the 1950 film *The Gunfighter*?
15. Who played Tony in the TV comedy series *Men Behaving Badly*?
16. In which 1933 Marx Brothers film did Groucho play the prime minister of a mythical kingdom?
17. Who had a top ten hit single in 1981 with *Romeo and Juliet*?
18. In which city was the 1996 film *Small Faces* set?
19. Which former member of the Moody Blues and Wings released an album in 1996 entitled *Reborn*?
20. Who directed, produced and starred in the 1982 film *Honkytonk Man*?

ANSWERS: *1 Edward G. Robinson, 2 Robert Powell, 3 Duran Duran, 4 Terry Gilliam, 5 Craig Charles, 6 Sale of the Century, 7 Fay Wray, 8 Franklin D. Roosevelt, 9 Dave Vanian, 10 Lou Carpenter, 11 Swimming With Sharks, 12 Cocteau Twins, 13 Friends, 14 Gregory Peck, 15 Neil Morrissey, 16 Duck Soup, 17 Dire Straits, 18 Glasgow, 19 Denny Laine, 20 Clint Eastwood.*

General Knowledge

Your rating: ● 0-5 Join a library ● 6-10 Keep at it ● 11-15 Join a quiz team ● 16-20 Join Mensa

1. Which sports car manufacturer designed the Volkswagen car which became known as the Beetle?
2. In what year was Prince Edward born?
3. Which British triple jumper set a new world record in the European Indoor Athletics Championships in Valencia in 1998?
4. To which English monarch was Catherine of Braganza married?
5. Which French couturier was the first to show a collection for men?
6. What name was given to the anti-Roman Catholic riots that took place in 1780?
7. What name is given to the religious dramas usually performed on Good Friday?
8. What is the formula for the toxic gas carbon monoxide?
9. Which senior churchman chairs Lambeth Conferences?
10. Which slow-moving arboreal mammal of South and Central America hangs upside down from branches feeding on leaves and fruit?
11. What might carry and deposit till and moraine?
12. Which Old Testament prophet was taken up to heaven in a chariot of fire?
13. What is the capital of the province of Kosovo?
14. What name is given to a painting or sculpture of Christ crowned with thorns, from the Latin for 'Behold the man'?
15. In Arthurian legend, who was King Arthur's enchantress sister?
16. Which Suffolk resort is famous for its annual music festival founded by Benjamin Britten?
17. In the New Testament, which of the Apostles is generally identified with Thaddeus?
18. Which brothers were the legendary leaders of the Jutes, the first Anglo-Saxon settlers in Britain?
19. In which constellation is the second-magnitude star Algol?
20. Which mite causes scabies in man and mange in animals?

ANSWERS: *1 Ferdinand Porsche, 2 1964, 3 Ashia Hansen, 4 Charles II, 5 Pierre Cardin, 6 Gordon riots, 7 Passion plays, 8 CO, 9 The Archbishop of Canterbury, 10 Sloth, 11 A glacier, 12 Elijah, 13 Pristina, 14 Ecce Homo, 15 Morgan le Fay, 16 Aldeburgh, 17 St Jude, 18 Hengist and Horsa, 19 Perseus, 20 Itch mite.*

General Knowledge

Your rating: ● **0-5 Join a library** ● **6-10 Keep at it** ● **11-15 Join a quiz team** ● **16-20 Join Mensa**

1. Which lark is noted for singing while hovering or as it rises almost vertically in the air?
2. Who wrote *Prufrock and Other Observations* and *Four Quartets*?
3. Which British soldier had his 1993 conviction for murdering a joyrider quashed by Northern Ireland's Court of Appeal in 1998?
4. Which sport is also known as freefall parachuting?
5. What name is given to luxury railway sleeping cars invented by a U.S. businessman who died in 1897?
6. Which Irish novelist and poet wrote *Dubliners* and *Portrait of the Artist as a Young Man*?
7. According to the Bible, what was Judas' monetary reward for betraying Jesus?
8. Which large constellation takes its name from the Latin for swan?
9. Which Irish nationalist politician who took part in the Easter Rising formed Fianna Fáil in 1926?
10. What was the name of the horse at the centre of the libel trial won by Lynda and Jack Ramsden and Kieren Fallon?
11. Who was the first president of Tanzania?
12. Which holiday resort in North Wales was designed by Clough Williams-Ellis?
13. What is the capital of the French département of Meurthe-et-Moselle?
14. Which British surgeon is regarded as the founder of antiseptic surgery?
15. In which country was the first of the Pugwash Conferences held?
16. Which Puccini opera was completed by Franco Alfano?
17. Which French town in the Calvados department is famous for the shrine of St Thérèse?
18. In ethology, what name is given to the form of learning in the first hours of life identified by Konrad Lorenz?
19. Which Australian composer became Master of the Queen's Musick in 1975?
20. On which Italian river does the city of Verona stand?

ANSWERS: *1 Skylark, 2 T. S. Eliot, 3 Lee Clegg, 4 Skydiving, 5 Pullman, 6 James Joyce, 7 Thirty pieces of silver, 8 Cygnus, 9 Eamon de Valera, 10 Top Cees, 11 Julius Nyerere, 12 Portmeirion, 13 Nancy, 14 Baron Joseph Lister, 15 Canada, 16 Turandot, 17 Lisieux, 18 Imprinting, 19 Malcolm Williamson, 20 Adige.*

General Knowledge

Your rating: ● **0-5 Join a library** ● **6-10 Keep at it** ● **11-15 Join a quiz team** ● **16-20 Join Mensa**

1. What relation is Peter Mandelson to Festival of Britain organiser Herbert Morrison?
2. What was the first truly synthetic fibre, introduced commercially in 1938?
3. Which American TV personality successfully defended a libel action brought against her by a consortium of cattlemen in 1998?
4. Which 1980 film starred Bob Hoskins and Helen Mirren?
5. Which English city houses the cathedral that is the largest church in Britain?
6. Cathay was the medieval European name for which Asian country?
7. Which saint is the reputed inventor of the alphabet used in Russian and other Slavic languages?
8. What colour are the flat broad-brimmed hats worn by cardinals?
9. Which organ of the body converts excess glucose into glycogen?
10. What is the smallest unit of a compound that can exist independently and retain its properties?
11. The collection of which British physician and naturalist formed the nucleus of the British Museum?
12. Which spice is obtained from the dried aril of a nutmeg?
13. What is the lightest metal?
14. What is the name of the Lowland Scots dialect in which Robert Burns wrote?
15. Charles Dickens was born in a suburb of which Hampshire city?
16. What name is given to celestial objects emitting extremely regular pulses of radiation, first discovered in 1967?
17. Who painted *Impression: Sunrise* that gave its name to the Impressionist movement?
18. What is the technical name for the collecting and studying of coins, medals and banknotes?
19. Which British theatre director is best known for *The Hostage* and *Oh, What a Lovely War*?
20. Which genus of plants includes plums, apricots, cherries, peaches and almonds?

ANSWERS: *1 Grandson, 2 Nylon, 3 Oprah Winfrey, 4 The Long Good Friday, 5 Liverpool, 6 China, 7 St Cyril, 8 Red, 9 The liver, 10 Molecule, 11 Sir Hans Sloane, 12 Mace, 13 Lithium, 14 Lallans, 15 Portsmouth, 16 Pulsars, 17 Claude Monet, 18 Numismatics, 19 Joan Littlewood, 20 Prunus.*

Sports

Your rating: ● 0-5 Wooden spoon ● 6-10 Bronze medal ● 11-15 Silver medal ● 16-20 Gold medal

1. In 1998, which Premiership football team signed the defender Jaap Stam, for £10.5 million?
2. Which country's rugby union side is known as the All Blacks?
3. How old was Cassius Clay when he became the 1960 Olympic light-heavyweight boxing champion?
4. For which two events did Merlene Ottey win gold medals at the 1990 Commonwealth Games?
5. For which club did Ronaldo leave Barcelona?
6. Which international rugby union side did Nick Farr-Jones captain 36 times between 1988 and 1992?
7. Who replaced Michael Atherton as captain of England's Test cricket team?
8. What was boxer Joe Frazier's nickname?
9. Which Austrian driver was killed during qualifying at the 1994 San Marino Grand Prix?
10. What is the name of Swansea City's home ground?
11. What colour ball is worth three points in snooker?
12. At which Olympics did gymnast Ecaterina Szabo's four golds and a silver make her the most successful competitor?
13. Which country knocked Germany out of the 1998 World Cup finals?
14. In which sport did Raymond Barneveld successfully defend his World Professional title in 1999?
15. Which nation won its first Olympic skiing medal in 1948, courtesy of Gretchen Fraser?
16. Who managed Leeds United for only 44 days?
17. How many points are awarded for a touchdown in American football?
18. In which city was Rory Underwood born?
19. Which British amateur golfer finished joint fourth in the Open at Royal Birkdale in 1998?
20. In which year did Donovan Bailey win the Olympic men's 100m event?

ANSWERS: *1 Manchester United, 2 New Zealand's, 3 19, 4 100m and 200m, 5 Inter Milan, 6 Australia, 7 Alec Stewart, 8 Smokin' Joe, 9 Roland Ratzenberger, 10 Vetch Field, 11 Green, 12 1984, 13 Croatia, 14 Darts, 15 USA, 16 Brian Clough, 17 Six, 18 Middlesbrough, 19 Justin Rose, 20 1996.*

General Knowledge

Your rating: ● 0-5 Join a library ● 6-10 Keep at it ● 11-15 Join a quiz team ● 16-20 Join Mensa

1. Which French film director, whose works include *La Grande Illusion*, was the son of an impressionist painter?
2. What name is given to the inability to read and write?
3. Which former Conservative and Unionist MP died in 1998 at the age of 85?
4. What name is given to the collection of securities held by an investor?
5. What is the name of the load line on a ship's hull introduced as a result of the Merchant Shipping Act of 1876?
6. Of which African country is Mbabane the capital?
7. Which carnivorous mammal has striped, spotted and brown varieties?
8. Which celestial object is also known as a quasi-stellar object or QSO?
9. Who wrote the novel series *A Dance to the Music of Time*?
10. Who was the famous daughter of the American Indian chief Powhatan?
11. In Hinduism, what name is given to the seventh incarnation of Vishnu?
12. By what name is the plant *Nigella damascena* better known?
13. Which pigment is responsible for the colouring of skin, hair and the iris of the eye?
14. Who wrote *The Portrait of a Lady* and *Washington Square*?
15. Which Austrian composer wrote the *London* and *Oxford* symphonies?
16. What name was given to the extended educational tour of Europe that was formerly fashionable among English gentlemen?
17. Which Scottish politician was the first parliamentary leader of the Labour Party?
18. What is the technical name for weakening of the bones?
19. Which king's eldest son was known as the Black Prince?
20. Which British fashion designer opened a Chelsea boutique called *Bazaar* and popularised the miniskirt?

ANSWERS: *1 Jean Renoir, 2 Illiteracy, 3 Enoch Powell, 4 Portfolio, 5 Plimsoll line, 6 Swaziland, 7 Hyena, 8 Quasar, 9 Anthony Powell, 10 Pocahontas, 11 Rama, 12 Love-in-a-mist, 13 Melanin, 14 Henry James, 15 Joseph Haydn, 16 Grand tour, 17 Keir Hardie, 18 Osteoporosis, 19 Edward III, 20 Mary Quant.*

General Knowledge

Your rating: ● 0-5 Join a library ● 6-10 Keep at it ● 11-15 Join a quiz team ● 16-20 Join Mensa

1. What name is given to the carved and painted poles erected by North American Indian tribes?
2. Which award for industry was established in 1965?
3. During which war was the New Model Army founded?
4. Who wrote *Bridget Jones's Diary*?
5. Which war involved a volunteer army known as the International Brigade?
6. Which town on the Thames is associated with a Royal Regatta, first held in 1839?
7. Which king defeated Richard III at the Battle of Bosworth Field?
8. What name is given to tropical birds of the order *Psittaciformes*?
9. Which Japanese city hosted the 1998 Winter Olympics?
10. By what name is the plant *Solanum tuberosum*, supposedly introduced into England by Sir Walter Raleigh, better known?
11. Which English Cavalier poet wrote *To Althea, from Prison*?
12. What name is given to an instrument used for measuring the relative density of a liquid?
13. In Greek mythology, who fell in love with Psyche?
14. What sort of creature is a kudu?
15. Which wood carver and sculptor is best known for the choir stalls and organ screen in St Paul's Cathedral?
16. On which river does the West Yorkshire town of Ilkley stand?
17. After which American physicist is the SI unit of inductance named?
18. Which present-day country contains the ancient country of Parthia?
19. What name is given to the sexually mature adult form of any insect?
20. Who was the British flight engineer in the Breitling Orbiter round-the-world balloon challenge?

ANSWERS: *1 Totem poles, 2 Queen's Award, 3 English Civil War, 4 Helen Fielding, 5 Spanish Civil War, 6 Henley-on-Thames, 7 Henry VII, 8 Parrot, 9 Nagano, 10 Potato, 11 Richard Lovelace, 12 Hydrometer, 13 Eros, 14 An antelope, 15 Grinling Gibbons, 16 River Wharfe, 17 Joseph Henry, 18 Iran, 19 Imago, 20 Andy Elson.*

General Knowledge

Your rating:
- 0-5 Join a library
- 6-10 Keep at it
- 11-15 Join a quiz team
- 16-20 Join Mensa

1. What name is given to fog containing a high proportion of smoke?
2. Which class of animals includes crocodiles, turtles, lizards and snakes?
3. What are the two major political parties in the United States?
4. What letter is represented by three dots in morse code?
5. Which historical conspiracy was invented by Titus Oates and Israel Tonge?
6. What name is given to the amount a borrower is charged for a loan, usually expressed as a percentage?
7. In which country did light cavalrymen known as hussars originate?
8. Which narcotic drug is obtained from opium and used in medicine for the relief of severe pain?
9. Which British-born American comedian was awarded an honorary knighthood in 1998?
10. In which country is the Grande Dixence Dam?
11. Which German city is the capital of Baden-Württemberg?
12. In mathematics, what name is given to a quantity that has both magnitude and direction?
13. Which Surrey village is the site of the National Rifle Association ranges?
14. What is the name of the ground in Jamaica that made cricket history in 1998 when a Test was abandoned because of a dangerous pitch?
15. Which Roman emperor was the stepson and successor of Augustus?
16. What form of puzzle was devised by Englishman Arthur Wynne and first published in the New York World in 1913?
17. Which natural substance is formed by pedogenesis?
18. Which country is also known as the Republic of China?
19. In which Italian ski resort were 20 people killed when an American military aircraft sliced through the steel wire supporting a cable car in 1998?
20. What are the three main categories into which rocks are divided?

ANSWERS: *1 Smog, 2 Reptiles (Reptilia), 3 The Democratic Party and the Republican Party, 4 S, 5 The Popish Plot, 6 Interest, 7 Hungary, 8 Morphine, 9 Bob Hope, 10 Switzerland, 11 Stuttgart, 12 Vector, 13 Bisley, 14 Sabina Park, 15 Tiberius, 16 Crossword, 17 Soil, 18 Taiwan, 19 Cavalese, 20 Igneous, sedimentary and metamorphic.*

Entertainment

Your rating:
- 0-5 Buy a TV
- 6-10 Keep at it
- 11-15 Join a quiz team
- 16-20 Enter a quiz show

1. From which country did the group Men At Work come?
2. Who starred as the magician's assistant in the 1996 film *Rough Magic*?
3. Who presented the golfing gameshow *Full Swing*?
4. Which rapper released an album in 1996 entitled *The Return Of The Real*?
5. Who played the assassin hired to kill President Charles de Gaulle in the 1973 film *The Day of the Jackal*?
6. Which *Bat Out Of Hell* was born Marvin Lee Aday?
7. Who won the Palme d'Or at Cannes in 1996 for her performance in the film *Secrets And Lies*?
8. Who played Cockney ex-con Wayne Todd in the TV series *Bad Boys*?
9. Under what name did Sice, the shaven-headed Boo Radleys singer release a solo album in 1996?
10. Who played Gregory in the 1982 film *Gregory's Girl*?
11. What was the title of Dennis Potter's sequel to the TV drama *Karaoke*?
12. Which folk-rock band were named after an island off Northumberland?
13. Who played Annalise Hartman in *Neighbours*?
14. Who played the wheelchair-bound Man With A Plan in the film *Things To Do In Denver When You're Dead*?
15. Which band released an album in 1996 entitled *Everything Must Go*?
16. Who played Henry Willows in the sitcom *Home to Roost*?
17. Which *Monty Python* star wrote and played the lead role in the 1983 film *The Missionary*?
18. Which of Batman's enemies was portrayed on the small screen by Burgess Meredith?
19. In which European country did glam-rock group Hanoi Rocks originate?

ANSWERS: *1 Australia, 2 Bridget Fonda, 3 Jimmy Tarbuck, 4 Ice T, 5 Edward Fox, 6 Meat Loaf, 7 Brenda Blethyn, 8 Karl Howman, 9 Eggman, 10 John Gordon Sinclair, 11 Cold Lazarus, 12 Lindisfarne, 13 Kimberley Davies, 14 Christopher Walken, 15 Manic Street Preachers, 16 John Thaw, 17 Michael Palin, 18 The Penguin, 19 Finland, 20 Jack Nicholson.*

General Knowledge

Your rating:
- 0-5 Join a library
- 6-10 Keep at it
- 11-15 Join a quiz team
- 16-20 Join Mensa

1. According to the Bible, which town was the birthplace of Jesus?
2. In Greek mythology, who was the messenger and herald of the gods?
3. In which English county is the market town of Cirencester situated?
4. Which metal is represented by the symbol K?
5. Which children's author created the characters Peter Rabbit, Jemima Puddle-Duck and Mrs Tittlemouse?
6. With which musical instrument was Pablo Casals primarily associated?
7. Who made history in 1997 by becoming the youngest-ever U.S. Masters champion?
8. What is the popular name for the British Merchant Navy's Red Ensign?
9. Which event in Scottish highland games involves carrying a tapering tree trunk vertically and throwing it forwards?
10. According to the Bible, the builders of which tower were caused to speak different languages by Jehovah?
11. With which instrument is jazz musician Humphrey Lyttelton primarily associated?
12. In Tibetan Buddhism, which title is held by the chief abbot who ranks second to the Dalai Lama?
13. Which alkaline fluid is secreted by the liver and stored in the gall bladder?
14. Which writer was fired by a Sunday newspaper over allegations that he took drugs on John Major's 1997 campaign tour?
15. Which European country held Beirut from World War I until it became capital of the newly-independent Lebanon?
16. Who was elected prime minister of Jamaica in 1972?
17. Which two acids are present in aqua regia?
18. Which British chemist originated the modern atomic theory of matter?
19. Which fruit comes from the tree *Prunus armeniaca*?
20. According to Greek mythology, how many Fates were there?

ANSWERS: *1 Bethlehem, 2 Hermes, 3 Gloucestershire, 4 Potassium, 5 Beatrix Potter, 6 Cello, 7 Tiger Woods, 8 Red Duster, 9 Caber tossing, 10 Tower of Babel, 11 Trumpet, 12 Panchen Lama, 13 Bile, 14 Will Self, 15 France, 16 Michael Manley, 17 Nitric acid and hydrochloric acid, 18 John Dalton, 19 Apricot, 20 Three.*

General Knowledge

Your rating:
- 0-5 Join a library
- 6-10 Keep at it
- 11-15 Join a quiz team
- 16-20 Join Mensa

1. Which Australian tennis player defeated Ivan Lendl to become Wimbledon singles champion in 1987?
2. Of which ocean is the Caribbean Sea a section?
3. From which animal do we get cashmere?
4. Which number system uses only two digits (0 and 1)?
5. Which city is the administrative centre of Devon?
6. Which organ is most affected by cirrhosis?
7. Which British political party was led by Jo Grimond from 1956 to 1967?
8. Which European country colonised Martinique in 1635?
9. Which unit used to express depths of water is equal to six feet?
10. According to Greek mythology, how many Muses were there?
11. Of which African country is Bangui the capital?
12. Which German novelist wrote *Buddenbrooks* and *Doctor Faustus*?
13. To which comedy actress was Paul Merton married for six years?
14. What was Bix Beiderbecke's real first name?
15. Who was the last king of Egypt?
16. Which chemical element is represented by the symbol Se?
17. Who was the first president of Zambia?
18. Which nerve connects the brain with the heart, lungs, stomach and gut?
19. Who was prime minister of Australia from 1931 to 1939?
20. In which gland can the islets of Langerhans be found?

ANSWERS: *1 Pat Cash, 2 Atlantic Ocean, 3 Goat, 4 Binary system, 5 Exeter, 6 Liver, 7 Liberal Party, 8 France, 9 Fathom, 10 Nine, 11 Central African Republic, 12 Thomas Mann, 13 Caroline Quentin, 14 Leon, 15 Farouk I, 16 Selenium, 17 Kenneth Kaunda, 18 Vagus nerve, 19 Joseph Lyons, 20 Pancreas.*

General Knowledge

Your rating:
- 0-5 Join a library
- 6-10 Keep at it
- 11-15 Join a quiz team
- 16-20 Join Mensa

1. Which advice organisation is represented by the initials CAB?
2. Of which Asian kingdom is Kathmandu the capital?
3. How many balls are used in a game of English billiards?
4. What sort of creature is a guinea pig?
5. Which political party did president Dwight D. Eisenhower represent?
6. Which river flows through Paris to the English Channel?
7. Which member of the Boomtown Rats received an honorary knighthood in 1986 for his fund raising for the starving of Africa?
8. Which British central bank was originally incorporated in 1694 and nationalised in 1946?
9. Which tower was built for the 1889 Centennial Exposition in Paris, and was the highest building in the world until 1930?
10. Which Christian church season begins on the Sunday nearest St Andrew's Day?
11. Which SI unit of electric charge is represented by the symbol C?
12. Which political party did the Adullamites originally represent?
13. Which Northamptonshire castle was the scene of Richard III's birth and the execution of Mary, Queen of Scots?
14. Who was Britain's poet laureate from 1930 to 1967?
15. By what acronym was the Council for Mutual Economic Assistance formed between communist countries in 1949 known?
16. Which British field marshal was deputy commander of NATO forces from 1951 to 1958?
17. Of which sea is Botany Bay an inlet?
18. What sort of creature is a babirusa?
19. Which word describes the art of combining two or more melodic lines simultaneously in music?
20. Through which three countries do the Ardennes hills extend?

ANSWERS: *1 Citizens' Advice Bureau, 2 Nepal, 3 Three, 4 Rodent, 5 Republican Party, 6 The Seine, 7 Bob Geldof, 8 The Bank of England, 9 Eiffel Tower, 10 Advent, 11 Coulomb, 12 Liberal Party, 13 Fotheringhay Castle, 14 John Masefield, 15 COMECON, 16 Montgomery, 17 Tasman Sea, 18 A wild pig, 19 Counterpoint, 20 France, Belgium and Luxembourg.*

Entertainment

Your rating: ● **0-5** Buy a TV ● **6-10** Keep at it ● **11-15** Join a quiz team ● **16-20** Enter a quiz show

1. Which former *ER* star played a criminal on the run in the film *From Dusk Till Dawn*?
2. Which Indian city was the subject of a 1996 documentary series narrated by Tim Pigott-Smith?
3. Who had a top ten hit single in 1981 with *Girls On Film*?
4. Who won a Best Actor Oscar for his performance in the 1975 film *One Flew Over the Cuckoo's Nest*?
5. Which former *Eurovision Song Contest* presenter was born Katarina Imperiali di Francabilla?
6. Which Irish punk band released the albums *Tonic For The Troops* and *Fine Art Of Surfacing*?
7. Who was the star of *Sean's Show* on TV?
8. Who starred as Tony Montana in the 1983 film *Scarface*?
9. Who had a hit single and album entitled *Return of the Mack* in 1996?
10. Which *Naked Gun* actor starred in the 1996 film *Spy Hard*?
11. Who played Cory in the TV show *Boy Meets World*?
12. Who played the title role in the 1989 film *Shirley Valentine*?
13. Which suave, moustached personality formerly hosted *Match of the Day* and major sporting events for the BBC?
14. Who played defence lawyer Martin Vail in *Primal Fear*?
15. Which *Neighbours* character was played by Anthony Engelman?
16. Which Sex Pistol released an album entitled *Who's He Think He Is When He's At Home* in 1996?
17. Who starred in the title role of the 1983 film *The Man With Two Brains*?
18. Who presented *Hotel Babylon* on TV?
19. Who had a top twenty hit single in 1979 with *Forever in Blue Jeans*?
20. Which former *They Think It's All Over* star was the compere of TV's *Saturday Live*?

ANSWERS: *1 George Clooney, 2 Calcutta, 3 Duran Duran, 4 Jack Nicholson, 5 Katie Boyle, 6 The Boomtown Rats, 7 Sean Hughes, 8 Al Pacino, 9 Mark Morrisson, 10 Leslie Nielsen, 11 Ben Savage, 12 Pauline Collins, 13 Des Lynam, 14 Richard Gere, 15 Stonefish Rebecchi, 16 Glen Matlock, 17 Steve Martin, 18 Dani Behr, 19 Neil Diamond, 20 Lee Hurst.*

General Knowledge

Your rating:
- 0-5 Join a library
- 6-10 Keep at it
- 11-15 Join a quiz team
- 16-20 Join Mensa

1. Which language is an official language of Canada, Belgium and Switzerland?
2. In which country was the actress Greta Garbo born?
3. Of which South American country is Asunción the capital?
4. To which British actor was Vivien Leigh married?
5. Which arm of the Atlantic Ocean is known as "La Manche" to the French?
6. Which Sioux Indian chief led the massacre of General Custer and his men at the Little Bighorn?
7. Which French composer wrote *The Sorcerer's Apprentice*?
8. Who was Britain's poet laureate from 1972 to 1984?
9. Which U.S. author wrote *The Fall of the House of Usher* and *The Murders in the Rue Morgue*?
10. In which sport do people compete for the Admiral's Cup?
11. Which government department administered the British navy until 1964?
12. In which African country can the Matopo Hills be found?
13. Which British director won the 1997 Best Director Oscar for *The English Patient*?
14. Which girl band featuring the twins Edele and Keavy Lynch went straight to number one with their first single, *C'est La Vie*?
15. Which metallic element is represented by the symbol Sb?
16. Which type of weapon is represented by the abbreviation ICBM?
17. Who was the first president of India?
18. What is the largest of the Volcano Islands?
19. Which British missionary was portrayed by Ingrid Bergman in the film *The Inn of the Sixth Happiness*?
20. What sort of creature is a ringlet?

ANSWERS: *1 French, 2 Sweden, 3 Paraguay, 4 Laurence Olivier, 5 The English Channel, 6 Sitting Bull, 7 Paul Dukas, 8 Sir John Betjeman, 9 Edgar Allan Poe, 10 Yachting, 11 Board of Admiralty, 12 Zimbabwe, 13 Anthony Minghella, 14 B*Witched, 15 Antimony, 16 Intercontinental ballistic missile, 17 Rajendra Prasad, 18 Iwo Jima, 19 Gladys Aylward, 20 A butterfly.*

General Knowledge

Your rating:

- 0-5 Join a library
- 6-10 Keep at it
- 11-15 Join a quiz team
- 16-20 Join Mensa

1. In the USA, what is the largest of the New England states?
2. Which churchman was president of Cyprus from 1960 to 1974?
3. Which gas is represented by the symbol O?
4. How many humps does an Arabian camel possess?
5. To which European country does the island of Corfu belong?
6. Which political party governed Great Britain from 1951 to 1964?
7. In which English county is Blackburn situated?
8. Which metal makes up the majority of the alloy bronze?
9. According to Arthurian legend, what was the capital of King Arthur's kingdom?
10. On which river is the Aswan High Dam situated?
11. Which British novelist won the Booker Prize for *The Sea, The Sea*?
12. Which Austrian-born filmmaker directed *Anatomy of a Murder*?
13. Which French poet wrote *Une saison en enfer*?
14. What sort of creature is an opossum?
15. Which Russian composer wrote *Scheherazade*?
16. Which lanthanide element is represented by the symbol Pr?
17. How are the Canadian provinces of Alberta, Manitoba, and Saskatchewan collectively known?
18. Which French dramatist wrote *Andromaque* and *Britannicus*?
19. By what nickname is Britain's most notorious environment protester Daniel Hooper commonly known?
20. Which German composer wrote the opera *Donnerstag aus Licht*?

ANSWERS: *1 Maine, 2 Archbishop Makarios, 3 Oxygen, 4 One, 5 Greece, 6 The Conservative Party, 7 Lancashire, 8 Copper, 9 Camelot, 10 The River Nile, 11 Dame Iris Murdoch, 12 Otto Preminger, 13 Arthur Rimbaud, 14 A marsupial, 15 Nikolai Rimsky-Korsakov, 16 Praseodymium, 17 Prairie Provinces, 18 Jean Racine, 19 Swampy, 20 Karlheinz Stockhausen.*

General Knowledge

Your rating: ● 0-5 Join a library ● 6-10 Keep at it ● 11-15 Join a quiz team ● 16-20 Join Mensa

1. Which British comic actor made his name on radio in *The Goon Show* and went on to star in *The Pink Panther* series of films?
2. Which school for young children literally means "children's garden" in German?
3. Which scientific term describes the bending of a beam of light as it passes from one medium to another?
4. What sort of creature is a collie?
5. Which U.S. civil-rights leader won the Nobel Peace Prize in 1964, and was assassinated in 1968?
6. What is the name for the close-grained white tissue which forms the tusks of elephants, walruses, and narwhals?
7. In which English county is the resort of Skegness situated?
8. Who became the leader of the Labour Party in 1983, following Michael Foot's resignation?
9. With which musical instrument is Julian Lloyd Webber associated?
10. What is the largest of the Shetland Islands?
11. Which French composer wrote the operas *Faust* and *Romeo and Juliet*?
12. What was the name of the Russian parliament from 1906 to 1917?
13. Which alkali metal is represented by the symbol Fr?
14. Which horse won the 1997 Cheltenham Gold Cup?
15. What sort of creature is a gourami?
16. Which Greek mathematician is famous for his book entitled *Elements*?
17. Of which African country was Yakubu Gowon head of state from 1966 to 1975?
18. Who wrote the Booker Prize-winning novel upon which the film *The English Patient* is based?
19. According to Greek mythology, by what name were the 12 children of Uranus and Gaea collectively known?
20. Which U.S. composer wrote the piano sonata *Concord, Mass*?

ANSWERS: *1 Peter Sellers, 2 Kindergarten, 3 Refraction, 4 A dog, 5 Martin Luther King, 6 Ivory, 7 Lincolnshire, 8 Neil Kinnock, 9 Cello, 10 Mainland, 11 Charles Gounod, 12 Duma, 13 Francium, 14 Mr Mulligan, 15 A fish, 16 Euclid, 17 Nigeria, 18 Michael Ondaatje, 19 Titans, 20 Charles Ives.*

Entertainment

Your rating: ● 0-5 Buy a TV ● 6-10 Keep at it ● 11-15 Join a quiz team ● 16-20 Enter a quiz show

1. Which *Top Gun* star played a political activist in the 1988 film *The House on Carroll Street*?
2. Which British group had a 1968 U.K. number one hit with *Lily the Pink*?
3. Which British comedian wrote and directed the 2000 film *Maybe Baby*?
4. Which Nineties drama series set in the Twenties starred Stella Gonet and Louise Lombard as sisters Beatrice and Evangeline?
5. Which former docu-soap star released her second album, *Inspiration*, in 2000?
6. Which child actress played *The Littlest Rebel* in the 1935 film?
7. Which comedy duo appeared *Unplanned* on ITV?
8. Which actor played Rose's fiancé Cal Hockley in the 1997 film *Titanic*?
9. Who served viewers a slice of *American Pie* on BBC 1?
10. What was the title of S Club 7's second album release?
11. In which 1999 Woody Allen movie did Sean Penn play fictitious Thirties jazz guitarist Emmet Ray?
12. What was the title of the Jewish comedy series which was Sid James' first solo vehicle?
13. Who released her solo debut album, *Hear My Cry*, in 2000?
14. Which 1967 film set in America's deep South starred Sidney Poitier and Rod Steiger?
15. What was Frankie Goes to Hollywood's second U.K. number one hit?
16. Which 1999 U.S. teen film starred *Sabrina, the Teenage Witch* actress Melissa Joan Hart?
17. Who originally had a U.K. hit with the track *Mambo Italiano*, in 1954?
18. Which veteran Irish actress played John Candy's mother in the 1991 film *Only the Lonely*?
19. Which *Coronation Street* character tragically lost both his wife and new-born son in 2000?
20. What was the title of Kool and the Gang's 1981 top five hit?

ANSWERS: *1 Kelly McGillis, 2 Scaffold, 3 Ben Elton, 4 The House of Eliott, 5 Jane McDonald, 6 Shirley Temple, 7 David Baddiel & Frank Skinner, 8 Billy Zane, 9 Ruby Wax, 10 7, 11 Sweet and Lowdown, 12 East End, West End, 13 Sonique, 14 In the Heat of the Night, 15 Two Tribes, 16 Drive Me Crazy, 17 Rosemary Clooney, 18 Maureen O'Hara, 19 Kevin Webster, 20 Get Down On It.*

General Knowledge

Your rating: ● **0-5** Join a library ● **6-10** Keep at it ● **11-15** Join a quiz team ● **16-20** Join Mensa

1. Which former prime minister became the Earl of Stockton?
2. What is the second largest country in the world?
3. What number wood in golf is a driver?
4. What was the name of the ship that carried the Pilgrim Fathers to America in 1620?
5. Which black American singer and actor had his passport withdrawn by the U.S. government in 1950?
6. What is the capital of Romania?
7. In which county did the custom of Trick or Treat originate?
8. Who illustrated the published version of *Salome* by Oscar Wilde?
9. With which athletics field event was Dick Fosbury associated?
10. Which American actress married Humphrey Bogart in 1945?
11. Which Austrian composer wrote *The Creation* and *The Seasons*?
12. In which U.S. state is the town of Tombstone, famous in Westerns?
13. Who created the detective Jemima Shore?
14. At which ground did England secure their fastest Test victory since 1912 when they beat the West Indies in the 4th Test in 2000?
15. Which British author wrote *Lavengro* and *The Romany Rye*?
16. In computing, what does the abbreviation OCR stand for?
17. Which drug used in premedication is derived from deadly nightshade?
18. *The Blaydon Races* song is associated with which football club?
19. Who wrote the lyrics for Andrew Lloyd Webber's musical *The Beautiful Game*?
20. Which marksman won Great Britain's second gold medal at the Sydney Olympics?

ANSWERS: *1 Harold Macmillan, 2 Canada, 3 1, 4 The Mayflower, 5 Paul Robeson, 6 Bucharest, 7 United States, 8 Aubrey Beardsley, 9 High jump, 10 Lauren Bacall, 11 Joseph Haydn, 12 Arizona, 13 Antonia Fraser, 14 Headingley, 15 George Borrow, 16 Optical character recognition, 17 Atropine, 18 Newcastle United, 19 Ben Elton, 20 Richard Faulds.*

General Knowledge

Your rating: ● 0-5 Join a library ● 6-10 Keep at it ● 11-15 Join a quiz team ● 16-20 Join Mensa

1. Which fungal infection of the feet is the commonest form of ring-worm?
2. What is the second largest city in the Republic of Ireland?
3. Which female comedian was a member of the *Not The Nine O'Clock News* team?
4. What animal has a name which means 'river horse'?
5. Which former coin was worth a quarter of an old penny?
6. Who was the first heavyweight boxer to win the world title four times?
7. Which ITV drama series is set in Larkhall womens prison?
8. In which Shakespeare play do three witches appear?
9. Which lyricist collaborated with Richard Rodgers on *Oklahoma*, *Carousel* and *The King and I*?
10. What does the abbreviation LCD stand for?
11. Which U.S. social scientist coined the term 'conspicuous con-sumption' in *The Theory of the Leisure Class*?
12. In Greek mythology, who was the daughter of Cassiopeia and Cepheus?
13. In what year was the original version of the film *The Fly* made?
14. Of which country did Bhumibol Adulyadej become king in 1946?
15. Which American author wrote the novels *Exodus* and *QB VII*?
16. What name is given to the tiles used in a mosaic?
17. Which country hosted the football World Cup in 1990?
18. What nationality is the novelist Margaret Atwood?
19. Which Indian religion and philosophy was founded by Vardhamana?
20. What is the birthstone of people born in July?

ANSWERS: *1 Athlete's foot, 2 Cork, 3 Pamela Stephenson, 4 Hippopotamus, 5 Farthing, 6 Muhammad Ali, 7 Bad Girls, 8 Macbeth, 9 Oscar Hammerstein II, 10 Liquid crystal display, 11 Thorstein Veblen, 12 Andromeda, 13 1958, 14 Thailand, 15 Leon Uris, 16 Tesserae, 17 Italy, 18 Canadian, 19 Jainism, 20 Ruby.*

General Knowledge

Your rating: ● 0-5 Join a library ● 6-10 Keep at it ● 11-15 Join a quiz team ● 16-20 Join Mensa

1. Which former American football star was acquitted of murder in October 1995?
2. Who was the manager of the Manchester United team that won the European Cup in 1968?
3. Which poet wrote *Songs of Innocence*?
4. What sort of animal is a Clydesdale?
5. Which French leader called the English a 'nation of shopkeepers"?
6. What nationality was the World War I spy Mata Hari?
7. Which legendary magician was counsellor to King Arthur?
8. Who wrote *I Sing the Body Electric*?
9. Which Australian-born feminist author wrote *The Female Eunuch*?
10. What is the largest city in China?
11. Which well-known novel by Graham Greene is set in Sierra Leone?
12. Of which river is the Aare River a tributary?
13. Which county did Ian Botham play cricket for from 1987-91?
14. By what name is the vitamin B1 also known?
15. Which American comedy duo performed the routine *Who's On First*?
16. What name is given to trees of the genus *Platanus*?
17. In which previously dry Essex resort did the *Lock and Barrel* pub open in September 2000?
18. Who was the first footballer to be sent off in an FA Cup final at Wembley?
19. Which famous Dublin theatre was established in 1904?
20. What name is given to the full moon nearest the autumn equinox?

ANSWERS: *1 O J Simpson, 2 Matt Busby, 3 William Blake, 4 A horse, 5 Napoleon, 6 Dutch, 7 Merlin, 8 Ray Bradbury, 9 Germaine Greer, 10 Shanghai, 11 The Heart of the Matter, 12 Rhine, 13 Worcestershire, 14 Thiamine, 15 Abbott and Costello, 16 Plane trees, 17 Frinton, 18 Kevin Moran, 19 Abbey Theatre, 20 Harvest moon.*

Entertainment

Your rating: ● **0-5** **Buy a TV** ● **6-10** **Keep at it** ● **11-15** **Join a quiz team** ● **16-20** **Enter a quiz show**

1. Which British actress starred alongside David Duchovny in the 2000 film *Return to Me*?
2. Which comedian's *Video Show* on TV featured a dance troupe called Hot Gossip?
3. What was the title of Babybird's 2000 album release?
4. Who directed and starred in the 1986 film sequel *Psycho III*?
5. Which Australian soap was axed by ITV in 2000 after more than 10 years?
6. What was the title of Black Legend's 2000 number one hit?
7. In which 2000 film did Dennis Quaid star as a Sixties fireman?
8. Which Nineties drama series about a group of young lawyers featured the characters Anna, Milly, Egg and Miles?
9. Which U.S. singer/songwriter released an album in 2000 entitled *The Bedroom Tapes*?
10. Which U.S. organization produced *Sesame Street* from its first show in the Sixties?
11. Which 1990 film set in Fifties Cuba starred Robert Redford as Jack Weil?
12. Which newsreader presented the 2000 *British Bravery Awards* on BBC 1 alongside Nick Ross?
13. What was MN8's biggest hit, which reached number two in 1995?
14. Which Hollywood actor starred as an aging baseball star in the 2000 film *For the Love of the Game*?
15. Which Italian singer had a 1988 top five hit with *Boys (Summertime Love)*?
16. In which 1990 film did Joan Plowright play Tracey Ullman's mother?
17. Which BBC 1 comedy series set in the world of barristers starred John Bird and Sarah Lancashire?
18. Which horror actor's performances included the Monster in 1935's *Bride of Frankenstein* and 1939's *Son of Frankenstein*?
19. What was the title of Thin Lizzy's first U.K. top ten hit, in 1973?
20. Which 2000 film starred Sandra Bullock as a would-be writer who goes through rehab?

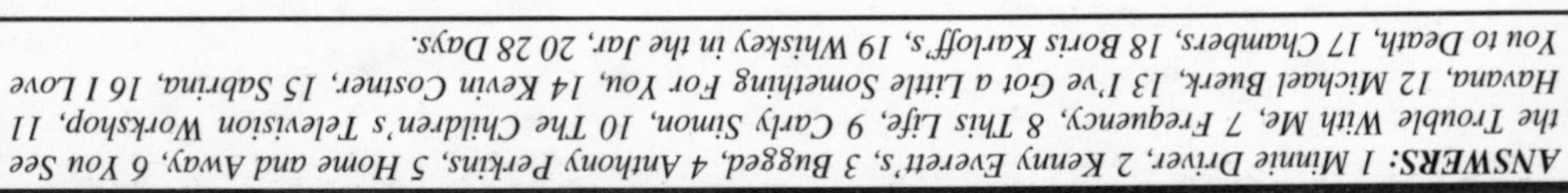

ANSWERS: *1 Minnie Driver, 2 Kenny Everett's, 3 Bugged, 4 Anthony Perkins, 5 Home and Away, 6 You See the Trouble With Me, 7 Frequency, 8 This Life, 9 Carly Simon, 10 The Children's Television Workshop, 11 Havana, 12 Michael Buerk, 13 I've Got a Little Something For You, 14 Kevin Costner, 15 Sabrina, 16 I Love You to Death, 17 Chambers, 18 Boris Karloff's, 19 Whiskey in the Jar, 20 28 Days.*

General Knowledge

Your rating: ● 0-5 Join a library ● 6-10 Keep at it ● 11-15 Join a quiz team ● 16-20 Join Mensa

1. Which young Jewish girl is famous for the diary she kept while her family hid from the Nazis in Amsterdam?
2. Who was the first Hanoverian king of Great Britain?
3. Bob Dylan recently won an Oscar for Best Song for which film?
4. Who was the director of the FBI from 1924 to 1972?
5. Which Russian leader was associated with the policies of glasnost and perestroika?
6. What was the composer Beethoven's first name?
7. Who wrote the novels on which the films *Grand Hotel* and *Hotel Berlin* were based?
8. Which star of the film *Home Alone* made his West End acting debut in 2000?
9. Who did Jesus raise from the dead in the New Testament?
10. What part of the body is affected by lumbago?
11. Which golfer captained the European Ryder Cup team in 1999?
12. Which novel by Elizabeth Gaskell was left unfinished at her death?
13. What do the initials stand for in the name of the American guitarist B.B. King?
14. Which former prime minister of Canada died in 2000 at the age of 80?
15. In algebraic chess notation, which figure begins the game on square e1?
16. Which prolific American author wrote *Riders of the Purple Sage*?
17. Who played *Edna the Inebriate Woman* on TV in 1971?
18. By what name is the perennial plant *Nigella damascena* better known?
19. Which U.S. lawman killed Billy the Kid?
20. What is the sixth book of the Old Testament?

ANSWERS: *1 Anne Frank, 2 George I, 3 Wonder Boys, 4 J Edgar Hoover, 5 Mikhail Gorbachev, 6 Ludwig, 7
Vicki Baum, 8 Macaulay Culkin, 9 Lazarus, 10 The back, 11 Mark James, 12 Wives and Daughters, 13 Blues
Boy, 14 Pierre Trudeau, 15 White's king, 16 Zane Grey, 17 Patricia Hayes, 18 Love-in-a-mist, 19 Pat Garrett,
20 Book of Joshua.*

General Knowledge

Your rating: ● 0-5 Join a library ● 6-10 Keep at it ● 11-15 Join a quiz team ● 16-20 Join Mensa

1. Which character in Greek mythology fell in love with his reflection?
2. Who wrote *On the Origin of Species by Means of Natural Selection*?
3. Who scored the winning goal of the 1996 FA Cup final?
4. What type of school is named from the German for 'children's garden'?
5. Which town is the administrative centre of Suffolk?
6. Which European country voted against adopting the Euro in a referendum in September 2000?
7. Which English novelist wrote *Three Men in a Boat*?
8. Which U.S. naval base in Hawaii was attacked by Japanese planes in 1941?
9. What is the French equivalent of 'Miss', referring to an unmarried female?
10. Which book is placed in hotel rooms by the organisation Gideons International?
11. What is the first name of the fictional detective Maigret?
12. Which boxer, born Archibald Lee Wright, held the world light-heavyweight title from 1952 to 1962?
13. What was the number on Sir Geoff Hurst's shirt that sold for £91,750 at Christie's?
14. Which fishing port is the most easterly town in Scotland?
15. What sort of creature is a mud puppy?
16. Which French cake was immortalised by Marcel Proust in his novel *Swann's Way*?
17. Who did Pat Cash beat in the final of Wimbledon in 1987?
18. What name is given to the outermost region of the sun's atmosphere?
19. To which English monarch was Sir Francis Walsingham principal secretary?
20. Which African country was represented by the swimmer Eric Moussambani at the Sydney Olympics?

ANSWERS: *1 Narcissus, 2 Charles Darwin, 3 Eric Cantona, 4 Kindergarten, 5 Ipswich, 6 Denmark, 7 Jerome K Jerome, 8 Pearl Harbor, 9 Mademoiselle, 10 The Bible, 11 Jules, 12 Archie Moore, 13 Ten, 14 Peterhead, 15 A salamander, 16 Madeleine, 17 Ivan Lendl, 18 Corona, 19 Elizabeth I, 20 Equatorial Guinea.*

General Knowledge

Your rating:
- **0-5 Join a library**
- **6-10 Keep at it**
- **11-15 Join a quiz team**
- **16-20 Join Mensa**

1. Which billionaire stood as a candidate in the U.S. presidential elections in 1992 and 1996?
2. Which American author wrote *The Sound and the Fury*?
3. Which political party's name means 'Party of Wales'?
4. Who claimed Britain's first Olympic boxing gold medal for 32 years at the Sydney Olympics?
5. Which Asian country changed its name to Myanmar in 1989?
6. Who was the first president of the United States?
7. Which English football team won the European Cup Winners Cup in 1985?
8. Who is the heroine of the *Tomb Raider* series of computer games?
9. Which leader of the Israelites anointed Saul as king and chose David as his successor?
10. Who wrote *The Wind in the Willows*?
11. What is another name for the gumshield of a boxer?
12. Which U.S. guitarist and composer was the leader of the Mothers of Invention?
13. In which Scottish town were the poems of Robert Burns first published?
14. To which continent is the chickadee native?
15. What name is given to a verbal device for aiding the memory, such as 'i before e, except after c'?
16. Which art critic wrote *Ways of Seeing*?
17. Which Italian conductor became the music director of Milan's La Scala in 1986?
18. What name is given to a marriage in which the wife and children do not succeed to the titles or property of the husband?
19. Who led the Labour Party from 1955 to 1963?
20. Which species of red algae is also called Irish moss?

ANSWERS: *1 Ross Perot, 2 William Faulkner, 3 Plaid Cymru, 4 Audley Harrison, 5 Burma, 6 George Washington, 7 Everton, 8 Lara Croft, 9 Samuel, 10 Kenneth Grahame, 11 Mouthpiece, 12 Frank Zappa, 13 Kilmarnock, 14 North America, 15 Mnemonic, 16 John Berger, 17 Riccardo Muti, 18 Morganatic marriage, 19 Hugh Gaitskell, 20 Carrageen.*

Entertainment

Your rating: ● **0-5** Buy a TV ● **6-10** Keep at it ● **11-15** Join a quiz team ● **16-20** Enter a quiz show

1. Which actor played psychiatrist Dr Roebuck in the Eighties series *Maybury*?
2. With whom did Whitney Houston duet on the 2000 U.K. top ten hit, *If I Told You That*?
3. Who played Denholm Elliott's son in the 1989 film *Killing Dad*?
4. Which *Coronation Street* character admitted to his wife that he'd had an affair with a work colleague in 2000?
5. What was the title of British soul singer Jamelia's debut album?
6. Which BBC 1 cooking contest show celebrated its tenth birthday in 2000?
7. Which actress and singer played the novelist Jacqueline Susann in the 2000 film *Isn't She Great*?
8. Which budget *Airline* was featured in the ITV docusoap?
9. Which former Boyzone member became the first to release a solo album, appropriately entitled *New Beginning*?
10. Which children's series originally featured characters such as Windy Miller, Captain Snort and Mickey Murphy?
11. Which 1967 film starred Sophia Loren and Omar Sharif?
12. Which British group had a U.K. top ten hit in 1971 with *Cousin Norman*?
13. In which 2000 film did Madonna and Rupert Everett play best friends?
14. Which girl's name provided Gerry Monroe with a U.K. top five hit in 1970?
15. Which Clint Eastwood-directed 1990 movie teamed him up with Charlie Sheen?
16. Which *Coronation Street* character set fire to his former fiancee's possessions after she ran off with his money in 2000?
17. What was the title of Technohead's 1996 U.K. top ten hit?
18. Which U.S. actor played an FBI agent undercover in the 2000 film *Big Momma's House*?
19. Which comedy actor starred alongside Nigel Havers as the other Guy in the Nineties comedy drama series *The Good Guys*?
20. Which former The Verve frontman released his debut album, *Alone With Everybody*, in 2000?

ANSWERS: *1 Patrick Stewart, 2 George Michael, 3 Richard E. Grant, 4 Martin Platt, 5 Drama, 6 Masterchef, 7 Bette Midler, 8 EasyJet, 9 Stephen Gately, 10 Camberwick Green, 11 More Than a Miracle, 12 Marmalade, 13 The Next Best Thing, 14 Sally, 15 The Rookie, 16 Jim McDonald, 17 I Wanna Be a Hippy, 18 Martin Lawrence, 19 Keith Barron, 20 Richard Ashcroft.*

General Knowledge

Your rating:
- 0-5 Join a library
- 6-10 Keep at it
- 11-15 Join a quiz team
- 16-20 Join Mensa

1. Which American singer had hits with *Only the Lonely*, *It's Over* and *Oh Pretty Woman*?
2. By what name is the charter granted by King John in 1215 known?
3. Iain Balshaw and Matt Dawson are internationals in which sport?
4. By what name is actor, writer and director Allen Stewart Konigsberg better known?
5. Which fungoid disease of trees was first described in the Netherlands?
6. Who wrote the orchestral suite *The Planets*?
7. Which British invention made its last Channel crossing in October 2000?
8. Who was infamously stripped of the 100m gold medal at the 1988 Olympic Games?
9. Which U.S. city is nicknamed the Windy City?
10. After which famous English clown are modern clowns nicknamed Joey?
11. Which symbol of rigid moral propriety was created in Thomas Morton's play *Speed the Plough*?
12. Where is the Interlagos motor racing circuit?
13. Which notorious East End criminal died in October 2000 at the age of 66?
14. What is the Russian word for 'fist', given to prosperous peasant farmers in pre-revolutionary Russia?
15. Which British designer created the Mini and the Morris Minor?
16. Montgomery Ward was an American pioneer of what form of retailing?
17. Which country won the mens hockey gold medal at the 1988 Olympic Games?
18. What is the oldest university in the United States?
19. In phonetics, what name is given to the speech sound used for example in the Cockney pronunciation of 'butter' or 'bottle'?
20. Which comedy by William Shakespeare features Helena and Bertram?

ANSWERS: *1 Roy Orbison, 2 Magna Carta, 3 Rugby union, 4 Woody Allen, 5 Dutch elm disease, 6 Gustav Holst, 7 Hovercraft, 8 Ben Johnson, 9 Chicago, 10 Joseph Grimaldi, 11 Mrs Grundy, 12 Brazil, 13 Reggie Kray, 14 Kulak, 15 Sir Alec Issigonis, 16 Mail order, 17 United Kingdom, 18 Harvard, 19 Glottal stop, 20 All's Well That Ends Well.*

General Knowledge

Your rating: ● 0-5 Join a library ● 6-10 Keep at it ● 11-15 Join a quiz team ● 16-20 Join Mensa

1. Which Dutch footballer was the European Footballer of the Year in 1971, 1973 and 1974?
2. Who created the fictional detective Adam Dalgliesh?
3. What was the name of the character played by Daniel Day Lewis in the film *Last of the Mohicans*?
4. Who was the first wife of Henry VIII?
5. Which ballerina and actress starred in the 1948 film *The Red Shoes*?
6. What sort of creature is a Tasmanian devil?
7. Where was the film Cinema Paradiso set?
8. Which British novelist wrote *King Solomon's Mines?*
9. What name is given to an extreme, irrational fear of a specific object or situation?
10. How much is the bull's-eye worth in darts?
11. Which American author wrote *The Beautiful and the Damned*?
12. Which British intelligence officer and Soviet agent warned Burgess and MacLean that they were under suspicion?
13. Who wrote the play *She Stoops to Conquer*?
14. Which horse has become the first to win the English and Irish Derbies and Prix de l'Arc de Triomphe in the same season?
15. What sort of creature is an agouti?
16. Which German swimmer was nicknamed The Albatross?
17. What was the first name of Cervantes, author of *Don Quixote*?
18. In which event did Steph Cook win Britain's 11th and final gold medal at the Sydney Olympics?
19. Which English tennis-playing brothers dominated Wimbledon from 1897 to 1906?
20. By what epithet was Richard Neville, Earl of Warwick known?

ANSWERS: 1 Johan Cruyff, 2 P D James, 3 Hawkeye, 4 Catherine of Aragon, 5 Moira Shearer, 6 A marsupial, 7 Sicily, 8 H Rider Haggard, 9 Phobia, 10 Fifty, 11 F Scott Fitzgerald, 12 Kim Philby, 13 Oliver Goldsmith, 14 Sinndar, 15 A rodent, 16 Michael Gross, 17 Miguel, 18 Modern Pentathlon, 19 Laurie and Reggie Doherty, 20 The Kingmaker.

General Knowledge

Your rating: ● **0-5** Join a library ● **6-10** Keep at it ● **11-15** Join a quiz team ● **16-20** Join Mensa

1. Which Norwegian composer wrote incidental music for the play *Peer Gynt*?
2. Who resigned as manager of the England national football team in 1977?
3. Which dog is the trademark of the main providers of intercity bus transportation in the U.S.?
4. How many gold medals did Marion Jones win at the Sydney Olympics?
5. Which female tennis player beat Bobby Riggs in a much-publicised Battle of the Sexes match in 1973?
6. What does a philatelist collect?
7. For which country did rugby league star Mal Meninga play?
8. What name is given to a plant that retains its leaves all year round?
9. Which gardens are formally known as The Royal Botanic Gardens?
10. By what name is the spectacular atmospheric display the aurora borealis better known?
11. Greensome and four-ball are terms used in which sport?
12. Which actor whose films include *M*, *Casablanca* and *The Maltese Falcon* was born Laszlo Loewenstein?
13. Is Solomon's seal a plant or an animal?
14. Which vacuum cleaner inventor won a multi-million pound court battle with Hoover in 2000?
15. Of which planet is Umbriel a satellite?
16. Which German composer is best known for his *Canon and Gigue in D Major*?
17. Which became the first African country to win a major soccer trophy when winning the 1996 Olympic Games football event?
18. Which veteran actor starred in the 2000 film *Where the Money Is*?
19. To which country is the burrowing parrot known as a kakapo native?
20. Which dramatist and architect designed Castle Howard and Blenheim Palace?

***ANSWERS:** 1 Edvard Grieg, 2 Don Revie, 3 Greyhound, 4 Three, 5 Billie Jean King, 6 Stamps, 7 Australia, 8 Evergreen, 9 Kew Gardens, 10 Northern lights, 11 Golf, 12 Peter Lorre, 13 A plant, 14 James Dyson, 15 Uranus, 16 Johann Pachelbel, 17 Nigeria, 18 Paul Newman, 19 New Zealand, 20 Sir John Vanbrugh.*

Entertainment

Your rating: ● 0-5 Buy a TV ● 6-10 Keep at it ● 11-15 Join a quiz team ● 16-20 Enter a quiz show

1. Which actress played the lead in the 1962 film *The Roman Spring of Mrs Stone*?
2. Which *EastEnders* teenager accused her maths tutor of attacking her in 2000?
3. Which New Jersey teenage rap duo released their debut album in 2000, entitled *We Didn't Say That!*?
4. Which comedian and actor played headmaster Ian George in the BBC 1 drama series *Hope & Glory*?
5. Which Hollywood actor provided the voice of Rocky the Rooster in the 2000 animated film *Chicken Run*?
6. In which U.S. city was the sitcom *Happy Days* set?
7. Which sex symbol made her film debut as Javotte Lemoine in 1952's *Le Trou normand*?
8. Which Canadian singer released an album entitled *Invincible Summer* in 2000, her first record of original material for five years?
9. Who played *The Greek Tycoon* Theo Tomasis in the 1978 film?
10. In which BBC 1 comedy series did Alan Davies star as reluctant adulterer Russel Boyd?
11. Which U.S. group claimed *It's a Love Thing* in the U.K. charts in 1981?
12. Which *Friends* actor starred in the 2000 film *Three to Tango*?
13. Which former *EastEnder* played barrister Sam Lucas in ITV's drama series *In Defence*?
14. Which British group had a *Rock 'N' Roll Winter* in the U.K. top ten in 1974?
15. Which Irish actor played the Black Prince in the 1987 film *Lionheart*?
16. Who presented the BBC 1 quiz show *The Syndicate*?
17. Which female singer featured on Incognito's 1991 U.K. top ten hit *Always There*?
18. Which 2000 film adaptation of a Noel Coward comedy starred Julie Andrews and Colin Firth?
19. Which Seventies sitcom starring Terry Scott and June Whitfield preceded *Terry and June*?
20. Which Australian popstar had a 2000 number one hit with *Spinning Around*?

ANSWERS: 1 Vivien Leigh, 2 Nicky diMarco, 3 Daphne & Celeste, 4 Lenny Henry, 5 Mel Gibson, 6 Milwaukee, Wisconsin, 7 Brigitte Bardot, 8 k.d. lang, 9 Anthony Quinn, 10 A Many Splintered Thing, 11 Whispers, 12 Matthew Perry, 13 Ross Kemp, 14 Wizzard, 15 Gabriel Byrne, 16 Nick Ross, 17 Jocelyn Brown, 18 Relative Values, 19 Happy Ever After, 20 Kylie Minogue.

General Knowledge

Your rating:
- **0-5 Join a library**
- **6-10 Keep at it**
- **11-15 Join a quiz team**
- **16-20 Join Mensa**

1. Which international men's team tennis trophy was first contested in 1900?
2. What is the first book of the Old Testament?
3. Which quiz show presented by Anne Robinson earned her the title of 'rudest person on television'?
4. In which Jules Verne novel does Phileas Fogg appear?
5. Which Scottish bacteriologist discovered penicillin?
6. What does a somnambulist do?
7. Which novel by Charles Dickens features the character Wackford Squeers?
8. What name is given to the tall yellow-flowered plants of the genus *Helianthus*?
9. In which sport did Britons Ben Ainslie, Iain Percy and Shirley Robertson win Olympic gold medals in Sydney?
10. What is the largest of all known animals?
11. Who is the author of the book *Angry Blond*?
12. Which organic compounds that destroy the ozone layer are known as CFCs?
13. Who directed the films *Somebody Up There Likes Me* and *The Sound of Music*?
14. Which Liverpool player scored the goal in Germany's 1-0 win over England at Wembley in 2000?
15. With which instruments is jazz musician Gene Krupa associated?
16. Which American car company owns Vauxhall?
17. Who was the first Australian cricketer to score over 7000 Test runs?
18. Which American author wrote *Double Indemnity* and *The Postman Always Rings Twice*?
19. Which Spanish soup containing tomatoes and peppers is served cold?
20. Which U.S. children's author and illustrator created Huckle Cat and Lowly Worm?

***ANSWERS:** 1 Davis Cup, 2 Genesis, 3 The Weakest Link, 4 Around the World in Eighty Days, 5 Sir Alexander Fleming, 6 Sleepwalk, 7 Nicholas Nickleby, 8 Sunflowers, 9 Sailing, 10 Blue whale, 11 Eminem, 12 Chlorofluorocarbons, 13 Robert Wise, 14 Dietmar Hamann, 15 Drums, 16 General Motors, 17 Greg Chappell, 18 James M Cain, 19 Gazpacho, 20 Richard Scarry.*

General Knowledge

Your rating:
- **0-5 Join a library**
- **6-10 Keep at it**
- **11-15 Join a quiz team**
- **16-20 Join Mensa**

1. Which animated character made his debut in the 1928 cartoon *Steamboat Willie*?
2. What is the points value of a drop goal in rugby league?
3. Which acute viral disease particularly associated with children is also called rubeola?
4. Who was ousted as president of Yugoslavia in 2000?
5. Which three-leaved plant was St Patrick said to have used to explain the Holy Trinity?
6. What is the brightest star in the night sky?
7. Which travel writer penned *Notes From a Small Island*?
8. In which lawn game can a player win by pegging out?
9. Which light metal has the chemical symbol Al?
10. Who became the world's most expensive footballer when he joined Newcastle United in 1996?
11. Which English author wrote *The History of Tom Jones*?
12. Who was the Roman equivalent of the Greek god Ares?
13. In which game did Mark Tracy become the world champion in 2000 on the village green at Ashton in Northamptonshire?
14. Which gemstone is the traditional birthstone for January?
15. Who directed the films *Salaam Bombay*, *Mississippi Masala* and *Kama Sutra*?
16. In which strait is the mirage known as Fata Morgana occasionally seen?
17. Which jockey rode West Tip to victory in the 1986 Grand National?
18. Which skin condition caused by inflammation around the sweat glands is also called miliaria?
19. In which country is the airline KLM based?
20. What sort of creature is a rorqual?

ANSWERS: *1 Mickey Mouse, 2 1, 3 Measles, 4 Slobodan Milosevic, 5 Shamrock, 6 Sirius, 7 Bill Bryson, 8 Croquet, 9 Aluminium, 10 Alan Shearer, 11 Henry Fielding, 12 Mars, 13 Conkers, 14 Garnet, 15 Mira Nair, 16 Strait of Messina, 17 Richard Dunwoody, 18 Prickly heat, 19 The Netherlands, 10 A whale.*

General Knowledge

Your rating:
- 0-5 Join a library
- 6-10 Keep at it
- 11-15 Join a quiz team
- 16-20 Join Mensa

1. Which Irish novelist wrote *Finnegans Wake*?
2. Cologne stands on the left bank of which river?
3. Which famous secret agent was created by Ian Fleming?
4. Who played Dr Tom Latimer in the TV sitcom *Don't Wait Up*?
5. Which sport involves the use of epees, sabres and foils?
6. What is the capital of Kenya?
7. Which U.S. actor starred in the films *Lust for Life* and *Spartacus*?
8. Of which Asian country was Cory Aquino the president from 1986 to 1992?
9. Which English author wrote *Gormenghast*?
10. Which singer recorded the albums *Off The Wall*, *Thriller* and *Bad*?
11. Which mineral has the lowest rating on the Mohs scale of hardness?
12. Which English-born actor won an Oscar for his performance in *A Double Life*?
13. At which Grand Prix did Michael Schumacher clinch the 2000 world title?
14. Which character in *Treasure Island* is particularly partial to cheese?
15. What is the English translation of the Russian poputchik, meaning a Communist sympathiser?
16. Which British group recorded the album *Parklife*?
17. Who was Scotland's First Minister who died in 2000?
18. Who wrote *A Kind of Loving*?
19. What was the real name of Nazi propagandist Lord Haw-Haw?
20. Who was the first president of the Committee of Public Safety in the French Revolution?

***ANSWERS:** 1 James Joyce, 2 The Rhine, 3 James Bond, 4 Nigel Havers, 5 Fencing, 6 Nairobi, 7 Kirk Douglas, 8 The Philippines, 9 Mervyn Peake, 10 Michael Jackson, 11 Talc, 12 Ronald Colman, 13 Japanese, 14 Ben Gunn, 15 Fellow traveller, 16 Blur, 17 Donald Dewar, 18 Stan Barstow, 19 William Joyce, 20 Georges Danton.*

Sports

Your rating: ● **0-5** **Wooden spoon** ● **6-10** **Bronze medal** ● **11-15** **Silver medal** ● **16-20** **Gold medal**

1. Which horse won the 1998 Cheltenham Gold Cup?
2. Which American sport do the New York Yankees and the Atlanta Braves compete in?
3. For which German football team did Kevin Keegan play?
4. In which year will Salt Lake City, USA host the Winter Olympics?
5. Which side did England knock out of the 1995 rugby union World Cup with a late Rob Andrew drop goal?
6. Which club signed Paul Ince from Manchester United in 1995?
7. In which year did Eric Bristow win his record fifth World Professional darts title?
8. Which Canadian was the 1997 Formula 1 World Motor Racing Champion?
9. How old was Ray Reardon when he became the oldest World Snooker Champion?
10. Which traditional Scottish sport first appeared officially at the 1998 Winter Olympics?
11. To whom did Michael Bentt lose a WBO world heavyweight title fight in 1994?
12. Which nation competes with England for the rugby union Calcutta Cup?

13. In which year did England win the football World Cup?
14. From which event was Ben Johnson disqualified after winning at the 1988 Olympics?
15. In 1980, Nadyezda Tkatchenko become the first athlete to exceed 5,000 points in which event?
16. Which British racing driver was World Championship runner-up from 1955 to 1958?
17. Which Scottish golfer won $1 million in 1998 as the Andersen Consulting World Champion?
18. For which event did Trevor Bickle win the gold medal at the 1962 Commonwealth Games?
19. What is the Argentinian rugby union side's nickname?
20. Which football team was coached by Daniel Passarella at the 1998 World Cup?

***ANSWERS:** 1 Cool Dawn, 2 Baseball, 3 Hamburg, 4 2002, 5 Australia, 6 Inter Milan, 7 1986, 8 Jacques Villeneuve, 9 45, 10 Curling, 11 Herbie Hide, 12 Scotland, 13 1966, 14 100m, 15 Pentathlon, 16 Stirling Moss, 17 Colin Montgomerie, 18 Pole vault, 19 The Pumas, 20 Argentina.*

General Knowledge

Your rating:
- 0-5 Join a library
- 6-10 Keep at it
- 11-15 Join a quiz team
- 16-20 Join Mensa

1. Which British novelist wrote *Stamboul Train*?
2. Which state of dormancy in winter is experienced by many creatures to avoid death by heat loss or food scarcity?
3. By which name, meaning "Great Soul", was the Indian nationalist leader Mohandas Gandhi known?
4. Which U.S. general directed the recapture of the SW Pacific as Allied commander in World War II?
5. What is the official language of Costa Rica?
6. Which island in the Irish Sea has Douglas as its capital?
7. The island of Bali is part of which Asian country?
8. In the high jump, what is the maximum number of attempts each competitor is allowed at each height?
9. In which state of the USA is the city of Los Angeles located?
10. Which Italian dictator formed an alliance with Hitler in 1936?
11. Which strait connects the Sea of Marmara with the Aegean Sea?
12. Which Greek comic dramatist wrote *Lysistrata* and *The Frogs*?
13. Of which Asian country is Vientiane the capital?
14. Which rare-earth metal is represented by the symbol La?
15. What sort of creature is a douroucouli?
16. Which British novelist wrote *The Small Back Room*?
17. In the 1930s, which Austrian zoologist identified the phenomenon of imprinting in young chicks?
18. According to the Christian calendar, on which date of the year does the Major Rogation occur?
19. Which Italian poet won the 1959 Nobel prize for literature?
20. Which Italian author wrote *The Triumph of Death*?

ANSWERS: *1 Graham Greene, 2 Hibernation, 3 Mahatma, 4 Douglas MacArthur, 5 Spanish, 6 Isle of Man, 7 Indonesia, 8 Three, 9 California, 10 Benito Mussolini, 11 The Dardanelles, 12 Aristophanes, 13 Laos, 14 Lanthanum, 15 Monkey, 16 Nigel Balchin, 17 Konrad Lorenz, 18 April the 25th, 19 Salvatore Quasimodo, 20 Gabriele D'Annunzio.*

General Knowledge

Your rating: ● 0-5 Join a library ● 6-10 Keep at it ● 11-15 Join a quiz team ● 16-20 Join Mensa

1. Which comedy duo starred in the 1930s films *Our Relations* and *Way Out West*?
2. In which English county can Cheddar Gorge be found?
3. Which sign of the zodiac is represented by a ram?
4. Which Russian dramatist wrote *Uncle Vanya* and *The Cherry Orchard*?
5. Of which European country is Krakow the third largest city?
6. Which reactive metal is represented by the symbol Ca?
7. Which silvery-white metal is represented by the symbol Al?
8. Which European river flows through Vienna, Budapest and Belgrade?
9. Which metal is represented by the symbol Pb?
10. What is the name for the goatskin pouch often worn with a kilt in traditional Highland dress?
11. Which British jazz musician married singer Cleo Laine?
12. Who resigned as foreign secretary of the U.K. following the Argentinian invasion of the Falkland Islands in 1982?
13. Which city on the River Vienne is the centre of the French porcelain industry?
14. Which British actor starred in the films *The Private Life of Henry VIII* and *Mutiny on the Bounty*?
15. Which Greek philosopher was appointed by Philip of Macedon to tutor his 13-year-old son Alexander?
16. Which British general was besieged for ten months in Khartoum in 1884-5?
17. Who was the prime minister of Great Britain from 1923 to 1924, 1924 to 1929, and 1935 to 1937?
18. According to Greek legend, which daughter of Minos helped Theseus to kill the Minotaur?
19. What sort of creature is an antlion?
20. Which British novelist and playwright wrote *The Bottle Factory Outing* and *The Dressmaker*?

ANSWERS: *1 Laurel and Hardy, 2 Somerset, 3 Aries, 4 Anton Chekhov, 5 Poland, 6 Calcium, 7 Aluminium, 8 The River Danube, 9 Lead, 10 Sporran, 11 John Dankworth, 12 Lord Carrington, 13 Limoges, 14 Charles Laughton, 15 Aristotle, 16 Charles Gordon, 17 Stanley Baldwin, 18 Ariadne, 19 An insect, 20 Beryl Bainbridge.*

General Knowledge

Your rating: ● **0-5** Join a library ● **6-10** Keep at it ● **11-15** Join a quiz team ● **16-20** Join Mensa

1. Which sport does one associate with Tony Jacklin?
2. Which Indian river is the Hindus' most sacred river?
3. What colour are emeralds?
4. According to Greek legend, what sort of monster was Medusa?
5. Of which island country is Antananarivo the capital?
6. Which Indian stateswoman was prime minister of her country from 1966 to 1977 and 1980 to 1984?
7. In which English county are the Cotswold Hills mainly situated?
8. Which British novelist wrote *The Spy Who Came in from the Cold*?
9. Which scientific term describes the lowest temperature that can theoretically be attained?
10. Which poet wrote *The Canterbury Tales*?
11. Which U.S. president was known as the "Hero of New Orleans"?
12. Of which island country is Roseau the capital?
13. Who became the only football club manager to play for the England national team in 1997?
14. What sort of creature is a takahe?
15. What was J Arthur Rank's first name?
16. What is the most widely-spoken language of India?
17. What has been the official residence of the presidents of France since 1873?
18. Which Italian film maker directed *La Notte* and *The Passenger*?
19. What is the capital of South Australia?
20. Which method of treating rubber with sulphur was patented by Charles Goodyear in 1844?

ANSWERS: 1 Golf, 2 The River Ganges, 3 Green, 4 A gorgon, 5 Madagascar, 6 Indira Gandhi, 7 Gloucestershire, 8 John Le Carré, 9 Absolute zero, 10 Geoffrey Chaucer, 11 Andrew Jackson, 12 Commonwealth of Dominica, 13 Stuart Pearce, 14 A bird, 15 Joseph, 16 Hindi, 17 Palais de l'Élysée, 18 Michelangelo Antonioni, 19 Adelaide, 20 Vulcanisation.

Entertainment

Your rating: ● 0-5 Buy a TV ● 6-10 Keep at it ● 11-15 Join a quiz team ● 16-20 Enter a quiz show

1. With which band is Louise Wener associated?
2. Who starred as *The Invisible Man* in the 1933 film?
3. Who had a number one hit single in 1973 with *Skweeze Me Pleeze Me*?
4. Which crooner played serial killer Daryll Lee Cullum in the film *Copycat*?
5. Who starred as Lucy in TV's *I Love Lucy*?
6. Which vocalist released an album entitled *Older* in 1996?
7. Who played Harry Palmer in the film *The Ipcress File*?
8. Which sitcom starred Alan Cumming and Forbes Masson as Air Scotia stewards Sebastian and Steve?
9. How is pop singer Marie McDonald McLaughlin Lawrie better known?
10. Who played Gary in the TV comedy series *Men Behaving Badly*?
11. Which 1996 film starred Meryl Streep and Liam Neeson as the parents of a 17-year-old murder suspect?
12. Which band released an album entitled *Walking Wounded* in 1996?
13. Which '70s U.S. drama series starred Richard Thomas as John-Boy?
14. Who starred as the absent-minded inventor in the film *Chitty Chitty Bang Bang*?
15. Who played director Nick Balmer in the TV drama *Karaoke*?
16. What is Madonna's middle name?
17. Who played Sandra in TV's *The Liver Birds*?
18. Which 1996 documentary film was about New York fashion designer Isaac Mizrahi?
19. Who played Mildred in the sitcom *George and Mildred*?
20. Which actor played Harry in the 1989 film *When Harry Met Sally*?

ANSWERS: *1 Sleeper, 2 Claude Rains, 3 Slade, 4 Harry Connick Jr., 5 Lucille Ball, 6 George Michael, 7 Michael Caine, 8 The High Life, 9 Lulu, 10 Martin Clunes, 11 Before And After, 12 Everything But The Girl, 13 The Waltons, 14 Dick Van Dyke, 15 Richard E. Grant, 16 Louise, 17 Nerys Hughes, 18 Unzipped, 19 Yootha Joyce, 20 Billy Crystal.*

General Knowledge

Your rating:
- 0-5 Join a library
- 6-10 Keep at it
- 11-15 Join a quiz team
- 16-20 Join Mensa

1. Which two Middle Eastern countries fought each other in a war that began in 1980?
2. What name is given to an earthed rod placed at the top of a tall building?
3. Which high-kicking dance originated in Paris in about 1830?
4. Who became the youngest footballer to play for England in the 20th century when he made his debut against Chile in 1998?
5. Of which U.S. state is Trenton the capital?
6. Who wrote *Silas Marner* and *The Mill on the Floss*?
7. What is the name of the largest minor planet or asteroid?
8. Which hypothetical substance did alchemists seek for its ability to turn base metals into gold?
9. What name is given to a place equipped with telescopes for studying the sky?
10. Which American author writes the *Goosebumps* series of novels?
11. Which composer wrote the opera for television *Amahl and the Night Visitors*?
12. What was the name of the Roman household gods associated with the storeroom?
13. Which German skier became the first skier ever to retain an Olympic downhill title in 1998?
14. Who was the foreign secretary who fought the minister of war Castlereagh in a duel in 1809?
15. Which French impressionist painter was the granddaughter of Fragonard and sister-in-law of Manet?
16. According to Jewish tradition, who was Adam's first wife?
17. Which Paris street on the Left Bank of the River Seine is home to the French Foreign Office?
18. Who directed the films *M* and *Metropolis*?
19. In which U.S. state is the city of Milwaukee?
20. Which breed of working dog is sometimes known as a bobtail?

ANSWERS: *1 Iran and Iraq, 2 Lightning conductor, 3 Cancan, 4 Michael Owen, 5 New Jersey, 6 George Eliot, 7 Ceres, 8 Philosopher's stone, 9 Observatory, 10 R L Stine, 11 Gian Carlo Menotti, 12 Penates, 13 Katja Seizinger, 14 George Canning, 15 Berthe Morisot, 16 Lilith, 17 Quai d'Orsay, 18 Fritz Lang, 19 Wisconsin, 20 Old English sheepdogs.*

General Knowledge

Your rating:
- **0-5 Join a library**
- **6-10 Keep at it**
- **11-15 Join a quiz team**
- **16-20 Join Mensa**

1. Which woodwind instrument is the smallest member of the flute family?
2. In mathematics, what name is given to the likelihood that something will occur?
3. At which Premiership football team did Gianluca Vialli replace Ruud Gullit as player-manager?
4. Of which Middle Eastern country is Amman the capital?
5. Who wrote *My Cousin Rachel* and *Rebecca*?
6. Which disease of the central nervous system is represented by the abbreviation MS?
7. Of which English county is Northallerton the administrative centre?
8. What does the abbreviation JP stand for?
9. Which member of the *Beyond the Fringe* revue studied medicine at Cambridge?
10. What is the name of Anthony Gormley's controversial sculpture which stands next to the A1 at Gateshead?
11. To the nearest whole number, what percentage of the mass of the solar system resides in the sun?
12. Which legal holiday is celebrated in America on the first Monday in September?
13. What name is given to a minute noncellular particle that can reproduce only in living cells?
14. What is the name of the channel between New Zealand's North Island and South Island?
15. What was the name of the imperial Roman bodyguard created by Augustus in 27 BC?
16. Which German composer wrote *The Raft of the Medusa* and *The Bassarids*?
17. By what name is the tree *Ficus elastica* known?
18. Which rare genetic disorder is believed to have been the cause of the madness of George III?
19. Which pop group is Danbert Nobacon associated with?
20. To which genus of plants do the sensitive plants belong?

ANSWERS: *1 Piccolo, 2 Probability, 3 Chelsea, 4 Jordan, 5 Daphne Du Maurier, 6 Multiple sclerosis, 7 North Yorkshire, 8 Justice of the Peace, 9 Jonathan Miller, 10 Angel of the North, 11 100, 12 Labor Day, 13 Virus, 14 Cook Strait, 15 Praetorian Guard, 16 Hans Werner Henze, 17 Rubber plant, 18 Porphyria, 19 Chumbawumba, 20 Mimosa.*

General Knowledge

Your rating: ● 0-5 Join a library ● 6-10 Keep at it ● 11-15 Join a quiz team ● 16-20 Join Mensa

1. Which gas is the main constituent of natural gas and marsh gas?
2. What name is given to trees of the genus *Larix*?
3. How many Academy Award nominations did the film *Titanic* receive?
4. Which Russian writer wrote the novel *Anna Karenina*?
5. Which red hair dye is obtained from the shrub *Lawsonia inermis*?
6. By what name was Charles Stratton known when he was publicly exhibited by P T Barnum?
7. Which Germanic people invaded England, especially Kent, along with the Angles and Saxons in the 5th century AD?
8. In concert pitch, to what note are orchestral instruments tuned?
9. What was the former name of the Indian city of Kanpur, scene of massacre during the Indian Mutiny?
10. Of which country is Piraeus the chief port?
11. What name is given to the state of perfect serenity that is the goal of Buddhism?
12. Which vitamin is also known as retinol?
13. What was the name of the German camp doctor at Auschwitz who was known as the Angel of Death?
14. Which snooker player won the 1998 Benson and Hedges Masters with a re-spotted black?
15. What was the name of the flintlike stone formerly used to test the purity of gold and silver?
16. Which Austrian-born educationalist wrote *Deschooling Society*?
17. Which U.S. poet and critic broadcast fascist propaganda during World War II?
18. What sort of creature is a prairie dog?
19. Which austere Protestant sect was founded by J N Darby?
20. By what name is Roman scholar Gaius Plinius Secundus, author of the encyclopedia *Natural History*, better known?

ANSWERS: *1 Methane, 2 Larch, 3 14, 4 Count Leo Tolstoy, 5 Henna, 6 General Tom Thumb, 7 Jutes, 8 A, 9 Cawnpore, 10 Greece, 11 Nirvana, 12 Vitamin A, 13 Josef Mengele, 14 Mark Williams, 15 Touchstone, 16 Ivan Illich, 17 Ezra Pound, 18 A rodent, 19 Plymouth Brethren, 20 Pliny the Elder.*

Entertainment

Your rating: ● 0-5 Buy a TV ● 6-10 Keep at it ● 11-15 Join a quiz team ● 16-20 Enter a quiz show

1. Who starred as Glenn Holland in the film *Mr Holland's Opus*?
2. Which country won the 1996 Eurovision Song Contest?
3. Who played the imprisoned writer in the 1990 film *Misery*?
4. Which sci-fi film and TV series featured the evil Cylons?
5. In which city were the group The Human League formed?
6. Who was the British director of the 1996 shipwreck film *White Squall*?
7. Which former Grateful Dead drummer composed a piece featuring 100 percussionists for the 1996 Olympic Games?
8. Which newsreader presented the current affairs series *3-D*?
9. What does BAFTA stand for?
10. Which *EastEnders* character was played by Deepak Verma?
11. Who had a top ten hit single in 1977 with *Something Better Change*?
12. Who played nightclub owner Armand in the film *The Birdcage*?
13. Which former punk rock vocalist reported on complementary therapies for TV's *Watchdog Healthcheck*?
14. Which singer/songwriter released an album in 1996 entitled *All This Useless Beauty*?
15. Who wrote, produced, co-directed and starred in the 1942 film *In Which We Serve*?
16. Who presented the gameshow *Small Talk*?
17. Who had a top ten hit single in 1988 with *Smooth Criminal*?
18. Which actress won the 1999 Best Actress Oscar for her performance in *Shakespeare in Love*?
19. Who starred in *Going Straight* and *Open All Hours*?
20. Which former *Baywatch* star appeared in the film *Barb Wire*?

ANSWERS: *1 Richard Dreyfuss, 2 Ireland, 3 James Caan, 4 Battlestar Galactica, 5 Sheffield, 6 Ridley Scott, 7 Mickey Hart, 8 Julia Somerville, 9 British Academy of Film and Television Arts, 10 Sanjay Kapoor, 11 The Stranglers, 12 Robin Williams, 13 Toyah Willcox, 14 Elvis Costello, 15 Noel Coward, 16 Ronnie Corbett, 17 Michael Jackson, 18 Gwyneth Paltrow, 19 Ronnie Barker, 20 Pamela Anderson Lee.*

General Knowledge

Your rating: ● 0-5 Join a library ● 6-10 Keep at it ● 11-15 Join a quiz team ● 16-20 Join Mensa

1. Which inlet of the Atlantic Ocean between N Spain and W France is noted for its rough seas and high tides?
2. What name is given to the programs run by a computer, as opposed to the physical equipment?
3. Which medical specialty deals with the problems and diseases of old age?
4. What was the pen name of Leslie Charles Bowyer Yin, creator of *The Saint*?
5. To what is the drug lysergic acid diethylamide usually abbreviated?
6. Which former capital of Japan is an anagram of its present capital?
7. In which country did the Red Brigades kill Aldo Moro in 1978?
8. Which ancient cities were destroyed by fire and brimstone, according to Genesis?
9. Of which organ of the body is the tricuspid valve a part?
10. Which Dutch headland has a seaport with a ferry link to Harwich?
11. Which infectious disease of birds is also called parrot disease?
12. In what year did the First Crusade begin?
13. Which archipelago, divided between Chile and Argentina, is separated from the South American mainland by the Strait of Magellan?
14. In which English county did Luddism begin in 1811?
15. By what name is the German pistol the Parabellum also known?
16. Of which country is Thursday Island a part?
17. In Greek mythology, which daughter of Tantalus was turned into a weeping stone?
18. What name is given to the grains of seed plants that contain the male gametes?
19. The diaries of which Labour minister were published in 1975 in spite of government attempts to suppress them?
20. What adjective is applied to substances capable of being broken down by living organisms?

ANSWERS: *1 Bay of Biscay, 2 Software, 3 Geriatrics, 4 Leslie Charteris, 5 LSD, 6 Kyoto, 7 Italy, 8 Sodom and Gomorrah, 9 Heart, 10 Hook of Holland, 11 Psittacosis, 12 1095, 13 Tierra del Fuego, 14 Nottinghamshire, 15 Luger, 16 Australia, 17 Niobe, 18 Pollen, 19 Richard Crossman, 20 Biodegradable.*

General Knowledge

Your rating:
- 0-5 Join a library
- 6-10 Keep at it
- 11-15 Join a quiz team
- 16-20 Join Mensa

1. Which Merseyside port is linked to Liverpool by road and rail tunnels?
2. In the Old Testament, who was the father of Joseph?
3. Which Rugby Union team was the first British winner of the Heineken Cup?
4. For which plant are the Netherlands, Lincolnshire and the Channel Islands the main commercial growing areas?
5. Which sign of the zodiac is between Leo and Libra?
6. Who wrote *The Golden Notebook* and *The Good Terrorist*?
7. Which Venetian traveller dictated an account of his travels to the Far East in the 13th century?
8. What name is given to a pathologically strong fear of a situation or thing?
9. What sort of creature is a monarch?
10. Which French art gallery contains the *Venus de Milo* and the *Mona Lisa*?
11. By what name was the Italian painter of the Venetian school Paolo Caliari known?
12. Which era of geological time comprises the Cambrian, Ordovician, Silurian, Devonian, Carboniferous and Permian periods?
13. Who was the father of King Edward the Elder?
14. Which tennis player won the men's singles at the 1998 Australian Open?
15. What name is given to compounds used to induce labour?
16. Which institution did Robert Raikes found in Gloucester in 1780?
17. What is the largest city in Alabama?
18. Which constellation is popularly known as the Southern Cross?
19. In which Dublin park were Thomas Burke and Lord Frederick Cavendish murdered in 1882?
20. What form of laryngitis occurs most commonly in children under five?

ANSWERS: *1 Birkenhead, 2 Jacob, 3 Bath, 4 Tulip, 5 Virgo, 6 Doris Lessing, 7 Marco Polo, 8 Phobia, 9 A butterfly, 10 Louvre, 11 Paolo Veronese, 12 Palaeozoic, 13 Alfred the Great, 14 Petr Korda, 15 Prostaglandins, 16 Sunday school, 17 Birmingham, 18 Crux, 19 Phoenix Park, 20 Croup.*

General Knowledge

Your rating:
- **0-5 Join a library**
- **6-10 Keep at it**
- **11-15 Join a quiz team**
- **16-20 Join Mensa**

1. Which Carthaginian general provoked the Second Punic War with Rome?
2. Which German-born physicist extended his theory of relativity to the general case in 1915 and received the 1921 Nobel Prize for Physics?
3. Which daughter of a famous rock star was appointed head designer of French fashion house Chloe in 1997?
4. What name is given to the form of capital punishment by which Jesus was executed?
5. What sort of creature is a gannet?
6. According to legend, which courtier did Dionysius seat at a banquet beneath a sword suspended by a single hair?
7. Which breed of spotted dog is named after an Adriatic coastal region?
8. Which small round beetles are mainly yellow or red with black spots?
9. What sort of creature is a Russian Blue?
10. Of which war was the Battle of Inkerman a decisive battle?
11. Between which two countries does the Cascade Range of volcanic mountains extend?
12. Of which mineral is aquamarine a variety?
13. Which Oscar-winning actor became ambassador to Japan for the Bahamas in 1977?
14. Which country was ruled by Casimir the Great from 1333 to 1370?
15. What is the largest inland sea in the world?
16. Which order of Roman Catholic monks was founded at Cîteaux, France in 1098?
17. What does the C stand for in the famous formula of Einstein's theory of relativity?
18. Which British caricaturist illustrated Charles Dickens's *Oliver Twist*?
19. Which alloy of copper and zinc, formerly used to imitate gold in jewellery, is named after a watchmaker?
20. What is the name of the science that studies the occurrence and movement of water on and over the surface of the earth?

ANSWERS: *1 Hannibal, 2 Albert Einstein, 3 Stella McCartney, 4 Crucifixion, 5 A bird, 6 Damocles, 7 Dalmatian, 8 Ladybirds, 9 A cat, 10 Crimean War, 11 Canada and USA, 12 Beryl, 13 Sidney Poitier, 14 Poland, 15 Caspian Sea, 16 Cistercians, 17 The speed of light, 18 George Cruikshank, 19 Pinchbeck, 20 Hydrology.*

Entertainment

Your rating: ● 0-5 Buy a TV ● 6-10 Keep at it ● 11-15 Join a quiz team ● 16-20 Enter a quiz show

1. Who was the original host of the gameshow *Blankety Blank*?
2. Who played Jim Hawkins's mother in the film *Muppet Treasure Island*?
3. Which heavy metal group released an album in 1996 entitled *Load*?
4. Which 1939 Alfred Hitchcock film was based on a Daphne du Maurier novel?
5. Which singer co-hosted the TV show *You Bet!*?
6. Which British reggae band had a top ten hit single in 1980 with *Food For Thought*?
7. Which Oscar-winning actress played the young hero's mother in the 1996 film *Angus*?
8. Which *Carry On* star played the head of the family in the sitcom *Bless This House*?
9. Which Hispanic female vocalist released an album in 1996 entitled *Destiny*?
10. Who starred as the defence attorney who falls in love with her client in the film *Jagged Edge*?
11. Who was the host of the food quiz show *Eat Your Words*?
12. With which musical instrument is Branford Marsalis primarily associated?
13. Who played FBI Special Agent Fox Mulder in *The X Files*?
14. Which 1996 film starred Woody Harrelson and Wesley Snipes as cops?
15. Which rock 'n' roll legend released an album called *A Man Amongst Men* in 1996?
16. Which *EastEnders* character is played by Dean Gaffney?
17. Who played dance instructor Johnny Castle in the film *Dirty Dancing*?
18. Who presented the gameshow *Lucky Numbers*?
19. Which British actor played crooked cop Norman Stansfield in the 1994 film *Leon*?
20. Which *Goon Show* regular could be seen on TV in *Potty Time*?

ANSWERS: *1 Terry Wogan, 2 Jennifer Saunders, 3 Metallica, 4 Jamaica Inn, 5 Darren Day, 6 UB40, 7 Kathy Bates, 8 Sid James, 9 Gloria Estefan, 10 Glenn Close, 11 Loyd Grossman, 12 Saxophone, 13 David Duchovny, 14 Money Train, 15 Bo Diddley, 16 Robbie Jackson, 17 Patrick Swayze, 18 Shane Richie, 19 Gary Oldman, 20 Michael Bentine.*

General Knowledge

Your rating: ● 0-5 Join a library ● 6-10 Keep at it ● 11-15 Join a quiz team ● 16-20 Join Mensa

1. According to Greek mythology, which woman had a box which when opened released all the varieties of evil and retained only hope?
2. Of which body of water is the Adriatic Sea a section?
3. Which device for detecting and counting ionizing radiation and particles is named after a German physicist?
4. In which English county is the resort of Weymouth situated?
5. With which musical instrument is Larry Adler associated?
6. In antiquity, which Greek village was the principal sanctuary and oracle of Apollo?
7. What is the second largest continent?
8. What is a nimbostratus?
9. Which natural phenomena is seismology primarily concerned with?
10. A tigon is a hybrid resulting from the mating of which two animals?
11. Which British theatre director directed the films *Lord of the Flies* and *King Lear*?
12. What is a straight line that a two-dimensional curve approaches but never meets as the curve is extended infinitely?
13. Which British show jumper won Olympic bronze medals in 1960 and 1968 and the world championship in 1970?
14. Which Italian Renaissance painter and engraver married the daughter of Jacopo Bellini?
15. Which London borough was created in 1965 from the former metropolitan boroughs of Hampstead, Holborn and St. Pancras?
16. Which Serbian secret society were responsible for the assassination of the archduke Francis Ferdinand in 1914?
17. Of which range of hills is Coombe Hill the highest point?
18. Which Roman road ran from Exeter through Cirencester to Lincoln?
19. Which unit of weight for precious stones is equal to two milligrams?
20. Which son of Percival in Arthurian legend is the title of a Wagner opera?

ANSWERS: *1 Pandora, 2 Mediterranean Sea, 3 Geiger counter, 4 Dorset, 5 Harmonica, 6 Delphi, 7 Africa, 8 A cloud, 9 Earthquakes, 10 Lioness and tiger, 11 Peter Brook, 12 Asymptote, 13 David Broome, 14 Andrea Mantegna, 15 Camden, 16 Black Hand, 17 Chiltern Hills, 18 Fosse Way, 19 Point, 20 Lohengrin.*

General Knowledge

Your rating: ● 0-5 Join a library ● 6-10 Keep at it ● 11-15 Join a quiz team ● 16-20 Join Mensa

1. Which South American country launched an invasion of the Falkland Islands in April 1982?
2. Which Canadian city was the venue for the 1976 Olympics?
3. According to the Bible, which miraculous food fell with the dew to sustain the Israelites in the wilderness?
4. What sort of creature is a cormorant?
5. Which constellation of the zodiac means "twins" in Latin?
6. Which political party did President John F. Kennedy represent?
7. Which organisation was founded by the Geneva Convention of 1864?
8. At which sport was Jack Dempsey a world champion from 1919 to 1926?
9. What is a lyre?
10. In which part of the body can one find the metacarpals and the phalanges?
11. Which British composer wrote *On Hearing the First Cuckoo in Spring*?
12. In which state of the USA can the Garden of the Gods be found?
13. Who was the first Valois king of France?
14. What sort of creature is a gar?
15. Who was the president of France from 1913 to 1920?
16. In which former Yugoslav republic is the port of Pula situated?
17. Which nation was defeated by the Balkan League in the first Balkan War of 1912 to 1913?
18. What sort of creature is a thrips?
19. Who was Robert Runcie's predecessor as Archbishop of Canterbury?
20. Which British poet wrote *1914 and Other Poems*?

ANSWERS: *1 Argentina, 2 Montreal, 3 Manna, 4 A bird, 5 Gemini, 6 Democratic Party, 7 International Red Cross, 8 Boxing, 9 An ancient stringed instrument, 10 The hand, 11 Frederick Delius, 12 Colorado, 13 Philip VI, 14 A fish, 15 Raymond Poincaré, 16 Croatia, 17 Turkey, 18 An insect, 19 Donald Coggan, 20 Rupert Brooke.*

General Knowledge

Your rating: ● 0-5 Join a library ● 6-10 Keep at it ● 11-15 Join a quiz team ● 16-20 Join Mensa

1. Which French term meaning "blue ribbon" is used to describe food that achieves a degree of excellence?
2. In which state of the USA is the subtropical swampy area known as the Everglades situated?
3. What is the study of the movements of the heavenly bodies in relation to their presumed influence upon human affairs?
4. What is the world's third largest ocean?
5. What sort of creature is a bustard?
6. On 29 May 1953 the summit of which mountain was reached by Edmund Hillary and Sherpa Tenzing Norgay?
7. Which U.S. comedy writer, actor, and filmmaker directed *Young Frankenstein*?
8. How is an eggplant otherwise known?
9. In which European country is Lake Garda situated?
10. According to legend, which magic sword did Arthur succeed in drawing from a stone?
11. Which Roman Christian martyr is the patron saint of music?
12. To which country do the Antipodes Islands belong?
13. The islands of Zanzibar and Pemba are parts of which African country?
14. Which very hard grey dense metallic element is represented by the symbol Ta?
15. Which French composer wrote the ballets *Coppélia* and *Sylvia*?
16. Which river rises in the Rocky Mountains and forms the border between Texas and Mexico?
17. Which unit of length is equal to the mean distance between the earth and the sun?
18. Who was the first Bourbon king of Spain?
19. Which Spanish poet and dramatist wrote *The House of Bernarda Alba*?
20. Which Egyptian goddess was the sister and wife of Osiris?

ANSWERS: *1 Cordon Bleu, 2 Florida, 3 Astrology, 4 The Indian Ocean, 5 A bird, 6 Mount Everest, 7 Mel Brooks, 8 Aubergine, 9 Italy, 10 Excalibur, 11 St. Cecilia, 12 New Zealand, 13 Tanzania, 14 Tantalum, 15 Leo Delibes, 16 Rio Grande, 17 Astronomical unit, 18 Philip V, 19 Federico Garcia Lorca, 20 Isis.*

Entertainment

Your rating: ● 0-5 Buy a TV ● 6-10 Keep at it ● 11-15 Join a quiz team ● 16-20 Enter a quiz show

1. Which 1990 film starred Steven Seagal as a former Drug Enforcement Agency troubleshooter?
2. Which ITV comedy drama series featured Michelle Collins as ex-dancer Maxine Gaines?
3. Which former boy band member hit the U.K. number one spot in 2000 with *Life is a Rollercoaster*?
4. Which sports presenter hosted BBC TV's Wimbledon 2000 coverage along with Sue Barker?
5. Who directed the 2000 film sequel *Mission: Impossible 2*?
6. Which Channel 4 legal comedy drama series starred Calista Flockhart in the title role?
7. Which Steps song featured on their 2000 U.K. top five double A-side, along with *When I Said Goodbye*?
8. Which comedy series of the Sixties starred former *The Army Game* actors Alfie Bass and Bill Fraser?
9. Which 1992 film set in the world of drug dealing starred Willem Dafoe and Susan Sarandon?
10. Which *Tomorrow's World* presenter also co-hosted the BBC 1 series about animal behaviour, *Barking Mad*?
11. Which British group had a U.K. top ten hit in 1986 with *Suspicious Minds*?
12. Which actor provided the voice of the orphan mouse *Stuart Little* in the 2000 movie of the same name?
13. What was the title of Jon Secada's 1992 U.K. top five hit?
14. Which English king did Robert Shaw play in the 1966 film *A Man For All Seasons*?
15. Which ex-*EastEnder* became the presenter of BBC 1's *Battersea Dogs' Home* in 2000?
16. Which U.S. grunge group had a 1992 U.K. top ten hit with *Come As You Are*?
17. Which British author wrote the book upon which the 2000 film *High Fidelity* was based?
18. In which year did Sandie Shaw, representing the U.K., win the Eurovision Song Contest with a rendition of *Puppet on a String*?
19. What was the name of Prince's character in the 1984 film *Purple Rain*?
20. Which Irish band had a 2000 U.K. number one hit with *Breathless*?

ANSWERS: 1 *Marked For Death*, 2 *Up Rising*, 3 Ronan Keating, 4 John Inverdale, 5 John Woo, 6 *Ally McBeal*, 7 *Summer of Love*, 8 *Bootsie and Snudge*, 9 *Light Sleeper*, 10 Philippa Forrester, 11 Fine Young Cannibals, 12 Michael J Fox, 13 *Just Another Day*, 14 Henry VIII, 15 Patsy Palmer, 16 Nirvana, 17 Nick Hornby, 18 1967, 19 The Kid, 20 The Corrs.

General Knowledge

Your rating: ● **0-5** Join a library ● **6-10** Keep at it ● **11-15** Join a quiz team ● **16-20** Join Mensa

1. Which Hollywood actor was born Archibald Leach in Bristol?
2. Is colour blindness more common in men or women?
3. Which American novelist wrote *Moby Dick*?
4. What nationality is Liverpool goalkeeper Sander Westerveld?
5. In which South American country did the tango originate?
6. Who was the third wife of Henry VIII?
7. What is the largest triumphal arch in the world?
8. In which English county is Woburn Abbey?
9. What is the maximum weight in ounces of an ice hockey puck?
10. Which U.S. actor starred in *Elmer Gantry*, *The Birdman of Alcatraz* and *Local Hero*?
11. Against which team did England gain the first point of their 2002 World Cup qualifying campaign?
12. Which Norwegian explorer and scientist won the Nobel peace prize in 1922?
13. Which English author writes crime fiction under the pseudonym Dan Kavanagh?
14. Which British playwright wrote *Serjeant Musgrave's Dance* and *The Workhouse Donkey*?
15. In which U.S. state is the city of Tacoma?
16. By what name is the European bison also known?
17. Davo Karnicar was the first man to ski non-stop down which mountain?
18. Who was the Formula One world champion in 1991?
19. Which former Labour minister wrote the book *The Unconventional Minister*?
20. What is the second largest city in Zimbabwe?

ANSWERS: *1 Cary Grant, 2 Men, 3 Herman Melville, 4 Dutch, 5 Argentina, 6 Jane Seymour, 7 The Arc de Triomphe in Paris, 8 Bedfordshire, 9 6, 10 Burt Lancaster, 11 Finland, 12 Fridtjof Nansen, 13 Julian Barnes, 14 John Arden, 15 Washington, 16 Wisent, 17 Mount Everest, 18 Ayrton Senna, 19 Geoffrey Robinson, 20 Bulawayo.*

General Knowledge

Your rating: ● 0-5 Join a library ● 6-10 Keep at it ● 11-15 Join a quiz team ● 16-20 Join Mensa

1. Which U.S. railroad engineer became a folk hero after his death on the Cannonball Express in 1900?
2. In which year did Tiger Woods win his first major in golf?
3. Which Disney film features the voices of Julianna Margulies and Joan Plowright?
4. In which European city is the Colosseum?
5. What is Australia's national anthem?
6. With which sport is Joe Namath associated?
7. Who wrote the novel *English Passengers*?
8. What is the world's second highest mountain?
9. Which character in the New Testament asked for the head of John the Baptist?
10. Of which country was Morarji Desai prime minister from 1977 to 1979?
11. Which novelist wrote *The Green Hat*?
12. What was the only major encounter between the British and German fleets in World War I?
13. In what year did Sirimavo Bandaranaika become the world's first female prime minister?
14. What were P G Wodehouse's first names?
15. In which Shakespeare play does Duke Vincentio disguise himself as a friar?
16. Which sport was invented by James A Naismith?
17. What was the name of the BBC test card girl?
18. Which Chartist leader was transported in 1840 after leading the Newport rising?
19. What does GATT stand for?
20. Which city in Wiltshire was formerly called New Sarum?

ANSWERS: *1 Casey Jones, 2 1997, 3 Dinosaur, 4 Rome, 5 Advance Australia Fair, 6 American football, 7 Matthew Kneale, 8 K2, 9 Salome, 10 India, 11 Michael Arlen, 12 Battle of Jutland, 13 1960, 14 Pelham Grenville, 15 Measure for Measure, 16 Basketball, 17 Carol Hershey, 18 John Frost, 19 General Agreement on Tariffs and Trade, 20 Salisbury.*

General Knowledge

Your rating:
- **0-5 Join a library**
- **6-10 Keep at it**
- **11-15 Join a quiz team**
- **16-20 Join Mensa**

1. Which cricket ground is the headquarters of the MCC?
2. What name is given to the property or money given by a bride's family to her husband?
3. Which sex symbol made her screen debut in the 1948 film *Scudda-Hoo, Scudda-Hay*?
4. On which childrens TV show did Leslie Crowther begin his career?
5. Which Mongol leader was originally called Temujin?
6. What sort of creature is a coot?
7. Of which country is the drachma the basic currency unit?
8. What was the first comet whose return was predicted?
9. Who played Joan of Arc in the 1948 film of that name?
10. What is the first book of the Old Testament?
11. Which U.S. author wrote *The Scarlet Letter* and *The House of the Seven Gables*?
12. Of which metal is cuprite an important ore?
13. What unit of electric charge is defined as the quantity of electricity conveyed by one ampere in one second?
14. Which was the first live-action Disney feature?
15. What name is given to a coral reef surrounding a lagoon?
16. In German folklore, what name is given to a person's double?
17. Which Austrian composer wrote the *Surprise*, *Military* and *Drumroll* symphonies?
18. Which actor wrote an autobiography entitled *What's It All About*?
19. Which ancient Greek city was the site of a famous oracle in the temple of Apollo?
20. Which Dutch artist painted *Broadway Boogie Woogie*?

ANSWERS: *1 Lord's, 2 Dowry, 3 Marilyn Monroe, 4 Crackerjack, 5 Genghis Khan, 6 A bird, 7 Greece, 8 Halley's Comet, 9 Ingrid Bergman, 10 Genesis, 11 Nathaniel Hawthorne, 12 Copper, 13 Coulomb, 14 Treasure Island, 15 Atoll, 16 Doppelganger, 17 Joseph Haydn, 18 Michael Caine, 19 Delphi, 20 Piet Mondrian*

Entertainment

Your rating: ● **0-5** Buy a TV ● **6-10** Keep at it ● **11-15** Join a quiz team ● **16-20** Enter a quiz show

1. Which BBC 1 comedy drama series featured former *Goodnight Sweetheart* star Elizabeth Carling as Charlotte, a superstar pop singer?
2. What was the title of the fourth album by The Corrs, released in 2000?
3. Which 2000 film starred Mel Gibson as an 18th-century American landowner?
4. Which Sixties sitcom by Johnny Speight starred Eric Sykes and Spike Milligan?
5. Which 1974 film set in Brooklyn starred Michael Sarrazin and Barbra Streisand as husband and wife?
6. With whom did Freddie Mercury duet on the 1987 and 1992 U.K. top ten hit *Barcelona*?
7. Which English resort was the holiday destination for *Coronation Street*'s Jack and Vera Duckworth and party in 2000?
8. What was the title of Spandau Ballet's only U.K. number one hit?
9. Which star of TV's *ER* appeared in the 2000 British film *Essex Boys*?
10. Which former *Coronation Street* actress joined the cast of BBC 1's *Playing the Field* as midfielder Holly?
11. Which British band hit the U.K. number one spot in 1989 with *Belfast Child*?
12. Which futuristic 1992 film's cast included Emilio Estevez, Mick Jagger, Rene Russo and Anthony Hopkins?
13. Which U.S. city was the setting for Ross and Rachel's drunken marriage in the sitcom *Friends*?
14. What was Dusty Springfield's 1966 U.K. number one hit called?
15. Which 2000 children's film based on a series of well-known books starred Alec Baldwin and Peter Fonda?
16. What did the car's name KITT stand for in the Eighties series *Knight Rider*?
17. Which female vocalist returned to the U.K. top five in 2000 with a song entitled *2 Faced*?
18. Which controversial Channel 4 series began in 2000 with ten volunteers moving in to a house filled with cameras?
19. Which comic actor played Sydney in the ITV comedy series *Pay and Display*?
20. Which Monty Python team member directed the 1977 film *Jabberwocky*?

ANSWERS: *1 Border Cafe, 2 In Blue, 3 The Patriot, 4 Curry and Chips, 5 For Pete's Sake, 6 Montserrat Caballe, 7 Blackpool, 8 True, 9 Alex Kingston, 10 Gaynor Faye, 11 Simple Minds, 12 Freejack, 13 Las Vegas, 14 You Don't Have to Say You Love Me, 15 Thomas and the Magic Railroad, 16 Knight Industries Two Thousand, 17 Louise, 18 Big Brother, 19 James Bolam, 20 Terry Gilliam.*

General Knowledge

Your rating: ● 0-5 Join a library ● 6-10 Keep at it ● 11-15 Join a quiz team ● 16-20 Join Mensa

1. Who was the first gymnast to score a perfect 10 in Olympic competition?
2. Which actor made his final film appearance as Proximo in *Gladiator*?
3. Who created *Rumpole of the Bailey*?
4. *Qui Veut Gagner des Millions* is a French version of which British TV quiz show?
5. From which country does the white wine Tokay come?
6. With which instrument is jazz musician John Coltrane associated?
7. Who originally sang *Love is Like a Butterfly*, which became the theme tune of the sitcom *Butterflies*?
8. In which Italian city is the Doges' Palace?
9. Who was Bonnie Parker's partner in crime?
10. Which part of the eye varies in size to regulate the amount of light passing to the retina?
11. Who played Detective Inspector Maggie Forbes in *The Gentle Touch* on television?
12. Which American author wrote *The Catcher in the Rye*?
13. Who was the first woman to scale Mount Everest alone and without bottled oxygen?
14. Which country beat South Africa in the final of the Alfred Dunhill Cup at St Andrews in 2000?
15. What is the state capital of Iowa?
16. Which British dramatist wrote *Trelawny of the 'Wells'*?
17. At which film festival are the Golden Lions awarded?
18. Which ship launched in 1906 became the basis of battleship design for more than 50 years?
19. Who was the first leader of the Labour Party in the House of Commons?
20. Who wrote the music for the ballet *Coppélia*?

ANSWERS: *1 Nadia Comaneci, 2 Oliver Reed, 3 John Mortimer, 4 Who Wants To Be A Millionaire, 5 Hungary, 6 Saxophone, 7 Dolly Parton, 8 Venice, 9 Clyde Barrow, 10 Pupil, 11 Jill Gascoigne, 12 J D Salinger, 13 Alison Hargreaves, 14 Spain, 15 Des Moines, 16 Sir Arthur Wing Pinero, 17 Venice, 18 Dreadnought, 19 Keir Hardie, 20 Leo Delibes.*

General Knowledge

Your rating:
- 0-5 Join a library
- 6-10 Keep at it
- 11-15 Join a quiz team
- 16-20 Join Mensa

1. Which English admiral circumnavigated the globe from 1577 to 1580?
2. Of which U.S. state is Dover the capital?
3. What was Flipper in the 1960s TV series of that name?
4. What is removed from seawater in a desalination plant?
5. Which American novelist wrote *Gentlemen Prefer Blondes*?
6. To which philosopher does the adjective Cartesian relate?
7. From which planet do the invaders come in *The War of the Worlds* by H G Wells?
8. What name is given to the handrail fixed to the walls of a ballet studio?
9. Which British cartoonist created the *Mr Men* and *Little Miss* series of books?
10. What is inflamed in a case of dermatitis?
11. Which French fashion designer launched the first ready-to-wear collection for men in 1960?
12. Who was the first black officer to hold the highest military post in the United States?
13. Which novel by Jeffrey Archer describes the competition between four men to become prime minister?
14. By what name was the powerful defoliant sprayed by U.S. forces in Vietnam known?
15. Which animal is also called a honey badger?
16. For what is epistaxis the medical term?
17. Which pop star bought a piano that belonged to John Lennon for more than £1 million at auction in October 2000?
18. Who won the 1985 Whitbread Award for fiction for his novel *Hawksmoor*?
19. Who was the Greek goddess of agriculture?
20. Which food additive is also known as MSG?

ANSWERS: *1 Sir Francis Drake, 2 Delaware, 3 A dolphin, 4 Salt, 5 Anita Loos, 6 René Descartes, 7 Mars, 8 Barre, 9 Roger Hargreaves, 10 The skin, 11 Pierre Cardin, 12 Colin Powell, 13 First Among Equals, 14 Agent Orange, 15 Ratel, 16 Nosebleed, 17 George Michael, 18 Peter Ackroyd, 19 Demeter, 20 Monosodium glutamate.*

General Knowledge

Your rating:
- **0-5 Join a library**
- **6-10 Keep at it**
- **11-15 Join a quiz team**
- **16-20 Join Mensa**

1. Which novel by Thomas Hardy tells the story of Michael Henchard?
2. Which actor's childhood nickname was Tootsie?
3. Which boy band has become the first act to have six number one singles in a row?
4. What name is given to July 15, which is supposed to set the weather for 40 days thereafter?
5. To what sort of cleric does the adjective episcopal relate?
6. What sort of creature is a guppy?
7. Which character in David Copperfield by Charles Dickens is famous for his false humility?
8. What is normally the outermost planet in our solar system?
9. Which Walt Disney film is based on a story about a deer by Felix Salten?
10. What name is given to a fear of closed or confined spaces?
11. Who was the first actress to receive two Oscars before the age of thirty?
12. Which Belgian city was the site of the first battle between British and German forces in World War I?
13. The actor Ivan Owen was the voice of which popular TV glove puppet?
14. Which large triangular muscle covering the shoulder serves to raise the arm laterally?
15. What was Cecil B DeMille's middle name?
16. Which part of a church contains the choir?
17. What was the pen name of Samuel Langhorne Clemens?
18. Which hoisting device used on ships is named after a 17th-century English hangman?
19. Who was the fifth wife of Henry VIII?
20. Which actress starred in the film thriller *What Lies Beneath*?

ANSWERS: *1 The Mayor of Casterbridge, 2 Dustin Hoffman, 3 Westlife, 4 St Swithin's Day, 5 Bishop, 6 A fish, 7 Uriah Heep, 8 Pluto, 9 Bambi, 10 Claustrophobia, 11 Jodie Foster, 12 Mons, 13 Basil Brush, 14 Deltoid (deltoideus), 15 Blount, 16 Chancel, 17 Mark Twain, 18 Derrick, 19 Catherine Howard, 20 Michelle Pfeiffer.*

Entertainment

Your rating:
- **0-5 Buy a TV**
- **6-10 Keep at it**
- **11-15 Join a quiz team**
- **16-20 Enter a quiz show**

1. Which DJ and pianist released his debut album *Sincere* in 2000, featuring the U.K. top ten single *Crazy Love*?
2. Which 2000 sci-fi sequel starring Christopher Lambert followed his escape from a futuristic prison?
3. What was *Hong Kong Phooey*'s everyday alias in the Seventies cartoon series?
4. Which 2000 album release was a collaboration between Jimmy Page and the Black Crowes?
5. Who played *The Man With the Golden Gun* in the 1974 Bond film?
6. Who was the presenter of the ITV show *Find a Fortune*?
7. Which British duo had a 1988 U.K. number one hit with *Heart*?
8. Which 2000 film by Chen Kaige was set in the reign of Ying Zheng in third century China?
9. What was the title of Alvin Stardust's 1974 U.K. number one hit?
10. Which Oscar-winning actress played Susan Traherne in *Plenty*, a 1985 film set just after the Second World War?
11. Which U.S. band asked *What's the Frequency, Kenneth* in the U.K. top ten in 1994?
12. Which rapper starred as a Cincinatti arch-criminal nick-named 'God' in the 2000 film *In Too Deep*?
13. What was the name of the Orkans' leader who Mork reported back to at the end of every episode of the sitcom *Mork and Mindy*?
14. Which girl group had a 2000 U.K. top five hit with *Jumpin' Jumpin'*?
15. Which Western star appeared in the films *Rio Grande*, *Rio Bravo* and *Rio Lobo*?
16. Who persuaded *EastEnders*' Ian Beale to sign papers beginning his divorce from Melanie in 2000?
17. Which former member of Boyzone released a self-titled debut solo album in 2000?
18. Which former *Coronation Street* actor joined the cast of the drama series *Where the Heart Is* in 2000?
19. In which 2000 film did George Clooney star as the skipper of the *Andrea Gail*, a swordfishing-boat?
20. Who introduced us to her *Sunshine Food* in a BBC 2 series?

ANSWERS: *1 M.J. Cole, 2 Fortress 2, 3 Penrod 'Penry' Pooch, 4 Live at the Greek, 5 Christopher Lee, 6 Carol Vorderman, 7 Pet Shop Boys, 8 The Emperor and the Assassin, 9 Jealous Mind, 10 Meryl Streep, 11 R.E.M., 12 LL Cool J, 13 Orson, 14 Destiny's Child, 15 John Wayne, 16 Steve Owen, 17 Ronan Keating (Ronan), 18 Phil Middlemiss, 19 The Perfect Storm, 20 Sophie Grigson.*

General Knowledge

Your rating: ● 0-5 Join a library ● 6-10 Keep at it ● 11-15 Join a quiz team ● 16-20 Join Mensa

1. Which child star sang *On the Good Ship Lollipop* in the 1934 film *Bright Eyes*?
2. On whose book was the film *Fahrenheit 451* based?
3. Which Australian singer sang *Dancing Queen* at the Olympic Games closing ceremony after entering the stadium on a giant flip-flop?
4. In which country did the dance the turkey trot originate?
5. Which narcotic was removed from Coca-Cola's formula in 1905?
6. What is the French equivalent of Mister?
7. The Seattle-based television comedy *Frasier* is a spin-off from *Cheers* - which was set where?
8. In Arthurian legend, what was the seat of King Arthur's court?
9. What was the name of the lion cub raised by George and Joy Adamson, as recounted in *Born Free*?
10. In which U.S. city is Carnegie Hall?
11. Who wrote *The Ordeal of Richard Feverel*?
12. Which American silent film star was known as 'The Man of a Thousand Faces'?
13. From which British port did John Cabot set sail on the Matthew in 1497?
14. Which nonsense poem by Lewis Carroll is subtitled *An Agony in Eight Fits*?
15. Who won Best Score Oscars for *Out of Africa* and *Dances With Wolves*?
16. What name is given to the two dots placed above a vowel in German?
17. What nationality is the gymnast Andreea Raducan who was stripped of an Olympic gold medal after failing a drugs test?
18. Which zodiac sign governs the period from February 19 to March 20?
19. What sort of creature is a moccasin?
20. Which American author wrote *The Case of Charles Dexter Ward*?

ANSWERS: *1 Shirley Temple, 2 Ray Bradbury, 3 Kylie Minogue, 4 United States, 5 Cocaine, 6 Monsieur, 7 Boston, 8 Camelot, 9 Elsa, 10 New York City, 11 George Meredith, 12 Lon Chaney, 13 Bristol, 14 The Hunting of the Snark, 15 John Barry, 16 Umlaut, 17 Romanian, 18 Pisces, 19 A snake, 20 H P Lovecraft.*

General Knowledge

Your rating:
- 0-5 Join a library
- 6-10 Keep at it
- 11-15 Join a quiz team
- 16-20 Join Mensa

1. Which American composer wrote *An American in Paris* and *Porgy and Bess*?
2. What were the first names of aviation pioneers the Wright brothers?
3. What is the surname of the little people in the Mary Norton book *The Borrowers*?
4. Who resigned as England football manager in October 2000?
5. Which Walt Disney film is based on a story by Carlo Collodi?
6. What is the chief addictive ingredient of tobacco?
7. *The Man of Property* was the first of which series of novels?
8. Which bone is also called the thighbone?
9. Which British actor played Sherlock Holmes on TV from 1984 to 1995?
10. What is the capital of Portugal?
11. What is the value of the pink ball in snooker?
12. Which English surgeon was the founder of antiseptic medicine?
13. What name is given to the seafood picnic traditional in the New England region of the United States?
14. Which child actor appeared in the films *The Little Vampire*, *Stuart Little* and *Jerry Maguire*?
15. From which two places did the Bren gun get its name?
16. Which Indian novelist wrote *A Suitable Boy*?
17. Which horse won the Derby in 1981?
18. Which 19th-century Irish nationalist MP's career was ended by proof of his affair with Katherine O'Shea?
19. What name is given to the natural painkillers secreted by the brain that resemble opiates?
20. Who directed the 1960 film *La Dolce Vita*?

ANSWERS: *1 George Gershwin, 2 Orville and Wilbur, 3 Clock, 4 Kevin Keegan, 5 Pinocchio, 6 Nicotine, 7 The Forsyte Saga, 8 Femur, 9 Jeremy Brett, 10 Lisbon, 11 Six, 12 Joseph Lister, 13 Clambake, 14 Jonathan Lipnicki, 15 Brno and Enfield, 16 Vikram Seth, 17 Shergar, 18 Charles Stewart Parnell, 19 Endorphins, 20 Federico Fellini*

General Knowledge

Your rating:
- **0-5 Join a library**
- **6-10 Keep at it**
- **11-15 Join a quiz team**
- **16-20 Join Mensa**

1. Which actor starred in *Yes, Minister* and *The Good Life*?
2. By what first name was world heavyweight boxing champion Charles Liston known?
3. Which major conflict was also called the War Between the States?
4. Roald Dahl wrote the script for which Bond film?
5. Which English poet wrote *A Shropshire Lad*?
6. From which garden were Adam and Eve expelled?
7. By what first name was English pirate Edward Teach known?
8. Which Australian TV soap was set at Coopers Crossing?
9. Which Hungarian composer became Richard Wagner's father-in-law?
10. For which football team did Billy Bremner play from 1959 to 1976?
11. In which golf competition did Europe beat the United States at Loch Lomond in October 2000?
12. Which Oscar-winning actor was born Muni Weisenfreund in 1895?
13. Whose first novel was called *Kate Hannigan*?
14. Which Scottish racing driver was the world champion in 1963 and 1965?
15. Who directed *The Dirty Dozen* and *The Killing of Sister George*?
16. With which instrument is jazz musician Jack Teagarden associated?
17. Who made his directorial debut with *Star Trek III: The Search For Spock*?
18. Which soft white clay is also known as china clay?
19. Of which American orchestra was Sir Georg Solti the music director from 1969 to 1991?
20. Which English novelist wrote *A Kind of Loving*?

ANSWERS: *1 Paul Eddington, 2 Sonny, 3 American Civil War, 4 You Only Live Twice, 5 A E Housman, 6 Garden of Eden, 7 Blackbeard, 8 The Flying Doctors, 9 Franz Liszt, 10 Leeds United, 11 Solheim Cup, 12 Paul Muni, 13 Catherine Cookson, 14 Jim Clark, 15 Robert Aldrich, 16 Trombone, 17 Leonard Nimoy, 18 Kaolin, 19 Chicago Symphony Orchestra, 20 Stan Barstow.*

Sports

Your rating: ● 0-5 Wooden spoon ● 6-10 Bronze medal ● 11-15 Silver medal ● 16-20 Gold medal

1. Which British sprinter won the silver medal in the 200m at the Sydney Olympics?
2. In which country was the gymnast Nadia Comaneci born?
3. Lazio football club is based in which Italian city?
4. Which British player won the U.S. Masters in 1991?
5. What colour ball is worth five points in snooker?
6. Which cyclist won his second successive Tour de France in 2000?
7. At which weight did Cassius Clay win gold at the 1960 Rome Olympics?
8. The 1994 Winter Olympics host town Lillehammer is in which country?
9. How many furlongs must a horse cover to complete one mile?
10. What number shirt does a full back traditionally wear in rugby union?
11. Which Fijian golfer won the 2000 U.S. Masters?
12. The goalkeeper Thomas Sorensen plays for which Premiership club?
13. Who won the cricket County Championship seven times from 1959-69?
14. How many yards long is a croquet lawn?
15. Which horse won the Derby in 1991?
16. Which French international goalkeeper joined Manchester United in 2000?
17. Who did England beat 60-26 at Twickenham in 1998?
18. What was the name of the boat sailed by Ellen MacArthur in the recent Vendee Globe solo round-the-world yacht race?
19. Who reached the final of the snooker World Championship eight times from 1981-89?
20. What nationality is the golfer Jose-Maria Olazabal?

ANSWERS: *1 Darren Campbell, 2 Romania, 3 Rome, 4 Ian Woosnam, 5 Blue, 6 Lance Armstrong, 7 Light heavyweight, 8 Norway, 9 8, 10 15, 11 Vijay Singh, 12 Sunderland, 13 Yorkshire, 14 35, 15 Generous, 16 Fabien Barthez, 17 Wales, 18 Kingfisher, 19 Steve Davis, 20 Spanish.*

General Knowledge

Your rating: ● 0-5 Join a library ● 6-10 Keep at it ● 11-15 Join a quiz team ● 16-20 Join Mensa

1. Which round yellow Dutch cheese has a red outer coating?
2. With which sport was Jonah Barrington most famously associated?
3. Which star of *The Sound of Music* has confirmed that she will never sing again?
4. By what name is the clavicle more commonly known?
5. Which Russian composer wrote scores for the ballets Swan Lake and The Nutcracker?
6. Of which country was Karachi the first capital?
7. Which of these tennis players won Wimbledon in 1990?
8. What is the basic monetary unit of Italy?
9. Which singer had hits with *Saving All My Love For You* and *I Will Always Love You*?
10. What form of ESP takes its name from the French for 'clear seeing'?
11. Who wrote *To Serve Them All My Days*?
12. Which Roman emperor was the subject of two novels by Robert Graves?
13. In which U.S. state is the city of Branson?
14. Which rail company was the first to be stripped of its franchise in Britain?
15. What is the name for the film colour process introduced in movies in 1932?
16. Which French author wrote *Notre-Dame des Fleurs*?
17. Which country does wicketkeeper Adam Parore play for?
18. Of which former Soviet republic is Tbilisi the capital?
19. Which North Yorkshire river rises on Fylingdales Moor and flows to the River Ouse?
20. Who was elected as the new Speaker of the Commons in 2000?

ANSWERS: *1 Edam, 2 Squash, 3 Julie Andrews, 4 Collarbone, 5 Peter Tchaikovsky, 6 Pakistan, 7 Stefan Edberg, 8 Lira, 9 Whitney Houston, 10 Clairvoyance, 11 R F Delderfield, 12 Claudius, 13 Missouri, 14 Connex South Central, 15 Technicolor, 16 Jean Genet, 17 New Zealand, 18 Georgia, 19 River Derwent, 20 Michael Martin.*

General Knowledge

Your rating:
- 0-5 Join a library
- 6-10 Keep at it
- 11-15 Join a quiz team
- 16-20 Join Mensa

1. Which English actor starred in the films *The Scarlet Pimpernel*, *The Petrified Forest* and *Gone with the Wind*?
2. Who won the F.A. Cup in 1987?
3. Which former prime minister became the Earl of Avon in 1961?
4. To which hit horror film is *Book of Shadows* a sequel?
5. Which story from *The Thousand and One Nights* concerns a boy and a magic lamp?
6. What colour are the woolly leaves of the edelweiss?
7. In which country was the star of *Xena - Warrior Princess* Lucy Lawless born?
8. Who sang *Let The Bright Seraphim* at the Prince of Wales's wedding in 1981?
9. Which large coarse fern is also known as brake?
10. What colour is an emerald?
11. Which cartoon series is set in Bedrock?
12. Which Italian author wrote *The Name of the Rose*?
13. Who was the unsuccessful Republican candidate in the 1996 U.S. presidential election?
14. Which Merchant Ivory film starring Uma Thurman is based on a novel by Henry James?
15. In which war did the term Fifth Column originate?
16. What is the capital of Yemen?
17. Which novelist and poet did Ezra Pound compare to vile scum on a pond?
18. Which song did Julia Ward Howe write to the tune of *John Brown's Body*?
19. With which branch of the arts was Bill Brandt associated?
20. Which British dramatist wrote *Plenty*?

ANSWERS: *1 Leslie Howard, 2 Coventry City, 3 Sir Anthony Eden, 4 The Blair Witch Project, 5 Aladdin, 6 White, 7 New Zealand, 8 Kiri Te Kanawa, 9 Bracken, 10 Green, 11 The Flintstones, 12 Umberto Eco, 13 Bob Dole, 14 The Golden Bowl, 15 Spanish Civil War, 16 San'a, 17 G K Chesterton, 18 Battle Hymn of the Republic, 19 Photography, 20 David Hare.*

General Knowledge

Your rating: ● 0-5 Join a library ● 6-10 Keep at it ● 11-15 Join a quiz team ● 16-20 Join Mensa

1. Which naturalist and author wrote *My Family and Other Animals*?
2. The Dell is the home ground of which football team?
3. Which Russian chess player lost his world title to Vladimir Kramnik in 2000?
4. By what name was comedian William Claude Dukenfield better known?
5. Which comic actress starred in the TV series *I Love Lucy*?
6. In which European country are the Dolomites?
7. Gwendolen Harleth is the heroine of which novel by George Eliot?
8. What is the capital of Egypt?
9. Which aquatic mammal has common and bottle-nosed varieties?
10. What nationality was the racing driver Juan Manuel Fangio?
11. Which famous runner was nicknamed The Shifter?
12. Which American test pilot was the first man to fly through the sound barrier?
13. Who was the Chief Inspector of Schools who resigned in 2000?
14. Of which country is Mount Logan the highest mountain?
15. Who wrote *The Count of Monte Cristo*?
16. In which U.S. state is the city of Fairbanks?
17. Who wrote *The Winds of War*?
18. Which former world heavyweight boxing champion was known as 'the Cinderella Man'?
19. What sort of domestic appliance is the Contrarotator designed by James Dyson?
20. What is the fourth largest city in Scotland?

ANSWERS: *1 Gerald Durrell, 2 Southampton, 3 Garry Kasparov, 4 W C Fields, 5 Lucille Ball, 6 Italy, 7 Daniel Deronda, 8 Cairo, 9 Dolphin, 10 Argentinian, 11 Miruts Yifter, 12 Chuck Yeager, 13 Chris Woodhead, 14 Canada, 15 Alexandre Dumas, 16 Alaska, 17 Herman Wouk, 18 James J Braddock, 19 Washing machine, 20 Dundee.*

Entertainment

Your rating: ● **0-5** **Buy a TV** ● **6-10** **Keep at it** ● **11-15** **Join a quiz team** ● **16-20** **Enter a quiz show**

1. Which Welsh rock band had a hit with *A Design For Life* in 1996?
2. Who co-starred with Michelle Pfeiffer in the film *Up Close and Personal*?
3. In which game show did Des O'Connor invite contestants to "take the money" or "open the box"?
4. Which Martin Scorsese film was based on Nicholas Pileggi's book *Wiseguy*?
5. Which Canadian rocker released an album entitled *18 Til I Die* in 1996?
6. Who directed the 1996 film *Girl 6*?
7. Which sci-fi TV series featured the robot Twiki?
8. What was the title of Peter Gabriel's first four albums?
9. For which 1984 film did Haing S. Ngor win a Best Supporting Actor Oscar for his portrayal of Dith Pran?
10. Which 'Page 3 model' was the star of the TV series *Gayle's World*?
11. Who had a top ten hit single in 1979 with *Gimme Gimme Gimme (A Man After Midnight)*?
12. Which 1996 coming-of-age movie starred Demi Moore and Melanie Griffith?
13. Which foxy glove puppet had the catchphrase "Boom Boom"?
14. Who played the title role in the 1986 film *Lady Jane*?
15. Which *Monty Python* star created the children's animation series *Blazing Dragons*?
16. Which singer/songwriter released an album in 1996 entitled *Having It Both Ways*?
17. Who played Matthew Willows in the sitcom *Home to Roost*?
18. Which actor played Oscar Wilde in the 1997 biopic *Wilde*?
19. Which *EastEnders* character was played by Andrew Lynford?
20. Which Irish group released an album entitled *To*

ANSWERS: *1 Manic Street Preachers, 2 Robert Redford, 3 Take Your Pick, 4 Goodfellas, 5 Bryan Adams, 6 Spike Lee, 7 Buck Rogers in the 25th Century, 8 Peter Gabriel, 9 The Killing Fields, 10 Gayle Tuesday, 11 Abba, 12 Now And Then, 13 Basil Brush, 14 Helena Bonham Carter, 15 Terry Jones, 16 Tom Robinson, 17 Reece Dinsdale, 18 Stephen Fry, 19 Simon Raymond, 20 The Cranberries.*

General Knowledge

Your rating:
- 0-5 Join a library
- 6-10 Keep at it
- 11-15 Join a quiz team
- 16-20 Join Mensa

1. Which British composer wrote the music for the musicals *Evita* and *Jesus Christ Superstar*?
2. The kimono is the traditional costume of which country?
3. In which English county can the town of Matlock be found?
4. Which unit of mass is abbreviated to kg?
5. Which founder of the nursing profession was known as the Lady with the Lamp?
6. With which sport is Billie Jean King associated?
7. In France, which currency unit is equal to 100 centimes?
8. Which British author wrote *The Moon and Sixpence*?
9. Of which English county is Oxford the administrative centre?
10. How is the Cumbrian atomic power station Windscale known nowadays?
11. Who was the prime minister of Great Britain from 1955 to 1957?
12. Which channel separates the mainland of Australia from Tasmania?
13. Which alkaline-earth metal is represented by the symbol Be?
14. Which best-selling novelist wrote *Birds Of Prey*?
15. Which island off the NW coast of Wales was known as Mona to the Romans?
16. What is the fifth book of the New Testament?
17. What sort of creature is a bushmaster?
18. Which radioactive metal is represented by the symbol Ac?
19. Which French army officer was King of Naples from 1808 to 1815?
20. For which football team did Sir Stanley Matthews play from 1931 to 1947 and from 1961 to 1965?

ANSWERS: *1 Andrew Lloyd Webber, 2 Japan, 3 Derbyshire, 4 Kilogram, 5 Florence Nightingale, 6 Tennis, 7 Franc, 8 W. Somerset Maugham, 9 Oxfordshire, 10 Sellafield, 11 Anthony Eden, 12 Bass Strait, 13 Beryllium, 14 Wilbur Smith, 15 Anglesey, 16 Acts of the Apostles, 17 A snake, 18 Actinium, 19 Joachim Murat, 20 Stoke City.*

General Knowledge

Your rating:
- 0-5 Join a library
- 6-10 Keep at it
- 11-15 Join a quiz team
- 16-20 Join Mensa

1. Which British novelist wrote *Three Men in a Boat*?
2. Who became vice president of the USA under Ronald Reagan?
3. Which rock and roll musician wrote the songs *Johnny B. Goode*, and *Roll Over, Beethoven*?
4. In which English county can Hastings be found?
5. Which traditional Chinese system of healing involves inserting thin metal needles into selected points in the body?
6. In Italy, which currency unit is equal to 100 centesimi?
7. Which country's revolution was precipitated by the storming of the Bastille on 14 July 1789?
8. At which sport did David Gower captain England?
9. What is a dulcimer?
10. Which British author created the famous Larkin family in the 1958 novel *The Darling Buds of May*?
11. Which U.S. film maker directed *Stagecoach*?
12. Which British physician developed the first effective vaccine against smallpox?
13. Of which African country is Bujumbura the capital?
14. What sort of creature is a mangabey?
15. In the U.K., how many gallons are there in a bushel?
16. Of which country did Hassan II become king in 1961?
17. Which unit of magnetic flux is named after a 19th century Scottish physicist?
18. Which Korean businessman founded the Unification Church in 1954?
19. Who was chancellor of West Germany from 1969 to 1974?
20. To which French town was the papacy moved from 1309 to 1377?

***ANSWERS:** 1 Jerome K. Jerome, 2 George Bush, 3 Chuck Berry, 4 East Sussex, 5 Acupuncture, 6 Lira, 7 France, 8 Cricket, 9 A musical instrument, 10 H. E. Bates, 11 John Ford, 12 Edward Jenner, 13 Burundi, 14 A monkey, 15 Eight, 16 Morocco, 17 Maxwell, 18 Sun Myung Moon, 19 Willy Brandt, 20 Avignon.*

General Knowledge

Your rating:
- 0-5 Join a library
- 6-10 Keep at it
- 11-15 Join a quiz team
- 16-20 Join Mensa

1. In which English county can the resort of Eastbourne be found?
2. Which type of detachable blade was first developed in the French port of Bayonne?
3. Which jazz singer was known as *Lady Day*?
4. Of which religious movement is the Watch Tower Bible and Tract Society the legal publishing agency?
5. Which country is home to Ayers Rock, the largest monolith in the world?
6. The Great Red Spot can be seen in the atmosphere of which planet?
7. The Bay of Pigs is on the SW coast of which Caribbean country?
8. Which British pop singer starred in the film *The Man Who Fell to Earth*?
9. In which country was there a campaign to promote economic and industrial growth called the Great Leap Forward?
10. Which French singer and actor starred in the films *Love Me Tonight* and *Gigi*?
11. Which English judge is notorious for the harsh punishment and death sentences he imposed during the Bloody Assizes?
12. Which style of design derives its name from the 1925 Exposition Internationale des Arts Décoratifs et Industriels Modernes?
13. Which British author wrote *The Innocence of Father Brown*?
14. What do the initials LPG stand for?
15. Who gained the Russian throne in a coup in which her unpopular husband Emperor Peter III was murdered?
16. Which German town is famous as the home and burial place of Richard Wagner, who designed its Festival Theatre?
17. Which U.S. actress became known as the "It" girl?
18. What is the highest mountain in Argentina?
19. What sort of creature is a murex?
20. Which group made pop history in 1997 with a fourth consecutive number one in their first four singles?

ANSWERS: *1 East Sussex, 2 Bayonet, 3 Billie Holiday, 4 Jehovah's Witnesses, 5 Australia, 6 Jupiter, 7 Cuba, 8 David Bowie, 9 China, 10 Maurice Chevalier, 11 Baron Jeffreys of Wem, 12 Art Deco, 13 G. K. Chesterton, 14 Liquefied Petroleum Gas, 15 Catherine the Great, 16 Bayreuth, 17 Clara Bow, 18 Mount Aconcagua, 19 A mollusc, 20 The Spice Girls.*

Entertainment

Your rating: ● **0-5** Buy a TV ● **6-10** Keep at it ● **11-15** Join a quiz team ● **16-20** Enter a quiz show

1. Who played ticket collector Jack Skinner in the TV comedy *Oh, Doctor Beeching!*?
2. Which easy-listening combo released an album in 1996 entitled *A Groovy Place*?
3. Which *Supermarket Sweep* host presented *Pets Win Prizes* on TV?
4. In which 1998 film did Kate Winslet play Rose DeWitt Bukater?
5. Which nun was the star of a BBC series on the fine arts?
6. Who played FBI recruit Clarice Starling in the film *The Silence of the Lambs*?
7. Which duo had a top ten hit single in 1970 with *Young, Gifted and Black*?
8. Who played the bisexual butler in the 1996 film *The Grotesque*?
9. Which *EastEnders* character was played by Brian Croucher?
10. Which ex-Eternal singer released an album entitled *Naked* in 1996?
11. Who played the English butler in the film *Trading Places*?
12. Who starred as Edward VIII in the TV series *Edward and Mrs Simpson*?
13. Which half of a famous pop duo released a debut solo album entitled *Angel Clare* in 1973?
14. Who starred as the mysterious British spy in the 1996 film *The Rock*?
15. In which London park did the Sex Pistols play the first concert of their comeback tour in 1996?
16. Which British actor played Vincent Van Gogh in Robert Altman's film *Vincent and Theo*?
17. Who had a top ten hit single in 1989 with *You're History*?
18. Who starred as the middle-aged mum in John Schlesinger's 1996 film *Eye For An Eye*?
19. From which football ground was *The Crowd Are On The Pitch - Euro 96 Extravaganza* broadcast?
20. Which 1996 film starred Eddie Murphy as a vampire?

ANSWERS: *1 Paul Shane, 2 The Mike Flowers Pops, 3 Dale Winton, 4 Titanic, 5 Sister Wendy (Beckett), 6 Jodie Foster, 7 Bob and Marcia, 8 Sting, 9 Ted Hills, 10 Louise, 11 Denholm Elliott, 12 Edward Fox, 13 Art Garfunkel, 14 Sean Connery, 15 Finsbury Park, 16 Tim Roth, 17 Shakespears Sister, 18 Sally Field, 19 Old Trafford, 20 Vampire in Brooklyn.*

General Knowledge

Your rating: ● 0-5 Join a library ● 6-10 Keep at it ● 11-15 Join a quiz team ● 16-20 Join Mensa

1. Which British actress starred in the films *Stevie* and *Hopscotch*?
2. The Gorbals is a district of which Scottish city?
3. By what name was the unidentified murderer who killed at least six prostitutes in the East End of London in 1888 known?
4. What was the name of the survey of England that William I ordered to be carried out in 1086?
5. Which breed of dog was developed from the fox terrier by the Rev John Russell in the 19th century?
6. Which German Nazi politician became head of the SS in 1929 and also directed the Gestapo from 1936?
7. Which Swedish tennis player won the men's singles at Wimbledon for five consecutive years?
8. Of which ocean is the Bay of Bengal a section?
9. Which Soviet statesman signed a major arms limitation treaty with President Reagan in 1987?
10. Which Austrian motor-racing driver was world champion in 1975, 1977, and 1984?
11. Who succeeded Sir Keith Joseph as secretary of state for education and science?
12. Which Russian composer wrote *Rhapsody on a Theme of Paganini*?
13. What is the largest natural lake in Wales?
14. Which type of investment is represented by the acronym PEP?
15. Which British critic and novelist published under the pseudonym "Q"?
16. Of which two elements are boranes compounds?
17. Which Roman frontier defence work linked the Firths of Forth and Clyde?
18. The surname of which Norwegian army officer and Nazi collaborator has come to mean "traitor"?
19. Of which state of the USA is Harrisburg the capital?
20. What relations are footballers Les and Rio Ferdinand?

ANSWERS: *1 Glenda Jackson, 2 Glasgow, 3 Jack the Ripper, 4 The Domesday Book, 5 Jack Russell terrier, 6 Heinrich Himmler, 7 Bjorn Borg, 8 Indian Ocean, 9 Mikhail Gorbachev, 10 Niki Lauda, 11 Kenneth Baker, 12 Sergei Rachmaninov, 13 Lake Bala, 14 Personal Equity Plan, 15 Sir Arthur Quiller-Couch, 16 Boron and hydrogen, 17 The Antonine Wall, 18 Quisling, 19 Pennsylvania, 20 Cousins.*

General Knowledge

Your rating:
- 0-5 Join a library
- 6-10 Keep at it
- 11-15 Join a quiz team
- 16-20 Join Mensa

1. The Entente Cordiale of 1904 was an agreement between which two countries?
2. What is the largest artery called?
3. By what name was the policy of separate development of the white and non-white populations in South Africa known?
4. What is a balalaika?
5. By which acronym was the Australian and New Zealand Army Corps known?
6. In which county can the market town of Bakewell be found?
7. Which three countries formed the customs union known as Benelux?
8. In which African country is the town of Entebbe located?
9. Which historical event started in Pudding Lane, London in 1666?
10. What is ikebana?
11. Which mythical nation of female warriors were believed by the ancient Greeks to have invaded Attica?
12. Which art critic and social reformer wrote *Unto This Last*?
13. Which 1977 sci-fi film became the biggest box office hit in history after its re-release in the USA?
14. Ambergris is derived from the intestines of which creatures?
15. Which Moroccan middle-distance runner became the holder of world records in the 1500m, 2000m and 5000m in 1987?
16. Who was the first chancellor of the Federal Republic of Germany?
17. What sort of creature is a moloch?
18. Which British dramatist wrote *The Fair Penitent*?
19. Of which state of the USA is Madison the capital?
20. Which British poet wrote *Idylls of the King*?

ANSWERS: *1 France and Britain, 2 The aorta, 3 Apartheid, 4 A musical instrument, 5 ANZAC, 6 Derbyshire, 7 Belgium, the Netherlands and Luxembourg, 8 Uganda, 9 The Great Fire of London, 10 Japanese flower arrangement, 11 Amazons, 12 John Ruskin, 13 Star Wars, 14 Sperm whales, 15 Saïd Aouita, 16 Konrad Adenauer, 17 A lizard, 18 Nicholas Rowe, 19 Wisconsin, 20 Alfred Tennyson.*

General Knowledge

Your rating:
- **0-5 Join a library**
- **6-10 Keep at it**
- **11-15 Join a quiz team**
- **16-20 Join Mensa**

1. What is the name for the series of interconnected underground tunnels in which rabbits live?
2. Of which Middle East country is Haifa the main port?
3. Which 250 mile long footpath extends between Edale in Derbyshire and Kirk Yetholm in Scotland?
4. Which British author created the archetypal secret agent James Bond?
5. How is the respiratory infection pertussis commonly known?
6. What is the capital of Guatemala?
7. Of which Asian country is Honshu the largest island?
8. In a human being, which two respiratory organs are situated within the ribcage on either side of the heart?
9. Which mausoleum in Agra, India was constructed from pure white Makrana marble by over 20,000 workmen?
10. Which nun founded the Order of the Missionaries of Charity in Calcutta, and received the 1979 Nobel Peace Prize?
11. Which Massachusetts city is the birthplace of two US presidents - John Adams, and his son John Quincy Adams?
12. Which Bohemian folk dance is characterised by three steps and a hop?
13. Who became Queen of Denmark in 1972?
14. Which Sherpa mountaineer accompanied Sir Edmund Hillary on the first successful expedition to the summit of Mount Everest?
15. Which British diplomat and literary critic married the novelist Victoria Sackville-West in 1913?
16. What is the capital of the U.S. state of Florida?
17. Of which African country is Niamey the capital?
18. Which Chelsea striker scored the only goal in Italy's World Cup qualifier 1-0 victory over England in 1997?
19. Which drug obtained from the bark of trees was the first drug used to treat malaria?
20. Which silent film comedian starred in *Safety Last* and *The Freshman*?

ANSWERS: *1 Warren, 2 Israel, 3 The Pennine Way, 4 Ian Fleming, 5 Whooping cough, 6 Guatemala City, 7 Japan, 8 Lungs, 9 The Taj Mahal, 10 Mother Teresa, 11 Quincy, 12 Polka, 13 Margrethe II, 14 Tenzing Norgay, 15 Sir Harold Nicolson, 16 Tallahassee, 17 Niger, 18 Gianfranco Zola, 19 Quinine, 20 Harold Lloyd.*

Entertainment

Your rating: ● **0-5** **Buy a TV** ● **6-10** **Keep at it** ● **11-15** **Join a quiz team** ● **16-20** **Enter a quiz show**

1. Who played Edina in the BBC comedy series *Absolutely Fabulous*?
2. Who had a top ten hit single in 1984 with *Blue Jean*?
3. Who directed the 1984 film *Broadway Danny Rose*?
4. Who played Superman in TV's *The New Adventures of Superman*?
5. Which former Fairground Attraction singer released an album entitled *Candyfloss And Medicine* in 1996?
6. On which soap opera did Mandy's Munch Box appear?
7. Who had a top ten hit single in 1990 with *Birdhouse In Your Soul*?
8. Who produced and starred in the 1996 movie version of *Mission: Impossible*?
9. Who starred as Faith in the sitcom *Faith in the Future*?
10. Which star of *The New Adventures of Superman* played a femme fatale in the 1996 film *Heaven's Prisoners*?
11. Who played George in the classic sitcom *George and Mildred*?
12. What was the title of (The Artist Formerly Known As) Prince's last album for Warner Bros?
13. Who played Ted in the film *Bill & Ted's Excellent Adventure*?
14. In the TV series *Dr Quinn, Medicine Woman*, which character was played by Joe Lando?
15. Which reggae artist released an album in 1996 entitled *Man With The Fun*?
16. Who starred as Wild Bill Hickok in the 1996 film *Wild Bill*?
17. Who played Starsky in the TV series *Starsky and Hutch*?
18. Who had a top ten hit single in 1983 with *Buffalo Soldier*?
19. Who starred as Dr Max Lowe in the 1992 film *City of Joy*?
20. Which character in the TV drama series *Wycliffe* was played by Helen Masters?

ANSWERS: *1 Jennifer Saunders, 2 David Bowie, 3 Woody Allen, 4 Dean Cain, 5 Eddi Reader, 6 Emmerdale, 7 They Might Be Giants, 8 Tom Cruise, 9 Lynda Bellingham, 10 Teri Hatcher, 11 Brian Murphy, 12 Chaos And Disorder, 13 Keanu Reeves, 14 Byron Sully, 15 Maxi Priest, 16 Jeff Bridges, 17 Paul Michael Glaser, 18 Bob Marley and the Wailers, 19 Patrick Swayze, 20 DI Lucy Lane.*

General Knowledge

Your rating: ● 0-5 Join a library ● 6-10 Keep at it ● 11-15 Join a quiz team ● 16-20 Join Mensa

1. Which French philosopher is famous for the statement "I think, therefore I am"?
2. Of which country is Bangkok the capital?
3. How is the tympanic membrane commonly known?
4. In which Kent cathedral was Thomas à Becket martyred in 1170?
5. Which British microbiologist discovered the antibiotic penicillin?
6. Which African country was formerly known as Abyssinia?
7. What is the name of the principal Italian opera house which opened in Milan in 1776?
8. To what did East Pakistan change its name in 1972?
9. Followers of which religion regard the Koran as their sacred scripture?
10. In which country was Mozart born?
11. Which Paris-born postimpressionist painter moved to Tahiti in 1891?
12. What is the capital of Slovenia?
13. Which cricketer captained the West Indies from 1974 to 1978 and 1979 to 1985?
14. What sort of creature is an anole?
15. Who became life president of Malawi in 1971?
16. Which Japanese novelist and playwright wrote *Confessions of a Mask*?
17. Who became head of the Soviet secret police in 1938 and a member of the politburo in 1946?
18. Which former Soviet republic has Tallinn as its capital?
19. On which date does the feast of Lady Day occur?
20. Who was the first King of Saudi Arabia?

ANSWERS: *1 René Descartes, 2 Thailand, 3 The eardrum, 4 Canterbury cathedral, 5 Sir Alexander Fleming, 6 Ethiopia, 7 La Scala, 8 Bangladesh, 9 Islam, 10 Austria, 11 Paul Gauguin, 12 Ljubljana, 13 Clive Lloyd, 14 A lizard, 15 Hastings Banda, 16 Yukio Mishima, 17 Lavrenti Beria, 18 Estonia, 19 25th of March, 20 Ibn Saud.*

General Knowledge

Your rating:
- **0-5 Join a library**
- **6-10 Keep at it**
- **11-15 Join a quiz team**
- **16-20 Join Mensa**

1. Of which English county is Chichester the administrative centre?
2. Which U.S. science-fiction author wrote the novel *Fahrenheit 451*?
3. Which two countries collaborated on the supersonic aircraft Concorde?
4. In which European country can the Cantabrian Mountains be found?
5. How is acquired immune deficiency syndrome better known?
6. What is the positive electrode of an electrolytic cell called?
7. In the USA's political system, how is the upper house of Congress known?
8. Which 19th century French author wrote *Notre Dame de Paris*?
9. Which dictator ruled over Spain from 1939 until his death in 1975?
10. How many gods does a monotheist believe in?
11. Which Austrian composer wrote the operas *Wozzeck* and *Lulu*?
12. Of which country is Bandar Seri Begawan the capital?
13. Which English dramatist and poet wrote the satirical plays *Volpone* and *The Alchemist*?
14. Which member of Oasis caused outrage by suggesting that taking drugs was as normal as "having a cup of tea"?
15. What sort of creature is a nematode?
16. Which Irish monk founded the monastery at Lindisfarne?
17. Which son of Charles Martel founded the Carolingian dynasty?
18. Of which African country is Ougadougou the capital?
19. Which German composer wrote the song-cycle *Frauenliebe und Leben*?
20. Horace Walpole's *Castle of Otranto* and Ann Radcliffe's *The Mysteries of Udolpho* are examples of which English literary genre?

ANSWERS: *1 West Sussex, 2 Ray Bradbury, 3 Britain and France, 4 Spain, 5 AIDS, 6 Anode, 7 The Senate, 8 Victor Hugo, 9 General Franco, 10 One, 11 Alban Berg, 12 Brunei, 13 Ben Jonson, 14 Noel Gallagher, 15 A worm, 16 St Aidan, 17 Pepin the Short, 18 Burkina Faso, 19 Robert Schumann, 20 The gothic novel.*

General Knowledge

Your rating: ● **0-5** Join a library ● **6-10** Keep at it ● **11-15** Join a quiz team ● **16-20** Join Mensa

1. Which number is represented by the symbol M in Roman numerals?
2. Which six-a-side team game is played with sticks and a puck on a rink?
3. Who became Britain's prime minister in 1783, at the age of 24?
4. How is the notorious plant belladonna otherwise known?
5. Which five-sided building is the headquarters of the US Defense Department?
6. In which English county can the resort of Penzance be found?
7. In economics, what is represented by the initials PSBR?
8. Of which English county is Winchester the administrative centre?
9. Which Norwegian playwright and poet wrote *Peer Gynt* and *Hedda Gabler*?
10. On which river is Hampton Court situated?
11. Which lanthanide element is represented by the symbol Eu?
12. Who became first secretary of the Czechoslovak Communist Party in 1968?
13. Of which country is Lake Taupo the largest lake?
14. Which tennis star lost to Pete Sampras in successive Wimbledon semi finals?
15. Which British author wrote the novels *Pamela* and *Clarissa*?
16. What is the largest of the Swedish islands?
17. Who was the second man to walk on the moon?
18. Which cricket legend became the first living Australian to appear on an Australian postage stamp?
19. Which channel separates the Orkney Islands from the mainland of North Scotland?
20. How is the insecticide dichlorodiphenyltrichloroethane commonly known?

ANSWERS: 1 1,000, 2 Ice hockey, 3 William Pitt the Younger, 4 Deadly nightshade, 5 The Pentagon, 6 Cornwall, 7 Public Sector Borrowing Requirement, 8 Hampshire, 9 Henrik Ibsen, 10 Thames, 11 Europium, 12 Alexander Dubcek, 13 New Zealand, 14 Tim Henman, 15 Samuel Richardson, 16 Gotland, 17 Edwin "Buzz" Aldrin, 18 Sir Donald Bradman, 19 Pentland Firth, 20 DDT.

Entertainment

Your rating: ● **0-5** **Buy a TV** ● **6-10** **Keep at it** ● **11-15** **Join a quiz team** ● **16-20** **Enter a quiz show**

1. From which planet does Mork come in *Mork and Mindy*?
2. Which Irish group had a top ten hit in 1987 with *I Still Haven't Found What I'm Looking For*?
3. Which 1996 comedy film about ten-pin bowling starred Woody Harrelson and Bill Murray?
4. Which consumer-championing TV programme was presented by Anne Robinson?
5. Which reformed band released an album in 1996 entitled *Filthy Lucre - Live*?
6. Which Scottish actor played Bull in the post-Cold War TV thriller *The Writing on the Wall*?
7. Which singer starred as Susan in the film *Desperately Seeking Susan*?
8. Which Pretenders star made a guest appearance in an episode of the TV comedy *Friends*?
9. Who had a top ten hit in 1984 with *New Moon On Monday*?
10. Which 1996 film starred Janeane Garofalo as radio vet Dr. Abby?
11. In which TV series did military historian Professor Richard Holmes visit the sites of six famous battlefields?
12. Which US rock band released an album in 1996 entitled *Three Snakes And One Charm*?
13. Who played Johnny in the 1991 film *Frankie and Johnny*?
14. Which *Dallas* star also starred in the TV series *I Dream of Jeannie*?
15. Which female vocalist released an album entitled *Guilty* in 1996?
16. Which 1996 film starred Adam Sandler as a foul-mouthed golfer?
17. Which former Page 3 model presented *Page 3 - a Celebration* on TV?
18. Who directed the 1988 film *Frantic*?
19. Which British actress is married to John Thaw?
20. Who had a top ten hit in 1977 with *No More Heroes*?

ANSWERS: *1 Ork, 2 U2, 3 King Pin, 4 Watchdog, 5 Sex Pistols, 6 Bill Paterson, 7 Madonna, 8 Chrissie Hynde, 9 Duran Duran, 10 The Truth About Cats And Dogs, 11 War Walks, 12 The Black Crowes, 13 Al Pacino, 14 Larry Hagman, 15 Ruby Turner, 16 Happy Gilmore, 17 Samantha Fox, 18 Roman Polanski, 19 Sheila Hancock, 20 The Stranglers.*

General Knowledge

Your rating:
- **0-5 Join a library**
- **6-10 Keep at it**
- **11-15 Join a quiz team**
- **16-20 Join Mensa**

1. What is a euphonium?
2. Which British novelist wrote *Wuthering Heights*?
3. Which reddish-brown element is represented by the symbol Br?
4. In which European country can Mount Parnassus be found?
5. By what name are the fleet of 130 ships sent by Philip II of Spain in 1588 to invade England usually known?
6. Which city is known as Köln in German?
7. In which European country is the city of Gerona located?
8. Which U.S. novelist wrote *The Naked and the Dead*?
9. Which of the 12 Apostles is known as "Doubting" because he refused to believe in the resurrection until he had seen Christ?
10. With which sport is Shane Warne associated?
11. Which Democratic politician ran for the US presidency in 1952 and 1956, but was defeated both times by Eisenhower?
12. By what name are the eight blessings with which Jesus opened the Serman on the Mount usually known?
13. Which grandson of William the Conqueror was King of England from 1135 to 1154
14. Which Austrian composer wrote the song-cycle *Die Winterreise*?
15. What sort of creature is a numbat?
16. Which flat race for three-year-old horses was the earliest of the English Classics to be established?
17. Which fruit comes from the tree *Prunus persica*?
18. In which country is Nullarbor Plain situated?
19. Which point in the sky lies directly above an observer and 90 degrees from all points on his horizon?
20. Which German philosopher wrote *The World as Will and Idea*?

ANSWERS: *1 A brass musical instrument, 2 Emily Brontë, 3 Bromine, 4 Greece, 5 The Spanish Armada, 6 Cologne, 7 Spain, 8 Norman Mailer, 9 Thomas, 10 Cricket, 11 Adlai E. Stevenson, 12 Beatitudes, 13 Stephen, 14 Franz Schubert, 15 A marsupial, 16 St Leger, 17 Peach, 18 Australia, 19 Zenith, 20 Arthur Schopenhauer.*

General Knowledge

Your rating: ● 0-5 Join a library ● 6-10 Keep at it ● 11-15 Join a quiz team ● 16-20 Join Mensa

1. In which English county can the town of Maidenhead be found?
2. What is the hardest known mineral?
3. Which British rock band released an album entitled *Abbey Road*?
4. What sort of creature is a halibut?
5. To which English monarch was Catherine Parr married?
6. Which U.S. president delivered the Gettysburg Address in 1863?
7. To what family of musical instruments do the triangle, gong and xylophone belong?
8. Which term describes the time taken for half the atoms in a sample of a radioactive isotope to decay?
9. At which sport was Ray Reardon world champion six times in the 1970s?
10. Which city is the administrative centre of Cheshire?
11. Which protein hormone is secreted by the islets of Langerhans in response to a high concentration of glucose in the blood?
12. According to Greek mythology, which daughter of king Agenor of Tyre was carried to Crete by Zeus in the form of a bull?
13. Who replaced Kevin Keegan as manager of Newcastle United?
14. On which river does the Yorkshire town of Halifax lie?
15. Who is the patron saint of Russia?
16. Of which country was Malcolm Fraser prime minister from 1975 to 1983?
17. How are the states of Maine, New Hampshire, Vermont, Massachusetts, Rhode Island and Connecticut collectively known?
18. On which river does the town of Hawick stand?
19. In which present day country are the remains of the ancient city of Locri?
20. Which Irish politician of the late 19th century was a dominant political figure until cited in a divorce suit brought against Katherine O'Shea?

ANSWERS: *1 Berkshire, 2 Diamond, 3 The Beatles, 4 A fish, 5 Henry VIII, 6 Abraham Lincoln, 7 Percussion instruments, 8 Half-life, 9 Snooker, 10 Chester, 11 Insulin, 12 Europa, 13 Kenny Dalglish, 14 The River Calder, 15 St Nicholas, 16 Australia, 17 New England, 18 River Teviot, 19 Italy, 20 Charles Stewart Parnell.*

General Knowledge

Your rating:
- 0-5 Join a library
- 6-10 Keep at it
- 11-15 Join a quiz team
- 16-20 Join Mensa

1. Which constellation of the zodiac takes its name from the Latin for "bull"?
2. In which state of the USA is the city of Houston situated?
3. Which U.S. composer wrote *Rhapsody in Blue* and *An American in Paris*?
4. Which unit of power is often abbreviated to hp?
5. Which former film actor became president of the USA in 1981?
6. What is the name for a group of lions?
7. Which British novelist wrote *Jane Eyre*?
8. What is the capital of Colombia?
9. In which English county can the New Forest be found?
10. What was the name for the Nazi secret police formed in 1933 under Göring?
11. In which Hampshire village can the National Motor Museum be found?
12. What did the Indian state of Mysore change its name to in 1973?
13. Which British poet and scholar wrote *A Shropshire Lad*?
14. Which Brazilian tennis player was the women's singles champion at Wimbledon in 1959, 1960 and 1964?
15. What sort of creature is a white-eye?
16. Which Russian ballet impresario founded the Ballets Russes?
17. Which Roman road is now followed partly by the A429?
18. Which pollster successfully predicted the result of the 1936 U.S. presidential election?
19. Which composer of musicals became a life peer in the 1997 New Year Honours List?
20. In the New Testament, who was the first Christian martyr?

ANSWERS: *1 Taurus, 2 Texas, 3 George Gershwin, 4 Horsepower, 5 Ronald Reagan, 6 A pride, 7 Charlotte Brontë, 8 Bogota, 9 Hampshire, 10 The Gestapo, 11 Beaulieu, 12 Karnataka, 13 A. E. Housman, 14 Maria Bueno, 15 A bird, 16 Sergei Diaghilev, 17 Fosse Way, 18 George Gallup, 19 Sir Andrew Lloyd Webber, 20 St Stephen.*

Entertainment

Your rating: ● 0-5 Buy a TV ● 6-10 Keep at it ● 11-15 Join a quiz team ● 16-20 Enter a quiz show

1. Which actor was the fifth *Doctor Who* in the TV sci-fi series?
2. What was the title of Louise's third solo album, released in 2000?
3. Which 1973 film starred Rod Steiger and Robert Ryan as the heads of two feuding families?
4. What was Moby's first top ten hit, which entered the charts in 1991?
5. Which 2000 animated movie, set after the destruction of Earth, featured the voices of Matt Damon and Drew Barrymore?
6. Which part of the world did Paul O'Grady, Lily Savage's alter-ego, visit in a 2000 ITV travel series?
7. Which Eighties pop group had a 1982 U.K. top five hit with *Best Years of Our Lives*?
8. Who wrote the book upon which the 1990 film *The Russia House* was based?
9. Which actor played Vince Skinner in ITV's comedy series *The Thing About Vince*?
10. What was the title of the Sixties singer Bobby Rydell's only U.K. top ten hit?
11. Which star of *The Full Monty* played Fred in the 2000 prequel, *The Flintstones in Viva Rock Vegas*?
12. Which Eighties series, starring Tony Haygarth and Patsy Rowlands, featured a repairman who dreamed of visiting another planet?
13. Which British singer hit the top of the U.K. charts in 2000 with *Rock DJ*?
14. Which 1982 film about a search for gold featured Charlton Heston and Kim Basinger?
15. Which *Coronation Street* character left Weatherfield and his girlfriend Toyah in 2000 to 'find himself' in India?
16. Which British singer/songwriter scored a top five album in 2000 with *White Ladder*, featuring his hit song *Babylon*?
17. Which chat show host became a *National Lottery* presenter in 2000, fronting the travelling quiz show *On the Spot*?
18. Which former footballer featured alongside Nicolas Cage and Robert Duvall in the 2000 film *Gone in 60 Seconds*?
19. Who was the commander of the spacecraft in Gerry Anderson's Sixties puppet series *Fireball XL5*?
20. Which former Spice Girl had a U.K. number one hit with *I Turn to You* in 2000?

ANSWERS: *1 Peter Davison, 2 Elbow Beach, 3 The Lolly-Madonna War, 4 Go, 5 Titan AE, 6 The Orient, 7 Modern Romance, 8 John Le Carre, 9 Timothy Spall, 10 Wild One, 11 Mark Addy, 12 Kinvig, 13 Robbie Williams, 14 Mother Lode, 15 Spider Nugent, 16 David Gray, 17 Des O'Connor, 18 Vinnie Jones, 19 Colonel Steve Zodiac, 20 Melanie C.*

General Knowledge

Your rating:
- **0-5 Join a library**
- **6-10 Keep at it**
- **11-15 Join a quiz team**
- **16-20 Join Mensa**

1. Which tubes between the ovary and uterus are also called oviducts?
2. How many legs does a lobster have?
3. Which American golfer won the British Open in 1996?
4. In which country is the city of Eindhoven?
5. In which country was Albert Einstein born?
6. What is the standard currency unit of Japan?
7. Which actor's nickname was The Sex Thimble?
8. Which British actor starred in *Brief Encounter* and *The Third Man*?
9. Which small flute shares its name with a Scottish region?
10. Which Scottish novelist wrote *Rob Roy* and *The Heart of Midlothian*?
11. Which country hosted the football World Cup in 1982?
12. Which French composer wrote *The Sorcerer's Apprentice*?
13. Who was the Green Party candidate in the 2000 U.S. presidential election?
14. Which African-American Muslim organisation is led by Louis Farrakhan?
15. In which country was John Prescott born?
16. Which American author wrote *The Foxes of Harrow*?
17. Which Irish singer was voted the world's most beautiful woman in a poll in 2000?
18. Who was the famous ice dancing partner of Jayne Torvill?
19. What sort of creature is a prairie dog?
20. In which U.S. state is Dodge City?

ANSWERS: *1 Fallopian tubes, 2 Ten, 3 Tom Lehman, 4 The Netherlands, 5 Germany, 6 Yen, 7 Dudley Moore, 8 Trevor Howard, 9 Fife, 10 Sir Walter Scott, 11 Spain, 12 Paul Dukas, 13 Ralph Nader, 14 The Nation of Islam, 15 Wales, 16 Frank Yerby, 17 Andrea Corr, 18 Christopher Dean, 19 A rodent, 20 Kansas.*

General Knowledge

Your rating: ● 0-5 Join a library ● 6-10 Keep at it ● 11-15 Join a quiz team ● 16-20 Join Mensa

1. Which music-hall comedienne and singer was born Grace Stansfield?
2. Who was the leader of the mutiny on *HMS Bounty*?
3. What nationality is tennis player Gustavo Kuerten?
4. What was the tallest building in the world before the Chrysler Building in New York was completed in 1930?
5. Which actor starred in the *Death Wish* series of films?
6. What does 'prep' stand for when referring to a school?
7. Who scored his 12th Test century for South Africa in January 2001?
8. What is the oldest national park in the United States?
9. In what part of the body is the fibula?
10. Which fruit is known as an eggplant in the United States?
11. Who was born Michael Dumble-Smith?
12. Which American dancer died when her scarf caught in the wheel of a car?
13. What were the first names of the poet W.B. Yeats?
14. Which Canadian author won the 2000 Booker Prize for her novel *The Blind Assassin*?
15. What nationality was the golfer Bobby Locke?
16. In which English county is the new town of Skelmersdale?
17. What was the second Walt Disney film?
18. Who wrote the songs for the musicals *Guys and Dolls* and *Hans Christian Andersen*?
19. Of which country is Suva the capital?
20. The Faroe Islands is a self-governing region of which European country?

ANSWERS: *1 Dame Gracie Fields, 2 Fletcher Christian, 3 Brazilian, 4 Eiffel Tower, 5 Charles Bronson, 6 Preparatory, 7 Daryll Cullinan, 8 Yellowstone National Park, 9 The leg, 10 Avocado, 11 Michael Crawford, 12 Isadora Duncan, 13 William Butler, 14 Margaret Atwood, 15 South African, 16 Lancashire, 17 Pinocchio, 18 Frank Loesser, 19 Fiji, 20 Denmark.*

General Knowledge

Your rating: ● 0-5 Join a library ● 6-10 Keep at it ● 11-15 Join a quiz team ● 16-20 Join Mensa

1. Which form of recreation originated on paved areas along California beaches in the 1960s?
2. What is the name of *The Barber of Seville* in the play by Beaumarchais?
3. Who wrote *Tarzan of the Apes*?
4. In which Spanish city is the Prado Museum?
5. Which nut is also called a filbert?
6. In which English county is Bognor Regis?
7. What is the first name of Mr Micawber in *Great Expectations*?
8. Which British rower announced his retirement in 2000?
9. Which architect rebuilt St Paul's Cathedral after the Great Fire of London?
10. What is the boiling point of water at sea level on the Celsius scale?
11. Who captained the 1995 rugby union World Cup winners?
12. Which London theatre was rebuilt by a trust set up by the American actor Sam Wanamaker?
13. Of which country is Bratislava the capital?
14. Which French composer wrote *España* and *Le Roi malgé lui*?
15. What is the French name for the German city of Aachen?
16. Which British novelist wrote *The Alexandria Quartet*?
17. Where did Paula Radcliffe finish in the 10,000 metres final at the Sydney Olympics?
18. Which Stone Age village in the Orkneys was exposed by a storm in 1850?
19. Who was appointed as the England football team's first foreign coach?
20. Which English novelist wrote *Joseph Andrews*?

ANSWERS: *1 Skateboarding, 2 Figaro, 3 Edgar Rice Burroughs, 4 Madrid, 5 Hazelnut, 6 West Sussex, 7 Wilkins, 8 Steve Redgrave, 9 Sir Christopher Wren, 10 100 degrees, 11 Francois Pienaar, 12 The Globe, 13 Slovakia, 14 Emmanuel Chabrier, 15 Aix-la-Chapelle, 16 Lawrence Durrell, 17 4th, 18 Skara Brae, 19 Sven Goran Eriksson, 20 Henry Fielding.*

Entertainment

Your rating: ● 0-5 Buy a TV ● 6-10 Keep at it ● 11-15 Join a quiz team ● 16-20 Enter a quiz show

1. Which actor directed and starred in the 1992 film *Mac*?
2. What was Mike and the Mechanics' 1995 U.K. top twenty hit?
3. Which 2000 animated film featured the voices of Kevin Kline and Kenneth Branagh?
4. Which *Coronation Street* character was christened in 2000?
5. Who had a U.K. number one hit in 1983 with *Baby Jane*?
6. Which 1964 Howard Hawks film starred Rock Hudson as a fishing equipment salesman?
7. What was the title of the Orb's 1993 U.K. top ten hit?
8. Which Oscar-winning French actress starred in the 2000 film *La Veuve de Saint-Pierre*?
9. Who wrote and starred as the Sheriff of Nottingham in the former children's series *Maid Marian and Her Merry Men*?
10. Which U.S. singer returned to the U.K. top five in 2000 with *Doesn't Really Matter*?
11. Which actor starred as a theatrical entrepreneur and serial killer in the 1968 film *No Way to Treat a Lady*?
12. Which *EastEnders* family left the Square in 2000 for a life in Leicester?
13. Which U.K. garage artist released his debut album, *Born to Do It*, in 2000?
14. In which Scottish city was the BBC 2 drama series *Tinsel Town* set?
15. Which 2000 film memoir about a young boy and his dog featured Kevin Bacon and Diane Lane as the boy's parents?
16. Which British sporting team's progress over a four-year period was depicted in the 2000 video diary series *Gold Fever*?
17. With which song did Spiller beat Victoria Beckham to the number one spot in 2000?
18. Who narrated the former children's series *Roobarb and Custard*?
19. On whose novel was the 1979 Otto Preminger film *The Human Factor* based?
20. Which BBC 1 fly-on-the-wall documentary series focused on the lives of people in an area of West London?

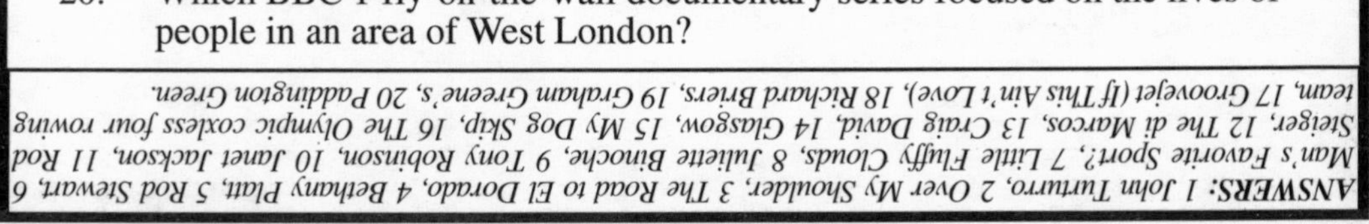

ANSWERS: *1 John Turturro, 2 Over My Shoulder, 3 The Road to El Dorado, 4 Bethany Platt, 5 Rod Stewart, 6 Man's Favorite Sport?, 7 Little Fluffy Clouds, 8 Juliette Binoche, 9 Tony Robinson, 10 Janet Jackson, 11 Rod Steiger, 12 The di Marcos, 13 Craig David, 14 Glasgow, 15 My Dog Skip, 16 The Olympic coxless four rowing team, 17 Groovejet (If This Ain't Love), 18 Richard Briers, 19 Graham Greene's, 20 Paddington Green.*

General Knowledge

Your rating: • 0-5 Join a library • 6-10 Keep at it • 11-15 Join a quiz team • 16-20 Join Mensa

1. Which American singer-songwriter wrote *Blowin' in the Wind*?
2. What is the capital of Colombia?
3. Which boxer won heavyweight gold at the 1968 Olympics?
4. Who was the British prime minister at the start of World War II?
5. Which American author wrote *The Fall of the House of Usher*?
6. How many players are there in a hockey team?
7. What was the real rank of *Biggles* author Captain W E Johns?
8. Which comic actor played the title role in the film *The Grinch*?
9. By what first name is the British decathlete Francis Morgan Thompson known?
10. Which lizard is noted for its ability to change colour?
11. Who was the Formula One world champion in 1976?
12. Which German poet and dramatist wrote *Mother Courage and Her Children*?
13. Who painted *Woman with Crossed Arms*, which sold for more than £38 million at auction in 2000?
14. In computing, what does HTML stand for?
15. What sort of creature is a looper?
16. Which Italian poet wrote the libretti for Mozart's *Don Giovanni* and *Cosi fan tutte*?
17. In which imaginary country was *The Prisoner of Zenda* set?
18. Which state underwent several recounts to decide the outcome of the 2000 U.S. presidential election?
19. What nationality was the 8th century poet Tu Fu?
20. Which Bavarian town was the site of the first concentration camp set up by the Nazis?

ANSWERS: *1 Bob Dylan, 2 Bogota, 3 George Foreman, 4 Neville Chamberlain, 5 Edgar Allan Poe, 6 Eleven, 7 Flying Officer, 8 Jim Carrey, 9 Daley, 10 Chameleon, 11 James Hunt, 12 Bertolt Brecht, 13 Pablo Picasso, 14 HyperText Markup Language, 15 A caterpillar, 16 Lorenzo da Ponte, 17 Ruritania, 18 Florida, 19 Chinese, 20 Dachau.*

General Knowledge

Your rating:
- 0-5 Join a library
- 6-10 Keep at it
- 11-15 Join a quiz team
- 16-20 Join Mensa

1. Which archangel announced the birth of Jesus to the Virgin Mary?
2. What is a two-man bobsleigh called?
3. Which beauty contest was invented by Eric Morley who died in 2000?
4. In which German city is the Brandenburg Gate?
5. Which British actress won an Oscar for *Howards End*?
6. Of which U.S. state is Boise the capital?
7. In which year was Panamanian boxer Roberto Duran born?
8. Who played Rick in the 1942 film *Casablanca*?
9. From which country does the wine Chablis come?
10. For what sort of swelling on the skin is furuncle the technical name?
11. What is the name of the the whaling ship in the novel *Moby-Dick*?
12. Which figure of speech is an intentional extravagant exaggeration?
13. From which English Premiership team was Chris Hutchings dismissed as manager in 2000?
14. Which Hungarian-born actress provided the voice of Bianca in the Disney *Rescuers* films?
15. What name is given to the use of obstructive delaying tactics in parliaments?
16. In which English county is the Vale of Eden?
17. What was artist John Callcott Horsley the first to design?
18. How many players make up an American football team?
19. What nationality was the singer and political activist Fela Kuti?
20. Which American author of 'hard-boiled' fiction had the middle name Mallahan?

ANSWERS: *1 Gabriel, 2 Boblet, 3 Miss World, 4 Berlin, 5 Emma Thompson, 6 Idaho, 7 1951, 8 Humphrey Bogart, 9 France, 10 Boil, 11 Pequod, 12 Hyperbole, 13 Bradford City, 14 Eva Gabor, 15 Filibustering, 16 Cumbria, 17 A Christmas card, 18 11, 19 Nigerian, 20 James M Cain.*

General Knowledge

Your rating: ● **0-5** Join a library ● **6-10** Keep at it ● **11-15** Join a quiz team ● **16-20** Join Mensa

1. Which marine creature has hermit, spider and king varieties?
2. Who wrote the novel *Sophie's Choice*?
3. Which former country was also known as the GDR?
4. *The Remorseful Day* was the last episode of which TV drama series starring John Thaw?
5. Which Texas city has an American football team called the Cowboys?
6. In which country is *Le Figaro* a daily newspaper?
7. Which American novelist wrote *The Turn of the Screw*?
8. In which sport might you see a Salchow or an Axel?
9. Santa Claus is a modification of which saint's name?
10. Who has become the first First Lady to be elected to the U.S. Senate?
11. With which sport was Geoff Capes most famously associated?
12. What was the name of *Othello*'s wife in Shakespeare's play?
13. In the Old Testament, who was the favourite son of King David?
14. Which Bedfordshire town has the lowest rates of divorce and separation?
15. With which sport is Reggie Jackson associated?
16. Which English film studio was associated with comedies such as *Passport to Pimlico*?
17. What is Salman Rushdie's real first name?
18. Which river did George Washington cross on Christmas night in 1776?
19. For which month is emerald the traditional birthstone?
20. Which actor played Julian to Kenneth Williams's Sandy on *Round the Horne*?

ANSWERS: *1 Crab, 2 William Styron, 3 East Germany, 4 Inspector Morse, 5 Dallas, 6 France, 7 Henry James, 8 Ice skating, 9 St Nicholas, 10 Hillary Clinton, 11 Shot put, 12 Desdemona, 13 Absalom, 14 Biggleswade, 15 Baseball, 16 Ealing Studios, 17 Ahmed, 18 Delaware, 19 May, 20 Hugh Paddick.*

Entertainment

Your rating: ● **0-5** **Buy a TV** ● **6-10** **Keep at it** ● **11-15** **Join a quiz team** ● **16-20** **Enter a quiz show**

1. Which group had a 1982 U.K. top five hit with *Golden Brown*?
2. Which actor played a Marine colonel accused of massacring 83 civilian Yemenis in the 2000 film *Rules of Engagement*?
3. Which former docusoap star presented the BBC 1 series *The Toughest Job in Britain*?
4. What was the title of U2's 1991 U.K. number one hit?
5. Which British actress starred in the title role of the 1977 film *Julia*?
6. Which *Coronation Street* baddie found himself back out on the streets in 2000 after being cleared of the murder of Tony Horrocks?
7. Which U.S. group had U.K. number one hits in the Sixties with *Make It Easy On Yourself* and *The Sun Ain't Gonna Shine Anymore*?
8. Which 2000 film starred Leslie Grantham as a policeman and Amanda Redman as his barmaid wife?
9. Who was the original presenter of the music show *Top of the Pops*?
10. Which U.S. pop singer was fortunate enough to have a U.K. top five hit with *Lucky* in 2000?
11. Which 1990 film starred Steve Martin as an Italian-American criminal-turned-witness called Vinnie?
12. Who was the father of Sonia Jackson's baby Chloe in *EastEnders*?
13. Which founder member of the Fugees released his second solo album, *The Ecleftic*, in 2000?
14. Which newsreader fronted the ITV quiz show *The People Versus*?
15. Which actor played Professor Charles Xavier in the 2000 film version of *X-Men*?
16. Who played angel Jonathan Smith in the Eighties drama series *Highway to Heaven*?
17. Which pop legend knocked Spiller from the top of the U.K. charts in 2000 with her single *Music*?
18. Which 1971 film set on a South American island starred Kirk Douglas and Yul Brynner?
19. Who was the presenter of the BBC 1 wildlife series *Cousins*?
20. Which U.K. group had a top ten hit in 1996 with *Kevin Carter*?

ANSWERS: *1 The Stranglers, 2 Samuel L. Jackson, 3 Jeremy Spake, 4 The Fly, 5 Vanessa Redgrave, 6 Jez Quigley, 7 The Walker Brothers, 8 The Wedding Tackle, 9 Jimmy Savile, 10 Britney Spears, 11 My Blue Heaven, 12 Martin Fowler, 13 Wyclef Jean, 14 Kirsty Young, 15 Patrick Stewart, 16 Michael Landon, 17 Madonna, 18 The Light at the Edge of the World, 19 Charlotte Uhlenbroek, 20 Manic Street Preachers.*

General Knowledge

Your rating:
- 0-5 Join a library
- 6-10 Keep at it
- 11-15 Join a quiz team
- 16-20 Join Mensa

1. Who wrote the children's story *James and the Giant Peach*?
2. What sort of puzzle first appeared in the *New York World* in December 1913?
3. Which mythical monster is also called a yeti?
4. How many times did Oxford win the Boat Race during the 1980s?
5. Which country is known as Suomi in its native language?
6. In which sea are the Cayman Islands?
7. Who played the title role in the 1970 film musical *Scrooge*?
8. Which number lies between 1 and 5 on a dartboard?
9. Who is the Norse god of Thunder, after whom Thursday is named?
10. Which Welsh author wrote *Under Milk Wood*?
11. Which novel by Sir Laurens van der Post was filmed as *Merry Christmas Mr Lawrence*?
12. Which actor won an Oscar in 1950 for his performance in *Cyrano de Bergerac*?
13. Who was the unsuccessful Democratic candidate in the 1988 U.S. presidential election?
14. Who wrote the novel Princess Daisy?
15. In which country are the Plains of Abraham?
16. Which American composer wrote the opera *Einstein on the Beach*?
17. Which weather phenomenon takes its name from the Spanish for 'the child'?
18. Where is the TV detective series Taggart set?
19. Which French New Wave director made the films *Les Cousins* and *Les Biches*?
20. Which English poet wrote *Christmas Eve and Easter Day*?

ANSWERS: *1 Roald Dahl, 2 Crossword puzzle, 3 Abominable snowman, 4 Nine, 5 Finland, 6 Caribbean Sea, 7 Albert Finney, 8 20, 9 Thor, 10 Dylan Thomas, 11 The Seed and the Sower, 12 José Ferrer, 13 Michael Dukakis, 14 Judith Krantz, 15 Canada, 16 Philip Glass, 17 El Niño, 18 Glasgow, 19 Claude Chabrol, 20 Robert Browning.*

General Knowledge

Your rating:
- 0-5 Join a library
- 6-10 Keep at it
- 11-15 Join a quiz team
- 16-20 Join Mensa

1. How many months of the year have 31 days?
2. What was the pen name of Charles Lutwidge Dodgson?
3. What was the former name for the temperature scale now called Celsius?
4. *1* is the title of a greatest hits album by which 60s group?
5. Who was the first woman to make a solo flight across the Atlantic Ocean?
6. What name is given to a two-hulled sailing vessel?
7. Which horse won the Grand National in 1996?
8. According to tradition, which games were first held in 776 BC?
9. In which Czech city is Wenceslas Square?
10. Which American actor starred in *Angels With Dirty Faces* and *White Heat*?
11. Which Swedish tennis player won the Australian Open in 1983?
12. On which American city was the first Monopoly game based?
13. Which glamorous string quartet saw their album *Born* removed from the classical music charts after reaching No 2 in 2000?
14. In what year was the Channel Tunnel officially opened?
15. How many yards are there in a furlong?
16. With what style of music is Blind Lemon Jefferson associated?
17. What is the name of the home stadium of Leeds United?
18. Which British actor married the daughter of the playwright Eugene O'Neill in 1943?
19. Which scientific organisation is famous for its Christmas lectures?
20. Who wrote *Confessions of an English Opium-Eater*?

ANSWERS: *1 Seven, 2 Lewis Carroll, 3 Centigrade, 4 The Beatles, 5 Amelia Earhart, 6 Catamaran, 7 Rough Quest, 8 Olympic Games, 9 Prague, 10 James Cagney, 11 Mats Wilander, 12 Atlantic City, 13 Bond, 14 1994, 15 220, 16 Blues, 17 Elland Road, 18 Charlie Chaplin, 19 The Royal Institution, 20 Thomas de Quincey.*

General Knowledge

Your rating: ● 0-5 Join a library ● 6-10 Keep at it ● 11-15 Join a quiz team ● 16-20 Join Mensa

1. Which American author wrote *The Big Sleep* and *The Long Goodbye*?
2. What is the state capital of Utah?
3. Which of the Brontes wrote *The Tenant of Wildfell Hall*?
4. By what first name was Gabrielle Chanel known?
5. Which Hollywood great was the subject of the book *Mommie Dearest*?
6. For what sort of fabric is Chantilly famous?
7. Which king of England was crowned on Christmas Day 1066?
8. Which country hosted the football World Cup in 1978?
9. Which adult male singing voice is between tenor and bass?
10. In which country was media magnate Rupert Murdoch born?
11. Which star of *The X Files* played Lily Bart in the film *The House of Mirth*?
12. Which British runner refused to compete in the 100m at the 1924 Olympics because it was held on a Sunday?
13. What was the first name of the poet W H Auden?
14. Which American fighter aircraft is also called the Fighting Falcon?
15. Who was the French signatory to the Munich Agreement of 1938?
16. Which Christmas decoration grows as a parasite on trees?
17. What is another name for the hop step and jump?
18. Which actress and singer had a hit with the single *Cry Me a River* in the 1950s?
19. What name is given to the fruits of plants of the genus *Ficus*?
20. Which much-married former child star was born Joe Yule?

ANSWERS: *1 Raymond Chandler, 2 Salt Lake City, 3 Anne, 4 Coco, 5 Joan Crawford, 6 Lace, 7 William I (the Conqueror), 8 Argentina, 9 Baritone, 10 Australia, 11 Gillian Anderson, 12 Eric Liddell, 13 Wystan, 14 F-16, 15 Edouard Daladier, 16 Mistletoe, 17 Triple jump, 18 Julie London, 19 Figs, 20 Mickey Rooney.*

Entertainment

Your rating: ● 0-5 Buy a TV ● 6-10 Keep at it ● 11-15 Join a quiz team ● 16-20 Enter a quiz show

1. Which 2000 film starred Rachel Griffiths as an investigative journalist who changes places with her alter ego, a housewife?
2. Who presented BBC 2's *Edinburgh Review* in 2000?
3. Which female vocalist, in collaboration with ELO, had a 1980 U.K. number one hit with *Xanadu*?
4. Which 1982 film directed by *Happy Days*' Ron Howard also featured his former co-star Henry Winkler?
5. Who did *EastEnders*' Melanie surprisingly start dating in 2000 in order to get her own back on Steve Owen?
6. What was the title of the Shadows' first U.K. number one hit, in 1960?
7. Who directed the 2000 film *Timecode*, featuring Salma Hayek and Jeanne Tripplehorn?
8. From which U.S. drama series was *Knots Landing* a spin-off?
9. What was the title of Reef's 2000 album release?
10. What was the name of the character played by John Travolta in the films *Saturday Night Fever* and *Staying Alive*?
11. Which supermodel became Joey's roommate in the comedy series *Friends*?
12. Which song, a 2000 U.K. number one for A1, was originally a U.K. number two hit for A-Ha in 1985?
13. Who presented the 2000 *Britain's Strongest Man* competition coverage on BBC 1?
14. Which member of the *Ally McBeal* cast starred alongside Jackie Chan in the 2000 western comedy *Shanghai Noon*?
15. Who was the original host of the TV quiz show *Busman's Holiday*?
16. Which Channel 4 show's theme tune hit the U.K. top five in 2000?
17. Which 1988 film starred Timothy Dalton and Anthony Edwards as cancer patients?
18. Which British group had a 1987 U.K. top ten hit with *Running in the Family*?
19. Which British actor played a school football coach in the 2000 film *There's Only One Jimmy Grimble*?
20. Which member *of Coronation Street*'s Battersby clan left Weatherfield in 2000 to join Mark Baldwin on his travels?

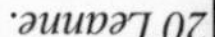

ANSWERS: *1 Me Myself I, 2 Mariella Frostrup, 3 Olivia Newton-John, 4 Night Shift, 5 Billy Mitchell, 6 Apache, 7 Mike Figgis, 8 Dallas, 9 Getaway, 10 Tony Manero, 11 Elle MacPherson, 12 Take on Me, 13 John Inverdale, 14 Lucy Liu, 15 Julian Pettifer, 16 Big Brother's, 17 Hawks, 18 Level 42, 19 Robert Carlyle, 20 Leanne.*

General Knowledge

Your rating: ● 0-5 Join a library ● 6-10 Keep at it ● 11-15 Join a quiz team ● 16-20 Join Mensa

1. What part of the body is affected by glaucoma?
2. In which year was the Grand National race declared void?
3. Which British actress starred in the 2000 remake of the 1967 film *Bedazzled*?
4. By what name was American lyricist Samuel Cohen known?
5. Which actor appeared in *Superman* and *Apocalypse Now*?
6. What is the longest river in Italy?
7. What is the value of the green ball in snooker?
8. In which political scandal of the 1970s was John D Ehrlichman involved?
9. Who wrote *A Christmas Carol*?
10. What is the capital of Chile?
11. Which city is West Sussex was called *Noviomagus Regnensium* by the Romans?
12. Who wrote *Rebecca of Sunnybrook Farm*?
13. Which British sprinter won the 100m at the world junior championships after passing up the chance to go to the Olympics?
14. By what name was Sir Henry Percy, who died in 1403, known?
15. Which blacklisted U.S. director made the films *The Servant* and *The Go-Between*?
16. What was the first name of the composer Mussorgsky?
17. Of which ocean is the Kara Sea an arm?
18. How many players make up a rugby union team?
19. What is the title of the Clement Moore poem that begins "Twas the night before Christmas"?
20. What nationality is the soprano Montserrat Caballe?

ANSWERS: *1 The eye, 2 1993, 3 Liz Hurley, 4 Sammy Cahn, 5 Marlon Brando, 6 River Po, 7 Three, 8 Watergate, 9 Charles Dickens, 10 Santiago, 11 Chichester, 12 Kate Wiggin, 13 Mark Lewis-Francis, 14 Hotspur, 15 Joseph Losey, 16 Modest, 17 Arctic Ocean, 18 Fifteen, 19 A Visit from St Nicholas, 20 Spanish.*

General Knowledge

Your rating:
- 0-5 Join a library
- 6-10 Keep at it
- 11-15 Join a quiz team
- 16-20 Join Mensa

1. Which newspaper was founded by Alfred Harmsworth in 1896?
2. What country does cricketer Lance Klusener represent?
3. Which English novelist wrote *Moll Flanders*?
4. In which European country is the ski resort of Kaprun?
5. Who is the patron saint of music?
6. With which sport was Dennis Andries most famously associated?
7. In which New York square do crowds traditionally gather on New Year's Eve?
8. Which Canadian comedian starred in the films *Planes, Trains and Automobiles* and *Cool Runnings*?
9. In which U.S. state is the city of Houston?
10. Which singer had hits with *Mistletoe and Wine* and *Saviour's Day*?
11. Which English team won football's U.E.F.A. Cup in 2001?
12. What is the literal meaning of the word cenotaph?
13. The Wish Tower and the Redoubt are features of which East Sussex seaside resort?
14. What is the name of the 203-carat diamond that thieves tried to steal from the Dome in 2000?
15. In which English county is The Wrekin?
16. Which American football team won the Super Bowl in 1997?
17. Which dog takes its name from the German for 'badger dog'?
18. In broadcasting, for which channel is CNN an abbreviation?
19. Which joint is also known as the carpus?
20. Christmas Island in the Indian Ocean is a territory of which country?

ANSWERS: *1 Daily Mail, 2 South Africa, 3 Daniel Defoe, 4 Austria, 5 St Cecilia, 6 Boxing, 7 Times Square, 8 John Candy, 9 Texas, 10 Cliff Richard, 11 Liverpool, 12 Empty tomb, 13 Eastbourne, 14 The Millennium Star, 15 Shropshire, 16 Green Bay Packers, 17 Dachshund, 18 Cable News Network, 19 Wrist, 20 Australia.*

General Knowledge

Your rating:
- 0-5 Join a library
- 6-10 Keep at it
- 11-15 Join a quiz team
- 16-20 Join Mensa

1. Which member of the Royal Family popularised the Christmas tree in the mid-19th century?
2. Which product did soap salesman William Wrigley Jr begin distributing in 1892?
3. On which river does Glasgow stand?
4. Which country won the cricket World Cup in 1975?
5. Which title was first granted to John Dryden?
6. By what first name was jazz drummer Bernard Rich known?
7. Which U.S. author wrote the book on which the film *The Grinch* is based?
8. Which rank did *Six Million Dollar Man* Steve Austin hold?
9. Which British golfer won the 2000 European Order of Merit title?
10. To which European city were Kevin's family travelling in the film *Home Alone*?
11. Which former British intelligence officer wrote the controversial book *Spycatcher*?
12. Of which country did Jean-Bédel Bokassa proclaim himself emperor in 1977?
13. What was the first name of *Ironside*?
14. How many players are there in a Gaelic football team?
15. What name is given to the Japanese art of flower arranging?
16. Of which Italian island is Cagliari the capital?
17. Which American novelist wrote Goodbye Columbus?
18. By what name is the plant *Helleborus niger* better known?
19. Which British contralto died in 1953 at the age of 41?
20. A daguerreotype was an early form of what?

ANSWERS: *1 Prince Albert, 2 Chewing gum, 3 River Clyde, 4 West Indies, 5 Poet laureate, 6 Buddy, 7 Dr Seuss, 8 Colonel, 9 Lee Westwood, 10 Paris, 11 Peter Wright, 12 Central African Republic, 13 Robert, 14 Fifteen, 15 Ikebana, 16 Sardinia, 17 Philip Roth, 18 Christmas rose, 19 Kathleen Ferrier, 20 Photograph.*

Sports

Your rating:
- ● **0-5** **Wooden spoon**
- ● **6-10** **Bronze medal**
- ● **11-15** **Silver medal**
- ● **16-20** **Gold medal**

1. Which British swimmer retained his Commonwealth 50m freestyle title in 1998 in a new Games record time?
2. In which event did Sally Gunnell win her 1992 Olympic gold medal?
3. Which football team was coached by Carlos Alberto Parreira at the 1994 World Cup?
4. Which Russian tennis player was knocked out of Wimbledon by Venus Williams in 1999?
5. Which international rugby union competition was first staged in 1987?
6. Which British club won the 1968 European Cup?
7. In which year were the first modern Olympic Games held?
8. Which snooker player is nicknamed 'Whirlwind'?
9. Against which team did Arsenal clinch the Double in 1998 by winning the F.A. Cup Final?
10. In which city were the 1998 Commonwealth Games held?
11. Which sport's matches are divided into chukkas?
12. Who did George Foreman beat to win the world heavyweight boxing title in January 1973?
13. Which football team won the League Cup in 1988?
14. Which driver was on pole position a record 65 times in his 161 Grands Prix starts?
15. In which Olympic event did Ed Moses win gold and set a new world record in 1976?
16. Which tennis player won the men's singles at the 1998 Australian Open?
17. Which rugby union club side play at the Recreation Ground?
18. In which sport is the Swaythling Cup contested?
19. Which British side did France beat 36-3 in the 1991 rugby union Five Nations championships?
20. Which two titles did Lasse Viren successfully defend at the 1976 Olympics?

***ANSWERS:** 1 Mark Foster, 2 400m hurdles, 3 Brazil, 4 Anna Kournikova, 5 The World Cup, 6 Manchester United, 7 1896, 8 Jimmy White, 9 Newcastle United, 10 Kuala Lumpur, 11 Polo's, 12 Joe Frazier, 13 Luton Town, 14 Ayrton Senna, 15 400m hurdles, 16 Petr Korda, 17 Bath, 18 Table tennis, 19 Wales, 20 5,000m & 10,000m.*

General Knowledge

Your rating: ● 0-5 Join a library ● 6-10 Keep at it ● 11-15 Join a quiz team ● 16-20 Join Mensa

1. Which part of the body is affected by lumbago?
2. Which Derbyshire town is famous for its church with a crooked spire?
3. By what acronym is the International Criminal Police Organisation usually known?
4. Does the Arctic Circle surround the North Pole or the South Pole?
5. Which country developed the Polaris missile?
6. What sort of creature is a barracuda?
7. Which electrician became leader of the Polish trade union Solidarity in 1980, and was awarded the 1983 Nobel Peace Prize?
8. In which English county is the port of Ramsgate situated?
9. Which New Testament evangelist was the author of the third Gospel?
10. In which Asian country can the city of Lahore be found?
11. What was the name for the line of demarcation between North and South Vietnam established by the Geneva Conference?
12. Which East Sussex village was the landing place of William the Conqueror?
13. What is the largest cemetery in the USA?
14. In which European country is the port of Narvik located?
15. Which French designer took over Dior's fashion house in 1957?
16. Which royal palace was the principal London residence of the monarch from 1697 until superseded by Buckingham Palace in 1837?
17. Which is the innermost and second smallest planet of the solar system?
18. Which two countries signed the 1569 Union of Lublin?
19. Who was the prime minister of Canada from 1968 to 1979 and 1980 to 1984?
20. What sort of creature is a scaup?

ANSWERS: *1 The back, 2 Chesterfield, 3 Interpol, 4 The North Pole, 5 USA, 6 A fish, 7 Lech Walesa, 8 Kent, 9 St Luke, 10 Pakistan, 11 The Seventeenth Parallel, 12 Pevensey, 13 The Arlington National Cemetery, 14 Norway, 15 Yves Saint-Laurent, 16 St James's Palace, 17 Mercury, 18 Poland and Lithuania, 19 Pierre Trudeau, 20 A duck.*

General Knowledge

Your rating: ● 0-5 Join a library ● 6-10 Keep at it ● 11-15 Join a quiz team ● 16-20 Join Mensa

1. In which continent are ostriches found in the wild?
2. Which organ is inflamed if one is suffering from hepatitis?
3. Which city was the site of the 1980 Summer Olympic Games?
4. Which fruit comes from the tree *Citrus paradisi*?
5. According to Greek mythology, which beautiful youth was punished by being made to fall in love with his own reflection?
6. With which musical instrument is French jazz musician Stephane Grappelli associated?
7. How many wives did King Henry VIII of England have?
8. Which word describes any animal without a backbone?
9. What nationality was the composer Jean Sibelius?
10. In which European country is Lake Lucerne situated?
11. Which Scottish chemist won the 1904 Nobel Prize for Chemistry for his work on noble gases?
12. At which Cumbrian town was the first British nuclear submarine built?
13. Which group of Nottingham frameworkers were severely repressed after destroying labour-saving machinery in 1811?
14. What sort of creature is a water moccasin?
15. What was the only cabinet post held by Enoch Powell?
16. Which Sikh ruler was known as the Lion of the Punjab?
17. Who directed the films *Jules et Jim* and *L'Enfant sauvage*?
18. Which Scottish river rises on Ben Lomond and flows through Stirling to Alloa?
19. Which U.S. poet wrote *Hugh Selwyn* and *Homage to Sextus Propertius*?
20. Where would you find a Mercator projection?

ANSWERS: *1 Africa, 2 The liver, 3 Moscow, 4 Grapefruit, 5 Narcissus, 6 The violin, 7 Six, 8 Invertebrate, 9 Finnish, 10 Switzerland, 11 Sir William Ramsay, 12 Barrow-in-Furness, 13 Luddites, 14 A snake, 15 Minister of health, 16 Maharaja Ranjit Singh, 17 François Truffaut, 18 The River Forth, 19 Ezra Pound, 20 On a map.*

General Knowledge

Your rating: ● **0-5** Join a library ● **6-10** Keep at it ● **11-15** Join a quiz team ● **16-20** Join Mensa

1. Which title was assumed by rulers of ancient Egypt?
2. Which presumed assassin of John F. Kennedy was killed by Jack Ruby?
3. Which British architect redesigned Buckingham Palace and Brighton's Royal Pavilion?
4. Of which chemical element is graphite a form?
5. What sort of creature is a whiting?
6. What do the initials RAF stand for?
7. Which explosive mixture invented by Alfred Nobel consists of 75% nitroglycerine and 25% kieselguhr?
8. Which pets are paraded at the annual British show Cruft's?
9. According to legend, which Greek mathematician shouted "Eureka!" after discovering a scientific principle in the bath?
10. At which naval battle in the Napoleonic wars was Nelson killed in the hour of victory?
11. Which extremely hard bluish-silver metal is represented by the symbol Os?
12. Which Czech filmmaker directed the 1976 film *One Flew over the Cuckoo's Nest*?
13. How many Noble Truths are the central beliefs of Buddhism based on?
14. Which Spice Girls song was the 1995 Christmas No. 1 single?
15. What sort of creature is a wallcreeper?
16. Of which French overseas region is Fort-de-France the capital?
17. Which type of acid takes its name from the Latin name for ant?
18. What is the largest inlet on the USA's Atlantic coast?
19. Which British novelist wrote *A Passage to India*?
20. What sort of plant is a peyote?

ANSWERS: *1 Pharaoh, 2 Lee Harvey Oswald, 3 John Nash, 4 Carbon, 5 A fish, 6 Royal Air Force, 7 Dynamite, 8 Dogs, 9 Archimedes, 10 The Battle of Trafalgar, 11 Osmium, 12 Milos Forman, 13 Four, 14 2 Become 1, 15 A bird, 16 Martinique, 17 Formic acid, 18 Chesapeake Bay, 19 E. M. Forster, 20 A cactus.*

Entertainment

Your rating:

- **0-5 Buy a TV**
- **6-10 Keep at it**
- **11-15 Join a quiz team**
- **16-20 Enter a quiz show**

1. Which former Blue Peter presenter co-hosted *Bright Sparks* on TV?
2. Which popular violinist released an album entitled *Kafka* in 1996?
3. Which David Croft comedy series was set in the 1960s in Hatley railway station?
4. Who had a top ten hit single in 1968 with *(Sittin' On) The Dock Of The Bay*?
5. Who starred as the English nobleman captured by the Sioux in the 1970 film *A Man Called Horse*?
6. Who starred as *Budgie* in the '70s TV series?
7. Which country music legend released an album entitled *Spirit* in 1996?
8. Who starred as ex-con George in the 1986 film *Mona Lisa*?
9. Which talkshow presenter controversially moved to the BBC before having her programme axed after bad publicity in 1999?
10. Which Irish blues guitarist released the albums *Against The Grain* and *Tattoo* in the '70s?
11. Who starred as the young bride-to-be in the film *How To Make An American Quilt*?
12. Which model and *Summer Holiday* presenter has a false leg?
13. Which ex-husband of Julia Roberts released an album entitled *The Road To Ensenada* in 1996?
14. Which U.S. sitcom starred Téa Leoni as a photojournalist?
15. Which actor played Jack Dawson in the hit 1998 film *Titanic*?
16. Who had a number one hit single in 1991 with the re-released *Should I Stay Or Should I Go*?
17. Who starred as Dutch in the 1987 film *Predator*?
18. Who played Lois Lane in TV's *The New Adventures of Superman*?
19. Who played the title role in the 1996 film *The Juror*?
20. Who starred as *The Fugitive* in the '60s TV series?

ANSWERS: *1 Diane Louise Jordan, 2 Nigel Kennedy, 3 Oh, Doctor Beeching!, 4 Otis Redding, 5 Richard Harris, 6 Adam Faith, 7 Willie Nelson, 8 Bob Hoskins, 9 Vanessa Feltz, 10 Rory Gallagher, 11 Winona Ryder, 12 Heather Mills, 13 Lyle Lovett, 14 Naked Truth, 15 Leonardo DiCaprio, 16 The Clash, 17 Arnold Schwarzenegger, 18 Teri Hatcher, 19 Demi Moore, 20 David Janssen.*

General Knowledge

Your rating: ● 0-5 Join a library ● 6-10 Keep at it ● 11-15 Join a quiz team ● 16-20 Join Mensa

1. In which English county can the resorts of Southend-on-Sea and Clacton be found?
2. What do the initials BBC stand for?
3. What is the title of the spiritual ruler of Tibet?
4. Which poisonous element is represented by the symbol As?
5. Which British dramatist wrote *Absurd Person Singular* and *Bedroom Farce*?
6. Who was the first wife of Henry VIII of England?
7. What sort of creature is a sprat?
8. Which word describes criminal damage committed by fire?
9. Which major airport is in the Greater London borough of Hounslow?
10. What sort of creature is a painted lady?
11. For which English monarch was Holbein the Younger court painter and designer?
12. Of which planet is Titan the largest satellite?
13. What is the name of the sheep which was successfully cloned at the Roslin Institute in Edinburgh in 1997?
14. Which gas makes up approximately 98 per cent of the atmosphere of the planet Venus?
15. Which British poet wrote the volume of poems entitled *Look, Stranger!*?
16. According to Greek mythology, who was the twin sister of Apollo?
17. Which British novelist created the character Horatio Hornblower?
18. Of which South American country is Mount Chimborazo the highest point?
19. Which U.S. novelist and dramatist wrote *The Skin of Our Teeth*?
20. Which British admiral was commander of the grand fleet from 1914 to 1916?

ANSWERS: *1 Essex, 2 British Broadcasting Corporation, 3 Dalai Lama, 4 Arsenic, 5 Alan Ayckbourn, 6 Catherine of Aragon, 7 A fish, 8 Arson, 9 Heathrow, 10 A butterfly, 11 Henry VIII, 12 Saturn, 13 Dolly, 14 Carbon dioxide, 15 W. H. Auden, 16 Artemis, 17 C. S. Forester, 18 Ecuador, 19 Thornton Wilder, 20 John Jellicoe.*

General Knowledge

Your rating: ● **0-5** **Join a library** ● **6-10** **Keep at it** ● **11-15** **Join a quiz team** ● **16-20** **Join Mensa**

1. In which continent can Lake Titicaca be found?
2. What sort of creature was Laika, who became the first animal in space in 1957?
3. Which U.S. actor and film maker directed *Annie Hall* and *Manhattan*?
4. In which European country can the city of Maastricht be found?
5. Which strong transition metal is represented by the symbol Ti?
6. In English law, what do the initials QC stand for?
7. What was the surname of the physician whose 1852 *Thesaurus of English Words and Phrases* has been revised in numerous editions?
8. Squirrels, mice, rats and chincillas are examples of what sort of mammals?
9. Which Russian composer wrote *Pictures at an Exhibition* and *A Night on the Bare Mountain*?
10. Which port is the largest city in New Zealand?
11. Which U.S. short-story writer wrote *Rip Van Winkle* and *The Legend of Sleepy Hollow*?
12. Who was prime minister of France from 1938 to 1940?
13. Of which Caribbean country is Santo Domingo the capital?
14. According to Greek legend, which prophet advised the Greeks to build the wooden horse by which they gained entry to Troy?
15. What is an earthstar?
16. Which author of the detective novel *Trent's Last Case* invented a humorous verse form consisting of two rhyming couplets?
17. Where, in North Scotland, was the site of the world's first experimental fast-breeder reactor?
18. Which British tribe was led by Boadicea or Boudicca?
19. How is the classic Chinese work on divination the Book of Changes otherwise known?
20. Which city is the capital of the Indian state of Andhra Pradesh?

ANSWERS: *1 South America, 2 A dog, 3 Woody Allen, 4 The Netherlands, 5 Titanium, 6 Queen's Counsel, 7 Roget, 8 Rodents, 9 Modest Mussorgsky, 10 Auckland, 11 Washington Irving, 12 Edouard Daladier, 13 Dominican Republic, 14 Calchas, 15 A fungus, 16 Edmund Clerihew Bentley, 17 Dounreay, 18 Iceni, 19 I Ching, 20 Hyderabad.*

General Knowledge

Your rating: ● 0-5 Join a library ● 6-10 Keep at it ● 11-15 Join a quiz team ● 16-20 Join Mensa

1. What is the largest province in Canada?
2. In which century did the Great Plague of London take place?
3. What sort of creature is a springbok?
4. What do the initials UFO stand for?
5. What is the organ that supplies oxygen and nutrients to a fetus called?
6. Of which English monarch was Jane Seymour the third wife?
7. In which Italian city can St Mark's Cathedral be found?
8. Which Roman goddess was identified with the Greek Aphrodite as goddess of love?
9. Which dramatist and poet wrote *The Importance of Being Earnest*?
10. In which country can the Bog of Allen be found?
11. What is the highest peak in Washington state?
12. Which navigational instrument is shaped in an arc of the sixth part of a circle?
13. Who is the only First Lady of the USA to have won a Grammy award?
14. Which country NE of Madagascar has Victoria as its capital?
15. Which filmmaker directed the films *The Go-Between* and *The Servant*?
16. Of which common mineral is rock crystal a pure variety?
17. What do the initials ISBN stand for?
18. What sort of bird is a lory?
19. Which British novelist wrote *Goodbye to Berlin*?
20. Of which state of the USA is Frankfort the capital?

ANSWERS: *1 Quebec, 2 The 17th century, 3 Antelope, 4 Unidentified flying object, 5 The placenta, 6 Henry VIII, 7 Venice, 8 Venus, 9 Oscar Wilde, 10 The Republic of Ireland, 11 Mount Rainier, 12 Sextant, 13 Hillary Clinton, 14 Seychelles, 15 Joseph Losey, 16 Quartz, 17 International Standard Book Number, 18 A parrot, 19 Christopher Isherwood, 20 Kentucky.*

Entertainment

Your rating: ● **0-5** **Buy a TV** ● **6-10** **Keep at it** ● **11-15** **Join a quiz team** ● **16-20** **Enter a quiz show**

1. Which Channel 4 comedy series starred Beatie Edney as a young woman looking for love?
2. Which song did both Norman Greenbaum and Doctor and the Medics take to number one?
3. Which actress played a young American governess in the 1996 film *A Month By The Lake*?
4. Who starred on TV as *Dr Quinn: Medicine Woman*?
5. Which New Wave American songstress released her first album for eight years in 1996, entitled *Gone Again*?
6. Which *Easy Rider* star directed *The Last Movie*?
7. Who, along with Zoe Ball, retired from presenting the Saturday morning TV show *Live & Kicking* in 1999?
8. Which singer/songwriter had a top ten hit in 1965 with *Subterranean Homesick Blues*?
9. Which former *EastEnders* actress presented *Genderquake* on TV?
10. Which rock star played a house-painter in the film *Moonlight And Valentino*?
11. By what nickname was '60s TV chef Graham Kerr known?
12. Which Latin-influenced jazz/pop trumpeter released an album entitled *Second Wind* in 1996?
13. Which British actor played the ex-Nazi who leaves his jungle hideaway for New York in the 1976 film *Marathon Man*?
14. Which surgeon in TV's *Chicago Hope* is played by Mandy Patinkin?
15. Which Canadian musician collaborated with Crazy Horse on the 1996 album *Broken Arrow*?
16. Who directed the 1986 film *Pirates*?
17. Which psychic TV show was presented by Susie Johns?
18. Which British pop group had a top ten hit in 1986 with *Suburbia*?
19. Which *Frasier* star played a submarine captain in the 1996 film *Down Periscope*?
20. Who starred in the TV series *Maverick* and *The Rockford Files*?

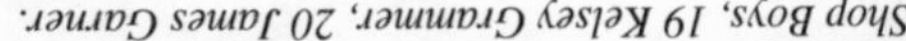

ANSWERS: *1 Dressing For Breakfast, 2 Spirit in the Sky, 3 Uma Thurman, 4 Jane Seymour, 5 Patti Smith, 6 Dennis Hopper, 7 Jamie Theakston, 8 Bob Dylan, 9 Susan Tully, 10 Jon Bon Jovi, 11 The Galloping Gourmet, 12 Herb Alpert, 13 Laurence Olivier, 14 Jeffrey Geiger, 15 Neil Young, 16 Roman Polanski, 17 Sixth Sense, 18 Pet Shop Boys, 19 Kelsey Grammer, 20 James Garner.*

General Knowledge

Your rating:
- 0-5 Join a library
- 6-10 Keep at it
- 11-15 Join a quiz team
- 16-20 Join Mensa

1. Which parts of the body do doctors known as ophthalmologists specialise in?
2. Which acute viral infection transmitted by animals is alternatively known as hydrophobia?
3. In which country did the alcoholic drink tequila originate?
4. What sort of insects belong to the family *Formicidae*?
5. Which English county contains Lizard Point, the most southerly point of the British Isles?
6. Of which country is Uncle Sam the personification?
7. Of which Mediterranean island is Nicosia the capital?
8. In which European city was the world's first urban underground railway built?
9. In which athletics event do competitors use a pole to lever themselves over a horizontal bar?
10. What is the name for the middle value of a set of numbers arranged in order of magnitude?
11. Antibodies to which bacterial infection may be discovered by the Schick test?
12. According to Greek legend, which sorceress helped Jason to steal the Golden Fleece?
13. What is the name for a line on a map joining points of equal temperature?
14. What sort of creature is a lumpsucker?
15. Who was the president of West Germany from 1974 to 1979?
16. Which French dramatist wrote *Le Bourgeois gentilhomme* and *Le Malade imaginaire*?
17. Which Danish composer wrote the opera *Saul and David*?
18. Who was the Archduchess of Austria from 1740 to 1780?
19. Which Welsh novelist wrote *How Green Was My Valley*?
20. What sort of creature is a hoopoe?

ANSWERS: *1 Eyes, 2 Rabies, 3 Mexico, 4 Ants, 5 Cornwall, 6 USA, 7 Cyprus, 8 London, 9 Pole vault, 10 Median, 11 Diphtheria, 12 Medea, 13 Isotherm, 14 A fish, 15 Walter Scheel, 16 Molière, 17 Carl Nielsen, 18 Maria Theresa, 19 Richard Llewellyn, 20 A bird.*

General Knowledge

Your rating:
- **0-5 Join a library**
- **6-10 Keep at it**
- **11-15 Join a quiz team**
- **16-20 Join Mensa**

1. Which London soccer stadium was the site of the 1948 Olympic Games?
2. What is the capital of Ecuador?
3. Which gas makes up more than seventy-five per cent of the earth's atmosphere?
4. Which state of the USA was founded by the English Quaker William Penn?
5. What name is given to the structure that connects a fetus to the placenta in the womb?
6. Which Turkish city used to be known as Constantinople?
7. What is the second largest continent in the world?
8. Which British school of acting is represented by the acronym RADA?
9. What sort of creature is an affenpinscher?
10. According to Greek mythology, which brother of Prometheus was forced to hold up the pillars separating heaven from earth?
11. Which version of the Bible was produced by St. Jerome in the 4th century AD?
12. Which committee was established by the U.S. House of Representatives in 1935 to investigate subversive organisations?
13. Which daughter of Henry VII of England was Regent of Scotland from 1513 to 1514?
14. Which statesman acquired California for the USA whilst serving as president from 1845 to 1849?
15. Which lanthanide element is represented by the symbol Tb?
16. Which German filmmaker directed the films *Madame De* and *Lola Montes*?
17. What name is given to the study of sound waves inaudible to the human ear?
18. Who succeeded Asquith as prime minister of Great Britain?
19. Who was the Roman god of fire?
20. Which British bowler was at the centre of the bodyline controversy during the 1932-33 tour of Australia?

ANSWERS: *1 Wembley, 2 Quito, 3 Nitrogen, 4 Pennsylvania, 5 The umbilical cord, 6 Istanbul, 7 Africa, 8 Royal Academy of Dramatic Art, 9 A dog, 10 Atlas, 11 The Vulgate, 12 The Un-American Activities Committee, 13 Margaret Tudor, 14 James K. Polk, 15 Terbium, 16 Max Ophuls, 17 Ultrasonics, 18 David Lloyd George, 19 Vulcan, 20 Harold Larwood.*

General Knowledge

Your rating:
- 0-5 Join a library
- 6-10 Keep at it
- 11-15 Join a quiz team
- 16-20 Join Mensa

1. In which ocean can the Marianas Trench be found?
2. How is light amplification by stimulated emission of radiation commonly known?
3. Which country in the Mediterranean was awarded the George Cross for its resistance to German attack during World War II?
4. Which Swedish actress went to Hollywood in 1939 and subsequently starred in the films *Casablanca* and *Gaslight*?
5. What is the second largest of the Channel Islands?
6. Which London street between the Strand and Ludgate Circus used to house the offices of most of the UK's national newspapers?
7. The Anschluss of 1938 was a union between which two countries?
8. What sort of creature is a gudgeon?
9. Of which European country is Bergen the second largest city?
10. What was the nickname of King Edmund II?
11. Which U.S. aviator was the first woman to fly solo across the Atlantic Ocean?
12. What is the name for chemical compounds that have the same molecular formulae but different arrangements of atoms?
13. Which British novelist wrote *Tom Brown's Schooldays*?
14. Which 15th century English author wrote *Morte d'Arthur*?
15. Which is the third planet from the sun?
16. What name is used by biblical scholars to describe the first five books of the Old Testament?
17. Which Old Testament woman became the queen of the Persian King Ahasuerus?
18. Which country is the smallest island in the Greater Antilles?
19. Which Holy Roman Emperor replaced Pope John XII with Leo VIII and established bishoprics to control his domains?
20. Which manned Soviet space stations were first launched into earth orbit in 1971?

ANSWERS: *1 The Pacific, 2 Laser, 3 Malta, 4 Ingrid Bergman, 5 Guernsey, 6 Fleet Street, 7 Austria and Germany, 8 A fish, 9 Norway, 10 Ironside, 11 Amelia Earhart, 12 Isomers, 13 Thomas Hughes, 14 Sir Thomas Malory, 15 The earth, 16 Pentateuch, 17 Esther, 18 Puerto Rico, 19 Otto the Great, 20 Salyut.*

Entertainment

Your rating: ● **0-5** Buy a TV ● **6-10** Keep at it ● **11-15** Join a quiz team ● **16-20** Enter a quiz show

1. Who plays Dr Frasier Crane in the US sitcom *Frasier*?
2. Which Motown singer had a top ten hit single in 1980 with *I'm Coming Out*?
3. Which 1996 Jim Jarmusch film featured performances from Johnny Depp, Robert Mitchum, John Hurt and Iggy Pop?
4. Who played Jack Roan in the TV series *Atletico Partick*?
5. Which former Take That star had a number one hit in 1996 with *Forever Love*?
6. Who played Veronica in the 1989 film *Heathers*?
7. Which *Children's ITV* magazine show was presented by Dannii Minogue and Sally Gray?
8. Which band had a number one hit in 1975 with *I'm Not In Love*?
9. Who produced, directed, and starred in the title role of the 1990 film *Dick Tracy*?
10. Who reprised his radio role as the head of the family in the TV version of *The Glums*?
11. Who starred as the cable TV installer in the film *The Cable Guy*?
12. Which James singer collaborated on an album in 1996 with *Twin Peaks* composer Angelo Badalamenti?
13. Who played the title role in the 1969 film version of *Hello Dolly!*?
14. Who first presented *Whose Line Is It Anyway* on TV?
15. Which Manchester band had a top twenty hit in 1991 with *I Wanna Be Adored*?
16. Which 1996 Disney animated film was based on a story by Victor Hugo?
17. Which spin-off from the TV comedy *Porridge* followed Fletcher's progress out of jail?
18. Which flautist released an album entitled *The Celtic Minstrel* in 1996?
19. Who starred in the title role of the 1992 film *My Cousin Vinny*?
20. Who played Mike Barratt in the BBC hospital drama *Casualty*?

ANSWERS: *1 Kelsey Grammer, 2 Diana Ross, 3 Dead Man, 4 Gordon Kennedy, 5 Gary Barlow, 6 Winona Ryder, 7 The Scoop, 8 10 C. C., 9 Warren Beatty, 10 Jimmy Edwards, 11 Jim Carrey, 12 Tim Booth, 13 Barbra Streisand, 14 Clive Anderson, 15 The Stone Roses, 16 The Hunchback of Notre Dame, 17 Going Straight, 18 James Galway, 19 Joe Pesci, 20 Clive Mantle.*

General Knowledge

Your rating: ● **0-5** **Join a library** ● **6-10** **Keep at it** ● **11-15** **Join a quiz team** ● **16-20** **Join Mensa**

1. Which political party formed an alliance with the Social Democratic Party in 1981?
2. Which British poet authored the volumes *The Whitsun Weddings* and *High Windows*?
3. What sort of creature is a mallard?
4. In which Scandinavian country is the port of Malmo situated?
5. By what name was the day in 1944 on which the Allied invasion of Normandy was launched from Britain known?
6. According to Greek legend, which Cretan monster had a bull's head and a man's body?
7. The magnitude of which natural phenomena is measured according to the Richter Scale?
8. Which constellation of the zodiac means "Scales" in Latin?
9. Which star of the films *Niagara* and *Gentlemen Prefer Blondes* had the first names Norma Jean?
10. Which type of winter sport is divided into Alpine and Nordic varieties?
11. Who was the secretary of state for education and science from 1981 to 1986?
12. What is the capital of Tibet?
13. What sort of creature is a skimmer?
14. Under what name did Jyoti Mishra top the charts with the song *Your Woman - Abort, Retry, Fail*?
15. By what name were the 400 Church of England clergy who refused to swear allegiance to William III and Mary II in 1690 known?
16. Which British novelist created *Tristram Shandy*?
17. Which Berkshire village is associated with several protest marches organised by CND between 1958 and 1963?
18. In which country can the Liaodong Peninsula be found?
19. Which British novelist wrote *The Saliva Tree* and *Last Orders*?
20. Who became Holy Roman Emperor in 1519 on the death of his grandfather Maximilian I?

ANSWERS: *1 The Liberal Party, 2 Philip Larkin, 3 A duck, 4 Sweden, 5 D-Day, 6 Minotaur, 7 Earthquakes, 8 Libra, 9 Marilyn Monroe, 10 Skiing, 11 Sir Keith Joseph, 12 Lhasa, 13 A bird, 14 White Town, 15 Nonjurors, 16 Laurence Sterne, 17 Aldermaston, 18 China, 19 Brian Aldiss, 20 Charles V.*

General Knowledge

Your rating:
- 0-5 Join a library
- 6-10 Keep at it
- 11-15 Join a quiz team
- 16-20 Join Mensa

1. Which modern day country was once home to the Aztecs?
2. Which British motor racing driver won 27 Grand Prix victories and was world champion in 1969, 1971 and 1973?
3. What name is given to the marks which appear on the body of a living person that resemble the five wounds that Christ received at the crucifixion?
4. Which term describes an industry in which the market is supplied by one supplier?
5. Which British novelist wrote *The Strange Case of Dr Jekyll and Mr Hyde*?
6. Which government archives organisation is represented by the initials PRO?
7. The Azores are part of which European country?
8. What name was given to the Nazi regime that succeeded the Weimar Republic and ended with Germany's defeat in World War II?
9. Which Welsh poet wrote the popular radio play *Under Milk Wood*?
10. Which body tissue consists of the dermis and the epidermis?
11. Of which country was Peter Fraser prime minister from 1940 to 1949?
12. Which British novelist wrote *Titus Groan*?
13. Which Scottish city is situated on the North Sea coast between the mouths of the Rivers Don and Dee?
14. Which actor was voted best comedy actor for *Jerry Maguire* in the 1997 Golden Globe awards?
15. Which Czech long-distance runner won three gold medals at the 1952 Helsinki Olympics?
16. In which town was the National Library of Wales established in 1911?
17. By what nickname was World War One air ace Manfred von Richthofen usually known?
18. On which river does the French city of Metz lie?
19. What sort of creature is a Percheron?
20. According to Greek legend, which dryad was the wife of Orpheus?

ANSWERS: *1 Mexico, 2 Jackie Stewart, 3 Stigmata, 4 Monopoly, 5 Robert Louis Stevenson, 6 Public Record Office, 7 Portugal, 8 The Third Reich, 9 Dylan Thomas, 10 Skin, 11 New Zealand, 12 Mervyn Peake, 13 Aberdeen, 14 Tom Cruise, 15 Emil Zatopek, 16 Aberystwyth, 17 The Red Baron, 18 River Moselle, 19 A horse, 20 Eurydice.*

General Knowledge

Your rating: ● 0-5 Join a library ● 6-10 Keep at it ● 11-15 Join a quiz team ● 16-20 Join Mensa

1. Of which group of islands is Alderney the third largest?
2. Which U.S. president founded the Peace Corps in 1961?
3. In which English county can the Peak District be found?
4. Which Hollywood actor starred in the films *Destry Rides Again* and *Harvey*?
5. On which date of the year does the feast day of St Valentine occur?
6. Which two cathedral cities provide the Church of England with its two Archbishops?
7. Is the Aberdeen Angus a breed of beef or dairy cattle?
8. Which Tibetan word is an alternative name for the Abominable Snowman?
9. Which type of medically useful electromagnetic radiation was originally called Roentgen rays?
10. Of which European country is Valletta the capital?
11. Which cinema idol of the 1920s starred in the films *The Sheik* and *Blood and Sand*?
12. Which British novelist wrote *The Cruel Sea*?
13. Which state of the USA is home to the Valley of Ten Thousand Smokes?
14. Who was sacked from Radio One after playing a round of golf when he should have been presenting the breakfast show?
15. Which royal dynasty of France succeeded the Capetians in 1328?
16. What is the capital of Tonga?
17. How many North American colonies originally became the United States of America in 1776?
18. What is the smallest and easternmost of the Great Lakes?
19. Which Italian filmmaker directed the 1968 film version of *Romeo and Juliet*?
20. Which novel by Charles Dickens features a raven called Grip?

ANSWERS: *1 Channel Islands, 2 John F. Kennedy, 3 Derbyshire, 4 James Stewart, 5 February 14th, 6 Canterbury and York, 7 Beef, 8 Yeti, 9 X-rays, 10 Malta, 11 Rudolf Valentino, 12 Nicholas Monsarrat, 13 Alaska, 14 Chris Evans, 15 Valois, 16 Nuku'alofa, 17 Thirteen, 18 Lake Ontario, 19 Franco Zeffirelli, 20 Barnaby Rudge.*

Entertainment

Your rating: ● **0-5** Buy a TV ● **6-10** Keep at it ● **11-15** Join a quiz team ● **16-20** Enter a quiz show

1. What was the title of the 1995 UK top five hit by the Nightcrawlers featuring John Reid?
2. Which actor played the title role in the 1973 film *Hitler - The Last Ten Days*?
3. Which US vocalist had a 1966 UK number one hit with *These Boots Are Made For Walking*?
4. Which 2000 film about a set of Siamese twins was written by and starred real-life twins Michael and Mark Polish?
5. In which eighties sitcom did Geoffrey Palmer star as Major Harry Kitchener Wellington Truscott?
6. What was the title of Robbie Williams' third album release?
7. Which biblical figure did Richard Gere play in a 1985 film of the same name?
8. To which holiday destination did *Emmerdale*'s Roy Glover head in 2000 to start a new life?
9. What was Modjo's 2000 UK number one hit single?
10. Which actress played Warren Clarke's wife in the BBC 1 drama series *Down to Earth*?
11. Who played *Nurse Betty* in the 2000 film of that name?
12. Which former Chancellor of the Exchequer's daughter launched her own cookery series on Channel 4 in 2000?
13. Which girl group's 2000 debut album was entitled *The Way It Is*?
14. What was the name of David Hasselhoff's character in the TV series *Baywatch*?
15. Which actress played *Jane Eyre* in the 1971 film version of the story?
16. Which sitcom duo embarked on a tour of Australia in the 2000 series *Men Down Under*?
17. Which flamboyant singer reached the UK number one spot posthumously in 1993 with *Living on My Own*?
18. Who directed the 2000 film *Snatch*?
19. Which actor played Jim in the comedy series *The Royle Family*?
20. Who wrote the novels upon which the seventies films *The Stud* and *The Bitch* were based?

ANSWERS: *1 Push the Feeling On, 2 Alec Guinness, 3 Nancy Sinatra, 4 Twin Falls Idaho, 5 Fairly Secret Army, 6 Sing When You're Winning, 7 King David, 8 Ibiza, 9 Lady (Hear Me Tonight), 10 Pauline Quirke, 11 Renee Zellweger, 12 Nigella Lawson (Nigella Bites), 13 Madasun's, 14 Mitch Bucannon, 15 Susannah York, 16 Martin Clunes & Neil Morrissey, 17 Freddie Mercury, 18 Guy Ritchie, 19 Ricky Tomlinson, 20 Jackie Collins.*

General Knowledge

Your rating: ● 0-5 Join a library ● 6-10 Keep at it ● 11-15 Join a quiz team ● 16-20 Join Mensa

1. Which British monarch died in January 1901?
2. What is the first name of the South African author J M Coetzee?
3. Which pop star ran up a £293,000 bill for flowers?
4. Coronas, cheroots and panatelas are types of what?
5. Which American actor starred in the films *Cool Hand Luke* and *The Hustler*?
6. How many Olympic gold medals did Sebastian Coe win?
7. Who wrote *The God of Small Things*?
8. From which German castle overlooking the Mulde River did 32 POWs successfully escape in World War II?
9. Which degenerative brain disorder is the most common form of dementia?
10. In which game was José Raúl Capablanca world champion from 1921 to 1927?
11. What was the name of Dick Dastardly's car in the cartoon *Wacky Races*?
12. After which Roman god is January named?
13. Which Spanish composer, best known for his *Concierto de Aranjuez*, was born in 1901?
14. Under what name was Michael Caine knighted?
15. Which bone is also called the talus?
16. What name is given to the night of anti-Jewish rioting on the night of November 9 1938?
17. In which series of films did the maniac Michael Myers appear?
18. Which Spanish surrealist artist painted *The Persistence of Memory*?
19. What is the fifth book of the Old Testament?
20. Which English novelist wrote *Eating People is Wrong* and *The History Man*?

ANSWERS: *1 Queen Victoria, 2 John, 3 Sir Elton John, 4 Cigars, 5 Paul Newman, 6 Two, 7 Arundhati Roy, 8 Colditz, 9 Alzheimer's disease, 10 Chess, 11 The Mean Machine, 12 Janus, 13 Joaquin Rodrigo, 14 Sir Maurice Micklewhite, 15 Ankle bone, 16 Kristallnacht, 17 Halloween, 18 Salvador Dali, 19 Deuteronomy, 20 Malcolm Bradbury.*

General Knowledge

Your rating:
- 0-5 Join a library
- 6-10 Keep at it
- 11-15 Join a quiz team
- 16-20 Join Mensa

1. Which English novelist wrote *The Ipcress File*?
2. In which city was the TV series *Quincy* set?
3. Which member of the Royal Family was photographed wringing a pheasant's neck in November 2000?
4. Of which organisation was John Reith director general from 1927 to 1938?
5. Which Russian city was formerly called Leningrad?
6. What sort of creature is a Russian Blue?
7. Who played the Acid Queen in the film *Tommy*?
8. In which sport is a shuttlecock used?
9. Which Turkish city was formerly called Constantinople and Byzantium?
10. What is the capital of Finland?
11. What was the first name of novelist D H Lawrence?
12. Which female American sprinter won Olympic gold medals in 1984, 1988 and 1992?
13. Who plays the third son of the devil in the film *Little Nicky*?
14. Cinnabar is the chief ore of which metallic element?
15. Whom did Neil Kinnock succeed as leader of the Labour Party?
16. By what forename was American jockey James Forman Sloan known, which became rhyming slang?
17. Which Charlie Chaplin film was banned in America?
18. Which English physicist and mathematician was born on Christmas Day in 1642?
19. In which Welsh town is the National Library of Wales?
20. Who was the first chancellor of West Germany?

ANSWERS: *1 Len Deighton, 2 Los Angeles, 3 The Queen, 4 BBC, 5 St Petersburg, 6 A cat, 7 Tina Turner, 8 Badminton, 9 Istanbul, 10 Helsinki, 11 David, 12 Evelyn Ashford, 13 Adam Sandler, 14 Mercury, 15 Michael Foot, 16 Tod, 17 Limelight, 18 Sir Isaac Newton, 19 Aberystwyth, 20 Konrad Adenauer.*

General Knowledge

Your rating: ● 0-5 Join a library ● 6-10 Keep at it ● 11-15 Join a quiz team ● 16-20 Join Mensa

1. Kurt Cobain was lead singer with which grunge rock group?
2. Who was born William Jefferson Blythe III in 1946?
3. What was the name of the character played by Richard Wilson in *One Foot in the Grave*?
4. Who was the first man to run a mile in less than four minutes?
5. Which oriental eating utensils originated in China?
6. Aer Lingus is the national airline of which country?
7. Which Dorset town is called Casterbridge in the novels of Thomas Hardy?
8. In which county is the town of Penzance?
9. By what name was William F Cody better known?
10. Which popular pianist died in November 2000 at the age of 75?
11. Who wrote the novel *Roots: The Saga of an American Family*?
12. By what collective name were tennis players Jean Borotra, Jacques Brugnon, Henri Cochet and René Lacoste known?
13. Which Turkish dish comprises thin layers of filo pastry containing nuts and honey?
14. In what year was there an unofficial truce on Christmas Day during World War I?
15. Which chemical element has the symbol B?
16. Who directed the films *The Graduate* and *Who's Afraid of Virginia Woolf*?
17. What was the name of the lion in the Chronicles of Narnia?
18. Which English novelist wrote *The Middle Ground* and *The Needle's Eye*?
19. How much did John Duthie win in the world's most lucrative poker tournament in 2000?
20. Which former Soviet leader was head of the KGB from 1967 to 1982?

ANSWERS: *1 Nirvana, 2 Bill Clinton, 3 Victor Meldrew, 4 Sir Roger Bannister, 5 Chopsticks, 6 Republic of Ireland, 7 Dorchester, 8 Cornwall, 9 Buffalo Bill, 10 Russ Conway, 11 Alex Haley, 12 The Four Musketeers, 13 Baklava, 14 1914, 15 Boron, 16 Mike Nichols, 17 Aslan, 18 Margaret Drabble, 19 £1 million, 20 Yuri Andropov.*

Entertainment

Your rating: ● **0-5** **Buy a TV** ● **6-10** **Keep at it** ● **11-15** **Join a quiz team** ● **16-20** **Enter a quiz show**

1. Which US boy band had a UK number one hit in 1989 with *You Got It (The Right Stuff)*?
2. Which was the first film of the *National Lampoon's* series to star Chevy Chase?
3. Which UK band had a 1967 UK top five hit with *Itchycoo Park*?
4. Which Oscar-winning actor played the title role in the 2000 film *Titus*?
5. Which comic actor's TV roles have included Trigger in *Only Fools and Horses* and Owen Newitt in *The Vicar of Dibley*?
6. What was the title of reggae rapper Glamma Kid's 2000 debut album release?
7. Which actress and author wrote the novel upon which the 1990 film *Postcards From the Edge* was based?
8. Which round-the-world yachtsman joined Lenny Henry on *Lenny's Big Atlantic Adventure*, screened on BBC 1 in 2000?
9. Which US R & B quartet released their fifth album, *Nathan Michael Shawn Wanya*, in 2000?
10. Which *EastEnders* character passed away in 2000 after enjoying her birthday party?
11. Which 2000 spoof horror film was directed and co-written by Keenan Ivory Wayans?
12. Which early nineties sitcom starred Penelope Keith as MP Jean Price?
13. What were the names of *The Blues Brothers* played by John Belushi and Dan Ackroyd in the 1980 film?
14. From which country are the guitar band Barenaked Ladies?
15. Which 1975 film starred James Caan and Robert Duvall as mercenaries who end up stalking each other?
16. Which ITV game show, presented by Cilla Black, challenged family members to complete certain tasks to win prizes?
17. Which Swedish duo had *The Look* in the UK top ten in 1989?
18. Which English actress starred opposite John Turturro in the 2000 film *The Luzhin Defence*?
19. Which 2000 BBC 1 drama featured Judi Dench as a saxophone-playing pensioner?
20. What was the Who's first UK top ten hit, which entered the chart in 1965?

ANSWERS: *1 New Kids on the Block, 2 National Lampoon's Vacation, 3 Small Faces, 4 Anthony Hopkins, 5 Roger Lloyd Pack's, 6 Kidology, 7 Carrie Fisher, 8 Tony Bullimore, 9 Boyz II Men, 10 Ethel Skinner, 11 Scary Movie, 12 No Job For a Lady, 13 Jake & Elwood, 14 Canada, 15 The Killer Elite, 16 Cilla's Moment of Truth, 17 Roxette, 18 Emily Watson, 19 The Last of the Blonde Bombshells, 20 I Can't Explain.*

General Knowledge

Your rating: ● 0-5 Join a library ● 6-10 Keep at it ● 11-15 Join a quiz team ● 16-20 Join Mensa

1. Which English adventurer and courtier to Elizabeth I was executed in 1618?
2. Which British poet wrote *Waving at Trains* and *The Stowaway*?
3. Which actress starred in *Dangerous Liaisons* and *Fatal Attraction*?
4. Judith Keppel was the first person to win £1 million on which TV quiz show?
5. In which country did the rottweiler originate?
6. Has the tug-of-war ever been an Olympic event?
7. What is the surname of Little Nell in *The Old Curiosity Shop* by Charles Dickens?
8. What name is given to a cosmic body of immense gravity from which nothing can escape?
9. Which comic strip featured Olive Oyl and J Wellington Wimpy?
10. With which religious sect is *The Watchtower* associated?
11. Which TV family had a maid called Alice?
12. Who was head of Fighter Command during the Battle of Britain?
13. What is the second brightest star in the night sky?
14. Who scored the try that gave England victory over Australia at Twickenham in November 2000?
15. With which Italian motor company is the Agnelli family associated?
16. Which English poet was born in Cockermouth in 1770?
17. Which of the Monty Python team wrote *Rutland Weekend Television*?
18. Of which Canadian province is St John's the capital?
19. Which was the first of the Great Lakes to be seen by Europeans?
20. Which American actor starred in *The Third Man* and *Under Capricorn*?

ANSWERS: *1 Sir Walter Raleigh, 2 Roger McGough, 3 Glenn Close, 4 Who Wants To Be a Millionaire?, 5 Germany, 6 Yes (1900-20), 7 Trent, 8 Black hole, 9 Popeye, 10 Jehovah's Witnesses, 11 The Brady Bunch, 12 Hugh Dowding, 13 Canopus, or Alpha Carinae, 14 Dan Luger, 15 Fiat, 16 William Wordsworth, 17 Eric Idle, 18 Newfoundland, 19 Lake Huron, 20 Joseph Cotten.*

General Knowledge

Your rating: ● 0-5 Join a library ● 6-10 Keep at it ● 11-15 Join a quiz team ● 16-20 Join Mensa

1. Which organisation controls horse racing and racehorse breeding in Great Britain?
2. Who provided the voices for the TV cartoon characters Roobarb and Custard?
3. Which French entertainer starred in the films *Love in the Afternoon* and *Gigi*?
4. Who became the world's most expensive defender when he joined Leeds United from West Ham United?
5. Which insect is commonly called a daddy longlegs?
6. What was the title of Robert Flaherty's 1922 documentary film about Eskimos?
7. Which member of The Beatles wrote the book *A Spaniard in the Works*?
8. What is the capital of Jersey?
9. Which Derbyshire town is renowned for its church with a crooked spire?
10. What name is given to painful involuntary contraction of muscle?
11. Which film star was known as Duke?
12. Which Anglo-Irish novelist wrote *Good Behaviour* and *Time After Time*?
13. Of which planet is Hyperion a satellite?
14. Which arts prize was won by German photographer Wolfgang Tillmans in 2000?
15. What were the first names of author GK Chesterton?
16. Which long-necked wading bird has crowned, whooping and sand-hill varieties?
17. What was the first film to be directed by Danny DeVito?
18. Which country won the 2000 Rugby League World Cup?
19. Which Canadian-born actress and dancer married Al Jolson in 1928?
20. Which Italian poet wrote *The Divine Comedy*?

ANSWERS: *1 The Jockey Club, 2 Richard Briers, 3 Maurice Chevalier, 4 Rio Ferdinand, 5 Crane fly, 6 Nanook of the North, 7 John Lennon, 8 St Helier, 9 Chesterfield, 10 Cramp, 11 John Wayne, 12 Molly Keane, 13 Saturn, 14 Turner Prize, 15 Gilbert Keith, 16 Crane, 17 Throw Momma From the Train, 18 Australia, 19 Ruby Keeler, 20 Dante Alighieri.*

General Knowledge

Your rating:
- 0-5 Join a library
- 6-10 Keep at it
- 11-15 Join a quiz team
- 16-20 Join Mensa

1. Which novel by Michael Ondaatje was adapted into an Oscar-winning film?
2. What was the name of the submarine in *Voyage to the Bottom of the Sea*?
3. Which pop superstar played a one-off concert at the Brixton Academy which was broadcast on the Internet in 2000?
4. What sort of puzzles originated as educational devices to teach geography?
5. Which actor first played James Bond in *GoldenEye*?
6. By what name is the wild primrose Primula veris known?
7. Who wrote the original *Tales of the Unexpected*?
8. What is the name of the prime minister's official country residence?
9. Who was the first man to win Olympic gold medals at 200m and 400m?
10. Who knocked out Gentleman Jim Corbett to become world heavyweight boxing champion in 1897?
11. Which best-selling novelist wrote *Going Home* and *Mixed Blessings*?
12. Which courtier of Dionysius the Elder had to sit beneath a sword hanging by a single thread?
13. Who wrote and directed the film *Boogie Nights*?
14. Which European country has become the first to legalise euthanasia?
15. For what form of fuel is LPG an abbreviation?
16. Which English poet wrote *The Village* and *The Borough*?
17. How many Rocky films have there been?
18. Which former Sunderland and England forward was known as the 'Clown Prince of Soccer'?
19. Who succeeded Yuri Andropov as leader of the Soviet Union in 1984?
20. Which award-winning French actress made her Hollywood debut in *Heaven's Gate*?

ANSWERS: *1 The English Patient, 2 Seaview, 3 Madonna, 4 Jigsaw puzzles, 5 Pierce Brosnan, 6 Cowslip, 7 Roald Dahl, 8 Chequers, 9 Michael Johnson, 10 Bob Fitzsimmons, 11 Danielle Steel, 12 Damocles, 13 Paul Thomas Anderson, 14 The Netherlands, 15 Liquefied petroleum gas, 16 George Crabbe, 17 5, 18 Len Shackleton, 19 Konstantin Chernenko, 20 Isabelle Huppert.*

Entertainment

Your rating: ● **0-5 Buy a TV** ● **6-10 Keep at it** ● **11-15 Join a quiz team** ● **16-20 Enter a quiz show**

1. Which *Fatal Attraction* actress starred in the 1991 film *Meeting Venus* as a lead soprano in the fictional Opera Europa?
2. Which former *Casualty* star played DC Mel Silver in the 2000 BBC 1 thriller *Waking the Dead*?
3. Which eighties group had a 1984 UK top five hit with *Doctor Doctor*?
4. Who directed the 2000 rites-of-passage drama *Liberty Heights*?
5. Which sixties sitcom featured *Carry On* stars such as Hattie Jacques, Charles Hawtrey and Joan Sims?
6. Which pop group had a 2000 UK top five hit with *Natural*?
7. In which 1989 film set in World War II did Nick Nolte star as a former US sergeant living in the Borneo jungle?
8. Which ITV medical drama series featured a female doctor called Alex Redman, played by Maggie O'Neill?
9. What was the title of Madonna's eighth studio album?
10. Which former *This Life* star appeared in the 2000 BBC 1 drama *A Likeness in Stone*?
11. Which 2000 Coen brothers film starred George Clooney as a thirties conman?
12. Which former *Doctor Who* played Professor Geoffrey Hoyt in the nineties drama series *Medics*?
13. Which legendary comic duo first appeared on screen together in a scene in the short film *A Lucky Dog*?
14. With which US singer did Westlife collaborate with on their 2000 UK number one hit, *Against All Odds*?
15. Which 1974 film set in South Africa starred Roger Moore as a mine foreman?
16. Which Channel 5 gameshow challenged ten contestants to escape from a prison in order to win a cash prize?
17. Which US vocalist had a 1959 UK number one hit with *Dream Lover*?
18. Which *Pulp Fiction* actor starred in the 2000 remake of the movie *Shaft*?
19. Who emerged as the winner of the first series of the Channel 4 gameshow phenomenon *Big Brother*?
20. Which British group had a 1984 UK top ten hit with *Heaven Knows I'm Miserable Now*?

ANSWERS: *1 Glenn Close, 2 Claire Goose, 3 Thompson Twins, 4 Barry Levinson, 5 Our House, 6 S Club 7, 7 Farewell to the King, 8 Peak Practice, 9 Music, 10 Andrew Lincoln (who played Egg), 11 O Brother, Where Art Thou?, 12 Tom Baker, 13 Laurel & Hardy, 14 Mariah Carey, 15 Gold, 16 Jailbreak, 17 Bobby Darin, 18 Samuel L. Jackson, 19 Craig Phillips, 20 The Smiths.*

General Knowledge

Your rating:
- ● 0-5 Join a library
- ● 6-10 Keep at it
- ● 11-15 Join a quiz team
- ● 16-20 Join Mensa

1. Which English novelist wrote *Brave New World* and *Eyeless in Gaza*?
2. Which film star was born Charles Carter?
3. Which dramatist wrote *Major Barbara* and *Pygmalion*?
4. In which building was the 2000 Miss World contest held?
5. Which town is West Bengal gives its name to a high-quality tea?
6. What name is given to a long narrow sea inlet resulting from marine inundation of a glacial valley?
7. Who wrote *The Carpetbaggers* and *The Betsy*?
8. Who became prime minister of France in June 1997?
9. What name is given to the period from about 476 to 1000 AD in western Europe?
10. Which football team beat Stoke City 8-0 in a 2000 Worthington Cup tie?
11. On which river does Chepstow stand?
12. Which member of the dog family is also called a prairie wolf?
13. Which American jazz trumpeter died in Spain in 1995?
14. In which city was the film *Bullitt* set?
15. What is the capital of Tanzania?
16. Which hand tool was used for threshing grain until the mid-19th century?
17. Which French revolutionary leader was murdered by Charlotte Corday?
18. Of what would a person suffering from hypertrichosis have an abnormal amount?
19. With which writer is the director Roger Corman associated?
20. Which member of the Royal Family was elevated to the Order of the Thistle in 2000?

ANSWERS: *1 Aldous Huxley, 2 Charlton Heston, 3 George Bernard Shaw, 4 The Millennium Dome, 5 Darjeeling, 6 Fjord, or fiord, 7 Harold Robbins, 8 Lionel Jospin, 9 Dark Ages, 10 Liverpool, 11 River Wye, 12 Coyote, 13 Don Cherry, 14 San Francisco, 15 Dodoma, 16 Flail, 17 Jean-Paul Marat, 18 Hair, 19 Edgar Allan Poe, 20 The Princess Royal.*

General Knowledge

Your rating: ● 0-5 Join a library ● 6-10 Keep at it ● 11-15 Join a quiz team ● 16-20 Join Mensa

1. Which American actor starred in *Cape Fear*, *Thunder Road* and *The Winds of War*?
2. What is the first name of the fictional detective Miss Marple?
3. Which former England manager joined Middlesbrough as first-team coach in 2000?
4. In which country did reggae music originate?
5. Which holiday is observed on the first Monday in September in the U.S.?
6. What nationality was the composer Dmitry Shostakovich?
7. Who was the *Housesitter* of Steve Martin in the 1992 film?
8. How many points does a Star of David have?
9. Which American actor starred in *Dirty Harry* and *Play Misty for Me*?
10. In which county is Chester-le-Street?
11. Which musical has won the most Oscars?
12. Which English actress starred in film versions of *Pygmalion* and *Major Barbara*?
13. In Greek mythology, who was the husband of Helen of Troy?
14. Which country beat Australia to win the Davis Cup for the first time?
15. Of which U.S. state is Bismarck the capital?
16. Which American soul singer founded the Blue Notes?
17. Who wrote the novel *The Magic Toyshop*?
18. Which British dramatist wrote *The Caretaker* and *The Birthday Party*?
19. What is the brightest star in the constellation Leo?
20. Which Pakistan cricketer made his 100th Test appearance in 2000?

***ANSWERS:** 1 Robert Mitchum, 2 Jane, 3 Terry Venables, 4 Jamaica, 5 Labor Day, 6 Russian, 7 Goldie Hawn, 8 Six, 9 Clint Eastwood, 10 Durham, 11 West Side Story, 12 Dame Wendy Hiller, 13 Menelaus, 14 Spain, 15 North Dakota, 16 Harold Melvin, 17 Angela Carter, 18 Harold Pinter, 19 Regulus, 20 Wasim Akram.*

General Knowledge

Your rating: ● 0-5 Join a library ● 6-10 Keep at it ● 11-15 Join a quiz team ● 16-20 Join Mensa

1. Which novel by Mary Norton first featured the Clock family?
2. Who played the lead in the film *Life of Brian*?
3. Which former England cricket captain died in 2000 at the age of 67?
4. What were Marilyn Monroe's real first names?
5. Which British racing driver won the Formula 1 world championship in 1962 and 1968?
6. Who was president of France from 1981 to 1995?
7. Who wrote *Uncle Silas* and *In a Glass Darkly*?
8. What title was given to the eldest son of a French king from 1350 to 1830?
9. Which Canadian province's name means 'New Scotland'?
10. In which athletics event was a cannon ball formerly used?
11. Which fictional diarist was created by Helen Fielding?
12. Which actor, whose films included *The Sting* and *Jaws*, wrote *The Man in the Glass Booth*?
13. What was the title of the BBC's controversial four-part drama about the 1916 Easter Rising?
14. Which American jazz pianist was known as Fatha?
15. What is the largest lake in Europe?
16. Which fish is also called a suckerfish?
17. What was the first name of Crocodile Dundee?
18. In which London borough is Heathrow Airport?
19. Which South African province was formerly known as Natal?
20. Which Nazi politician led the SS from 1929 and the Gestapo from 1936?

ANSWERS: *1 The Borrowers, 2 Graham Chapman, 3 Lord (Colin) Cowdrey of Tonbridge, 4 Norma Jean, 5 Graham Hill, 6 François Mitterrand, 7 Sheridan Le Fanu, 8 Dauphin, 9 Nova Scotia, 10 Shot put, 11 Bridget Jones, 12 Robert Shaw, 13 Rebel Heart, 14 Earl Hines, 15 Lake Ladoga, 16 Remora, 17 Michael, 18 Hillingdon, 19 KwaZulu/Natal, 20 Heinrich Himmler.*

Sports

Your rating: ● 0-5 Wooden spoon ● 6-10 Bronze medal ● 11-15 Silver medal ● 16-20 Gold medal

1. Which university won the 2000 Boat Race?
2. How many players make up a cricket team?
3. When was British showjumper Harvey Smith born?
4. What nationality is teenage swimming sensation Ian Thorpe, who won three gold medals and one silver at the Sydney Olympics?
5. At which Olympics did Allan Wells win Olympic gold in the 100m?
6. Which American golfer smashed several records in winning the 2000 US Open at Pebble Beach?
7. Fratton Park is the home of which football club?
8. Bernard Laporte is the French national coach in which sport?
9. What nationality was motor racing legend Jim Clark?
10. Paul Hunter and Peter Ebdon are professionals in which sport?
11. Which American tennis player won the men's singles title at the 2000 Australian Open?
12. Who beat the Brisbane Broncos 20-18 to win the rugby league World Club Challenge in January 2001?
13. Which British swimmer won the 200m breaststroke gold medal at the 1976 Olympics?
14. Which British boxer lost a world title fight to Roberto Duran in June 1972?
15. Which country won the cricket World Cup in 1987?
16. At which racecourse did jockeys Frankie Dettori and Ray Cochrane survive a plane crash in June 2000?
17. Mick the Miller is a famous name from which sport?
18. Which team lost in the final of the FA Cup in 1992?
19. Which golfer won the US Masters in 1995?
20. In which weight division did Robin Reid win bronze at the 1992 Olympics?

***ANSWERS:** 1 Oxford, 2 11, 3 1938, 4 Australian, 5 Moscow, 6 Tiger Woods, 7 Portsmouth, 8 Rugby union, 9 Scottish, 10 Snooker, 11 Andre Agassi, 12 St Helens, 13 David Wilkie, 14 Ken Buchanan, 15 Australia, 16 Newmarket, 17 Greyhound racing, 18 Sunderland, 19 Ben Crenshaw, 20 Light-middleweight.*

General Knowledge

Your rating: ● 0-5 Join a library ● 6-10 Keep at it ● 11-15 Join a quiz team ● 16-20 Join Mensa

1. Which Swiss tennis player is the daughter of former Czech tennis star Melanie Molitor?
2. Who wrote *The Old Men at the Zoo* and *Anglo-Saxon Attitudes*?
3. Which strait separates Anglesey from the Welsh mainland?
4. How many dalmatians are there in Disney's sequel to *101 Dalmatians*?
5. What is the name of the alphabet used for writing Russian?
6. In which U.S. city is Shea Stadium?
7. In which country is the Paul Theroux novel *Saint Jack* set?
8. What name is given to the hypothetical intermediate form between human beings and their anthropoid ancestors?
9. In what year did Sir Edmund Hillary reach the summit of Mount Everest?
10. Which soap opera celebrated its 40th anniversary in 2000?
11. In which film did Humphrey Bogart play Charlie Allnut?
12. In literature and drama, what name is given to an extended speech by one person?
13. By what name is Mendelssohn's Fourth Symphony known?
14. Which American rapper reached Number 1 in the singles charts with *Stan*?
15. Of which former Soviet state is Bishkek the capital?
16. Which Canadian novelist wrote *What's Bred in the Bone*?
17. Who was *The Girl Who Cant Help It*?
18. By what name is 16th-century astrologer Michel de Notredame better known?
19. By what name was jazz composer and pianist Ferdinand Joseph La Menthe known?
20. Which English poet wrote *The Task* and the hymn *God Moves in a Mysterious Way*?

ANSWERS: *1 Martina Hingis, 2 Angus Wilson, 3 Menai Strait, 4 102, 5 Cyrillic alphabet, 6 New York City, 7 Singapore, 8 Missing Link, 9 1953, 10 Coronation Street, 11 The African Queen, 12 Monologue, 13 Italian Symphony, 14 Eminem, 15 Kyrgyzstan, 16 Robertson Davies, 17 Jayne Mansfield, 18 Nostradamus, 19 Jelly Roll Morton, 20 William Cowper.*

General Knowledge

Your rating:
- **0-5 Join a library**
- **6-10 Keep at it**
- **11-15 Join a quiz team**
- **16-20 Join Mensa**

1. Which English novelist wrote *Goodbye Mr Chips* and *Random Harvest*?
2. Which Irish author wrote *The Ballroom of Romance*?
3. Which U.S. actress starred in *Anatomy of a Murder*, *Days of Wine and Roses* and *The Omen*?
4. Who was voted BBC Sports Personality of the Year in 2000?
5. Which British administrator originated the penny postage system?
6. In which European country is the city of Modena?
7. For which film did *Under the Sea* win the Oscar for Best Song?
8. What name is given to a document giving proof of goods being loaded on a ship?
9. Which American golfer won the first of his six U.S. Masters titles in 1963?
10. What name is given to the art of creating and arranging dances?
11. In which sport was the father of Grace Kelly an Olympic gold medallist?
12. Which jazz group was formed by Milt Jackson, John Lewis, Kenny Clarke and Percy Heath in 1952?
13. Who was the first American racing driver to win the Formula 1 world championship?
14. Which American pair won golf's World Cup in 2000?
15. What is the smaller of the two main islands of New Zealand?
16. Which English-born writer wrote *The American Way of Death*?
17. In which film was the main character Benjamin Braddock?
18. By what name was Joseph Merrick known when he appeared in freak shows?
19. Which English prince was the father of Henry IV?
20. Which breed of dog is noted for its blue-black tongue?

ANSWERS: *1 James Hilton, 2 William Trevor, 3 Lee Remick, 4 Steve Redgrave, 5 Sir Rowland Hill, 6 Italy, 7 The Little Mermaid, 8 Bill of lading, 9 Jack Nicklaus, 10 Choreography, 11 Rowing, 12 Modern Jazz Quartet, 13 Phil Hill, 14 Tiger Woods and David Duval, 15 North Island, 16 Jessica Mitford, 17 The Graduate, 18 The Elephant Man, 19 John of Gaunt, 20 Chow chow.*

General Knowledge

Your rating: • **0-5** **Join a library** • **6-10** **Keep at it** • **11-15** **Join a quiz team** • **16-20** **Join Mensa**

1. Which English monarch was known as the Virgin Queen?
2. Who created *The Saint*?
3. Which country was the first visiting cricket side to beat Pakistan in a Test match in Karachi?
4. What nationality was former world heavyweight boxing champion Ingemar Johansson?
5. Which detective died in Agatha Christie's 1975 novel *Curtain*?
6. From which country does the cheese Pont-l'Éveque come?
7. What is the name of the captain in *Twenty Thousand Leagues Under the Sea*?
8. What is the name of the volcano that destroyed Pompeii?
9. In which Asian country is the city of Pondicherry?
10. Which motor racing commentator announced his retirement in 2000?
11. Who narrated the TV series *The World At War*?
12. Which countries are connected by the Khyber Pass?
13. Who plays the father in the film *Meet The Parents*?
14. Which communist movement ruled Cambodia from 1975 to 1979?
15. In which country is the port of Mocha, which gives its name to a type of coffee?
16. Which German composer wrote the opera *König Hirsch*?
17. Who was *Sorry* on TV for 43 episodes?
18. Which American puppeteer created *The Muppets*?
19. Which island of the Netherlands Antilles gives its name to a liqueur flavoured with orange peel?
20. In which film did Katharine Hepburn first co-star with Spencer Tracy?

ANSWERS: *1 Elizabeth I, 2 Leslie Charteris, 3 England, 4 Swedish, 5 Hercule Poirot, 6 France, 7 Captain Nemo, 8 Vesuvius, 9 India, 10 Murray Walker, 11 Laurence Olivier, 12 Pakistan and Afghanistan, 13 Robert De Niro, 14 Khmer Rouge, 15 Yemen, 16 Hans Werner Henze, 17 Ronnie Corbett, 18 Jim Henson, 19 Curaçao, 20 Woman of the Year.*

Entertainment

Your rating: ● **0-5** **Buy a TV** ● **6-10** **Keep at it**
● **11-15** **Join a quiz team** ● **16-20** **Enter a quiz show**

1. Which character in the TV series *Due South* was played by David Marciano?
2. Which 1996 Steven Spielberg-produced disaster movie was about tornados?
3. Who played Hyacinth in the sitcom *Keeping Up Appearances*?
4. Which in-depth ITV current affairs programme was presented by Dermot Murnaghan?
5. Which Northern Ireland pop group called their debut album *1977*?
6. Who starred as Sara Woodruff in the 1981 film *The French Lieutenant's Woman*?
7. Which TV cartoon company brought us *The Flintstones*, *The Jetsons* and *Scooby Doo*?
8. Which rock 'n' roll legend had a top ten hit in 1964 with *No Particular Place To Go*?
9. Which British actor directed the 1996 film *Rainbow*?
10. Which *ER* character is played by Anthony Edwards?
11. Which duo released a compilation of tunes in 1996 entitled *Walk Right Back*?
12. Who starred in the title role of the film *Crocodile Dundee*?
13. In which Wisconsin city was the TV series *Happy Days* set?
14. Which actress starred as Emma Peel in the 1998 film version of *The Avengers*?
15. Which group had a top twenty hit in 1975 with *Now I'm Here*?
16. In which city was Hal Salwen's 1996 movie *Denise Calls Up* set?
17. Who was the host of *The Big Big Talent Show* on TV?
18. Which former 4 Non Blondes singer released a solo album in 1996 entitled *In Flight*?
19. Who played Philip Marlowe in the 1946 film *The Big Sleep*?
20. What was the name of Paul Merton's second TV series for Channel 4?

ANSWERS: *1 Ray Vecchio, 2 Twister, 3 Patricia Routledge, 4 The Big Story, 5 Ash, 6 Meryl Streep, 7 Hanna-Barbera, 8 Chuck Berry, 9 Bob Hoskins, 10 Dr Mark Greene, 11 The Everly Brothers, 12 Paul Hogan, 13 Milwaukee, 14 Uma Thurman, 15 Queen, 16 New York, 17 Jonathan Ross, 18 Linda Perry, 19 Humphrey Bogart, 20 Paul Merton: The Second Series.*

General Knowledge

Your rating: ● 0-5 Join a library ● 6-10 Keep at it ● 11-15 Join a quiz team ● 16-20 Join Mensa

1. In which New York City street are the majority of the leading commercial theatres situated?
2. What is measured in watts?
3. Which King of England was nicknamed 'The Lionheart'?
4. What sort of creature is an osprey?
5. In which English county is the port of Plymouth situated?
6. In which English county can the majority of the Broads be found?
7. Which element used in atomic bombs is represented by the symbol Pu?
8. Which star of the film *One Flew Over the Cuckoo's Nest* won an Oscar for his performance in *Terms of Endearment*?
9. With which sport is Joe Frazier associated?
10. Which pop singer starred in the film *Summer Holiday* and had a hit with *We Don't Talk Anymore*?
11. With which musical instrument is the Russian-born musician Isaac Stern associated?
12. Which British civil engineer is best known for his construction of the suspension bridge over the Menai Strait?
13. Which Austrian novelist wrote *The Death of Virgil*?
14. Which silvery-white semiconductor is represented by the symbol Te?
15. In which European country can the Arlberg Pass be found?
16. What is the maximum length of time that the House of Lords may veto a finance bill?
17. What is the longest nerve in the body?
18. Who succeeded his grandfather Edward III as King of England?
19. What is measured using the Beaufort Scale?
20. Which volcano in SW Washington erupted in May 1980 causing widespread destruction?

***ANSWERS:** 1 Broadway, 2 Power, 3 Richard I, 4 A bird, 5 Devon, 6 Norfolk, 7 Plutonium, 8 Jack Nicholson, 9 Boxing, 10 Cliff Richard, 11 Violin, 12 Thomas Telford, 13 Hermann Broch, 14 Tellurium, 15 Austria, 16 One month, 17 The sciatic nerve, 18 Richard II, 19 Wind speed, 20 Mount St Helens.*

General Knowledge

Your rating:
- 0-5 Join a library
- 6-10 Keep at it
- 11-15 Join a quiz team
- 16-20 Join Mensa

1. Which British prime minister resigned in May 1940 after his policy of appeasement towards Hitler failed?
2. In which limb would you find the humerus, ulna and radius?
3. From which Italian city does Parmesan cheese take its name?
4. With which sport is Jack Nicklaus associated?
5. What sort of creature is a chameleon?
6. In which ocean can the Isles of Scilly be found?
7. In which Swiss city are the International Red Cross and the World Health Organisation based?
8. Which British actor played the monster in the 1931 film *Frankenstein*?
9. What can be measured in pascals, millimetres of mercury, or millibars?
10. Of which English county is Maidstone the administrative centre?
11. Of which state of the USA is Concord the capital?
12. Which French novelist and dramatist wrote *Our Lady of the Flowers*?
13. Which Dutch lens grinder built the first telescope?
14. What is the chief river of British Columbia?
15. What sort of creature is a colobus?
16. Which U.S. magician and escapologist was born Erich Weiss?
17. Which Austrian composer wrote the song cycle *Das Lied von der Erde*?
18. In which English county can the prehistoric fortress known as Maiden Castle be found?
19. In which language were the Dharmashastra written originally?
20. What is the capital of Sri Lanka?

ANSWERS: *1 Neville Chamberlain, 2 The arm, 3 Parma, 4 Golf, 5 A lizard, 6 The Atlantic Ocean, 7 Geneva, 8 Boris Karloff, 9 Pressure, 10 Kent, 11 New Hampshire, 12 Jean Genet, 13 Hans Lippershey, 14 Fraser River, 15 A monkey, 16 Harry Houdini, 17 Gustav Mahler, 18 Dorset, 19 Sanskrit, 20 Colombo.*

General Knowledge

Your rating:
- **0-5 Join a library**
- **6-10 Keep at it**
- **11-15 Join a quiz team**
- **16-20 Join Mensa**

1. Which Swiss national hero is reputed to have shot an apple from his son's head with a crossbow at 80 paces?
2. Of which Central American republic is Managua the capital?
3. To which country did Sardinia cede the city of Nice in 1860?
4. Which hard silvery metal is represented by the symbol Ni?
5. What sort of creature is a narwhal?
6. In which English county is the resort of Newquay situated?
7. Which son of Ernest I, Duke of Saxe-Coburg-Gotha married Queen Victoria in 1840?
8. What can be measured in kelvins, degrees Celsius or degrees Fahrenheit?
9. Which U.S. artist achieved notoriety in the 1960s with his paintings of soup cans and portraits of Marilyn Monroe?
10. Which British novelist wrote *Kipps*?
11. Of which Canadian province is Edmonton the capital?
12. Which child film star of the 1930s was appointed U.S. ambassador to Ghana in 1974?
13. Which former member of the Beatles was made a knight in the 1997 New Year Honours List?
14. Who was the last Emperor of Russia?
15. What sort of creature is a bleak?
16. Which unit of distance used in astronomy is approximately equal to 3.26 light-years?
17. Who became Queen of the Netherlands in 1980?
18. Which British novelist wrote *Agnes Gray*?
19. How many cubic metres are equivalent to one stere?
20. Which British composer wrote the music to the choral song *Jerusalem*?

ANSWERS: *1 William Tell, 2 Nicaragua, 3 France, 4 Nickel, 5 A whale, 6 Cornwall, 7 Albert, 8 Temperature, 9 Andy Warhol, 10 H. G. Wells, 11 Alberta, 12 Shirley Temple (Black), 13 Paul McCartney, 14 Nicholas II, 15 A fish, 16 Parsec, 17 Beatrix, 18 Anne Brontë, 19 One, 20 Sir Hubert Parry.*

Entertainment

Your rating: ● 0-5 Buy a TV ● 6-10 Keep at it ● 11-15 Join a quiz team ● 16-20 Enter a quiz show

1. Which star of *The Man From UNCLE* was the host of TV's *Danger Theatre*?
2. Who had a top ten hit single in 1980 with *She's Out of My Life*?
3. Which England rugby player co-presented TV's *Body Heat* with Sally Gunnell?
4. Which *Absolutely Fabulous* star played Spiker in the 1996 film *James And The Giant Peach*?
5. What was the name of Constable Benton Fraser's canine sidekick in *Due South*?
6. Which US rock band released an album entitled *She's The One* in 1996?
7. Who directed the 1991 film *The Commitments*?
8. Who played Rose in the TV series *Upstairs, Downstairs*?
9. Which Beatles song did Billy Bragg take to number one in 1988?
10. Which 1996 dolphin film starred Paul Hogan and Elijah Wood?
11. Which Australian actress/singer co-presented *The Big Breakfast*'s *Eggs on Legs* roadshow in 1996?
12. Which London band released an album in 1996 entitled *Son Of The Great Outdoors*?
13. Who starred as the prince of Zamunda in the film *Coming to America*?
14. Which 1996 BBC series examined the lives of British expatriates in Florida?
15. Who had a number one hit single in 1974 with *Seasons in the Sun*?
16. Which *Jurassic Park* star played a computer genius in *Independence Day*?
17. Which British character actress starred in the title role of the award-winning *Edna the Inebriate Woman*?
18. Which former Alarm singer released an album entitled *Feel Free* in 1996?
19. Who starred in the title role of the 1965 film *Doctor Zhivago*?
20. Which car maintenance series was presented on TV by Julia Carling?

ANSWERS: *1 Robert Vaughn, 2 Michael Jackson, 3 Jeremy Guscott, 4 Joanna Lumley, 5 Diefenbaker, 6 Tom Petty and the Heartbreakers, 7 Alan Parker, 8 Jean Marsh, 9 She's Leaving Home, 10 Flipper, 11 Dannii Minogue, 12 Nervous, 13 Eddie Murphy, 14 Florida Folk, 15 Terry Jacks, 16 Jeff Goldblum, 17 Patricia Hayes, 18 Mike Peters, 19 Omar Sharif, 20 Where's the Jack?*

General Knowledge

Your rating: ● 0-5 Join a library ● 6-10 Keep at it ● 11-15 Join a quiz team ● 16-20 Join Mensa

1. Which U.S. novelist wrote *Little Women*?
2. At the start of a game of chess, how many pieces are on the board?
3. The city of Strasbourg was returned to which country after World War I?
4. How many legs does a spider have?
5. What name is given to all chemical compounds which contain carbon and hydrogen?
6. How often does football's World Cup take place?
7. Where can polar bears be found, the North Pole or the South Pole?
8. According to the New Testament, how many Apostles were chosen by Jesus?
9. Scotch, rye and bourbon are types of which alcoholic drink?
10. Of which metal is steel an alloy?
11. Which British philosopher and mathematician collaborated with Bertrand Russell on *Principia Mathematica*?
12. Which nation was defeated by the Turks at the Battle of Varna in 1444?
13. Which forest is the setting for Shakespeare's *As You Like It*?
14. According to Greek legend, who was the father of Apollo?
15. Of which present-day African country is the former kingdom of Barotseland a part?
16. Which British poet wrote the verse drama *Prometheus Unbound*?
17. Which two countries agreed to the Alcock Convention of 1869?
18. Which transition metal is represented by the symbol Sc?
19. Which kingdom of Anglo-Saxon England was ruled by Penda and Offa?
20. Which U.S. tennis player was the first to win all four major singles titles (Australian, French, U.S. and Wimbledon)?

ANSWERS: *1 Louisa May Alcott, 2 32, 3 France, 4 Eight, 5 Hydrocarbons, 6 Every four years, 7 The North Pole, 8 Twelve, 9 Whisky, 10 Iron, 11 A. N. Whitehead, 12 Hungary, 13 Forest of Arden, 14 Zeus, 15 Zambia, 16 Percy Shelley, 17 Britain and China, 18 Scandium, 19 Mercia, 20 Don Budge.*

General Knowledge

Your rating: ● **0-5** Join a library ● **6-10** Keep at it ● **11-15** Join a quiz team ● **16-20** Join Mensa

1. Which British ice-dance partnership won the 1984 Olympic gold medal?
2. How was the Strategic Defence Initiative announced by Ronald Reagan in 1983 popularly known?
3. How many arms does an octopus have?
4. Who directed the films *Close Encounters of the Third Kind* and *Jaws*?
5. In which English county is the resort of Torquay located?
6. Which chemical is used to make drinks "fizzy"?
7. Which building complex in Washington DC gave its name to a political scandal leading to the resignation of Richard Nixon?
8. Which festive shrub of the genus *Ilex* has spiny green leaves and female flowers which develop into red berries?
9. Which jazz saxophonist was nicknamed "Bird"?
10. What nationality was the painter Claude Monet?
11. Which British poet collaborated with Coleridge on 1798's *Lyrical Ballads*?
12. Which noble gas is represented by the symbol Rn?
13. In which London street is the Cenotaph situated?
14. According to Greek legend, which son of Priam abducted Helen of Troy?
15. Which Swedish author wrote *Confessions of a Fool* and *The Dance of Death*?
16. Of which South American country was Getulio Vargas president from 1930 to 1945?
17 Which U.S. soldier and diplomat wrote the bestseller *Ben-Hur*?
18. Which *Toy Story* doll caused frantic parents to pay up to ten times its asking price after being sold out in November 1996?
19. Which type of sleeve without shoulder seams was named after a British field marshal?
20. Which Spanish novelist wrote *The Four Horsemen of the Apocalypse*?

ANSWERS: *1 Jayne Torvill and Christopher Dean, 2 Star wars, 3 Eight, 4 Steven Spielberg, 5 Devon, 6 Carbon dioxide, 7 Watergate, 8 Holly, 9 Charlie Parker, 10 French, 11 William Wordsworth, 12 Radon, 13 Whitehall, 14 Paris, 15 August Strindberg, 16 Brazil, 17 Lew Wallace, 18 Buzz Lightyear, 19 Raglan sleeve, 20 Vicente Blasco Ibanez.*

General Knowledge

Your rating:
- 0-5 Join a library
- 6-10 Keep at it
- 11-15 Join a quiz team
- 16-20 Join Mensa

1. By what nickname was jazz musician Thomas Waller usually known?
2. Which radioactive metallic element is represented by the symbol Ra?
3. Of which trade union did Arthur Scargill become president in 1981?
4. Of which East European country did General Jaruzelski become leader in 1981?
5. Which composer wrote *The Messiah*?
6. What sort of twins were Chang and Eng, who were born in 1811 joined at the hip?
7. In which sea is the island of Sicily situated?
8. Which is the better poker hand, two pairs or a straight flush?
9. What sort of creature is a wallaby?
10. With which musical instrument is Paul Tortelier associated?
11. Who directed the films *Repulsion* and *Rosemary's Baby*?
12. Of which country was Paul Spaak prime minister from 1938-39 and 1947-50?
13. Which racing driver was 1996 BBC Television Sports Personality of the Year?
14. In which constellation can Polaris (the North Star) be found?
15. Which Nigerian dramatist and poet was awarded the 1986 Nobel prize for literature?
16. What was Vanuata Republic known as until 1980?
17. Which British novelist wrote *On the Beach*?
18. Scapa Flow is a section of which ocean?
19. Which cabinet post was held by William Whitelaw from 1979 to 1983?
20. Which French town is the capital of the Vienne department?

ANSWERS: *1 Fats, 2 Radium, 3 The National Union of Mineworkers, 4 Poland, 5 Handel, 6 Siamese twins, 7 The Mediterranean Sea, 8 Straight flush, 9 A marsupial, 10 The cello, 11 Roman Polanski, 12 Belgium, 13 Damon Hill, 14 Ursa Minor, 15 Wole Soyinka, 16 New Hebrides, 17 Nevil Shute, 18 The Atlantic Ocean, 19 Home Secretary, 20 Poitiers.*

Entertainment

Your rating: ● **0-5** Buy a TV ● **6-10** Keep at it ● **11-15** Join a quiz team ● **16-20** Enter a quiz show

1. Which duo had a top ten hit in 1975 with *Please Mr Postman*?
2. Who starred as 19-year-old Lucy in the film *Stealing Beauty*?
3. Which sport was the subject of Channel 4's *Blitz!*?
4. Who refused to set off for Oasis's 1996 US tour saying, "I am sick of living my life in hotels. I need to be happy"?
5. Which character in the Channel 4 comedy series *Father Ted* was played by Ardal O' Hanlon?
6. Who played bereaved father Freddy Gale in Sean Penn's *The Crossing Guard*?
7. Which British group had a top ten single in 1989 with *Song For Whoever*?
8. Which *EastEnders* star presented the DIY programme *The Terrace*?
9. Who played Margaret Schlegel in the 1992 film *Howards End*?
10. Which Hanna-Barbera cartoon series of the Seventies was about a meek janitor with a double life as a disaster-prone super-detective?
11. Which American rock band signed a £53 million deal with Warner Bros in 1996 for their next five albums?
12. Who starred as a woman on death row in the 1996 film *Last Dance*?
13. Which former *Brookside* star played Welsh teenager Sioned in the TV series *Cadfael*?
14. Which rock group had a top ten hit single in 1981 with *Start Me Up*?
15. Which ex-footballer talked to fellow owners of *Golden Boots* on BBC 1 in 1998?
16. Who directed the 1983 film *The King of Comedy*?
17. Which quintet had a number one hit single with *Wannabe* in 1996?
18. Who played Pussy Galore in the 1964 film *Goldfinger*?
19. Who played Richie Cunningham in the TV comedy *Happy Days*?
20. Who had a top ten hit single in 1967 with *If I Were A Rich Man*?

ANSWERS: 1 *The Carpenters*, 2 *Liv Tyler*, 3 *American football*, 4 *Liam Gallagher*, 5 *Father Dougal*, 6 *Jack Nicholson*, 7 *The Beautiful South*, 8 *Mike Reid*, 9 *Emma Thompson*, 10 *Hong Kong Phooey*, 11 *REM*, 12 *Sharon Stone*, 13 *Anna Friel*, 14 *The Rolling Stones*, 15 *Gary Lineker*, 16 *Martin Scorsese*, 17 *The Spice Girls*, 18 *Honor Blackman*, 19 *Ron Howard*, 20 *Topol*.

General Knowledge

Your rating: ● 0-5 Join a library ● 6-10 Keep at it ● 11-15 Join a quiz team ● 16-20 Join Mensa

1. From which collection of stories do *Aladdin* and *Ali Baba* come?
2. Which Irish pop singer instigated the Band Aid project *Do They Know It's Christmas*?
3. What are the two official languages of Gibraltar?
4. Which legendary Greek king of Ithaca was the hero of Homer's *Odyssey*?
5. What sort of creature is an albatross?
6. What nationality was the composer Franz Joseph Haydn?
7. Which U.S. singer and actress starred in the films *Hello Dolly* and *A Star is Born*?
8. What is measured in ohms?
9. According to Greek legend, which king of Thebes fulfilled the prophecy that he would kill his father and marry his mother?
10. Of which European country is Rotterdam the second largest city?
11. Which British doctor and philanthropist founded the first of his homes for destitute children at Stepney, London in 1867?
12. Which Roman writer is famous for his love poems addressed to a married woman named Lesbia?
13. Who became the USA's first female secretary of state in 1996?
14. Which Jewish festival commemorates the revolt of the Maccabees?
15. Which Nobel Prize-winning U.S. novelist wrote *The Good Earth*?
16. What sort of creature is a viscacha?
17. Which German city is the capital of Lower Saxony?
18. According to Greek legend, who killed the Hydra?
19. Of which state of the USA is Juneau the capital?
20. What sort of creature is an albacore?

ANSWERS: *1 Arabian Nights, 2 Bob Geldof, 3 English and Spanish, 4 Odysseus, 5 A seabird, 6 Austrian, 7 Barbra Streisand, 8 Electrical resistance, 9 Oedipus, 10 Netherlands, 11 Thomas Barnardo, 12 Catullus, 13 Madeleine Albright, 14 Hanukkah, 15 Pearl S. Buck, 16 A rodent, 17 Hanover, 18 Heracles, 19 Alaska, 20 A fish.*

General Knowledge

Your rating: ● 0-5 Join a library ● 6-10 Keep at it ● 11-15 Join a quiz team ● 16-20 Join Mensa

1. In geometry, how many minutes are in a degree?
2. The Balearic and Canary Islands are part of which European country?
3. Which U.S. actor starred in the films *The Bank Dick* and *My Little Chickadee*?
4. What sort of creature is a chow chow?
5. Which British prime minister is remembered for his speech during the 1959 election asserting "you've never had it so good"?
6. With which sport is J.P.R. Williams associated?
7. In which state of the USA is the city of Pasadena situated?
8. Which unit of pressure is represented by the symbol Pa?
9. Which singer/songwriter released an album entitled *Planet Waves*?
10. Of which Caribbean country was François "Papa Doc" Duvalier the president?
11. Of which African country is Brazzaville the capital?
12. Which religious movement was founded in New York in 1848 by John Thomas?
13. Which U.S. novelist wrote *The Naked Lunch*?
14. Of which country was Adnan Menderes prime minister from 1950 to 1960?
15. Which road was built between Rome and Capua about 312 BC by the statesman Appius Claudius?
16. Who was prime minister of the Union of South Africa from 1924 to 1939?
17. In which city are the headquarters of the University of California situated?
18. Of which European country is Durrës the main port?
19. Which synthetic transuranic element is represented by the symbol No?
20. Which British novelist wrote *The French Lieutenant's Woman*?

ANSWERS: *1 Sixty, 2 Spain, 3 W. C. Fields, 4 A dog, 5 Harold Macmillan, 6 Rugby Union, 7 California, 8 Pascal, 9 Bob Dylan, 10 Haiti, 11 The People's Republic of Congo, 12 Christadelphians, 13 William Burroughs, 14 Turkey, 15 Appian Way, 16 James Hertzog, 17 Berkeley, 18 Albania, 19 Nobelium, 20 John Fowles.*

General Knowledge

Your rating:
- 0-5 Join a library
- 6-10 Keep at it
- 11-15 Join a quiz team
- 16-20 Join Mensa

1. What nationality was the painter and sculptor Edgar Degas?
2. With which sport is Alain Prost associated?
3. In which country can Cape Town and Table Mountain be found?
4. What is inflammation of the vermiform appendix called?
5. Which general was president of France from 1959 to 1969?
6. Which system of voting is represented by the initials PR?
7. Is a cathode negatively or positively charged?
8. Followers of which religion observe the Passover?
9. In which year did the Battle of Hastings take place?
10. Which region of Italy is known as Toscana in Italian?
11. Who became general secretary of the Trades Union Congress in 1984?
12. Which general led a successful coup on 13 September 1923 and was dictator of Spain until 1930?
13. What sort of creature is a noctule?
14. Of which state of the USA is Cheyenne the capital?
15. Which British chemist first extracted oxygen from mercuric oxide?
16. What was the state of Tuvalu known as until 1976?
17. Which name was officially adopted in 1943 for the reports of debates in the UK's parliament?
18. Which river flows from Plynlimmon through Monmouth joining the River Severn near Chepstow?
19. Who was the last Danish King of England?
20. Which Greek novelist wrote *Zorba the Greek*?

ANSWERS: *1 French, 2 Motor racing, 3 South Africa, 4 Appendicitis, 5 Charles de Gaulle, 6 Proportional representation, 7 Negatively, 8 Judaism, 9 1066, 10 Tuscany, 11 Norman Willis, 12 Miguel Primo de Rivera, 13 A bat, 14 Wyoming, 15 Joseph Priestley, 16 Ellice Islands, 17 Hansard, 18 The River Wye, 19 Hardecanute, 20 Nikos Kazantzakis.*

Entertainment

Your rating: ● **0-5** **Buy a TV** ● **6-10** **Keep at it** ● **11-15** **Join a quiz team** ● **16-20** **Enter a quiz show**

1. Who played Princess Catherine Radziwill in the 1996 TV drama *Rhodes*?
2. Who had a top ten hit single in 1966 with *Rainy Day Women Nos. 12 & 35*?
3. Who starred as an accident-prone young woman in the film *Boys*?
4. Who starred on TV as *The Fall Guy*?
5. Which British group had a number one hit single in 1966 with *Pretty Flamingo*?
6. Who played Eddie in the BBC 2 comedy series *Bottom*?
7. Which female vocalist released an album entitled *Man* in 1996?
8. Who starred as Laura in the 1991 film *Sleeping With The Enemy*?
9. Who played Reggie's military-obsessed brother-in-law Jimmy in TV's *The Legacy of Reginald Perrin*?
10. Which avant-garde composer explored the relationship of silence to music in his *4' 53"*?
11. Which firefighting drama series was set in Blackwall Fire Station?
12. Who starred as an algebra teacher in the 1996 film *Diabolique*?
13. Which US rock band released an album entitled *New Adventures in Hi-Fi*?
14. Which TV personality was born Magnus Sigursteinnson?
15. Which British actor co-starred with Laurence Olivier in the 1973 film *Sleuth*?
16. Who had a top ten hit single in 1967 with *Purple Haze*?
17. Which *Blockbusters* host presented the panel game show *Call My Bluff*?
18. Which wall was the subject of Margarethe von Trotta's 1996 film *The Promise*?
19. Which British pop band released an album entitled *Bilingual* in 1996?
20. Which former Olympic swimmer replaced Zoe Ball as presenter of *The Big Breakfast*?

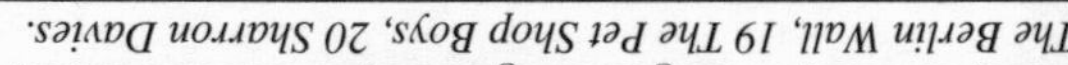

ANSWERS: *1 Frances Barber, 2 Bob Dylan, 3 Winona Ryder, 4 Lee Majors, 5 Manfred Mann, 6 Adrian Edmondson, 7 Neneh Cherry, 8 Julia Roberts, 9 Geoffrey Palmer, 10 John Cage, 11 London's Burning, 12 Sharon Stone, 13 REM, 14 Magnus Magnusson, 15 Michael Caine, 16 The Jimi Hendrix Experience, 17 Bob Holness, 18 The Berlin Wall, 19 The Pet Shop Boys, 20 Sharron Davies.*

General Knowledge

Your rating: ● 0-5 Join a library ● 6-10 Keep at it ● 11-15 Join a quiz team ● 16-20 Join Mensa

1. In which state of the USA can the city of Cincinnati be found?
2. How was silent film comedian Joseph Francis Keaton better known?
3. What is the currency unit of Australia?
4. How is the roof of the mouth otherwise known?
5. In which English county can the towns of Watford, Hemel Hempstead and Stevenage be found?
6. Which term describes an integer greater than one that has no integral factors except itself and one?
7. Of which Asian country was Ferdinand Marcos president from 1965 to 1986?
8. According to the New Testament, which apostle denied Christ three times?
9. Which unit of frequency is abbreviated to Hz?
10. Which British poet wrote *Endymion* and the ode *To a Nightingale*?
11. According to Greek mythology, which wife of King Menelaus was abducted by Paris thus precipitating the Trojan War?
12. The Trobriand Islands are part of which country?
13. Who was the president of the Soviet Union from 1977 to 1982?
14. Which Oscar-winning actor married the daughter of playwright Arthur Miller?
15. Which English churchman was Lord Chancellor under Henry VIII from 1515 to 1529?
16. Tritium is a radioactive isotope of which gas?
17. Which French feminist and companion of Jean-Paul Sartre wrote *The Second Sex*?
18. What is the longest river in Scotland?
19. Who was the king of Romania from 1914 to 1927?
20. Who directed the films *On the Waterfront* and *East of Eden*?

ANSWERS: *1 Ohio, 2 Buster Keaton, 3 Dollar, 4 The palate, 5 Hertfordshire, 6 Prime number, 7 The Philippines, 8 St Peter, 9 Hertz, 10 John Keats, 11 Helen, 12 Papua New Guinea, 13 Leonid Brezhnev, 14 Daniel Day-Lewis, 15 Cardinal Thomas Wolsey, 16 Hydrogen, 17 Simone de Beauvoir, 18 The Tay, 19 Ferdinand, 20 Elia Kazan.*

General Knowledge

Your rating:
- 0-5 Join a library
- 6-10 Keep at it
- 11-15 Join a quiz team
- 16-20 Join Mensa

1. On which Greek island was the Duke of Edinburgh born?
2. What is bezique?
3. Which German tennis player won the men's singles title at Wimbledon in 1985 at the age of 17?
4. Cape Horn is the most southerly point of which continent?
5. In which country was Charlie Chaplin born?
6. Which Italian town was the birthplace of St Francis, the founder of the Franciscan Order?
7. To which group of islands do Guernsey, Jersey and Sark belong?
8. Which hero of Greek mythology beheaded Medusa?
9. In which country can wombats be found in the wild?
10. Charcoal is a form of which chemical?
11. Which British actor starred in the films *Major Barbara* and *The Blue Bird*?
12. Who was the supreme god in Babylonian mythology?
13. What name is shared by an evergreen shrub and a gastropod mollusc?
14. What is bladderwrack?
15. Savai'i is the largest island of which country?
16. Which King of England was married to Margaret of Anjou?
17. What is the highest cataract in the world?
18. Which TV presenter was attacked in a Paris bar by footballer Stan Collymore in 1998?
19. What was William Gladstone's middle name?
20. Which British historian wrote *The Origins of the Second World War*?

ANSWERS: *1 Corfu, 2 A card game, 3 Boris Becker, 4 South America, 5 England, 6 Assisi, 7 Channel Islands, 8 Perseus, 9 Australia, 10 Carbon, 11 Robert Morley, 12 Marduk, 13 Periwinkle, 14 Seaweed, 15 Western Samoa, 16 Henry VI, 17 Angel Falls, 18 Ulrika Jonsson, 19 Ewart, 20 A. J. P. Taylor.*

General Knowledge

Your rating: ● 0-5 Join a library ● 6-10 Keep at it ● 11-15 Join a quiz team ● 16-20 Join Mensa

1. Which US actor starred in the films *Casablanca* and *The African Queen*?
2. Uttar Pradesh is a state of which country?
3. Which city was made the capital of newly independent Czechoslovakia in 1918?
4. Which light metallic element is represented by the symbol Li?
5. In which English county can the Forest of Dean be found?
6. Who was found guilty of killing Matthew Eappen?
7. Which two countries are linked by the Brenner Pass?
8. What sort of creature is a snapper?
9. How are adherents of the Church of Jesus Christ of Latter-Day Saints commonly known?
10. Which metallic element is represented by the symbol Fe?
11. Which mistress of Horatio Nelson gave birth to his daughter Horatia?
12. Which Greek goddess of the underworld was the daughter of Zeus and Demeter?
13. Who became Australia's soccer coach in 1996?
14. Which hard brittle metal is represented by the symbol Ir?
15. Which Irish-American novelist wrote *The Ginger Man* and *The Onion Eaters*?
16. The cathedral of which English city contains the tomb of Catherine of Aragon?
17. Which Italian city is the capital of Umbria?
18. Which King of England was known as the Sailor King?
19. Which Italian electrical engineer shared the 1909 Nobel Prize for Physics for his work on the transmission of radio waves?
20. What sort of creature is a glass snake?

ANSWERS: *1 Humphrey Bogart, 2 India, 3 Prague, 4 Lithium, 5 Gloucestershire, 6 Louise Woodward, 7 Austria and Italy, 8 A fish, 9 Mormons, 10 Iron, 11 Lady Emma Hamilton, 12 Persephone, 13 Terry Venables, 14 Iridium, 15 J. P. Donleavy, 16 Peterborough, 17 Perugia, 18 William IV, 19 Guglielmo Marconi, 20 A lizard.*

Sports

Your rating:
- 0-5 Wooden spoon
- 6-10 Bronze medal
- 11-15 Silver medal
- 16-20 Gold medal

1. Which qualifier reached the men's singles semi-finals at Wimbledon in 2000?
2. Which horse won the Grand National in 1975?
3. In which event did Daley Thompson win two Olympic gold medals?
4. What is the value of the black ball in snooker?
5. Gridiron is an informal name for which sport?
6. In which three events did U.S. athlete Marion Jones strike gold at the Sydney Olympics?
7. Which country does cricketer Matthew Hayden play for?
8. With which sport are David Tua and Hasim Rahman associated?
9. Who was the snooker world champion in 1979?
10. How many players make up a hockey team?
11. Which team won the Premiership title in May 2000 with a victory over Tottenham Hotspur?
12. Who scored 174 against Australia in the Centenary Test in 1977?
13. In which city will the 2004 Olympic Games be staged?
14. Which team lost to Celtic in the final of the 1967 European Cup?
15. Which horse did Bob Champion ride to win the Grand National in 1981?
16. Who scored the winning goal for Arsenal in the 1979 F.A. Cup Final?
17. Which team lost to Aston Villa in the final of the European Cup in 1982?
18. Which cyclist won the Tour de France from 1991-1995?
19. With which sport are Sean Long and Chris Joynt associated?
20. In which country was tennis star Monica Seles born?

ANSWERS: *1 Vladimir Voltchkov, 2 L'Escargot, 3 Decathlon, 4 7, 5 American football, 6 100m, 200m & 4 x 400m relay, 7 Australia, 8 Boxing, 9 Terry Griffiths, 10 11, 11 Manchester United, 12 Derek Randall, 13 Athens, 14 Inter Milan, 15 Aldaniti, 16 Alan Sunderland, 17 Bayern Munich, 18 Miguel Indurain, 19 Rugby league, 20 Yugoslavia.*

General Knowledge

Your rating:
- 0-5 Join a library
- 6-10 Keep at it
- 11-15 Join a quiz team
- 16-20 Join Mensa

1. Which poet and dramatist wrote *The Waste Land* and *The Cocktail Party*?
2. What are the chapters of *A Christmas Carol* by Charles Dickens called?
3. Which figure personifying Englishness was created by Scottish physician John Arbuthnot?
4. Who has become the 43rd President of the United States?
5. Which alloy of copper and nickel is used for coins?
6. With which branch of the arts is Merce Cunningham associated?
7. Who wrote *How to be a Domestic Goddess*?
8. Of which country did Ayatollah Khomeini become leader in 1979?
9. Which country has demanded the return of the Elgin Marbles?
10. In which French city is the Pompidou Centre?
11. In which country was movie actor Andy Garcia born?
12. Which English sculptor married painter Ben Nicholson in 1933?
13. What name is given to members of a Christian sect founded by John Thomas in New York in 1848?
14. Which publication launched in 1926 has merged with the NME?
15. What is the khamsin?
16. In what year did U.S. sprinter Bobby Morrow win the Olympic 100m and 200m?
17. For her performance in which film did Grace Kelly receive an Oscar in 1954?
18. What is the northernmost point of the British Isles?
19. Which suburb of Amsterdam is the centre of the Dutch broadcasting industry?
20. To which organ does the adjective hepatic relate?

***ANSWERS:** 1 T S Eliot, 2 Staves, 3 John Bull, 4 George W Bush, 5 Cupronickel, 6 Dance, 7 Nigella Lawson, 8 Iran, 9 Greece, 10 Paris, 11 Cuba, 12 Barbara Hepworth, 13 Christadelphians, 14 Melody Maker, 15 A wind, 16 1956, 17 Country Girl, 18 Muckle Flugga, 19 Hilversum, 20 Liver.*

General Knowledge

Your rating:
- 0-5 Join a library
- 6-10 Keep at it
- 11-15 Join a quiz team
- 16-20 Join Mensa

1. Which god of love is the Roman counterpart of Eros?
2. What was the name of the character played by John Malkovich in the film *Dangerous Liaisons*?
3. Which English king was known as Lackland?
4. Ethan Hawke played the title role in a 2000 film version of which Shakespeare play?
5. Which examination was used after 1944 to select children for grammar schools?
6. How many events are there in a heptathlon?
7. What was the name of the stately home in the TV series *To the Manor Born*?
8. Who wrote the novels *Silas Marner* and *Middlemarch*?
9. Which actor starred in *Chinatown* and *One Flew Over the Cuckoo's Nest*?
10. By what abbreviation is the resin polyvinyl chloride known?
11. Who wrote *My Brilliant Career*?
12. Which Welsh artist painted portraits of George Bernard Shaw, Dylan Thomas and James Joyce?
13. Which French footballer was World Footballer of the Year in 2000?
14. Which English county contained Parts of Holland?
15. Of which country did Jean Chrétien become prime minister in 1993?
16. What sort of creature is a curassow?
17. Which is the longest-running police TV series ever?
18. Which English artist is best known for *A Rake's Progress*?
19. In the Old Testament, which prophet was carried up to heaven in a fiery chariot?
20. In which U.S. state is the city of Nome?

ANSWERS: 1 Cupid, 2 Valmont, 3 King John, 4 Hamlet, 5 Eleven Plus, 6 Seven, 7 Grantleigh Manor, 8 George Eliot, 9 Jack Nicholson, 10 PVC, 11 Miles Franklin, 12 Augustus John, 13 Zinedine Zidane, 14 Lincolnshire, 15 Canada, 16 A bird, 17 Hawaii Five-O, 18 William Hogarth, 19 Elijah, 20 Alaska.

General Knowledge

Your rating: ● 0-5 Join a library ● 6-10 Keep at it ● 11-15 Join a quiz team ● 16-20 Join Mensa

1. Which port on the Isle of Wight is famous for its annual sailing regatta?
2. By what name is the I Ching also known?
3. Which film director married Madonna at Skibo Castle in 2000?
4. Of which country is Colombo the capital?
5. Which American jazz singer was known as 'Lady Day'?
6. Who wrote the play *Coriolanus*?
7. Who wrote the novels *A Summer Bird-Cage* and *The Ice Age*?
8. In what year did Elizabeth II become queen?
9. Which actress won an Oscar for her performance in the film *Roman Holiday*?
10. Who was the first person to see the resurrected Christ?
11. Which 1986 film features the Queen song *Who Wants to Live Forever*?
12. Which American football team did Chuck Noll lead to four Super Bowl victories?
13. What was the name of the ship in which Captain Cook discovered Australia?
14. Which British singer/songwriter was killed by a speedboat in 2000?
15. Who wrote *Le Morte d'Arthur*?
16. Which post was held by William Courtenay from 1381 to 1396?
17. In which year was the first Cannes Film Festival held?
18. Which English seaside resort became a city in 2000?
19. What type of musical composition was invented by Irish composer John Field?
20. Which musical comedy star was married to Jack Hulbert?

ANSWERS: *1 Cowes, 2 Book of Changes, 3 Guy Ritchie, 4 Sri Lanka, 5 Billie Holiday, 6 William Shakespeare, 7 Margaret Drabble, 8 1952, 9 Audrey Hepburn, 10 Mary Magdalene, 11 Highlander, 12 Pittsburgh Steelers, 13 Endeavour, 14 Kirsty MacColl, 15 Sir Thomas Malory, 16 Archbishop of Canterbury, 17 1946, 18 Brighton and Hove, 19 Nocturne, 20 Dame Cicely Courtneidge.*

Entertainment

Your rating:
- 0-5 Buy a TV
- 6-10 Keep at it
- 11-15 Join a quiz team
- 16-20 Enter a quiz show

1. Which actress played an orphaned teenage horse rider in the 1978 film *International Velvet*?
2. Which ITV show exposed real-life cowboy builders by using hidden cameras?
3. Which U.S. vocalist duetted with Joe Cocker on the 1983 U.K. top ten single *Up Where We Belong*?
4. Which 2000 film starred Edward Norton as a priest and Ben Stiller as a rabbi?
5. Who was Gary's original flatmate, played by Harry Enfield, in the sitcom *Men Behaving Badly*?
6. Which British singer had a 2000 U.K. top five hit with *Something Deep Inside*?
7. Which actor played criminal Tony Montana in the 1983 film *Scarface*?
8. Which TV chef embarked on a *Gourmet Express* on BBC 2?
9. Which 2000 Kylie Minogue album release featured her UK number one hit *Spinning Around*?
10. Which sports presenter guided us through *The Day Down Under* as part of the BBC's Olympics 2000 coverage?
11. Which 2000 film starred Clint Eastwood, Tommy Lee Jones, James Garner and Donald Sutherland as former airmen pulled out of retirement by NASA?
12. Which Eighties TV programme was the first British police series to have an ethnic hero, played by David Yip?
13. Which Spice Girl had a 2000 U.K. top five hit with *Tell Me*?
14. Which actor starred as Sylvester Stallone's prison warden in the 1989 film *Lock Up*?
15. Who wrote the novel upon which the BBC 1 drama *Other People's Children* was based?
16. Which group had a 1968 U.K. number one with *Blackberry Way*?
17. Which film-making brothers were behind the 2000 movie *Me, Myself & Irene*?
18. Which BBC 1 fly-on-the-wall series following environmental health officers was narrated by John Peel?
19. Who had a U.K. number one hit in 1979 with *We Don't Talk Anymore*?
20. Which sex symbol actress of the fifties and sixties was born Vera Jayne Palmer in 1933?

ANSWERS: *1 Tatum O'Neal, 2 House of Horrors, 3 Jennifer Warnes, 4 Keeping the Faith, 5 Dermot, 6 Billie Piper, 7 Al Pacino, 8 Ainsley Harriott, 9 Light Years, 10 John Inverdale, 11 Space Cowboys, 12 The Chinese Detective, 13 Melanie B, 14 Donald Sutherland, 15 Joanna Trollope, 16 Move, 17 The Farrelly Brothers, 18 A Life of Grime, 19 Cliff Richard, 20 Jayne Mansfield.*

General Knowledge

Your rating: ● 0-5 Join a library ● 6-10 Keep at it ● 11-15 Join a quiz team ● 16-20 Join Mensa

1. Which member of the Marx Brothers adopted an Italian accent?
2. Who beat Southampton 4-3 in the F.A. Cup in February 2001?
3. Which Scottish town became a city in 2000?
4. Who is the hero of John Buchan's novel *The Thirty-Nine Steps*?
5. Which code used in telegraphy uses dots and dashes?
6. What is the square root of 121?
7. Who wrote *The Remains of the Day*?
8. What nationality was the explorer Ferdinand Magellan?
9. Who was the only U.S. president to resign from office?
10. How many arms does a squid have?
11. Which ex-*Neighbours* star had a hit single entitled *Mona* in 1990?
12. Which Australian tennis player is the only woman to have achieved the grand slam in both doubles and singles?
13. Which barrister and author wrote the play *A Voyage Round My Father*?
14. Of which African country was Kwame Nkrumah the first president?
15. In what year did the Siege of Leningrad begin?
16. Which English novelist wrote *The Pumpkin Eater* and *Long Distance*?
17. Which actor made his film debut in the 1958 movie *The Cry Baby Killer*?
18. Yves Saint Laurent was ordered to take down posters featuring which British model in 2000?
19. By what nickname was James Edward Stuart known?
20. What sort of creature is a noctule?

ANSWERS: *1 Chico, 2 Tranmere Rovers, 3 Inverness, 4 Richard Hannay, 5 Morse code, 6 Eleven, 7 Kazuo Ishiguro, 8 Portuguese, 9 Richard Nixon, 10 Ten, 11 Craig McLachlan, 12 Margaret Court, 13 John Mortimer, 14 Ghana, 15 1941, 16 Penelope Mortimer, 17 Jack Nicholson, 18 Sophie Dahl, 19 The Old Pretender, 20 A bat.*

General Knowledge

Your rating: ● **0-5** **Join a library** ● **6-10** **Keep at it** ● **11-15** **Join a quiz team** ● **16-20** **Join Mensa**

1. Which French oceanographer and filmmaker invented the aqualung?
2. What was the title of actor David Niven's first autobiography?
3. Which model turned actress played Leeloo in *The Fifth Element*?
4. What was the pen name of mathematician and author Charles Lutwidge Dodgson?
5. Which English composer wrote *The Enigma Variations*?
6. In which English county is Marwell Zoological Park?
7. Television series *Drop the Dead Donkey* was set in which TV newsroom?
8. Which London square contained London's principal fruit, flower and vegetable market for over 300 years?
9. By what nickname was Mary I or Mary Tudor known?
10. Which Swedish chemist invented dynamite?
11. In which novel by Tolstoy does Konstantin Levin appear?
12. Which English Metaphysical poet wrote *To His Coy Mistress*?
13. Electronics entrepreneur Sir Alan Sugar sold his controlling interest in which Premiership club in 2000?
14. Who translated the first printed English Bible?
15. In what organ of the body is the pons?
16. Which country hosted the football World Cup in 1966?
17. In which English county are the Potteries?
18. Which U.S. president was associated with the Square Deal?
19. Which music hall star wrote the song *My Old Dutch*?
20. What sort of creature is a jacana?

ANSWERS: *1 Jacques Cousteau, 2 The Moon's a Balloon, 3 Milla Jovovich, 4 Lewis Carroll, 5 Sir Edward Elgar, 6 Hampshire, 7 Globelink News, 8 Covent Garden, 9 Bloody Mary, 10 Alfred Nobel, 11 Anna Karenina, 12 Andrew Marvell, 13 Tottenham Hotspur, 14 Miles Coverdale, 15 Brain, 16 England, 17 Staffordshire, 18 Theodore Roosevelt, 19 Albert Chevalier, 20 A bird.*

General Knowledge

Your rating:
- 0-5 Join a library
- 6-10 Keep at it
- 11-15 Join a quiz team
- 16-20 Join Mensa

1. Which American city hosted its first marathon in 1897?
2. Which film director produced the 1999 hit song *Everybody's Free (To Wear Sunscreen)*?
3. Which 70s TV series was made into a film starring Cameron Diaz, Drew Barrymore and Lucy Liu?
4. What is the longest river in Spain?
5. In which European country is Katowice?
6. What nationality was the artist Franz Marc?
7. In which category did British boxer Audley Harrison win his gold medal at the Sydney Olympics?
8. What sort of canoe was originally used by Greenland Eskimos for hunting and fishing?
9. Which rock group recorded the album *(What's The Story) Morning Glory*?
10. Who wrote the play *Romeo and Juliet*?
11. In what year did *This is Your Life* begin in Britain?
12. Which North African dish consists of semolina served with meat, vegetables and spices?
13. To which English monarch was Mary of Teck consort?
14. Which Mexican volcano erupted at the end of 2000?
15. What name was given to Church of England priests who refused to take oaths of allegiance to William and Mary?
16. What was the first name of West Indian cultural historian C. L. R. James?
17. Which British novelist wrote *The Citadel*?
18. Which actor won a Best Supporting Actor Oscar for *The Treasure of the Sierra Madre*?
19. The hypothalamus is part of which organ of the body?
20. Which former world heavyweight boxing champion was born Arnold Cream?

ANSWERS: *1 Boston, 2 Baz Luhrmann, 3 Charlie's Angels, 4 Ebro River, 5 Poland, 6 German, 7 Super heavy-weight, 8 Kayak, 9 Oasis, 10 William Shakespeare, 11 1955, 12 Couscous, 13 George V, 14 Popocatepetl, 15 Nonjurors, 16 Cyril, 17 A J Cronin, 18 Walter Huston, 19 The brain, 20 Jersey Joe Walcott.*

Entertainment

Your rating: ● **0-5** Buy a TV ● **6-10** Keep at it ● **11-15** Join a quiz team ● **16-20** Enter a quiz show

1. Who played *Inspector Clouseau* in the 1968 film of that name?
2. On which satirical Channel 4 programme did Ricky Gervais appear as a reporter before launching his own comedy chat show?
3. What was the title of Texas' first U.K. top ten hit?
4. In which 2000 film did Antonio Banderas and Woody Harrelson play two boxers?
5. Who was the original presenter of the British version of *Family Fortunes*?
6. Which former Dire Straits member released his second solo album, *Sailing to Philadelphia*, in 2000?
7. Who directed Roger Daltrey in 1975's *Lisztomania*?
8. Who played Robert Lindsay's wife in the BBC 1 sitcom *My Family*?
9. Which indie band released an album entitled *Kid A* in 2000?
10. Which actress starred as *Buffy the Vampire Slayer* in the BBC 2 series?
11. What was the title of Billie Piper's second album?
12. Which actor played Claudius in the Seventies drama series *I, Claudius*?
13. Which actor played an alcoholic Scottish poet in the 1983 film *Reuben, Reuben*?
14. What was the title of the Police's 1981 U.K. number one single?
15. In which 2000 Paul Verhoeven film did Kevin Bacon star as a scientist who makes himself invisible?
16. Whose *Weird Weekends* were the subject of a BBC 2 documentary series?
17. In which year did Oasis celebrate their second number one hit single, *Don't Look Back in Anger*?
18. Which actor played *The Spy Who Came in from the Cold* in the 1966 film of that name?
19. What was the surname of the *EastEnders* sisters who performed at the Vic's karaoke night as the Nolans in 2000?
20. What was the Supremes' first UK number one, which hit the charts in 1964?

ANSWERS: *1 Alan Arkin, 2 The 11 O'Clock Show, 3 I Don't Want a Lover, 4 Play it to the Bone, 5 Bob Monkhouse, 6 Mark Knopfler, 7 Ken Russell, 8 Zoe Wanamaker, 9 Radiohead, 10 Sarah Michelle Gellar, 11 Walk of Life, 12 Derek Jacobi, 13 Tom Conti, 14 Every Little Thing She Does is Magic, 15 Hollow Man, 16 Louis Theroux's, 17 1996, 18 Richard Burton, 19 Slater, 20 Baby Love.*

General Knowledge

Your rating:
- 0-5 Join a library
- 6-10 Keep at it
- 11-15 Join a quiz team
- 16-20 Join Mensa

1. What form of exercise was popularised by Bill Bowerman in a 1967 book?
2. The film *The Deep* was about the search for what beneath the sea?
3. Which British actress starred in *The Killing of Sister George* and *Entertaining Mr Sloane*?
4. In which South American country did Prince William spend ten weeks as part of an Operation Raleigh expedition?
5. What sort of dog has Labrador and golden varieties?
6. In which English county is Jodrell Bank?
7. Which fictitious court was the setting for the television drama series *Crown Court*?
8. In music, what name is given to three or more notes sounded together?
9. What sort of beer takes its name from the German for 'store'?
10. With which European country is the dance the czardas associated?
11. Which French dramatist wrote the 1897 play *Cyrano de Bergerac*?
12. Who won the F.A. Cup in 1972?
13. Which great Czech distance runner died in 2000 at the age of 78?
14. What name is given to an aquatic mammal with four limbs modified into flippers?
15. Which American poet wrote *The Bridge*?
16. What nationality was the composer Paul Hindemith?
17. Which fictional character made his first appearance in the novel *The Little White Bird*?
18. What sort of plant is a lady's slipper?
19. Who designed the wedding dress worn by Catherine Zeta Jones when she married Michael Douglas?
20. At which public school are most of the boys known as Oppidans?

ANSWERS: *1 Jogging, 2 Treasure, 3 Beryl Reid, 4 Chile, 5 Retriever, 6 Cheshire, 7 Fulchester Crown Court, 8 Chord, 9 Lager, 10 Hungary, 11 Edmond Rostand, 12 Leeds United, 13 Emil Zatopek, 14 Pinniped, 15 Hart Crane, 16 German, 17 Peter Pan, 18 An orchid, 19 Christian Lacroix, 20 Eton College.*

General Knowledge

Your rating: ● **0-5** Join a library ● **6-10** Keep at it ● **11-15** Join a quiz team ● **16-20** Join Mensa

1. Which sociologist, historian and economist co-wrote *The Communist Manifesto* with Friedrich Engels?
2. What name is given to the mature female of domesticated cattle?
3. What nationality is the novelist Chinua Achebe?
4. Who was the father of Queen Mary II, wife of King William III?
5. Which winter sports resort hosted the 1960 Winter Olympics?
6. In what decade was the Treaty on the Non-proliferation of Nuclear Weapons signed?
7. Which film won the Oscar for Best Picture in 1970?
8. Which U.S. city associated with the motor industry was founded by Antoine de la Mothe Cadillac?
9. In what year did the Princess of Wales die?
10. Which actress plays *Ally McBeal* on TV?
11. Which English author wrote *Love in a Cold Climate*?
12. In which 1969 television comedy series did Spike Milligan play an Asian with an Irish father?
13. Who was the skipper of the accident-prone catamaran Team Philips?
14. What nationality was the composer Carl Nielsen?
15. Which French tennis player won the first of her six Wimbledon singles titles in 1919?
16. What was the first name of the furniture designer Hepplewhite?
17. Which British boxer needed emergency surgery after a fight in December 2000?
18. What name is given to a monologue in which a character in a play speaks his thoughts aloud?
19. Who scored the winning goal of the 1979 European Cup final?
20. What was the title of the ruler of Egypt from 1867 to 1914?

ANSWERS: *1 Karl Marx, 2 Cow, 3 Nigerian, 4 James II, 5 Squaw Valley, 6 1960s, 7 Midnight Cowboy, 8 Detroit, 9 1997, 10 Calista Flockhart, 11 Nancy Mitford, 12 Curry and Chips, 13 Pete Goss, 14 Danish, 15 Suzanne Lenglen, 16 George, 17 Paul Ingle, 18 Soliloquy, 19 Trevor Francis, 20 Khedive.*

General Knowledge

Your rating: ● **0-5** Join a library ● **6-10** Keep at it ● **11-15** Join a quiz team ● **16-20** Join Mensa

1. Which Christian sacrament is also called Holy Communion and the Lord's Supper?
2. Which American comic actor wrote *Don't Stand Too Close to a Naked Man*?
3. Which American film director received an honorary knighthood in 2001?
4. What is the highest active volcano in Europe?
5. Which famous square is on the east side of the Kremlin in Moscow?
6. What sort of creature is a kudu?
7. Which television series featured Anthony Valentine as Major Horst Mohn?
8. In computing, what does DTP stand for?
9. In which English county is the resort of Sidmouth?
10. Which drink was first sold by the Compagnie de Limonadiers in Paris in 1676?
11. What is the sequel to the film *101 Dalamatians* called?
12. Which U.S. president was known as 'Old Hickory'?
13. With which branch of mathematics is Euclid chiefly associated?
14. Which Danish comedian and pianist died in 2000 at the age of 91?
15. Who directed the films *Invasion of the Body Snatchers*, *Dirty Harry* and *The Shootist*?
16. Which rare gas has the chemical symbol Kr?
17. Who wrote *How to Win Friends and Influence People*?
18. Which American golfer won the British Open, U.S. Open and U.S. Masters in 1953?
19. What was the Greek name for Khufu, builder of the Great Pyramid at Giza?
20. In which U.S. state is Diamond Head?

ANSWERS: *1 The Eucharist, 2 Tim Allen, 3 Steven Spielberg, 4 Mount Etna, 5 Red Square, 6 An antelope, 7 Colditz, 8 Desktop publishing, 9 Devon, 10 Lemonade, 11 102 Dalmatians, 12 Andrew Jackson, 13 Geometry, 14 Victor Borge, 15 Don Siegel, 16 Krypton, 17 Dale Carnegie, 18 Ben Hogan, 19 Cheops, 20 Hawaii.*

Entertainment

Your rating: ● **0-5** Buy a TV ● **6-10** Keep at it ● **11-15** Join a quiz team ● **16-20** Enter a quiz show

1. Which former Bond girl starred alongside Jon Favreau in the 2000 film *Love & Sex*?
2. What was Miss Piggy's surname in the TV show *The Muppets*?
3. Which British actress played a ballet teacher in the 2000 film *Billy Elliot*?
4. Which girl group had a 2000 U.K. number one hit with *Black Coffee*?
5. Which 1970 film set in World War II featured Michael Caine, Cliff Robertson and Henry Fonda?
6. Which *Coronation Street* character told her husband she wanted to divorce him in 2000 after his affair with a work colleague was revealed?
7. What was the title of Spice Girl Melanie B's debut solo album?
8. Who replaced Hugh Scully as presenter of BBC 1's *Antiques Roadshow*?
9. Which 75-year-old actor starred as a convicted bank robber in the 2000 film *Where the Money Is*?
10. What was the nickname of the character Peter Jenkins in the children's drama series *Grange Hill*?
11. Which British band released their seventh studio album, *Painting It Red*, in 2000?
12. Which 1972 film featured Yul Brynner playing a mysterious bomber?
13. Which former *EastEnders* actor starred as DC Jack Mowbray in the ITV drama series *Without Motive*?
14. Which U.S. group had a 1977 number one hit in the U.K. with *Show You the Way to Go*?
15. Which former newsreader presented the BBC 1 series *The Crime Squad*?
16. What was the title of the Bond theme with which Wings had a UK top ten hit in 1973?
17. Which 1967 musical film starring Tommy Steele was based on H.G. Wells' novel *Kipps*?
18. Which BBC 1 sitcom starred *Rab C. Nesbitt*'s Gregor Fisher and *The Vicar of Dibley* actor James Fleet?
19. Which British group's first U.K. top ten hit was 1993's *How Can I Love You More*?
20. Which 2000 British film featured Tim Curry as a club-owning drugs dealer called Damian?

ANSWERS: *1 Famke Janssen, 2 Lee, 3 Julie Walters, 4 All Saints, 5 Too Late the Hero, 6 Gail Platt, 7 Hot, 8 Michael Aspel, 9 Paul Newman, 10 Tucker, 11 The Beautiful South, 12 Fuzz, 13 Ross Kemp, 14 The Jacksons, 15 Sue Lawley, 16 Live and Let Die, 17 Half a Sixpence, 18 Brotherly Love, 19 M People, 20 Sorted.*

General Knowledge

Your rating:
- **0-5 Join a library**
- **6-10 Keep at it**
- **11-15 Join a quiz team**
- **16-20 Join Mensa**

1. Which Hampshire city is on a peninsula between the estuaries of the Rivers Test and Itchen?
2. Which science fiction author wrote the novel *Hothouse*?
3. Which pop star married Lisa Marie Presley in 1994?
4. Which Norwegian dramatist wrote *A Doll's House*?
5. Which Mongol emperor was the grandson of Genghis Khan?
6. What is the principal mountain system of Mexico?
7. Which film featured the character Lurch?
8. By what name was Russian tsar Ivan IV known?
9. By what first name was American gangster Benjamin Siegel known?
10. Which ancient Greek physician is regarded as the father of medicine?
11. What was *Red Dwarf* in the television comedy series of that name?
12. Which American retail chain was founded by Sam Walton in 1962?
13. What is the capital of Sierra Leone?
14. What name is given to the study of human improvement by genetic means?
15. By what name were supporters of the Youth International Party known?
16. Which American tennis player won the men's singles at Wimbledon in 1947?
17. Who wrote *My Family and Other Animals*?
18. Which Oscar-winning American actor died in December 2000 at the age of 78?
19. Which Italian composer was elected to the Central Committee of the Italian Communist Party in 1975?
20. What sort of creature is a krait?

ANSWERS: *1 Southampton, 2 Brian Aldiss, 3 Michael Jackson, 4 Henrik Ibsen, 5 Kublai Khan, 6 Sierra Madre, 7 The Addams Family, 8 Ivan the Terrible, 9 Bugsy, 10 Hippocrates, 11 A spaceship, 12 Wal-Mart, 13 Freetown, 14 Eugenics, 15 Yippies, 16 Jack Kramer, 17 Gerald Durrell, 18 Jason Robards, 19 Luigi Nono, 20 A snake.*

General Knowledge

Your rating: ● 0-5 Join a library ● 6-10 Keep at it ● 11-15 Join a quiz team ● 16-20 Join Mensa

1. Which American white supremacist organisation is represented by the initials KKK?
2. Who was kidnapped in the 1953 film *The Kidnappers*?
3. Which British rower was awarded a knighthood in the 2001 New Year Honours List?
4. Of which Italian island is Palermo the capital?
5. Which Australian tree is also called a gum tree?
6. With which musical instrument is Fritz Kreisler associated?
7. Which American author wrote the novels *Show Boat* and *Giant*?
8. Who wrote *Barefoot in the Park* and *The Odd Couple*?
9. For which country did cricketer Richie Benaud play?
10. Which American city is known as the 'City of Brotherly Love'?
11. Who wrote the sitcoms *Beast* and *Men Behaving Badly*?
12. Which pretender to the English crown worked in the royal kitchens after his capture at the Battle of Stoke?
13. What is the name of Patrick Stewart's character in *Star Trek: The Next Generation*?
14. Which Jerzy Kosinski novel was filmed in 1979 starring Peter Sellers?
15. What is the SI unit of radiation dose equivalent?
16. Which New Zealand rugby player was known as 'Pine Tree'?
17. Who wrote *The Wonderful Wizard of Oz*?
18. Which volcano between Java and Sumatra erupted catastrophically in 1883?
19. By what name was Polish-born ballet dancer and teacher Cyvia Rambam known?
20. Which musical composition takes its name from the French for 'study'?

ANSWERS: *1 Ku Klux Klan, 2 A baby, 3 Steve Redgrave, 4 Sicily, 5 Eucalyptus, 6 Violin, 7 Edna Ferber, 8 Neil Simon, 9 Australia, 10 Philadelphia, 11 Simon Nye, 12 Lambert Simnel, 13 Captain Jean-Luc Picard, 14 Being There, 15 Sievert, 16 Colin Meads, 17 L Frank Baum, 18 Krakatoa, 19 Dame Marie Rambert, 20 Etude.*

General Knowledge

Your rating:
- 0-5 Join a library
- 6-10 Keep at it
- 11-15 Join a quiz team
- 16-20 Join Mensa

1. Which Mediterranean island was invaded by Turkish troops in 1974?
2. Which author also writes under the name Barbara Vine?
3. Which TV character beat Westlife to the coveted Christmas number one spot in 2000?
4. Who wrote the novel *Gormenghast*?
5. Which town is the administrative centre of Kent?
6. With what sort of books is Karl Baedeker associated?
7. Where was the film *The Sundowners* set?
8. What name is given to a musical composition for four instruments?
9. In the Old Testament, who interpreted the writing on the wall at Belshazzar's feast?
10. What is the capital of Malaysia?
11. Who wrote the novel *All Quiet on the Western Front*?
12. Which hymn is named from the first word of the Latin for "my soul magnifies the Lord"?
13. What was the pen name of authors Frederic Dannay and Manfred B. Lee?
14. Which character in *The Archers* is played by Trevor Harrison?
15. Who was principal conductor of the Bavarian Radio Symphony Orchestra from 1961 to 1979?
16. Which American TV show host was known as 'the Great Stone Face'?
17. Which TV series featured the characters Ludicrus and Nausius?
18. In which city is the former cathedral Hagia Sophia?
19. In which story by Nathaniel Hawthorne is Hester Prynne the main character?
20. What is the second most abundant mineral in the Earth's crust after feldspar?

***ANSWERS:** 1 Cyprus, 2 Ruth Rendell, 3 Bob the Builder, 4 Mervyn Peake, 5 Maidstone, 6 Travel guide-books, 7 Australia, 8 Quartet, 9 Daniel, 10 Kuala Lumpur, 11 Erich Maria Remarque, 12 Magnificat, 13 Ellery Queen, 14 Eddie Grundy, 15 Rafael Kubelik, 16 Ed Sullivan, 17 Up Pompeii, 18 Istanbul, 19 The Scarlet Letter, 20 Quartz.*

Entertainment

Your rating: ● 0-5 Buy a TV ● 6-10 Keep at it ● 11-15 Join a quiz team ● 16-20 Enter a quiz show

1. Who starred as a US marshal working for the Witness Protection Programme in the film *Eraser*?
2. Which *Soldier Soldier* actress replaced Minnie Driver as single mum and landlady Ellie in the TV series *My Good Friend*?
3. Which former Take That star had a hit single with George Michael's *Freedom*?
4. Which former Bond girl played Laura in the sitcom *The Upper Hand*?
5. Which 1991 Peter Medak film was based on the true story of the controversial hanging of Derek Bentley for the murder of a policeman?
6. Who had a top ten hit single in 1972 with *All the Young Dudes*?
7. Which Northern Ireland entertainer presented *After the Break* on TV?
8. Who directed the 1996 comedy film *The Stupids*?
9. Who co-presented *Rough Guide to the World* on TV with Simon O'Brien?
10. From which city do the band Pulp come?
11. Who played Robinson Crusoe in the 1975 film *Man Friday*?
12. In which BBC series did Danny Brown set out to wreak revenge on practical jokers?
13. Which Elvis Presley hit did the Pet Shop Boys take to number one in 1987?
14. Which US police drama series won nine Emmy awards in 1981?
15. Which *Fresh Prince of Bel Air* star played a fighter pilot in *Independence Day* and an alien-buster in *Men in Black*?
16. Who was the presenter of Channel 4's *Moviewatch*?
17. Which band had a hit single with *Born Slippy* in 1996?
18. Who starred as John Sedley in the 1989 film *Johnny Handsome*?
19. Which comedy writing partnership wrote the sitcom *Hi-De-Hi*?
20. Which Oscar-winning actor made his directorial debut with the film *August*, based on Chekhov's *Uncle Vanya*?

ANSWERS: *1 Arnold Schwarzenegger, 2 Lesley Vickerage, 3 Robbie Williams, 4 Honor Blackman, 5 Let Him Have It, 6 Mott the Hoople, 7 Patrick Kielty, 8 John Landis, 9 Magenta De Vine, 10 Sheffield, 11 Peter O'Toole, 12 The Fall Guy, 13 Always On My Mind, 14 Hill Street Blues, 15 Will Smith, 16 Johnny Vaughan, 17 Underworld, 18 Mickey Rourke, 19 Jimmy Perry and David Croft, 20 Anthony Hopkins.*

General Knowledge

Your rating: ● 0-5 Join a library ● 6-10 Keep at it ● 11-15 Join a quiz team ● 16-20 Join Mensa

1. Which British singer had Christmas number ones with *Mistletoe and Wine* in 1988 and *Saviour's Day* in 1990?
2. Which Christian sect is formally known as the Society of Friends?
3. In Egyptian mythology, the sphinx has the body of which animal?
4. Of which South African city is Soweto a suburb?
5. What is the highest numbered compartment on a roulette wheel?
6. Which Belgian village was the site of a famous battle on 18 June 1815 which ended the Napoleonic Wars?
7. In which county is the town of Sheerness situated?
8. Which British music-hall comedian starred in the films *Oh, Mr Porter!* and *Ask a Policeman?*
9. What is the largest of the Society Islands?
10. Who wrote the play *Twelfth Night*?
11. Which German composer wrote the operas *Salome* and *Der Rosenkavalier*?
12. Of which constellation is Spica the brightest star?
13. Which U.S. actress played Cruella de Vil in Disney's live action film *101 Dalmatians*?
14. What sort of creature is a takahe?
15. Which U.S. novelist wrote *The Scarlet Letter*?
16. Through which two countries does the River Tagus flow?
17. Which word describes the point in the orbit of the moon at which it is furthest from the earth?
18. Which Russian composer wrote *The Rite of Spring*?
19. In which South American country can the River Xingu be found?
20. Which U.S. novelist wrote *The Man with the Golden Arm*?

ANSWERS: *1 Cliff Richard, 2 Quakers, 3 A lion, 4 Johannesburg, 5 36, 6 Waterloo, 7 Kent, 8 Will Hay, 9 Tahiti, 10 William Shakespeare, 11 Richard Strauss, 12 Virgo, 13 Glenn Close, 14 A flightless bird, 15 Nathaniel Hawthorne, 16 Spain and Portugal, 17 Apogee, 18 Igor Stravinsky, 19 Brazil, 20 Nelson Algren.*

General Knowledge

Your rating: • 0-5 Join a library • 6-10 Keep at it • 11-15 Join a quiz team • 16-20 Join Mensa

1. Which songbird of the thrush family has an olive-brown plumage with an orange-red breast, throat and forehead?
2. Which pop group consisted of Mel C, Emma, Geri, Victoria and Mel B?
3. Which Dickens story features Ebenezer Scrooge?
4. Which Soviet leader intoduced the policies of glasnost and perestroika?
5. Which chemical element is represented by the symbol C?
6. In which former colony did Robert Clive of Plassey establish British supremacy in the 18th century?
7. Of which 1980s political party was Shirley Williams co-founder?
8. Which U.S. actress starred in the films *Kramer vs. Kramer* and *Out of Africa*?
9. What was the capital of the Soviet Union?
10. Which Austrian composer wrote many waltzes including *The Blue Danube*?
11. At the end of World War II, which two countries were divided by the Oder-Neisse Line?
12. Which Hertfordshire town was built in 1903 as England's first garden city?
13. Which U.S. dramatist wrote *The Little Foxes*?
14. Which French composer is famous for his *Symphonie espagnole*?
15. Which Spanish Dominican friar was appointed head of the Spanish Inquisition in 1483?
16. What is a manometer used to measure?
17. Which gas is represented by the symbol Xe?
18. At which ancient capital of Normandy was Joan of Arc tried and burned?
19. Which British psychiatrist wrote *The Divided Self*?
20. On which river does the English city of Sheffield lie?

***ANSWERS:** 1 Robin, 2 The Spice Girls, 3 A Christmas Carol, 4 Mikhail Gorbachev, 5 Carbon, 6 India, 7 The Social Democratic Party, 8 Meryl Streep, 9 Moscow, 10 Johann Strauss (the Younger), 11 Germany and Poland, 12 Letchworth, 13 Lillian Hellman, 14 Edouard Lalo, 15 Tomas de Torquemada, 16 Pressure differences, 17 Xenon, 18 Rouen, 19 R. D. Laing, 20 River Don.*

General Knowledge

Your rating: ● 0-5 Join a library ● 6-10 Keep at it
● 11-15 Join a quiz team ● 16-20 Join Mensa

1. Of which European country is the island Lesbos a part?
2. To what did boxer Cassius Clay change his name?
3. Which U.S. dramatist wrote *Cat on a Hot Tin Roof*?
4. What are hay fever sufferers allergic to?
5. Of which African country is Harare the capital?
6. What was the honourable way of death for Japanese samurai who wished to avoid shame or demonstrate sincerity?
7. Which acid is a solution in water of the pungent gas hydrogen chloride?
8. Which opera singer collaborated with Elton John on the single *Live Like Horses*?
9. Which traditional Christmas decoration grows as a partial parasite on various trees?
10. Of which metal is ferrite a compound?
11. Which Czech composer's ninth symphony is entitled *From the New World*?
12. To what did Basutoland change its name in 1966?
13. Who was the president of the USA from 1885 to 1889 and 1893 to 1897?
14. Which artificial transuranic element is represented by the symbol Fm?
15. Which French novelist wrote *Eugénie Grandet* and *Le Père Goriot*?
16. Which building was designed by Joseph Paxton to house the Great Exhibition of 1851?
17. What is the capital of New York state?
18. Which German physicist was the first to develop quantum theory?
19. Which sister of the Emperor Augustus married Mark Antony?
20. Which French novelist wrote *The Vatican Cellars* and *The Counterfeiters*?

ANSWERS: *1 Greece, 2 Muhammad Ali, 3 Tennessee Williams, 4 Pollen, 5 Zimbabwe, 6 Hara-kiri, 7 Hydrochloric acid, 8 Luciano Pavarotti, 9 Mistletoe, 10 Iron, 11 Antonin Dvorak, 12 Kingdom of Lesotho, 13 Stephen Grover Cleveland, 14 Fermium, 15 Honoré de Balzac, 16 Crystal Palace, 17 Albany, 18 Max Planck, 19 Octavia, 20 André Gide.*

Sports

Your rating: ● **0-5** **Wooden spoon** ● **6-10** **Bronze medal**
● **11-15** **Silver medal** ● **16-20** **Gold medal**

1. Which English football team won the 1998 Coca Cola Cup?
2. Which players wear red caps in the sport of water polo?
3. Which event first appeared at the 1964 Winter Olympics?
4. Which British boxer lost two world title fights to Steve Collins in 1995?
5. Which French footballer scored 13 goals in the 1958 World Cup finals?
6. How many tries did rugby union's Rory Underwood score for England against Fiji at Twickenham in 1989?
7. Why were the equestrian events for the 1956 Melbourne Olympic Games held in Stockholm, Sweden?
8. What nationality was motor racing driver Nelson Piquet?
9. Which Italian team won the 1969 European Cup?
10. Which medal did Peter Elliott win in the 1500m at the 1988 Olympics?
11. Which snooker player won the 1998 Benson and Hedges Masters with a re-spotted black?
12. Which section of the World Championship Triathlon is 10km long?
13. In which sport was Greg Louganis the first person to exceed 700 points?
14. Which American Football team did quarterback Joe Elway lead to victory in the 1998 Super Bowl?
15. Which British athlete successfully defended her Commonwealth Games 10,000m title in 1990?
16. Which rugby union club side play at Stoop Memorial Ground?
17. Which famous basketball team was founded in 1927?
18. From which club did Kenny Dalglish join Liverpool in 1977?
19. In which year were the Winter Olympics held in Grenoble, France?
20. Who succeeded Ron Saunders as manager of Aston Villa?

ANSWERS: *1 Chelsea, 2 Goalkeepers, 3 Luge tobogganing, 4 Chris Eubank, 5 Just Fontaine, 6 Five, 7 Because of Australian quarantine laws, 8 Brazilian, 9 AC Milan, 10 Silver, 11 Mark Williams, 12 Running, 13 Highboard diving, 14 Denver Broncos, 15 Liz McColgan, 16 Harlequins, 17 The Harlem Globetrotters, 18 Celtic, 19 1968, 20 Tony Barton.*

General Knowledge

Your rating:
- 0-5 Join a library
- 6-10 Keep at it
- 11-15 Join a quiz team
- 16-20 Join Mensa

1. Which 19th century Dutch painter cut off part of his own left ear?
2. In which London street is the official residence of the prime minister?
3. Which British organisation is represented by the initials VSO?
4. What sort of creature is a chub?
5. In which English county is the port of Dover situated?
6. Who became the first Norman king of England in 1066?
7. Which word describes the rate of change of a body's velocity?
8. Who was Britain's prime minister from 1940 to 1945?
9. Is a gorilla a monkey or an ape?
10. In which country is the mountain range known as the Apennines?
11. What is the hottest and driest part of the USA called?
12. Which British tennis player won the men's singles title at Wimbledon from 1934 to 1936?
13. What is a pyrometer used to measure?
14. What is palaeography a study of?
15. Which gigantic statue of the sun god Helios was one of the Seven Wonders of the World?
16. Which South African novelist wrote *A Story Like the Wind*?
17. Which two ranges of chalk hills are separated by the Weald?
18. Which Electress of Hanover was the mother of Britain's King George I?
19. Which town in central S Turkey was the birthplace of St Paul?
20. Which brittle grey-white metalloid is represented by the symbol Ge?

ANSWERS: *1 Vincent Van Gogh, 2 Downing Street, 3 Voluntary Service Overseas, 4 A fish, 5 Kent, 6 William the Conqueror, 7 Acceleration, 8 Winston Churchill, 9 An ape, 10 Italy, 11 Death Valley, 12 Fred Perry, 13 High temperatures, 14 Ancient handwriting, 15 The Colossus of Rhodes, 16 Sir Laurens van der Post, 17 North and South Downs, 18 Sophia, 19 Tarsus, 20 Germanium.*

General Knowledge

Your rating:
- 0-5 Join a library
- 6-10 Keep at it
- 11-15 Join a quiz team
- 16-20 Join Mensa

1. How many musical instruments accompany the singing of an 'a cappella' piece of music?
2. Which European country is known as Sverige in its native language?
3. Who is the patron saint of Wales?
4. Which two contrasting but complementary principles lie at the root of traditional Chinese cosmology?
5. Which insects secrete royal jelly?
6. What is the popular name for the awards presented by the Academy of Motion Picture Arts and Sciences?
7. Which bird was said to live for 500 years before being consumed by fire, out of the ashes of which a new bird would arise?
8. On which river does the annual boat race between Oxford and Cambridge Universities take place?
9. Which word describes the periodic movement of animal populations between one region and another?
10. What sort of creature is a boa?
11. Which two countries joined with Austria-Hungary for the Triple Alliance of 1882?
12. With which City of London street is the Central Criminal Court associated?
13. Who was the last Democrat President before Bill Clinton to be re-elected for a second term?
14. Who became King of Norway in 1957?
15. By what name was soprano Maria Anna Kalageropoulos better known?
16. Which chemical substance is produced by the Haber-Bosch process?
17. Which British actress was known as the *Jersey Lily*?
18. What is the largest Fijian island?
19. Which New York Stock Exchange index is the principal indicator of share price movements in the USA?
20. Which type of artistic image was named after an 18th century French finance minister?

ANSWERS: *1 None, 2 Sweden, 3 St. David, 4 Yin and yang, 5 Bees, 6 Oscars, 7 Phoenix, 8 The Thames, 9 Migration, 10 A snake, 11 Germany and Italy, 12 The Old Bailey, 13 Franklin D. Roosevelt, 14 Olaf V, 15 Maria Callas, 16 Ammonia, 17 Lillie Langtry, 18 Viti Levu, 19 The Dow-Jones index, 20 Silhouette.*

General Knowledge

Your rating:
- 0-5 Join a library
- 6-10 Keep at it
- 11-15 Join a quiz team
- 16-20 Join Mensa

1. Which British writer of children's books created the *Famous Five* and *Secret Seven*?
2. What is the name of the factory in Llantrisant, South Wales in which the UK's coins are made?
3. Of which country is Yokohama the second largest city?
4. What is a sweet william?
5. With which sport is Lee Janzen associated?
6. Which sea mammal is the largest living creature?
7. Followers of which religion observe the holy day Yom Kippur?
8. Which spirit is mixed with tomato juice to make a Bloody Mary?
9. What is an ammeter used to measure?
10. Chiropody is a paramedical specialty that deals with which parts of the body?
11. What is the capital of United Arab Emirates?
12. Which English cathedral contains the tomb of St Swithin?
13. What is the capital of the Republic of Trinidad and Tobago?
14. What sort of creature is a sika?
15. Followers of which religion worship the Trimurti?
16. What does the acronym ACAS stand for?
17. Which organisation was founded by Peter Benenson in 1961 with the aim of defending freedom of speech throughout the world?
18. According to Greek mythology, who was the goddess of epic poetry and the chief of the nine Muses?
19. Which Russian-born US aeronautical engineer invented the first successful helicopter?
20. What sort of creature is a chuckwalla?

ANSWERS: *1 Enid Blyton, 2 The Royal Mint, 3 Japan, 4 A plant, 5 Golf, 6 Blue whale, 7 Judaism, 8 Vodka, 9 Electric current, 10 The feet, 11 Abu Dhabi, 12 Winchester Cathedral, 13 Port-of-Spain, 14 A deer, 15 Hinduism, 16 Advisory Conciliation and Arbitration Service, 17 Amnesty International, 18 Calliope, 19 Igor Sikorsky, 20 A lizard.*

Entertainment

Your rating: ● **0-5** Buy a TV ● **6-10** Keep at it ● **11-15** Join a quiz team ● **16-20** Enter a quiz show

1. Who starred on TV as *Magnum P. I.* ?
2. Who starred as Joey in the film *Stop! Or My Mom Will Shoot*?
3. Which daytime quiz show is presented by Rob Curling?
4. Which jazz-funk/disco outfit hit the charts in 1996 with the single *Virtual Insanity*?
5. Who directed the 1984 film *The Cotton Club*?
6. Who presented the TV discussion show *The Time ... the Place*?
7. Which US rock group had a No 1 hit in 1976 with *If You Leave Me Now*?
8. Who starred as Larry Sanders in TV's *The Larry Sanders Show*?
9. Which British actor starred as Juan in the 1996 film *The Perez Family*?
10. Which rock group fronted by Shirley Manson had a hit single with *Stupid Girl* in 1996?
11. Which former *EastEnders* actress played Chris Cross in the TV drama series *The Hello Girls*?
12. Who directed the 1989 film *The Cook, The Thief, His Wife and Her Lover*?
13. Which Australian comedian is the creator of Dame Edna Everage and Sir Les Patterson?
14. Which reggae band had a No 1 hit single in 1982 with *Pass the Dutchie*?
15. Who played car mechanic George Malley in the 1996 film *Phenomenon*?
16. Which children's TV presenter left the BBC in 1996 to host ITV's *The Noise*?
17. For which British heavy rock band does Joe Elliott sing?
18. Which *Cardiac Arrest* star played Edinburgh lawyer Lorna in Screen One's *Truth or Dare*?
19. Which Ridley Scott film was based on the novel *Do Androids Dream of Electric Sheep*?
20. Whose 70th birthday was celebrated by ITV in 1998 by the return of *Sunday Night at the London Palladium*?

ANSWERS: *1 Tom Selleck, 2 Sylvester Stallone, 3 Turnabout, 4 Jamiroquai, 5 Francis Coppola, 6 John Stapleton, 7 Chicago, 8 Garry Shandling, 9 Alfred Molina, 10 Garbage, 11 Letitia Dean, 12 Peter Greenaway, 13 Barry Humphries, 14 Musical Youth, 15 John Travolta, 16 Andi Peters, 17 Def Leppard, 18 Helen Baxendale, 19 Blade Runner, 20 Bruce Forsyth's.*

General Knowledge

Your rating:
- 0-5 Join a library
- 6-10 Keep at it
- 11-15 Join a quiz team
- 16-20 Join Mensa

1. Which London residence of the British monarch was redesigned by Nash for George IV?
2. Of which state of the USA is Richmond the capital?
3. What are incisors, canines and molars?
4. Which British novelist wrote *Robinson Crusoe* and *Moll Flanders*?
5. Which South African clergyman won the Nobel Peace Prize in 1984?
6. Which wall was built in 1961 to curb the flow of refugees from East Germany to West Germany?
7. With which instrument is Australian musician John Williams associated?
8. What sort of creature is a teal?
9. By what nickname was the British pirate Edward Teach known?
10. Which British novelist created the detective Lord Peter Wimsey?
11. What nationality was the composer Heitor Villa-Lobos?
12. Of which former Soviet republic is Tbilisi the capital?
13. Who was the first vice president of the USA?
14. Who was the president of the Soviet Union from 1983 to 1984?
15. Which British novelist wrote *Barchester Towers* and *Phineas Finn*?
16. What sort of creature is a trogon?
17. Which English religious leader founded the Quakers?
18. Which sea channel between Denmark and Sweden links the Kattegat and the Baltic Sea?
19. By what name was the UK's royal house known before the name Windsor was adopted in 1917?
20. Which Italian film-maker directed *The Damned* and *Death in Venice*?

ANSWERS: *1 Buckingham Palace, 2 Virginia, 3 Teeth, 4 Daniel Defoe, 5 Desmond Tutu, 6 The Berlin Wall, 7 Guitar, 8 A duck, 9 Blackbeard, 10 Dorothy L. Sayers, 11 Brazilian, 12 Georgia, 13 John Adams, 14 Yuri Andropov, 15 Anthony Trollope, 16 A bird, 17 George Fox, 18 The Sound, 19 Saxe-Coburg-Gotha, 20 Luchino Visconti.*

General Knowledge

Your rating: ● **0-5** Join a library ● **6-10** Keep at it ● **11-15** Join a quiz team ● **16-20** Join Mensa

1. Of which Mediterranean island is Palermo the capital?
2. Which measure of the fineness of gold is equal to the number of parts of gold by weight in 24 parts of the alloy?
3. Which Apollo mission was aborted after an in-flight explosion?
4. Who was Archbishop of Canterbury from 1980 to 1991?
5. Of which country was David Ben-Gurion the first prime minister?
6. Which Swedish chemist left £1.75 million as a foundation for annual awards for Peace, Physics, Chemistry, Literature and Medicine?
7. Which Indian-born British novelist won the Booker prize in 1981 for *Midnight's Children*?
8. Which kingdom was ruled by Tutankhamen from 1361 to 1352 BC?
9. Of which political party was Norman Tebbit chairman from 1985 to 1987?
10. Which constellation of the zodiac lies between Leo and Libra?
11. From what natural substance is lanolin extracted?
12. Which Irish author wrote the novel *Casualties of Peace*?
13. Which country was known as Dahomey until 1975?
14. Which legendary Spartan king was the husband of Helen and the brother of Agamemnon?
15. Which Ugandan president was overthrown by Idi Amin in 1971?
16. By what name was Italian painter Michelangelo Merisi known?
17. By what name were the two identical spacecraft that went into orbit around Mars in 1976 known?
18. In which Spanish city can one find the Prado art gallery?
19. Which British novelist wrote *Anna of the Five Towns* and *Clayhanger*?
20. Who was prime minister of South Africa from 1919 to 1924 and from 1939 to 1948?

ANSWERS: *1 Sicily, 2 Carat, 3 Apollo 13, 4 Robert Runcie, 5 Israel, 6 Alfred Nobel, 7 Salman Rushdie, 8 Egypt, 9 Conservative Party, 10 Virgo, 11 Wool, 12 Edna O'Brien, 13 Benin, 14 Menelaus, 15 Milton Obote, 16 Caravaggio, 17 Viking probes, 18 Madrid, 19 Arnold Bennett, 20 Jan Smuts.*

General Knowledge

Your rating:
- **0-5 Join a library**
- **6-10 Keep at it**
- **11-15 Join a quiz team**
- **16-20 Join Mensa**

1. In which English county can the Mendip Hills be found?
2. Which British novelist and dramatist wrote *The Good Companions* and *An Inspector Calls*?
3. Of which South American country is Caracas the capital?
4. Which Middle East political group is represented by the initials PLO?
5. Which German composer wrote the overture to *A Midsummer Night's Dream*?
6. Which Old Testament figure was instructed to build an ark for his family and representatives of each animal species?
7. On which date in which year did the USA's Declaration of Independence take place?
8. In which year did the Apollo 11 lunar module land on the moon?
9. Of which country did Kurt Waldheim become president in 1986?
10. Which U.S. actor starred in the films *The Cincinnati Kid* and *Papillon*?
11. Which British publisher was the director of a peerage which was first published in 1802?
12. What is a cimbalom?
13. Who was the prime minister of Great Britain from 1908 to 1916?
14. Which political party leader sang in a rock band called Ugly Rumours as a student?
15. In which cathedral was St Thomas à Becket murdered in 1170?
16. Which British actor starred in the films *Doctor in the House* and *Providence*?
17. What is the chief river in Burma?
18. Who was the prime minister of Italy from 1963 to 1968 and from 1974 to 1976?
19. Which treatment for mental disorders is represented by the initials ECT?
20. What are the three middle names of the Prince of Wales?

ANSWERS: *1 Somerset, 2 J. B. Priestley, 3 Venezuela, 4 Palestine Liberation Organisation, 5 Felix Mendelssohn, 6 Noah, 7 July 4th 1776, 8 1969, 9 Austria, 10 Steve McQueen, 11 John Debrett, 12 A musical instrument, 13 Herbert Asquith, 14 Tony Blair, 15 Canterbury Cathedral, 16 Dirk Bogarde, 17 Irrawaddy River, 18 Aldo Moro, 19 Electroconvulsive therapy, 20 Philip Arthur George.*

Entertainment

Your rating: ● **0-5** **Buy a TV** ● **6-10** **Keep at it**
● **11-15** **Join a quiz team** ● **16-20** **Enter a quiz show**

1. Which *Back to the Future* star played Caroline in Channel 4's *Caroline in the City*?
2. Which country singer released an album entitled *Trail of Tears* in 1996?
3. Who starred as Wayne in the film *Wayne's World*?
4. Which father and son starred as Cecil Rhodes in the BBC's £10 million series, *Rhodes*?
5. Which 'Bard of Barking' released an album entitled *William Bloke* in 1996?
6. In which hospital was TV's *Casualty* set?
7. Which singer/songwriter originally recorded the songs *After Midnight* and *Cocaine*, which were later covered by Eric Clapton?
8. Who starred in the title role of the1996 big-screen adaptation of Jane Austen's *Emma*?
9. Who presented the TV quiz show *Incognito*?
10. Which British group released an album in 1996 entitled *Coming Up*?
11. Which popular drama series centred on the activities of the King's Own Fusiliers?
12. Who produced and starred in the 1984 film *Tightrope*?
13. Which group had a top ten hit single in 1984 with *Radio Gaga*?
14. Which British actor won an Emmy in 1996 for best actor in a mini-series for *Rasputin*?
15. Which *Pulp Fiction* star appeared in the film *A Time To Kill*?
16. Who starred as the man in TV's *Man About the House*?
17. Which Sixties icon released a live album in 1996 entitled *20th Century Blues*?
18. Who won a Best Actor Oscar for his role in the 1969 film *True Grit*?
19. In which country was the documentary series *The Flying Vet* set?
20. Who starred as the secretary-turned-stripper in the film *Striptease*?

ANSWERS: *1 Lea Thompson, 2 Billy Ray Cyrus, 3 Mike Myers, 4 Martin and Joe Shaw, 5 Billy Bragg, 6 Holby City Hospital, 7 J. J. Cale, 8 Gwyneth Paltrow, 9 Peter Smith, 10 Suede, 11 Soldier, Soldier, 12 Clint Eastwood, 13 Queen, 14 Alan Rickman, 15 Samuel L. Jackson, 16 Richard O'Sullivan, 17 Marianne Faithfull, 18 John Wayne, 19 Australia, 20 Demi Moore.*

General Knowledge

Your rating: ● **0-5** Join a library ● **6-10** Keep at it ● **11-15** Join a quiz team ● **16-20** Join Mensa

1. The Sorbonne is part of which European city's university?
2. Which British novelist wrote *The Rachel Papers* and *The Moronic Inferno*?
3. What was the name of the ruling dynasty of England from 1485 to 1603?
4. Which Irish dramatist wrote *Juno and the Paycock*?
5. The Yukon is a territory of which country?
6. What nationality was the pianist and composer Franz Liszt?
7. What is the capital of Peru?
8. What is the first name of the Queen's sister?
9. Which militant organisation is represented by the initials IRA?
10. What sort of creature is an ocelot?
11. Which French surrealist wrote the novel *Nadja*?
12. Which electrical component consists of two conductor or semi-conductor plates separated by a dielectric?
13. By what name are the Kentucky Derby, the Preakness Stakes, and the Belmont Stakes collectively known?
14. Of which country was D. S. Senanayake the first prime minister?
15. Which boxer took the world heavyweight title from Joe Walcott in 1952 and retired undefeated in 1956?
16. Which German dramatist and poet wrote *The Caucasian Chalk Circle*?
17. Which British portrait painter became the first president of the Royal Academy in 1768?
18. Which British novelist wrote *The Needle's Eye* and *The Middle Ground*?
19. Which crooner co-starred with Danny Kaye in the 1954 film *White Christmas*?
20. Which Scottish explorer wrote *Travels in the Interior Districts of Africa*?

ANSWERS: *1 Paris, 2 Martin Amis, 3 The Tudors, 4 Sean O'Casey, 5 Canada, 6 Hungarian, 7 Lima, 8 Margaret, 9 Irish Republican Army, 10 A wild cat, 11 André Breton, 12 Capacitor, 13 The Triple Crown, 14 Ceylon, 15 Rocky Marciano, 16 Bertolt Brecht, 17 Sir Joshua Reynolds, 18 Margaret Drabble, 19 Bing Crosby, 20 Mungo Park.*

General Knowledge

Your rating:
- 0-5 Join a library
- 6-10 Keep at it
- 11-15 Join a quiz team
- 16-20 Join Mensa

1. Which slapstick policemen featured in several silent films produced by Mack Sennett?
2. The mountain range known as the Pyrenees lies between which two major European countries?
3. What do the initials LED stand for?
4. According to Greek mythology, who was the goddess of love?
5. Which star of the films *East of Eden* and *Rebel without a Cause* became a cult hero following his death in a car crash in 1955?
6. What was the federation of Serbia, Montenegro, Croatia, Slovenia and Bosnia-Herzegovina named in 1927?
7. What sort of creature is an aphid?
8. Of which country is Islamabad the capital?
9. Which British author created the character Sherlock Holmes?
10. Of which state of the USA is Phoenix the capital?
11. Which U.S. novelist wrote Slaughterhouse Five?
12. What sort of creature is an accentor?
13. What is the highest female singing voice?
14. Which French filmmaker directed *Mouchette* and *Lancelot du Lac*?
15. Who was King of the Scots from 1165 to 1214?
16. What was the Central American country of Belize known as until 1973?
17. What is the capital of Lithuania?
18. Which Greek dramatist wrote the plays *Oedipus Rex* and *Antigone*?
19. Which German city was the birthplace of Mendelssohn and Brahms?
20. How are fluorine, chlorine, bromine, iodine and astatine collectively known?

ANSWERS: *1 The Keystone Kops, 2 France and Spain, 3 Light-emitting diode, 4 Aphrodite, 5 James Dean, 6 Yugoslavia, 7 An insect, 8 Pakistan, 9 Sir Arthur Conan Doyle, 10 Arizona, 11 Kurt Vonnegut, 12 A bird, 13 Soprano, 14 Robert Bresson, 15 William the Lion, 16 British Honduras, 17 Vilnius, 18 Sophocles, 19 Hamburg, 20 Halogens.*

General Knowledge

Your rating:
- 0-5 Join a library
- 6-10 Keep at it
- 11-15 Join a quiz team
- 16-20 Join Mensa

1. In which continent is the Republic of Senegal located?
2. For which artform is Donatello famous?
3. Of which South American country was Juan Peron president from 1946 to 1955?
4. Which popular tinned fish is sometimes known as tunny?
5. What is the official currency unit of Belgium?
6. Of which country is Seoul the capital?
7. What is the capital of Iceland?
8. In which part of the body would you find the iris?
9. What sort of creature is a rhea?
10. Which amphitheatre in Rome is 188 metres long and 156 metres wide?
11. What was the Royal Ballet known as until 1956?
12. What sort of creature is a midshipman?
13. Which Italian poet wrote the epic *Rinaldo* and the pastoral drama *Aminta*?
14. In which two countries can Lake Maggiore be found?
15. Which Austrian philosopher wrote *Tractatus Logico-Philosophicus*?
16. What is the third largest state of the USA?
17. Which English agriculturalist is best known for his invention of the seed drill in 1701?
18. Of which Republic of Ireland county is Lifford the county town?
19. What sort of creature was a tarpan?
20. Of which country is P'yongyang the capital?

ANSWERS: *1 Africa, 2 Sculpture, 3 Argentina, 4 Tuna, 5 The Belgian Franc, 6 South Korea, 7 Reykjavik, The eye, 9 A bird, 10 The Colosseum, 11 The Sadler's Wells Ballet, 12 A fish, 13 Torquato Tasso, 14 Italy and Switzerland, 15 Wittgenstein, 16 California, 17 Jethro Tull, 18 Donegal, 19 A horse, 20 North Korea.*

Entertainment

Your rating: ● **0-5** Buy a TV ● **6-10** Keep at it ● **11-15** Join a quiz team ● **16-20** Enter a quiz show

1. Which actor played eight roles in the 2000 film sequel *Nutty Professor II: The Klumps*?
2. Which Australian entertainer was accompanied during his early 1960s TV appearances by Coojee Bear, a koala puppet?
3. Which Irish band returned to the U.K. charts with the number one single *Beautiful Day* in 2000?
4. What was the subtitle of the 1988 film *Halloween 4*?
5. Which actress played Dr Victoria Merrick in the BBC 1 drama series *Holby City*?
6. What was the title of All Saints' second album?
7. Which former *Blue Peter* presenter became one of the new team fronting BBC 1's *Live and Kicking* in 2000?
8. Which 2000 animated Disney film featured an iguanodon called Aladar?
9. Which newsreader presented the eventful *National Television Awards 2000*, screened on ITV?
10. Which Hollywood actor's early films included 1981's *Taps* and 1983's *Losin' It*?
11. Who played bar owner Sam Malone in the U.S. sitcom *Cheers*?
12. Which British band had a U.K. top ten hit in 1991 with *No Son of Mine*?
13. Which detective, created by Ruth Rendell, was played on TV by George Baker?
14. Which 2000 *American Pie*-esque film was co-produced by *Ghostbusters'* Ivan Reitman?
15. Which ITV drama series set in a slimming club was written by Kay Mellor?
16. What was the title of the Real McCoy's 1995 U.K. top ten hit?
17. Who directed and co-produced the 1988 film *The Milagro Beanfield War*?
18. Which US series starred James Gandolfini as a New Jersey gangster?
19. Which diva had a U.K. top five hit in 1989 with *This Time I Know It's For Real*?
20. Which star of *The X-Files* appeared in the 2000 film *The House of Mirth*?

ANSWERS: *1 Eddie Murphy, 2 Rolf Harris, 3 U2, 4 The Return of Michael Myers, 5 Lisa Faulkner, 6 Saints and Sinners, 7 Katy Hill, 8 Dinosaur, 9 Sir Trevor McDonald, 10 Tom Cruise's, 11 Ted Danson, 12 Genesis, 13 (Detective Chief) Inspector Wexford, 14 Road Trip, 15 Fat Friends, 16 Run Away, 17 Robert Redford, 18 The Sopranos, 19 Donna Summer, 20 Gillian Anderson.*

General Knowledge

Your rating:
- 0-5 Join a library
- 6-10 Keep at it
- 11-15 Join a quiz team
- 16-20 Join Mensa

1. Which English poet wrote *The Rime of the Ancient Mariner*?
2. Where did Ivor the Engine live?
3. Which well-known cycle race was first held in 1903?
4. On which island was the BBC series *Castaway 2000* set?
5. Which English fashion designer opened the boutique *Bazaar* on the King's Road in 1957?
6. Of which U.S. state is Cheyenne the capital?
7. What is the name of the lioness in *Born Free* by Joy Adamson?
8. What is the hardest naturally-occurring substance known?
9. What is the highest mountain in the British Isles?
10. Who directed the film *2001: A Space Odyssey*?
11. Which film was advertised as having a cast of 125 000?
12. Which actress was the eldest child of Roger Kemble?
13. Who invented the vacuum flask?
14. Which composer became a Companion of Honour in the 2001 New Year Honours List?
15. What was the surname of the uncle and nephew who discovered the North Magnetic Pole?
16. Which member of the Royal Family has the title Baron Greenwich?
17. Who is the author of the *River Cottage Cookbook*?
18. In which Australian city is the newspaper *The Age* published?
19. Which Greek poet is said to have introduced actors into dramatic performances?
20. Which condiment has the chemical formula NaCl?

ANSWERS: *1 Samuel Taylor Coleridge, 2 (In the top left-hand corner of) Wales, 3 Tour de France, 4 Taransay, 5 Mary Quant, 6 Wyoming, 7 Elsa, 8 Diamond, 9 Ben Nevis, 10 Stanley Kubrick, 11 Ben Hur, 12 Sarah Siddons, 13 Sir James Dewar, 14 Sir Harrison Birtwistle, 15 Ross, 16 Prince Philip, 17 Hugh Fearnley-Whittingstall, 18 Melbourne, 19 Thespis, 20 Salt.*

General Knowledge

Your rating: ● 0-5 Join a library ● 6-10 Keep at it ● 11-15 Join a quiz team ● 16-20 Join Mensa

1. Which well-known British medical journal was established in 1823?
2. What is added to vodka to make a screwdriver?
3. What nationality was the poet Gabriela Mistral who won the 1945 Nobel Prize for literature?
4. Who was the third president of the United States?
5. Which poison is represented by the letters CN?
6. In the Bible, which hostile power is associated with Gog?
7. What is the occupation of Illya in the film *Never On Sunday*?
8. In which London park is London Zoo?
9. How many reeds does a clarinet have?
10. Which well-known astronomer was awarded a knighthood in the 2001 New Year Honours List?
11. What was the name of the city where television's *The Jetsons* lived?
12. Which novelist became the first Baron Tweedsmuir?
13. In Greek mythology, which swift-footed huntress lost a race when she stopped to pick up golden apples?
14. Which Somerset farmer runs the Glastonbury Festival?
15. What is the common name for the hallucinogenic drug Phencyclidine or PCP?
16. Which English artist painted *Mr and Mrs Clark and Percy*?
17. Which British author wrote the Mallen trilogy?
18. Which Austrian composer wrote the *Resurrection Symphony* and the *Symphony of a Thousand*?
19. In Greek mythology, who killed the Minotaur?
20. Which plant of the parsley family is also called Queen Anne's lace?

ANSWERS: *1 The Lancet, 2 Orange juice, 3 Chilean, 4 Thomas Jefferson, 5 Cyanide, 6 Magog, 7 Prostitute, 8 Regent's Park, 9 One, 10 Patrick Moore, 11 Orbit City, 12 John Buchan, 13 Atalanta, 14 Michael Eavis, 15 Angel dust, 16 David Hockney, 17 Catherine Cookson, 18 Gustav Mahler, 19 Theseus, 20 Wild carrot.*

General Knowledge

Your rating: • **0-5** Join a library • **6-10** Keep at it • **11-15** Join a quiz team • **16-20** Join Mensa

1. Which literary family is associated with Haworth Parsonage in West Yorkshire?
2. What was the affliction suffered by Jennifer Jones in the film *Love Letters*?
3. Which clarinettist had a hit with *Stranger on the Shore* in 1961?
4. What name is given to the apparent brightness of a celestial body in astronomy?
5. To which country do the Cyclades belong?
6. What name is given to the long loincloth traditionally worn by Hindu men?
7. Which Russian author wrote *The Brothers Karamazov*?
8. Who was vice president of the United States from 1989 to 1993?
9. Which member of *The Goons* received an honorary knighthood in the 2001 New Year Honours List?
10. What is the capital of Tasmania?
11. Which British author wrote *Ballet Shoes*?
12. Which Russian impresario founded the Ballets Russes in 1909?
13. Who lost his world heavyweight boxing title in the first championship bout under the Queensberry rules?
14. With which musical instrument is Coleman Hawkins associated?
15. Who wrote The English Constitution in 1867?
16. Which Italian poet won the 1959 Nobel prize for literature?
17. Borat Karabzhanov is a character created by which televison comedian?
18. Which actor starred in *Dr Zhivago* and *The Dresser*?
19. In Chinese philosophy, what name is given to the ethereal substance of which everything is composed?
20. What sort of creature is a thickhead?

ANSWERS: *1 The Brontës, 2 Amnesia, 3 Acker Bilk, 4 Magnitude, 5 Greece, 6 Dhoti, 7 Fyodor Dostoevsky, 8 Dan Quayle, 9 Spike Milligan, 10 Hobart, 11 Noel Streatfeild, 12 Sergey Diaghilev, 13 John L Sullivan, 14 (Tenor) Saxophone, 15 Walter Bagehot, 16 Salvatore Quasimodo, 17 Sacha Baron Cohen, 18 Tom Courtenay, 19 Ch'i, 20 A bird.*

Entertainment

Your rating: ● 0-5 Buy a TV ● 6-10 Keep at it ● 11-15 Join a quiz team ● 16-20 Enter a quiz show

1. Which US soul singer released an album entitled *Renaissance* in 2000?
2. What were the first names of the Harts in the U.S. drama series *Hart to Hart*?
3. Which British band hit the UK number one spot with *Stomp* in 2000?
4. Which 1990 Coen Brothers film starred Gabriel Byrne and Albert Finney?
5. Where did the *Coronation Street* siege take place in 2000?
6. Which girl band returned to the U.K. number one spot with their double-A side release *Holler/Let Love Lead the Way* in 2000?
7. Which BBC 1 series, presented by Robert Winston, investigated our bodies' ability to repair themselves?
8. Who played Michelle Pfeiffer's husband in the 2000 film *What Lies Beneath*?
9. Which comedy quiz show, fronted by Angus Deayton, moved to a new spot on BBC 1 in 2000?
10. Which U.K. band, fronted by Sharleen Spiteri, released a *Greatest Hits* album in 2000?
11. Which eighties comedy drama set in the world of snooker starred Robert Lindsay and Paul McGann?
12. Which 1990 film thriller starred Rob Lowe and James Spader?
13. In which English city was the Channel 4 drama series *North Square* set?
14. What was the title of the Hollies' 1965 U.K. number one single?
15. Which star of *Jerry Maguire* and *Stuart Little* appeared in the 2000 film *The Little Vampire*?
16. Which US vocalist had a U.K. top ten hit in 1989 with *I Drove All Night*?
17. In what type of car did Michael J. Fox travel through time in the *Back to the Future* movies?
18. Who played the title role in the BBC 1 drama series *The Scarlet Pimpernel*?
19. Which female group had a U.K. top ten hit in 1981 with *Attention to Me*?
20. Which star of the U.S. sitcom *Roseanne* appeared in the 2000 film *Coyote Ugly*?

ANSWERS: *1 Lionel Richie, 2 Jonathan & Jennifer, 3 Steps, 4 Miller's Crossing, 5 Fresco's supermarket, 6 Spice Girls, 7 Superhuman, 8 Harrison Ford, 9 Have I Got News For You, 10 Texas, 11 Give Us a Break, 12 Bad Influence, 13 Leeds, 14 I'm Alive, 15 Jonathan Lipnicki, 16 Cyndi Lauper, 17 A DeLorean, 18 Richard E. Grant, 19 The Nolans, 20 John Goodman.*

General Knowledge

Your rating: • 0-5 Join a library • 6-10 Keep at it • 11-15 Join a quiz team • 16-20 Join Mensa

1. Which American actor won a Best Actor Oscar for *To Kill a Mockingbird*?
2. Which future novelist appeared in the 1965 film *A High Wind in Jamaica*?
3. Which *Coronation Street* actor is the only member of the original cast still in the show?
4. In Greek mythology, what name was given to a one-eyed giant?
5. Which U.S. government agency of volunteers was founded by John F Kennedy in 1961?
6. *El Pais* is a daily newspaper of which country?
7. Which of the acting McGann brothers has appeared as Sean Reynolds in Emmerdale?
8. Of which U.S. state is Augusta the capital?
9. Which zodiac sign is also called the Twins?
10. Of which national park is Kinder Scout the highest point?
11. Which American writer claimed that men seldom make passes at girls who wear glasses?
12. Which Irish dancer and choreographer was born Edris Stannus?
13. Of which football team did David Jones become manager in January 2001?
14. Which Kenyan runner won the 1500m at the 1968 Olympics?
15. What was the apt middle name of union leader Jimmy Hoffa who mysteriously disappeared in 1975?
16. Which cat is also called a desert lynx?
17. How many Oscars were won by the 1994 film Forrest Gump?6
18. Which American author wrote *Saint Jack* and *The Mosquito Coast*?
19. What is the oldest of the three classic races that constitute the American Triple Crown?
20. Which darts player was made an MBE in the 2001 New Year Honours List?

ANSWERS: *1 Gregory Peck, 2 Martin Amis, 3 Bill Roache, 4 Cyclops, 5 Peace Corps, 6 Spain, 7 Stephen, 8 Maine, 9 Gemini, 10 Peak District, 11 Dorothy Parker, 12 Dame Ninette de Valois, 13 Wolverhampton Wanderers, 14 Kip Keino, 15 Riddle, 16 Caracal, 17 , 18 Paul Theroux, 19 Belmont Stakes, 20 Phil Taylor.*

General Knowledge

Your rating:
- **0-5 Join a library**
- **6-10 Keep at it**
- **11-15 Join a quiz team**
- **16-20 Join Mensa**

1. Which American actress became Princess Grace of Monaco?
2. Which Australian author wrote *The Chant of Jimmy Blacksmith*?
3. Which city hosted the 2001 F.A. Cup Final?
4. What was the former name of Ho Chi Minh City?
5. With which athletics event is Sergey Bubka associated?
6. Of which U.S. state is Jefferson City the capital?
7. The 1983 film *Scarface* was set in which city?
8. What name is given to the act of taking another person's writings and passing them off as one's own?
9. With which sport are Oksana Baiul and Elvis Stojko associated?
10. Of which country is Gelderland a province?
11. In which novel by Charles Dickens does the character Bill Sikes appear?
12. Which constellation contains the Coalsack?
13. In which country is Lake Athabasca?
14. From which Italian football team did Sven-Goran Eriksson resign as manager in 2001?
15. Which English philosopher wrote *Leviathan*?
16. In the Old Testament, which Midianite priest became Moses' father-in-law?
17. Television series *Diagnosis Murder* features an amateur sleuth whose main job is what?
18. Which English novelist wrote *Headlong Hall* and *Nightmare Abbey*?
19. What surname did Turkish leader Mustafa Kemal receive in 1934?
20. Which West Saxon king was grandson of Alfred the Great?

ANSWERS: *1 Grace Kelly, 2 Thomas Keneally, 3 Cardiff, 4 Saigon, 5 Pole vault, 6 Missouri, 7 Miami, 8 Plagiarism, 9 Ice skating, 10 The Netherlands, 11 Oliver Twist, 12 Crux, or Southern Cross, 13 Canada, 14 Lazio, 15 Thomas Hobbes, 16 Jethro, 17 Hospital doctor, 18 Thomas Love Peacock, 19 Atatürk, 20 Athelstan.*

General Knowledge

Your rating: ● **0-5** Join a library ● **6-10** Keep at it ● **11-15** Join a quiz team ● **16-20** Join Mensa

1. Which English poet wrote an *Ode to a Nightingale*?
2. Which star of *It Aint Half Hot Mum* was the voice of Sgt Major Zero in the childrens television series *Terrahawks*?
3. Which Oscar-winning actor stars in the film *Cast Away*?
4. Who was the first professional England cricketer to be knighted?
5. What is the capital of Greece?
6. How many players are there in an ice hockey team?
7. Who played a fallen priest in *Night of the Iguana*?
8. What name is given to a Japanese woman whose traditional occupation is to entertain men?
9. Which American dancer, actor and singer starred in *Singin' in the Rain* and *An American in Paris*?
10. Which American city hosted the 1996 Olympics?
11. Who wrote *The Joy Luck Club*?
12. Which American actress was the elder sister of Joan Fontaine?
13. What nickname was given to the M9A1 rocket launcher?
14. Which figure in the Profumo scandal has claimed that Sir Roger Hollis was the 'fifth man' in the 1960s spy ring?
15. What is the thickest and most powerful tendon in the human body?
16. Which device for detecting radiation was invented by Donald A Glaser?
17. Which American author wrote the Studs Lonigan trilogy?
18. To which continent is the bird called the cock-of-the-rock native?
19. Which singer and actor had hits with *Banana Boat Song* and *Mary's Boy Child* in 1957?
20. What is the highest-pitched woodwind instrument in an orchestra?

ANSWERS: *1 John Keats, 2 Windsor Davies, 3 Tom Hanks, 4 Jack Hobbs, 5 Athens, 6 Six, 7 Richard Burton, 8 Geisha, 9 Gene Kelly, 10 Atlanta, 11 Amy Tan, 12 Olivia de Havilland, 13 Bazooka, 14 Christine Keeler, 15 Achilles tendon, 16 Bubble chamber, 17 James T Farrell, 18 South America, 19 Harry Belafonte, 20 Piccolo.*

Sports

Your rating: ● 0-5 Wooden spoon ● 6-10 Bronze medal ● 11-15 Silver medal ● 16-20 Gold medal

1. Which county beat Glamorgan to win cricket's 2000 Benson and Hedges Cup final?
2. Which number lies between 7 and 8 on a dartboard?
3. Who beat Don Curry to become undisputed world welterweight boxing champion in 1986?
4. Which former middle-distance runner became a Tory MP in 1992?
5. What type of game is battledore?
6. Which Everton player gave away the penalty that led to France's Golden Goal victory over Portugal at Euro 2000?
7. Who was the snooker world champion in 1991?
8. How many players make up a water polo team?
9. With which sport are the Dallas Cowboys and the San Francisco 49ers associated?
10. Who was world heavyweight boxing champion from 1952-56?
11. Which classic horserace was won by Love Divine in June 2000?
12. How many dogs take part in a greyhound race in Britain?
13. Which team lost 5-1 to Rangers in the final of the Scottish Cup in 1996?
14. The marathon is how many miles and 385 yards long?
15. At which Olympics did Briton Matthew Pinsent win his first gold medal?
16. Which Australian athlete won the women's 400m in front of her home crowd at the Sydney Olympics?
17. Who did Pakistan beat in the final of the cricket World Cup in 1992?
18. Which horse won the Derby in 1971?
19. Naim Suleymanoglu from Turkey is a top name in which sport?
20. Which team beat Celtic 2-1 in the final of the 1970 European Cup?

***ANSWERS:** 1 Gloucestershire, 2 16, 3 Lloyd Honeyghan, 4 Seb Coe, 5 An ancient racket game, 6 Abel Xavier, 7 John Parrott, 8 7, 9 American football, 10 Rocky Marciano, 11 The Oaks, 12 Six, 13 Hearts, 14 26, 15 Barcelona, 16 Cathy Freeman, 17 England, 18 Mill Reef, 19 Weightlifting, 20 Feyenoord.*

General Knowledge

Your rating: ● 0-5 Join a library ● 6-10 Keep at it ● 11-15 Join a quiz team ● 16-20 Join Mensa

1. Which comet is shown in the Bayeux Tapestry?
2. What name is given to a musical composition for six instruments?
3. Which team were 1991-92 Football League Champions?
4. Of which European country is Piedmont a region?
5. Which Spanish painter was noted for his 'blue period' in the early 20th century?
6. In law, what name is given to person involved in a criminal act as an accessory or abettor?
7. In which decade was *Dr Zhivago* first published in the Soviet Union?
8. Which U.S. crime fighter headed a team of law officers known as 'the Untouchables'?
9. De Beers Consolidated Mines are the world's largest producer and distributor of which precious stones?
10. Which comedian plays *Mr Bean*?
11. In which country did television presenter Phillip Schofield begin his TV career?
12. Which rock group recorded the song *Smells Like Teen Spirit*?
13. What is the new corporate name for organisations run by the Post Office?
14. Which Australian tennis player won the men's singles at Wimbledon in 1956 and 1957?
15. In which South American country is the Atacama Desert?
16. What sort of creature is a gelada?
17. The film *Picnic at Hanging Rock* begins on which day?
18. Which British actor became a Companion of Honour in the 2001 New Year Honours List?
19. Which well-known Oxford Street department store has been awarded its first royal warrant?
20. What name was given to the public market district of a Persian town?

ANSWERS: *1 Halley's Comet, 2 Sextet, 3 Leeds United, 4 Italy, 5 Pablo Picasso, 6 Accomplice, 7 1980s, 8 Eliot Ness, 9 Diamonds, 10 Rowan Atkinson, 11 New Zealand, 12 Nirvana, 13 Consignia, 14 Lew Hoad, 15 Chile, 16 A monkey, 17 Valentines Day, 18 Paul Schofield, 19 Selfridges, 20 Bazaar.*

General Knowledge

Your rating:
- 0-5 Join a library
- 6-10 Keep at it
- 11-15 Join a quiz team
- 16-20 Join Mensa

1. Which American talk show host received an Oscar nomination for *The Color Purple*?
2. Who wrote the television drama *A Sense of Guilt*?
3. Which veteran British actor renewed his marriage vows in a church service in 2001?
4. How much is a 'double top' worth in darts?
5. Which Shakespeare play is set against the background of enmity between the Capulets and Montagues?
6. In securities and commodities trading, is a bear market rising or declining?
7. Who lost 2-0 to Chelsea in the 1997 FA Cup final?
8. With which composer is the German city of Bayreuth associated?
9. Which British heptathlete was made an OBE in the 2001 New Year Honours List?
10. What sort of creature is a jacamar?
11. Who played Peter in the film *Peter's Friends*?
12. Which American song is sung to the tune of *God Save the Queen*?
13. On which naval vessel did Charles Darwin serve as naturalist from 1831 to 1836?
14. Which Oscar-winning actor plays the Marquis de Sade in the film *Quills*?
15. What name is given to the series of chemical elements with atomic numbers 89 to 103?
16. Which Irish port was formerly called Queenstown?
17. After which author is the verse form the Clerihew named?
18. In the Old Testament, which powerful animal has 'limbs like bars of iron'?
19. Who directed the 1959 film *À Bout de Souffle*?
20. Which Apollo mission was manned by Charles Conrad, Alan Bean and Richard Gordon?

ANSWERS: *1 Oprah Winfrey, 2 Andrea Newman, 3 Sir John Mills, 4 Forty, 5 Romeo and Juliet, 6 Declining, 7 Middlesbrough, 8 Richard Wagner, 9 Denise Lewis, 10 A bird, 11 Stephen Fry, 12 My Country 'Tis of Thee, 13 The Beagle, 14 Geoffrey Rush, 15 Actinides, 16 Cobh, 17 E C Bentley, 18 Behemoth, 19 Jean-Luc Godard, 20 Apollo 12.*

General Knowledge

Your rating: ● **0-5** Join a library ● **6-10** Keep at it ● **11-15** Join a quiz team ● **16-20** Join Mensa

1. Which jockey won the Derby nine times between 1954 and 1983?
2. What is added to vodka to make a bloody Mary?
3. Who played Thora Blacklock in the sitcom *Meet the Wife*?
4. In which athletics event did Bob Beamon hold the world record for 23 years?
5. Which French singer is associated with the song *Non, Je Ne Regrette Rien*?
6. In which country is the resort of Acapulco?
7. What was Gor in the television drama series *First Born*?
8. Which member of the Marx Brothers was silent in their films?
9. Of which African country is Accra the capital?
10. In Greek mythology, who drowned when he flew too near the sun?
11. The film *Dr Ehrlich's Magic Bullet* is about the search for a cure for which disease?
12. Which American director made the films *Carrie*, *Scarface* and *The Untouchables*?
13. Who was the president of the Democratic Republic of Congo who was killed by a bodyguard in January 2001?
14. Which Irish author wrote *Borstal Boy*?
15. Against which disease can the BCG vaccine offer protection?
16. Who was U.S. secretary of state from 1949 to 1953?
17. How many *Police Academy* films have been made?
18. Which South African president shared the 1993 Nobel Peace prize with Nelson Mandela?
19. Who was the world No 1, knocked out of the 2001 Australian Open by Greg Rusedski?
20. In which English county is the market town of Thetford?

ANSWERS: *1 Lester Piggott, 2 Tomato juice, 3 Thora Hird, 4 Long jump, 5 Edith Piaf, 6 Mexico, 7 A man-gorilla hybrid, 8 Harpo, 9 Ghana, 10 Icarus, 11 Syphilis, 12 Brian De Palma, 13 Laurent Kabila, 14 Brendan Behan, 15 Tuberculosis, 16 Dean Acheson, 17 7, 18 F W de Klerk, 19 Gustavo Kuerten, 20 Norfolk.*

Entertainment

Your rating: ● 0-5 Buy a TV ● 6-10 Keep at it ● 11-15 Join a quiz team ● 16-20 Enter a quiz show

1. Which nineties drama series featured a couple played by Adam Faith and Zoe Wanamaker?
2. Which former *EastEnder* scored a U.K. top five hit with *I'm Over You* in 2000?
3. Which actor played the title role in the 1991 film *The Doctor*?
4. Which BBC 1 sitcom starring Richard Wilson embarked upon its final series in 2000?
5. What was the title of Steps' 2000 album release?
6. Which Oscar-nominated actor starred as Len Green in the BBC 1 drama series *The Sins*?
7. What was the subtitle of the 2000 film sequel *Blair Witch 2*?
8. Which *EastEnders* teenager gave birth to an unexpected baby in 2000?
9. Which member of the *Spin City* cast provided the voice for Tom in 1992's *Tom and Jerry: The Movie*?
10. What was the name of the character played by Ruth Madoc in the comedy series *Hi-De-Hi*?
11. Which Irish band released their tenth studio album, *All That You Can't Leave Behind*, in 2000?
12. Which Joe Orton play was adapted into a 1970 film starring Richard Attenborough and Lee Remick?
13. Which BBC 1 sitcom starred Caroline Aherne as Denise Best?
14. Which U.S. group had a U.K. top ten hit in 1991 with *Shiny Happy People*?
15. Which 2000 British film featured James Bolam as an ageing gangster?
16. Which brash TV interviewer hosted a self-titled BBC 2 dinner party chat show?
17. What was the title of the 1973 U.K. top ten hit by the British group Stealer's Wheel?
18. Which English actor played the mastermind of a London bank heist in the 1981 film *Loophole*?

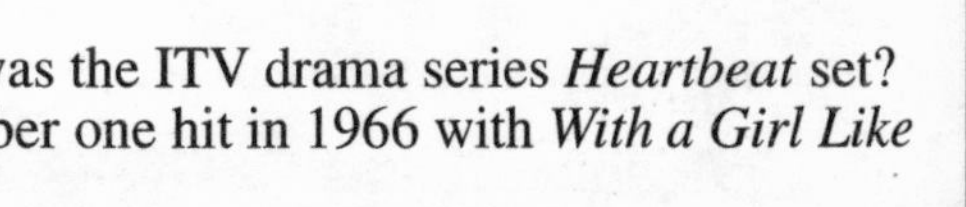

19. In which fictional Yorkshire village was the ITV drama series *Heartbeat* set?
20. Which British group had a U.K. number one hit in 1966 with *With a Girl Like You*?

ANSWERS: *1 Love Hurts, 2 Martine McCutcheon, 3 William Hurt, 4 One Foot in the Grave, 5 Buzz, 6 Pete Postlethwaite, 7 Book of Shadows, 8 Sonia Jackson, 9 Richard Kind, 10 Gladys Pugh, 11 U2, 12 Loot, 13 The Royle Family, 14 R.E.M., 15 It Was an Accident, 16 Ruby Wax (Ruby), 17 Stuck in the Middle With You, 18 Albert Finney, 19 Aidensfield, 20 The Troggs.*

General Knowledge

Your rating:
- **0-5 Join a library**
- **6-10 Keep at it**
- **11-15 Join a quiz team**
- **16-20 Join Mensa**

1. Which American actress founded United Artists with Charlie Chaplin, Douglas Fairbanks and D W Griffith?
2. What is the capital of the Lebanon?
3. Where was the actor Joaquin Phoenix born?
4. What name was given to the settlers who established the first permanent colony in New England in 1620?
5. Which London theatre was formerly called the Royal Victoria Hall?
6. Is the French wine Beaujolais red or white?
7. Which British historian wrote the best-selling biography *Elizabeth*?
8. Which American actor won a Best Actor Oscar for *Raging Bull*?
9. What name is given to a musical composition for five instruments?
10. Which member of the Royal Family broke his shoulder blade in a riding accident in 2001?
11. What is the surname of Emma in the novel by Jane Austen?
12. In which Shakespeare play does Lancelot Gobbo appear?
13. By what name do we know the Bahia de los Cochinos on the Cuban coast?
14. Which horse has become the first National Hunt horse to win £1 million in prize-money?
15. What was the real first name of jazz musician Bix Beiderbecke?
16. Which English poet wrote *The Listeners*?
17. Janeway and Chakotay are characters in which television sci-fi series?
18. With which sport is Lou Gehrig associated?
19. What name is given to the process of removing waste products from the blood?
20. Of which country is Geelong a major port?

ANSWERS: *1 Mary Pickford, 2 Beirut, 3 Puerto Rico, 4 Pilgrim Fathers, 5 The Old Vic, 6 Red, 7 David Starkey, 8 Robert De Niro, 9 Quintet, 10 Prince Charles, 11 Woodhouse, 12 The Merchant of Venice, 13 Bay of Pigs, 14 Istabraq, 15 Leon, 16 Walter de la Mare, 17 Star Trek: Voyager, 18 Baseball, 19 Dialysis, 20 Australia.*

General Knowledge

Your rating:
- 0-5 Join a library
- 6-10 Keep at it
- 11-15 Join a quiz team
- 16-20 Join Mensa

1. Do male or female sea horses carry the eggs until they hatch?
2. Who wrote *Doctor in the House*?
3. Which Italian jockey became an honorary MBE in the 2001 New Year Honours List?
4. What name is given to an Hindu prince ranking above a rajah?
5. Which French-born poet wrote *Cautionary Tales*?
6. In which country is Kruger National Park?
7. The singer Jane McDonald found fame as a result of which TV programme?
8. In which Canadian province is the city of Montreal?
9. Who wrote *The Cat in the Hat*?
10. Who was the most famous Australian bushranger of the 19th century?
11. Which Belgian artist painted *Golconda*, in which bowler-hatted men fall like rain?
12. Who wrote the music for the hymn *Onward Christian Soldiers*?
13. Before Steven Soderbergh in 2001 who was the last director to get two Best Director Oscar nominations in the same year?
14. What is the capital of Belize?
15. Which bird of the crow family has the Latin name *Pica pica*?
16. To which family of plants does cyclamen belong?
17. In which country are the headquarters of the multinational company Nestlé?
18. Who wrote *No Orchids for Miss Blandish*?
19. By what first name is Alexandra Pettifer, nee Legge-Bourke, commonly known?
20. In which Shakespeare play do Elbow and Mistress Overdone appear?

***ANSWERS:** 1 Male, 2 Richard Gordon, 3 Frankie Dettori, 4 Maharajah, 5 Hilaire Belloc, 6 South Africa, 7 The Cruise, 8 Quebec, 9 Dr Seuss, 10 Ned Kelly, 11 Rene Magritte, 12 Sir Arthur Sullivan, 13 Michael Curtiz, 14 Belmopan, 15 Magpie, 16 Primrose, 17 Switzerland, 18 James Hadley Chase, 19 Tiggy, 20 Measure for Measure.*

General Knowledge

Your rating:
- 0-5 Join a library
- 6-10 Keep at it
- 11-15 Join a quiz team
- 16-20 Join Mensa

1. What number is between 5 and 1 on a dartboard?
2. In Greek legend, by what part of his body was Achilles held when he was dipped in the River Styx?
3. Who was the top money-making film star in 1970?
4. In which English county is the town of Wisbech?
5. Which musical term literally means 'beautiful singing' in Italian?
6. Is the French wine Chablis red or white?
7. Who wrote *The Last Days of Pompeii*?
8. Which TV prankster was made an MBE in the 2001 New Year Honours List?
9. Which Scottish grocer founded a whisky blending industry in Kilmarnock in 1820?
10. What is the English name for the Italian city Napoli?
11. Which 17th-century author wrote the novel *Oroonoko*?
12. In which decisive naval battle did Octavian defeat Mark Antony in 31 BC?
13. Which Oscar-winning actor played a murder suspect in the film *Under Suspicion*?
14. Who wrote the novel *White Teeth*?
15. Of which U.S. state is Madison the capital?
16. By what name is Vittorio de Sica's film *Ladri di Biciclette* known in Britain?
17. What is Paul McCartney's real first name?
18. Which German physicist formulated the quantum theory?
19. In which film did Clint Eastwood co-star with his son Kyle?
20. Which British tenor sang in the first performances of all Benjamin Britten's operas?

***ANSWERS:** 1 Twenty, 2 Heel, 3 Paul Newman, 4 Cambridgeshire, 5 Bel canto, 6 White, 7 Edward Bulwer-Lytton, 8 Jeremy Beadle, 9 Johnny Walker, 10 Naples, 11 Aphra Behn, 12 Battle of Actium, 13 Gene Hackman, 14 Zadie Smith, 15 Wisconsin, 16 Bicycle Thieves, 17 James, 18 Max Planck, 19 Honkytonk Man, 20 Sir Peter Pears.*

Entertainment

Your rating: ● **0-5** Buy a TV ● **6-10** Keep at it ● **11-15** Join a quiz team ● **16-20** Enter a quiz show

1. Which City of Birmingham Symphony Orchestra conductor presented the Channel 4 series *Leaving Home*?
2. Which Plumstead band released an album in 1996 entitled *Girl Power*?
3. Which actor and actress played the lead roles in the 1970 film *Love Story*?
4. Which one of *The Munsters* was played by Fred Gwynne?
5. Who had a hit single in 1987 with *Shoplifters of the World Unite*?
6. Who starred as a man with four different alter-egos in the film *Multiplicity*?
7. Which former *Dangerfield* star played the head of a missing persons agency in the TV series *Beck*?
8. Which Status Quo star released an album entitled *King of the Doghouse* in 1996?
9. Who played idealistic law enforcer Eliot Ness in the 1987 film *The Untouchables*?
10. Which comedian/actor played *Jonathan Creek* in the BBC 1 crime mystery series?
11. Who starred as Snake Plissken in the 1996 film *Escape From LA*?
12. Which *Coronation Street* character was played by Angela Griffin?
13. Who had a number one hit single with *Return to Sender*?
14. Who won a Best Actor Oscar in 1987 for his role in *Wall Street*?
15. Which offbeat comedy drama series was set in the Alaskan town of Cicely?
16. Which Sixties-influenced British group released an album entitled *K* in 1996?
17. Which urban fantasy series was set in London Below and London Above?
18. Which *Pulp Fiction* star played a boxing promoter in the film *The Great White Hype*?
19. Which is the youngest of Michael Jackson's siblings?
20. What sort of creature was *Mister Ed* in the TV series?

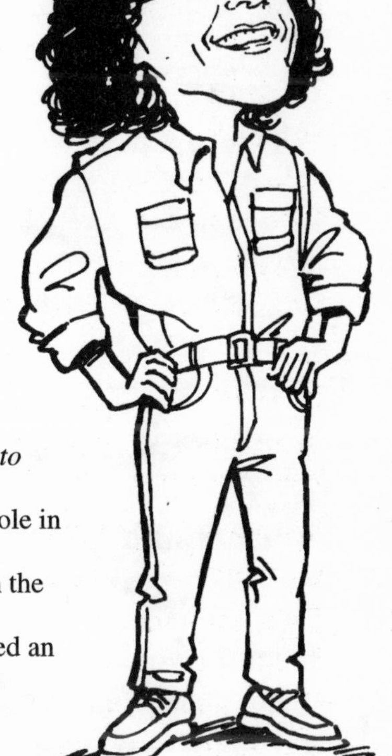

ANSWERS: *1 Simon Rattle, 2 Shampoo, 3 Ryan O'Neal and Ali MacGraw, 4 Herman Munster, 5 The Smiths, 6 Michael Keaton, 7 Amanda Redman, 8 Francis Rossi, 9 Kevin Costner, 10 Alan Davies, 11 Kurt Russell, 12 Fiona Middleton, 13 Elvis Presley, 14 Michael Douglas, 15 Northern Exposure, 16 Kula Shaker, 17 Neverwhere, 18 Samuel L. Jackson, 19 Janet Jackson, 20 A horse.*

General Knowledge

Your rating:
- **0-5 Join a library**
- **6-10 Keep at it**
- **11-15 Join a quiz team**
- **16-20 Join Mensa**

1. Which author wrote several comic novels featuring Bertie Wooster and his manservant Jeeves?
2. In which country is the resort of Acapulco situated?
3. At which sport was Steve Davis world champion in the 1980s?
4. Which word describes the use of live animals for experiments?
5. Which European country has French, German, Italian, and Romansch as its official languages?
6. What sort of creature is an ibis?
7. Which British novelist wrote *Lucky Jim* and *The Old Devils*?
8. Which Yorkshire city had the Roman name Eboracum?
9. Which coastal rescue organisation is represented by the initials RNLI?
10. Of which European country did Juan Carlos become king in 1975?
11. Which part of the body is inflamed if one suffers from encephalitis?
12. Which German boxer was the first European to win the world heavyweight title in the 20th century?
13. Which German director made the 1926 film *Metropolis*?
14. What is the largest breed of terrier?
15. Which British actress was married to the actor Sir Lewis Casson?
16. Which channel separates the mainland of South America from Tierra del Fuego?
17. In verse, which metrical foot consists of an unstressed syllable followed by a stressed syllable?
18. In which country was volleyball invented in 1895?
19. Which British physicist discovered the electron?
20. What sort of creature is a Lipizzaner?

ANSWERS: *1 P. G. Wodehouse, 2 Mexico, 3 Snooker, 4 Vivisection, 5 Switzerland, 6 A bird, 7 Kingsley Amis, 8 York, 9 Royal National Lifeboat Institution, 10 Spain, 11 The brain, 12 Max Schmeling, 13 Fritz Lang, 14 The Airedale terrier, 15 Dame Sybil Thorndike, 16 The Strait of Magellan, 17 Iamb, 18 USA, 19 Sir Joseph Thomson, 20 A horse.*

General Knowledge

Your rating: ● 0-5 Join a library ● 6-10 Keep at it ● 11-15 Join a quiz team ● 16-20 Join Mensa

1. Which two countries comprise the Iberian Peninsula?
2. Which unit of electromotive force is represented by the symbol V?
3. Which British adventure novelist wrote *She*?
4. Which British political party was led by Jeremy Thorpe from 1967 to 1976?
5. In which state of the USA is Yosemite National Park situated?
6. Can emus fly?
7. In which European country is the town of Ypres situated?
8. Which organisation is represented by the initials YMCA?
9. Of which country was Helmut Schmidt chancellor from 1974 to 1982?
10. Who was king of the United Kingdom from 1910 to 1936?
11. Which US actress starred in the films *Dark Victory* and *All About Eve*?
12. In which country was the conductor Sir Georg Solti born?
13. Which reactive alkaline-earth metal is represented by the symbol Sr?
14. Which contagious disease of many animals is also called wool-sorters' disease?
15. Which French man of letters wrote the satirical and philosophical fable *Candide*?
16. Which legendary Greek hero and son of Telamon fought Hector in single combat?
17. Which Nazi broadcaster was known as Lord Haw-Haw?
18. Who became the first prime minister of independent India in 1947?
19. Which English dramatist and poet wrote *Tamburlaine the Great*?
20. Which naturally occurring radioactive metal is represented by the symbol Th?

ANSWERS: 1 Portugal and Spain, 2 Volt, 3 Sir H. Rider Haggard, 4 The Liberal Party, 5 California, 6 No, 7 Belgium, 8 Young Men's Christian Association, 9 West Germany, 10 George V, 11 Bette Davis, 12 Hungary, 13 Strontium, 14 Anthrax, 15 Voltaire, 16 Ajax, 17 William Joyce, 18 Jawaharlal Nehru, 19 Christopher Marlowe, 20 Thorium.

General Knowledge

Your rating:
- **0-5 Join a library**
- **6-10 Keep at it**
- **11-15 Join a quiz team**
- **16-20 Join Mensa**

1. Which British athlete won Olympic gold medals in 1980 and 1984 for the decathlon?
2. Of which European country is Zürich the largest city?
3. Of which English county is Taunton the administrative centre?
4. What nationality is the operatic soprano Dame Joan Sutherland?
5. What sort of creature is a schnauzer?
6. Which organisation for young people is represented by the initials YHA?
7. Which non-metallic solid element is represented by the symbol P?
8. Of which French city did Jacques Chirac become mayor in 1977?
9. Which former English county used to comprise the North, West and East Ridings?
10. Who was the Norse god of thunder?
11. Which British author wrote the novels *Joseph Andrews* and *Tom Jones*?
12. Which war was precipitated by the Ems telegram?
13. Which author won the 1996 Booker Prize for fiction for his novel *Last Orders*?
14. What sort of creature is a rosella?
15. Which Irish political party has been led by John Costello, Liam Cosgrave, and Dr Garret FitzGerald?
16. Of which ocean is the Davis Strait a section?
17. Who was the last British king to appear in battle?
18. Which Russian novelist wrote *One Day in the Life of Ivan Denisovich*?
19. What is the capital of Fiji?
20. Which British art critic was director of the Victoria and Albert Museum from 1974 to 1987?

ANSWERS: *1 Daley Thompson, 2 Switzerland, 3 Somerset, 4 Australian, 5 A dog, 6 Youth Hostels Association, 7 Phosphorus, 8 Paris, 9 Yorkshire, 10 Thor, 11 Henry Fielding, 12 The Franco-Prussian War, 13 Graham Swift, 14 A parrot, 15 Fine Gael, 16 The Atlantic Ocean, 17 George II, 18 Aleksandr Solzhenitsyn, 19 Suva, 20 Sir Roy Strong.*

Entertainment

Your rating: ● **0-5** Buy a TV ● **6-10** Keep at it ● **11-15** Join a quiz team ● **16-20** Enter a quiz show

1. In TV's *Casualty*, what was the name of Baz Hayes's baby, born in 1996?
2. Which Sixties folk singer released an album entitled *Sutras* in 1996?
3. Which cockney actor starred as the gangland boss in the 1980 film *The Long Good Friday*?
4. Who had a number one hit single in 1978 with *Rivers of Babylon*?
5. Which British actor provided the voice for the last dragon alive in the family film *Dragonheart*?
6. Which Eighties pop star played feminist singer Niamh Connolly in an episode of the sitcom *Father Ted*?
7. Which girl group is made up of sisters Yonah, Cleo and Zainam?
8. Which *Men Behaving Badly* star narrated the children's TV show *Roger and the Rottentrolls*?
9. Which rock band released a live album entitled *From The Muddy Banks Of The Wishkah* in 1996?
10. Who presented *New Gamesmaster* on TV?
11. Who starred in the title role of the 1963 film *Hud*?
12. Which *Drop the Dead Donkey* character was played by Stephen Tompkinson?
13. Who had a top ten hit single in 1980 with *Games Without Frontiers*?
14. Who played the title role in the 1996 film version of *Jude*?
15. Who starred as the bashful priest in *Oh Brother* and *Oh Father* on TV?
16. Which country music diva released an album entitled *Treasures* in 1996?
17. Who won a Best Actress Oscar for the 1971 film *Klute*?
18. Who returned as a team captain of TV's *Have I Got News For You* in 1996 after missing the previous series?
19. Who had a number one hit single in 1985 with *I'm Your Man*?
20. Who played the title role in the 1996 remake of the film *The Nutty Professor*?

ANSWERS: *1 Louis, 2 Donovan, 3 Bob Hoskins, 4 Boney M, 5 Sean Connery, 6 Clare Grogan, 7 Cleopatra, 8 Martin Clunes, 9 Nirvana, 10 Dominik Diamond, 11 Paul Newman, 12 Damien Day, 13 Peter Gabriel, 14 Christopher Eccleston, 15 Derek Nimmo, 16 Dolly Parton, 17 Jane Fonda, 18 Paul Merton, 19 Wham!, 20 Eddie Murphy.*

General Knowledge

Your rating: ● 0-5 Join a library ● 6-10 Keep at it ● 11-15 Join a quiz team ● 16-20 Join Mensa

1. Which New Zealand mountaineer and explorer, along with Tenzing Norgay, was the first to reach the summit of Mount Everest?
2. According to Greek mythology, into which part of Achilles's body did Paris shoot a poisoned arrow?
3. Oahu is the most populous island of which US state?
4. Which Danish author of fairy tales wrote *The Little Mermaid*?
5. Which cricket ground has been the home of the Middlesex County Cricket Club since 1877?
6. In what year was the Queen Mother born?
7. What sort of creature is a gecko?
8. Which US novelist wrote *The Wonderful Wizard of Oz*?
9. What is the largest lake in England?
10. Who wrote *The Witches* and *The Twits*?
11. What is the shortest book in the Old Testament?
12. Who was secretary of state in Truman's cabinet from 1949 to 1953?
13. Victoria Falls is situated on the border of which two African countries?
14. Which British dramatist wrote *Five-Finger Exercise* and *Amadeus*?
15. Who is second to the Lord Chancellor in the judicial hierarchy?
16. Which French aviator was the first to fly the English Channel?
17. Of which metal is bauxite the chief ore?
18. Which British actor starred in the films *Mutiny on the Bounty* and *Ryan's Daughter*?
19. Of which state of the USA is Baton Rouge the capital?
20. Which French poet wrote the autobiographical novel *La Fanfarlo*?

ANSWERS: *1 Sir Edmund Hillary, 2 His heel, 3 Hawaii, 4 Hans Christian Andersen, 5 Lord's, 6 1900, 7 A lizard, 8 L. Frank Baum, 9 Windermere, 10 Roald Dahl, 11 The Book of Obadiah, 12 Dean Acheson, 13 Zimbabwe and Zambia, 14 Peter Shaffer, 15 Lord Chief Justice, 16 Louis Blériot, 17 Aluminium, 18 Trevor Howard, 19 Louisiana, 20 Charles Baudelaire.*

General Knowledge

Your rating: ● 0-5 Join a library ● 6-10 Keep at it ● 11-15 Join a quiz team ● 16-20 Join Mensa

1. Which US novelist wrote *Moby-Dick*?
2. How many pieces does each player start a game of draughts with?
3. Which reef off the coast of NE Australia is the largest coral reef in the world?
4. How is the grey metal wolfram otherwise known?
5. Which admiral was knighted by Elizabeth I on board the *Golden Hind* in 1581?
6. Who became the first Roman Catholic president of the USA in 1961?
7. In which county can Windsor Castle be found?
8. Rhodesia was named in honour of which British-born financier and statesman?
9. Alabaster is a form of which mineral?
10. Which London district is famous for its former power station and dogs' home?
11. How is hypermetropia commonly known?
12. Who was the first Archbishop of Canterbury?
13. Of which US state is Hartford the capital?
14. Which Briton did Dior appoint as its new designer in 1996?
15. Which U.S. novelist wrote *The Day of the Locust*?
16. Which British motor engineer broke the water-speed record three times between 1937 and 1939?
17. Which British admiral was setting sail from Tahiti in the Bounty when his crew mutinied?
18. Which state of the USA has Montpelier as its capital?
19. Of which country is Windhoek the capital?
20. Which Spanish novelist wrote *The Three-Cornered Hat*?

ANSWERS: *1 Herman Melville, 2 Twelve, 3 Great Barrier Reef, 4 Tungsten, 5 Sir Francis Drake, 6 John F. Kennedy, 7 Berkshire, 8 Cecil Rhodes, 9 Gypsum, 10 Battersea, 11 Longsightedness, 12 St Augustine, 13 Connecticut, 14 John Galliano, 15 Nathanael West, 16 Sir Malcolm Campbell, 17 William Bligh, 18 Vermont, 19 Namibia, 20 Pedro Antonio de Alarcón.*

General Knowledge

Your rating:
- 0-5 Join a library
- 6-10 Keep at it
- 11-15 Join a quiz team
- 16-20 Join Mensa

1. What is the minimum number of points necessary to win a table tennis game?
2. Which great circle lies around the earth at a latitude of zero degrees?
3. What nationality was the soprano Dame Nellie Melba?
4. What sort of creature is an anchovy?
5. At which racecourse is the Oaks run?
6. In which country is the Baltic port of Gdansk situated?
7. Andalusia is a region of which European country?
8. What is the official currency unit of Portugal?
9. Which group had hits with *Wonderwall* and *Stand By Me*?
10. In which county is the port of Gravesend situated?
11. According to Greek mythology, who was the only mortal Gorgon?
12. What sort of creature is a kagu?
13. Which King of the Belgians surrendered to the Germans in World War II?
14. Which British composer wrote *A Colour Symphony* and the opera *The Olympians*?
15. Which British novelist wrote *Voyage in the Dark* and *Good Morning, Midnight*?
16. Which French nun was known as the Little Flower of Jesus?
17. Which British actor starred in the 1930s films *The Scarlet Pimpernel* and *Pygmalion*?
18. In ancient Rome, what were thermae?
19. Which U.S. dramatist wrote *The Iceman Cometh* and *Long Day's Journey into Night*?
20. In which country did a volcano called Loki erupt in 1996?

ANSWERS: *1 Twenty-one, 2 The equator, 3 Australian, 4 A fish, 5 Epsom, 6 Poland, 7 Spain, 8 Escudo, 9 Oasis, 10 Kent, 11 Medusa, 12 A bird, 13 Leopold III, 14 Sir Arthur Bliss, 15 Jean Rhys, 16 St Thérèse, 17 Leslie Howard, 18 Public baths or hot springs, 19 Eugene O'Neill, 20 Iceland.*

Entertainment

Your rating: ● 0-5 Buy a TV ● 6-10 Keep at it ● 11-15 Join a quiz team ● 16-20 Enter a quiz show

1. Which Scottish comedian's *World Tour of Australia* appeared on TV?
2. Which African choral group collaborated with Paul Simon on *Homeless* from the *Graceland* album?
3. In which US city was most of the Keanu Reeves action film *Chain Reaction* set?
4. Which *London's Burning* character was played on TV by Zoe Heyes?
5. Under what name did Stephen Jones hit the charts in 1996 with the single *You're Gorgeous*?
6. Who starred in the title role of Franco Zeffirelli's 1990 film *Hamlet*?
7. Which James Bond actor starred in the Seventies TV series *The Persuaders*?
8. In 1990, En Vogue and Wilson Phillips both had top ten hit singles with different songs with the same name. What was it?
9. Who played Malvolio in Trevor Nunn's 1996 film version of *Twelfth Night*?
10. In which county was the ITV drama *Heartbeat* set?
11. Which female vocalist released an album entitled *Only Human* in 1996?
12. Which *EastEnders* character was played by Debbie Arnold?
13. Which James Bond star played a tough mine foreman in the film *Gold*?
14. Which male vocalist had a top ten hit in 1973 with *Rock On*?
15. Who played the mysterious Uncle Rory in the TV drama *The Crow Road*?
16. Who had a number one in 1982 with *Ebony and Ivory*?
17. Who presented the late-night live TV discussion programme *Weekly Planet*?
18. Who played golfer "Tin Cup" McAvoy in the 1996 comedy film *Tin Cup*?
19. Which Erle Stanley Gardner character was played on TV by Raymond Burr?
20. Which comedy double act starred in the 1945 film *Here Come The Co-Eds*?

ANSWERS: *1 Billy Connolly's, 2 Ladysmith Black Mambazo, 3 Chicago, 4 Carole Webb, 5 Babybird, 6 Mel Gibson, 7 Roger Moore, 8 Hold On, 9 Nigel Hawthorne, 10 Yorkshire, 11 Dina Carroll, 12 April Branning, 13 Roger Moore, 14 David Essex, 15 Peter Capaldi, 16 Paul McCartney with Stevie Wonder, 17 Jon Snow, 18 Kevin Costner, 19 Perry Mason, 20 Bud Abbott and Lou Costello.*

General Knowledge

Your rating: ● **0-5** Join a library ● **6-10** Keep at it ● **11-15** Join a quiz team ● **16-20** Join Mensa

1. Which US film actress married Prince Rainier III of Monaco in 1956?
2. On which planet is there a volcano called Olympus Mons?
3. Which British poet was married to the U.S. poet Sylvia Plath?
4. What sort of creature is a Doberman pinscher?
5. In which code is each letter of the alphabet and number represented by a sequence of dots and dashes?
6. In which continent can the Kalahari Desert be found?
7. Who played for Liverpool, Southampton, Newcastle United and Hamburg, where he was elected European Footballer of the Year?
8. Which sea connects with the Atlantic Ocean at Gibraltar, the Black Sea via the Sea of Marmara, and the Red Sea via the Suez Canal?
9. What was the surname of *Hud*, as played by Paul Newman in the 1963 film of the same name?
10. Which religious sect believes that Haile Selassie will arrange for the deliverance of the black races of the world?
11. Which West Yorkshire town is the north terminus of the Worth Valley Railway?
12. Who was Queen of England for nine days?
13. Which Slovakian city was the capital of Hungary until 1784?
14. At which racecourse is the Two Thousand Guineas run?
15. Which U.S. poet wrote *Tulips and Chimneys*, and the experimental novel *The Enormous Room*?
16. In which group of islands is Rarotonga?
17. According to the Old Testament, who was the first King of Israel?
18. Which German Nazi politician was ambassador to the UK from 1936 to 1938?
19. What is the capital of the Australian state of New South Wales?
20. Which international organisation was founded in 1929 to promote

ANSWERS: *1 Grace Kelly, 2 Mars, 3 Ted Hughes, 4 A dog, 5 Morse code, 6 Africa, 7 Kevin Keegan, 8 The Mediterranean Sea, 9 Bannon, 10 Rastafarianism, 11 Keighley, 12 Lady Jane Grey, 13 Bratislava, 14 Newmarket, 15 e. e. cummings, 16 The Cook Islands, 17 Saul, 18 Ribbentrop, 19 Sydney, 20 The Pony Club.*

General Knowledge

Your rating:
- 0-5 Join a library
- 6-10 Keep at it
- 11-15 Join a quiz team
- 16-20 Join Mensa

1. What nationality was the philosopher Bertrand Russell?
2. Of which country is Marrakesh the second largest city?
3. Which plant is St Patrick said to have adopted as a symbol of the holy trinity?
4. With which sport is Arnold Palmer associated?
5. Which British zoologist wrote *The Naked Ape* and *Manwatching*?
6. With which musical instrument is Ravi Shankar primarily associated?
7. Of which country is Riyadh the capital?
8. What is the world's largest and deepest ocean?
9. In which four-a-side stick-and-ball game do the players ride ponies?
10. Which title was used by the German emperors until 1917?
11. Who directed the films *Tootsie* and *Out of Africa*?
12. Who was the first Stuart King of England and Ireland?
13. Who was the goddess of the dawn in Roman mythology?
14. Which unit of measurement is equivalent to an explosion of one million tons of TNT?
15. Which British author wrote *Love in a Cold Climate*?
16. Which state of the USA has Trenton as its capital?
17. Which day of the week is named after the Roman god of agriculture?
18. Which French town is famous for its baroque palace, which was the residence of the French kings from 1678 to 1769?
19. Which British poet wrote *The Rape of the Lock*?
20. Which British admiral was nicknamed Old Grog?

ANSWERS: *1 British, 2 Morocco, 3 The shamrock, 4 Golf, 5 Desmond Morris, 6 The sitar, 7 Saudi Arabia, 8 The Pacific Ocean, 9 Polo, 10 Kaiser, 11 Sydney Pollack, 12 James I, 13 Aurora, 14 Megaton, 15 Nancy Mitford, 16 New Jersey, 17 Saturday, 18 Versailles, 19 Alexander Pope, 20 Edward Vernon.*

General Knowledge

Your rating:
- 0-5 Join a library
- 6-10 Keep at it
- 11-15 Join a quiz team
- 16-20 Join Mensa

1. Which precious metal is represented by the symbol Pt?
2. Which tax replaced domestic rates in Scotland in 1989 and the rest of the UK in 1990?
3. What sort of creature is a marmoset?
4. Which German composer wrote the operatic cycle *Der Ring des Nibelungen*?
5. Which cabinet post was held by Sir Geoffrey Howe from 1979 to 1983?
6. Which river flows from the Cheviot Hills to the North Sea, passing through Newcastle, Gateshead and Jarrow?
7. Which U.S. novelist wrote *The Adventures of Huckleberry Finn*?
8. Which English dramatist wrote *The Comedy of Errors* and *The Winter's Tale*?
9. Kale is a variety of which vegetable?
10. How many lines are in a sonnet?
11. Which British novelist wrote *Strangers and Brothers*?
12. According to Greek mythology, who was the sister and wife of Zeus?
13. Which radioactive element is represented by the symbol Po?
14. Which Spanish artist painted the *Rokeby Venus*?
15. What sort of creature is a dunnock?
16. Which river passes through Tonbridge, Maidstone, Rochester, Chatham and Gillingham?
17. Which Italian composer wrote the opera *I Pagliacci*?
18. In which Saudi Arabian city can the tomb of Mohammed be found?
19. Who was the Roman goddess of the hearth?
20. Which London borough was created in 1965 from the former municipal boroughs of Hornsey, Tottenham, and Wood Green?

ANSWERS: *1 Platinum, 2 The Community Charge (The poll tax), 3 A monkey, 4 Richard Wagner, 5 Chancellor of the exchequer, 6 The River Tyne, 7 Mark Twain, 8 William Shakespeare, 9 Cabbage, 10 Fourteen, 11 C. P. Snow, 12 Hera, 13 Polonium, 14 Velázquez, 15 A bird, 16 The River Medway, 17 Leoncavallo, 18 Medina, 19 Vesta, 20 Haringey.*

Sports

Your rating: ● **0-5** **Wooden spoon** ● **6-10** **Bronze medal** ● **11-15** **Silver medal** ● **16-20** **Gold medal**

1. Which British boxer defeated Wilfredo Vazquez to retain his WBO featherweight title in 1998?
2. The Nou Camp is the stadium of which football team?
3. How many Olympic gold medals did Russian gymnast Larissa Latynina win in 1956?
4. Which Canadian snooker player achieved the first maximum break in a World Championship?
5. Which British football team won the European Cup in 1967?
6. Which Austrian driver won the British Grand Prix in 1976, 1982 and 1984?
7. How many tries did New Zealand's Jonah Lomu score against England at the 1995 rugby union World Cup?
8. Which country staged the football World Cup finals in 1970?
9. Under what name did the former USSR team compete at the 1992 Barcelona Olympics?
10. What is the name of the ground in Jamaica that made cricket history in 1998 when the first Test was abandoned because of a dangerous pitch?
11. Which British athlete won gold in the 1500m at the 1986 Commonwealth Games?
12. For which country did David Campese win 92 international rugby union caps?
13. Which football team's home ground is Prenton Park?
14. In which event did swimmer Adrian Moorhouse win his 1988 Olympic gold medal?
15. In which field event of the 1998 European Athletics Championships did Britain claim both gold and silver medals as well as a new Championship record?
16. In which year were the Winter Olympics held in Calgary, Canada?
17. In which sport might one perform a flic-flac?
18. Against which country did Michael Owen find the net in May 1998 to become the youngest player ever to score for England?
19. Which rugby union player converted 140 penalty goals for Scotland between 1986 and 1995?
20. Which double did Michael Johnson achieve at the 1996 Olympic Games?

ANSWERS: *1 Prince Naseem Hamed, 2 Barcelona, 3 Four, 4 Cliff Thorburn, 5 Celtic, 6 Niki Lauda, 7 Four, 8 Mexico, 9 The Unified Team, 10 Sabina Park, 11 Steve Cram, 12 Australia, 13 Tranmere Rovers', 14 100m breast-stroke, 15 Javelin, 16 1988, 17 Gymnastics, 18 Morocco, 19 Gavin Hastings, 20 He won the 200m and 400m.*

General Knowledge

Your rating:
- **0-5 Join a library**
- **6-10 Keep at it**
- **11-15 Join a quiz team**
- **16-20 Join Mensa**

1. Which gas is represented by the symbol H?
2. Which British novelist wrote *The Mill on the Floss* and *Middlemarch*?
3. Which two oceans are connected by the Panama Canal?
4. In which sport might one use a foil, épée or sabre?
5. Which Labour politician was the UK's prime minister from 1964 to 1970 and 1974 to 1976?
6. Which small independent state is the seat of government of the Roman Catholic Church?
7. Which German Nazi politician was appointed minister of propaganda by Hitler in 1933?
8. Which word describes any horse that does not exceed 1.47 metres in height at maturity?
9. Which ancient Greek sculptures were sold to the British Museum in 1816 for £35,000?
10. Which Polish-born chemist discovered radium and polonium?
11. On which island is Pico de Teide, the highest mountain in Spain, situated?
12. Which U.S. novelist wrote *Ethan Frome*?
13. What is the name of the country Umberto Bossi wants to establish in northern Italy?
14. Who was the father of James I of England?
15. Who became King of Jordan in 1952?
16. Which Finnish runner won gold medals in the 5,000 and 10,000 metres at both the 1972 and 1976 Olympics?
17. What is the second largest of the Great Lakes in North America?
18. Which British novelist wrote *Vanity Fair*?
19. Who was the president of Egypt from 1956 to 1970?
20. Which international religious community was founded in New York in 1966 by Swami Prabhupada?

ANSWERS: *1 Hydrogen, 2 George Eliot, 3 Atlantic and Pacific, 4 Fencing 5 Harold Wilson, 6 Vatican City, 7 Joseph Goebbels, 8 Pony, 9 Elgin Marbles, 10 Marie Curie, 11 Tenerife, 12 Edith Wharton, 13 Padania, 14 Lord Darnley, 15 Hussein, 16 Lasse Viren, 17 Lake Huron, 18 William Makepeace Thackeray, 19 Nasser, 20 The International Society for Krishna Consciousness.*

General Knowledge

Your rating: ● 0-5 Join a library ● 6-10 Keep at it ● 11-15 Join a quiz team ● 16-20 Join Mensa

1. Of which country is Fujiyama the highest mountain?
2. Which sport is governed by the organisation FIFA?
3. What sort of creature is a snipe?
4. What is a thermometer used to measure?
5. Which British composer wrote the *Enigma Variations* and the *Pomp and Circumstance* marches?
6. In which continent are the pampas located?
7. How many points is the black ball worth in snooker?
8. What is the highest mountain in Wales?
9. What do the initials VAT stand for?
10. Which Roman god of love is identified with the Greek Eros?
11. Which Wiltshire cathedral has the highest spire in England?
12. Which King of the Scots is believed to be the author of the poem *The Kingis Quair*?
13. Which Irish poet won the Nobel prize for literature in 1923?
14. From 1350 to 1830, what was the title of the heirs to the French Crown?
15. Hydrolysis is the reaction of a chemical compound with which liquid?
16. Which Flemish artist painted the ceiling of the Banqueting House, Whitehall for Charles I?
17. According to the Old Testament, which prophet was taken into heaven without dying?
18. The young of which fish can be known as kelts?
19. Which Hollywood actor was branded "a cheating double-crosser" by his former lover Sondra Locke?
20. Which English inventor devised the spinning jenny, a machine which was named after his daughter?

ANSWERS: *1 Japan, 2 Football, 3 A bird, 4 Temperature, 5 Sir Edward Elgar, 6 South America, 7 Seven, 8 Snowdon, 9 Value-added tax, 10 Cupid, 11 Salisbury Cathedral, 12 James I, 13 W. B. Yeats, 14 Dauphin, 15 Water, 16 Rubens, 17 Elijah, 18 Salmon, 19 Clint Eastwood, 20 James Hargreaves.*

General Knowledge

Your rating:
- 0-5 Join a library
- 6-10 Keep at it
- 11-15 Join a quiz team
- 16-20 Join Mensa

1. A dilute solution of which sort of acid is used to make vinegar?
2. Which colour was the rose which was the emblem of the Lancastrians during the Wars of the Roses?
3. At the 1936 Berlin Olympics, which athlete did Hitler refuse to congratulate, despite winning four gold medals?
4. In which Italian city is the Brera Palace?
5. In Arthurian legend, which knight of the round table failed in the quest for the Holy Grail because of his love for Guinevere?
6. Which British novelist and poet wrote *Tess of the D'Urbervilles*?
7. Which mathematical term describes a quantity larger than any that can be specified?
8. In which English county is Dartmoor situated?
9. What do the initials NHS stand for?
10. What sort of creature is a ling?
11. Who was king of Italy from 1900 to 1946?
12. Which British director and actor founded the Mermaid Theatre?
13. Which British artist is famous for the four bronze lions at Trafalgar Square?
14. Which metallic element is represented by the symbol Tl?
15. Which British historical novelist wrote *Lorna Doone*?
16. Which spa town was the seat of the French government from 1940 to 1944?
17. Which metallic lanthanide element is represented by the symbol Ho?
18. Members of which Trotskyite faction were expelled from the Labour Party in 1986?
19. What is the smallest county in the Republic of Ireland?
20. Which publisher founded Penguin Books Ltd in 1935?

***ANSWERS:** 1 Acetic acid, 2 Red, 3 Jesse Owens, 4 Milan, 5 Lancelot, 6 Thomas Hardy, 7 Infinity, 8 Devon, 9 National Health Service, 10 A fish, 11 Victor Emmanuel III, 12 Baron Bernard Miles, 13 Sir Edwin Landseer, 14 Thallium, 15 R. D. Blackmore, 16 Vichy, 17 Holmium, 18 Militant Tendency, 19 Louth, 20 Sir Allen Lane.*

Entertainment

Your rating:	● 0-5	Buy a TV	● 6-10	Keep at it
	● 11-15	Join a quiz team	● 16-20	Enter a quiz show

1. Which 2000 film starred Guy Pearce as amnesiac salesman Leonard Shelby?
2. What type of creature was Ermintrude in the children's TV show *The Magic Roundabout*?
3. What was the title shared by the Baha Men's 2000 album release and their U.K. top five hit of the same year?
4. Which actress starred as teenager Anita in the 1992 film *Guncrazy*?
5. Which former *Casualty* star appeared as Rob Maguire in the ITV drama series *The Knock*?
6. Which British female group released their third album, *Forever*, in 2000?
7. Which *Changing Rooms* designer teamed up with Diarmuid Gavin to present the BBC 2 series *Home Front: Inside Out*?
8. Which model turned actress replaced Kathleen Turner in the role of Mrs Robinson in a West End production of *The Graduate* in 2000?
9. Who is the presenter of the BBC quiz show *The Weakest Link*?
10. Which 2000 Merchant Ivory film adaptation of a Henry James novel starred Uma Thurman as Charlotte Stant?
11. What did C.A.T.S. stand for in the title of the Eighties series *C.A.T.S. Eyes*?
12. What was the title of Westlife's second album?
13. Which *Monty Python* member wrote and starred in the 1983 film *The Missionary*?
14. Which chef presented his *Seafood Lovers Guide* on BBC 2?
15. Who duetted with Deniece Williams on the 1978 UK top five hit *Too Much Too Little Too Late*?
16. Which actor starred as Englishman turned native American *Grey Owl* in the 2000 film of that name?
17. Which actor narrated the ITV series *Britain at War in Colour*?
18. Which U.S. group had a 1973 U.K. top ten hit with *Love Train*?
19. In which U.S. city was the 1970 film *The Only Game in Town* set?
20. Which former *Casualty* actor starred as DCI Mortimer Marzec in the Channel 5 drama series *Headless*?

ANSWERS: *1 Memento, 2 A cow, 3 Who Let the Dogs Out, 4 Drew Barrymore, 5 Jonathan Kerrigan, 6 Spice Girls, 7 Laurence Llewelyn-Bowen, 8 Jerry Hall, 9 Anne Robinson, 10 The Golden Bowl, 11 Covert Activities Thames Section, 12 Coast to Coast, 13 Michael Palin, 14 Rick Stein, 15 Johnny Mathis, 16 Pierce Brosnan, 17 John Thaw, 18 The O'Jays, 19 Las Vegas, 20 Patrick Robinson.*

General Knowledge

Your rating: ● **0-5** **Join a library** ● **6-10** **Keep at it** ● **11-15** **Join a quiz team** ● **16-20** **Join Mensa**

1. Which famous building is at 1600 Pennsylvania Avenue, Washington D.C.?
2. Which movie star had wives called Movita and Tarita?
3. Who resigned from the Cabinet for the second time in two years in January 2001?
4. What name is given to members of the Order of the Reformed Cistercians of the Strict Observance?
5. Which Wild West frontiersman was shot dead while playing poker in Deadwood in 1876?
6. For what sort of drink is Armagnac famous?
7. Who took over from Loyd Grossman as the presenter of television's *Masterchef*?
8. What is the capital of Bolivia?
9. What name is given to crude iron obtained directly from a blast furnace?
10. In which athletics event might one see a Fosbury flop or Western roll?
11. Which gentleman murderer features in five novels by Patricia Highsmith?
12. What was the first name of the Scottish pirate Captain Kidd?
13. Which novel by Charles Dickens features the character Dolly Varden?
14. What is the capital of Namibia?
15. Which French-born conductor was music director of the Cleveland Orchestra from 1972 to 1982?
16. What nationality was the painter Daniel Maclise?
17. In 1933 what was the average time taken to make a film?
18. Who wrote *Five Children and It*?
19. In which European country is the city of Winterthur?
20. By what name was American rock-and-roll disc jockey Robert Weston Smith known?

ANSWERS: *1 The White House, 2 Marlon Brando, 3 Peter Mandelson, 4 Trappists, 5 Wild Bill Hickok, 6 Brandy, 7 Gary Rhodes, 8 La Paz, 9 Pig iron, 10 High jump, 11 Tom Ripley, 12 William, 13 Barnaby Rudge, 14 Windhoek, 15 Lorin Maazel, 16 Irish, 17 22 days, 18 Edith Nesbit, 19 Switzerland, 20 Wolfman Jack.*

General Knowledge

Your rating: ● 0-5 Join a library ● 6-10 Keep at it ● 11-15 Join a quiz team ● 16-20 Join Mensa

1. Which famous nanny was created by P. L. Travers?
2. What name is given to the winter dormancy of certain mammals?
3. What is the occupation of Lovejoy in stories by Jonathan Gash?
4. What is the only whale that has been observed to prey on other whales?
5. Which method of relaxation is represented by the letters TM?
6. In which country is the ancient Inca city of Machu Picchu?
7. Which soap opera did Oscar-winning actor Russell Crowe once appear in?
8. Which 19-year-old singer received the highest number of nominations for the 2001 Brit Awards but failed to win anything?
9. Is the French wine Sauternes red or white?
10. In which county is the town of Kidderminster?
11. To which prime minister was novelist Lady Caroline Lamb married?
12. Which play by Shakespeare features the characters Leontes and Perdita?
13. Who choreographed the ballet *Romeo and Juliet*, danced by Margot Fonteyn and Rudolf Nureyev in 1965?
14. Which former MI6 agent is the author of *The Big Breach*?
15. In which European country is Transylvania?
16. Who was the 14th president of the United States?
17. In which U.S. state was the 1986 film *Hoosiers* set?
18. Which Japanese city hosted the 1998 Winter Olympics?
19. Clara Furse became the first female chief executive of which institution?
20. Which novelist wrote *Whisky Galore*?

ANSWERS: *1 Mary Poppins, 2 Hibernation, 3 Antiques dealer, 4 Killer whale, 5 Transcendental Meditation, 6 Peru, 7 Neighbours, 8 Craig David, 9 White, 10 Worcester, 11 Viscount Melbourne, 12 The Winter's Tale, 13 Sir Kenneth Macmillan, 14 Richard Tomlinson, 15 Romania, 16 Franklin Pierce, 17 Indiana, 18 Nagano, 19 The London Stock Exchange, 20 Compton Mackenzie.*

General Knowledge

Your rating:
- 0-5 Join a library
- 6-10 Keep at it
- 11-15 Join a quiz team
- 16-20 Join Mensa

1. Which U.S. actor starred in *Double Indemnity* and *The Apartment*?
2. Who began presenting *Omnibus* on television in 1982?
3. What is the name of Bertie Wooster's manservant in P. G. Wodehouse's stories?
4. In Shakespeare's play, who kills *Macbeth*?
5. Which American tennis player won the women's singles at the 2001 Australian Open?
6. What name is given to a fishing vessel that uses a large conical net?
7. What is the name of the family featured in the film *Hook*?
8. Who became Emperor of the French in 1804?
9. Which legendary American Indian chief had a name meaning 'he makes rivers'?
10. Who was British prime minister from 1957 to 1963?
11. What was the occupation of the character played by Jack Lemmon in the film *How to Murder Your Wife*?
12. In Shakespeare's *The Tempest*, what is the name of the 'airy spirit' that does Prospero's bidding?
13. Who won the Whitbread Book of the Year Award for his novel *English Passengers*?
14. Which Florentine statesman and author wrote *The Prince*?
15. What is the state capital of Pennsylvania?
16. Which 17th-century radical sect was led by Gerrard Winstanley?
17. What were *The Oddball Couple* on television?
18. In which country is Winnipeg?
19. What is the highest mountain in Ireland?
20. Who wrote *The Treasure of the Sierra Madre*?

ANSWERS: *1 Fred MacMurray, 2 Barry Norman, 3 Jeeves, 4 Macduff, 5 Jennifer Capriati, 6 Trawler, 7 Banning, 8 Napoleon Bonaparte, 9 Hiawatha, 10 Harold Macmillan, 11 Cartoonist, 12 Ariel, 13 Matthew Kneale, 14 Niccolo Machiavelli, 15 Harrisburg, 16 The Diggers, 17 A dog and a cat, 18 Canada, 19 Carrauntoohill, 20 B Traven.*

Entertainment

Your rating: ● **0-5** Buy a TV ● **6-10** Keep at it ● **11-15** Join a quiz team ● **16-20** Enter a quiz show

1. What chart position did Elvis Presley's first U.K. hit, 1956's *Heartbreak Hotel*, reach?
2. In which 2000 film did Michael Douglas star as a professor of English?
3. Which actor played Detective Dave Starsky in the Seventies U.S. cop series *Starsky and Hutch*?
4. Which Brighton-based DJ released his second album, *Halfway Between the Gutter and the Stars*, in 2000?
5. Which actor played Wall Street vulture Lawrence Garfield in the 1991 film *Other People's Money*?
6. Which *EastEnders* character left Albert Square in 2000 after his extra-marital affair with his ex-wife was revealed?
7. Which Irish punk band's line-up on forming in 1975 was Bob Geldof on vocals, Johnnie Fingers on keyboards, Pete Briquette on bass and Gerry Cott and Garry Roberts on guitar?
8. Which writer performed his own monologues in *Telling Tales* on BBC 2?
9. Which band's U.S. and U.K. number one hits were compiled on the 2000 album *1*?
10. Which Channel 4 entertainment show replaced its usual host, Chris Evans, with a series of celebrity presenters for its last-ever series in 2000?
11. Which English actress played the Devil in the 2000 film *Bedazzled*?
12. Which actor played cult hero Reg Holdsworth in *Coronation Street*?
13. What was the title of the 2000 double live album release by Oasis?
14. Which actor played an android and his creator in the 1987 film *Making Mr. Right*?
15. In which *Airport* was BBC 1's docusoap set?
16. Which U.S. group had a 1965 U.K. number one hit with *Mr. Tambourine Man*?
17. In which 2000 film did Mark Wahlberg star as a ex-con drifting into gangsterism?
18. Which *Peak Practice* character, played by Gary Mavers, left the series in 2000?
19. What was the title of Taylor Dayne's 1988 U.K. top five single?
20. Which Scots actor starred in the title role of the 1991 film *The Pope Must Die*?

ANSWERS: 1 No. 2, 2 *Wonder Boys*, 3 Paul Michael Glaser, 4 Fatboy Slim, 5 Danny DeVito, 6 Frank Butcher, 7 Boomtown Rats, 8 Alan Bennett, 9 The Beatles, 10 *TFI Friday*, 11 Elizabeth Hurley, 12 Ken Morley, 13 *Familiar to Millions*, 14 John Malkovich, 15 Heathrow, 16 The Byrds, 17 *The Yards*, 18 Dr Andrew Attwood, 19 *Tell it to My Heart*, 20 Robbie Coltrane.

General Knowledge

Your rating:
- **0-5 Join a library**
- **6-10 Keep at it**
- **11-15 Join a quiz team**
- **16-20 Join Mensa**

1. Which major upland mass forms the 'backbone of England'?
2. Who was the first man to set foot on the Moon?
3. Who played Mac MacIntyre in the 1983 film *Local Hero*?
4. In which European country is the city of Maastricht?
5. Which carbohydrate is also called milk sugar?
6. What is the seat of the dukes of Bedford?
7. Which German author wrote the novel *Effi Briest*?
8. Which Steven Soderbergh film starred Michael Douglas and Catherine Zeta Jones?
9. Which alcoholic drink fermented from honey and water is also called metheglin?
10. Who wore the No 1 bib in the 2001 London Marathon?
11. In the children's television programme, what was the name of Noggin the Nog's wicked uncle?
12. Which pioneer of paperback publishing founded Penguin Books?
13. What is the meaning of the title 'Fidei Defensor' belonging to English monarchs?
14. Which American football team won Super Bowl XXXV?
15. Who wrote *The Day of the Triffids*?
16. In what year was Nelson Mandela released from prison?
17. Who illustrated the *Winnie-the-Pooh* stories by A. A. Milne?
18. In Greek mythology, which mountain nymph fell in love with Narcissus?
19. Which creatures are the principal food of the aardwolf?
20. Which tennis player beat Serena and Venus Williams in consecutive matches at the 2001 Australian Open?

ANSWERS: *1 The Pennines, 2 Neil Armstrong, 3 Peter Riegert, 4 The Netherlands, 5 Lactose, 6 Woburn Abbey, 7 Theodor Fontane, 8 Traffic, 9 Mead, 10 Sir Steve Redgrave, 11 Nogbad the Bad, 12 Sir Allen Lane, 13 Defender of the faith, 14 Baltimore Ravens, 15 John Wyndham, 16 1990, 17 E H Shepard, 18 Echo, 19 Termites, 20 Martina Hingis.*

General Knowledge

Your rating:
- **0-5** Join a library
- **6-10** Keep at it
- **11-15** Join a quiz team
- **16-20** Join Mensa

1. Which race meeting was established by Queen Anne in 1711?
2. Who wrote the televion comedy *Only Fools and Horses*?
3. Which Oscar-winning actor starred in the film *What Women Want*?
4. Who created the detective Philip Marlowe?
5. On which river does Manchester stand?
6. What is the capital of Jamaica?
7. Which actor's films included *Life With Father* and *The Thin Man*?
8. In the New Testament, what is the name of the site of the conclusive battle between the forces of good and evil?
9. Of which former Soviet state is Yerevan the capital?
10. What name was given to the 1974 bout between Muhammad Ali and George Foreman in Zaire?
11. Which British novelist wrote *The Citadel*?
12. Which Indian author created the fictional town of Malgudi?
13. Who won the men's singles at the 2001 Australian Open?
14. Which British folk singer and playwright wrote the song *The First Time Ever I Saw Your Face*?
15. What sort of creature is a piddock?
16. Which British novelist used the pseudonyms Jean Plaidy and Victoria Holt?
17. What was the name of the character played by Sandra Dickinson in *Hitch-Hikers Guide to the Galaxy*?
18. Which English actor was the first to play Hamlet, Macbeth, King Lear and Richard III?
19. Who succeeded Chris Woodhead as head of Ofsted?
20. Which English novelist wrote *East Lynne*?

ANSWERS: *1 Royal Ascot, 2 John Sullivan, 3 Mel Gibson, 4 Raymond Chandler, 5 River Irwell, 6 Kingston, 7 William Powell, 8 Armageddon, 9 Armenia, 10 The Rumble in the Jungle, 11 H E Bates, 12 R K Narayan, 13 Andre Agassi, 14 Ewan MacColl, 15 A mollusc, 16 Eleanor Hibbert, 17 Trillian, 18 Richard Burbage, 19 Mike Tomlinson, 20 Mrs Henry Wood.*

General Knowledge

Your rating:
- 0-5 Join a library
- 6-10 Keep at it
- 11-15 Join a quiz team
- 16-20 Join Mensa

1. Which American jazz musician was known as Satchmo?
2. Which was the first Gerry Anderson television series to use human rather than puppet actors?
3. Which of the British Isles has three legs on its flag?
4. What nationality is Abdul Baset Ali al-Megrahi who was convicted of the Lockerbie bombing?
5. Which Greek philosopher was tutor to Alexander the Great?
6. What is the westernmost peninsula of Cornwall?
7. In which film did Clark Gable co-star with Claudette Colbert?
8. What name is given to the Thursday forty days after Easter Sunday?
9. Who directed the films *Rear Window*, *Vertigo* and *North by Northwest*?
10. What is the first sign of the zodiac?
11. Where was the writer and film director Marguerite Duras born?
12. Which New Zealand-born author wrote *The Garden Party* and *Bliss*?
13. At which children's hospital in Liverpool did Professor Dick van Velzen work?
14. Which Shakespeare play is partly set in the Forest of Arden?
15. Of which planet is Deimos a satellite?
16. What does the C stand for in the computer abbreviation ASCII?
17. Which Scottish novelist wrote *Juan in America*?
18. Which Italian racing driver was world champion in 1952 and 1953?
19. Of which U.S. state is Lansing the capital?
20. To which continent is the mamba native?

ANSWERS: *1 Louis Armstrong, 2 UFO, 3 Isle of Man, 4 Libyan, 5 Aristotle, 6 Land's End, 7 It Happened One Night, 8 Ascension Day, 9 Sir Alfred Hitchcock, 10 Aries, 11 Vietnam, 12 Katherine Mansfield, 13 Alder Hey, 14 As You Like It, 15 Mars, 16 Code, 17 Eric Linklater, 18 Alberto Ascari, 19 Michigan, 20 Africa.*

Entertainment

Your rating:
- 0-5 Buy a TV
- 6-10 Keep at it
- 11-15 Join a quiz team
- 16-20 Enter a quiz show

1. Which BBC 1 series about money matters was presented by Sally Magnusson?
2. Which Irish vocalist had a U.K. top five hit in 1988 with *Missing You*?
3. Which actor played a businessman who comes face to face with himself as a child in the 2000 film *Disney's The Kid*?
4. Where did *The Flintstones* live in the cartoon series?
5. Which U.S. singer had a 2000 U.K. number one with *Can't Fight the Moonlight*?
6. Which 1969 film starring Michael Caine and Anthony Quinn was set on a Greek island?
7. Which *Brookside* character's death sparked a whodunit mystery in 2000?
8. What was the title of Martine McCutcheon's second album?
9. Which *Emmerdale* character died in a barn fire at the Sugden farm in 2000?
10. Which U.S. actor played *Little Nicky* in the 2000 film of that name?
11. Who presented the BBC 2 series *The House Detectives*?
12. Which pop legend released the live album *One Night Only*, recorded at Madison Square Garden in 2000?
13. In which seventies sitcom did John Alderton and Hannah Gordon star as a divorced couple?
14. Which 1960 film starred Spencer Tracy as a defence attorney and Gene Kelly as a cynical reporter?
15. Which actor starred as Pete Gifford in ITV's comedy drama series *Cold Feet*?
16. What was MC Tunes versus 808 State's 1990 U.K. top ten hit?
17. Which 2000 film starring Gwyneth Paltrow as a Las Vegas showgirl was directed by her father Bruce?
18. Whose *Wildlife Gardens* were created on BBC 2?
19. From which film was Olivia Newton-John's 1978 U.K.top five hit *Hopelessly Devoted to You* taken?
20. Which actress played Harvey Keitel's wife in the 1989 film *The January Man*?

ANSWERS: *1 Hard Cash, 2 Chris De Burgh, 3 Bruce Willis, 4 Bedrock, 5 LeAnn Rimes, 6 The Magus, 7 Susannah Morrisey's, 8 Wishing, 9 Sarah Sugden, 10 Adam Sandler, 11 Juliet Morris, 12 Elton John, 13 My Wife Next Door, 14 Inherit the Wind, 15 John Thomson, 16 The Only Rhyme That Bites, 17 Duets, 18 Charlie's (Charlie Dimmock's), 19 Grease, 20 Susan Sarandon.*

General Knowledge

Your rating:
- 0-5 Join a library
- 6-10 Keep at it
- 11-15 Join a quiz team
- 16-20 Join Mensa

1. Which actress was known as the 'Jersey Lily'?
2. For which novel is the Spanish author Miguel de Cervantes famous?
3. Michael Praed left the television series *Robin of Sherwood* to join which 1980s soap?
4. Who won a Best Actor Oscar for *The African Queen*?
5. Of which country is Managua the capital?
6. What was the first name of the French Postimpressionist painter Cezanne?
7. Who wrote the historical romance *Anthony Adverse*?
8. Which country did England beat in their opening match of the 2001 Six Nations Championship?
9. What sort of buns are traditionally eaten on Good Friday?
10. Which popular holiday destination is the easternmost of the Canary Islands?
11. Which film director entered a seminary in 1956?
12. Which British composer wrote *On Hearing the First Cuckoo in Spring*?
13. What is the surname of the Indian businessmen at the centre of the passport row that led to Peter Mandelson's resignation?
14. Which cartoon bird was created by Walter Lantz?
15. Of which country is Bangui the capital?
16. Which member of rock group The Faces died in 1997?
17. Who was the most commercially successful film director in the period 1985-90?
18. Which English novelist wrote *A Journal of the Plague Year*?
19. Buster Bloodvessel was the frontman of which eighties pop group?
20. What is the capital of the United Arab Emirates?

ANSWERS: *1 Lillie Langtry, 2 Don Quixote, 3 Dynasty, 4 Humphrey Bogart, 5 Nicaragua, 6 Paul, 7 Hervey Allen, 8 Wales, 9 Hot cross buns, 10 Lanzarote, 11 Martin Scorsese, 12 Frederick Delius, 13 Hinduja, 14 Woody Woodpecker, 15 Central African Republic, 16 Ronnie Lane, 17 Robert Zemeckis, 18 Daniel Defoe, 19 Bad Manners, 20 Abu Dhabi.*

General Knowledge

Your rating: ● 0-5 Join a library ● 6-10 Keep at it ● 11-15 Join a quiz team ● 16-20 Join Mensa

1. Which two countries contest The Ashes in cricket?
2. Which American author wrote *The Friendly Persuasion*?
3. Which actress starred with Bob Hope and Bing Crosby in a series of *Road to...* films?
4. On which TV show did Nigel Lythgoe and others create a new pop group?
5. Which modern animal is related to the mammoth?
6. Of which U.S. state is Phoenix the capital?
7. Which film director said "Aways make the audience suffer as much as possible"?
8. What name is given to the great fleet sent by King Philip II of Spain in 1588 to invade England?
9. Which American president was assassinated on Good Friday in 1865?
10. Of which organ is the cerebellum a part?
11. Which chat show host appeared in the 1988 film *Hairspray*?
12. Which British novelist is noted for her *Balkan Trilogy* and *Levant Trilogy*?
13. Who directed the films *The Last Picture Show* and *Paper Moon*?
14. Which England batsman joined Surrey from Middlesex in 2001?
15. Of which Asian country is Vientiane the capital?
16. Which martial arts actor and director fractured his skull when making the 1986 film *Armour of God*?
17. Who played televison's *Six Million Dollar Man*?
18. Which American actress was known as the 'Sweater Girl' in the 1940s?
19. By what first name was the baseball player Henry Aaron known?
20. Which German novelist wrote *The Magic Mountain* and *Buddenbrooks*?

ANSWERS: *1 England and Australia, 2 Jessamyn West, 3 Dorothy Lamour, 4 Popstars, 5 Elephant, 6 Arizona, 7 Alfred Hitchcock, 8 The (Spanish) Armada, 9 Abraham Lincoln, 10 The brain, 11 Ricki Lake, 12 Olivia Manning, 13 Peter Bogdanovich, 14 Mark Ramprakash, 15 Laos, 16 Jackie Chan, 17 Lee Majors, 18 Lana Turner, 19 Hank, 20 Thomas Mann.*

General Knowledge

Your rating: ● 0-5 Join a library ● 6-10 Keep at it ● 11-15 Join a quiz team ● 16-20 Join Mensa

1. Which classic American horse race is run on the first Saturday in May at Churchill Downs?
2. The title character of the film *Jackie Brown* was originally called what?
3. Which bird has green, lesser spotted and great spotted varieties?
4. What is the title of the film sequel to *The Silence of the Lambs*?
5. Which American media mogul founded CNN?
6. In which Scottish city did the murderers Burke and Hare operate?
7. Who wrote the autobiography *The Story of My Experiment with Truth*?
8. In the Old Testament, who was the father of Ishmael and Isaac?
9. Which actress starred in *Prime Suspect*?
10. In addition to Golgotha, by what name is the hill where Jesus was crucified known?
11. Which British novelist wrote *New Grub Street*?
12. Which French theologian was famous for his love for Héloïse?
13. Who defeated Jack Dempsey to become world heavyweight boxing champion in 1926?
14. Which actress, singer and songwriter was married to Roy Rogers?
15. The sackbut was a precursor of which musical instrument?
16. Which African country was formerly called Upper Volta?
17. In which city is the film *Bitter Sweet* set?
18. Which English poet and novelist wrote *The Edwardians* and *All Passion Spent*?
19. Who became the fastest woman to circumnavigate the globe alone in 2001?
20. Which British novelist wrote *Evelina* and *Camilla*?

ANSWERS: *1 Kentucky Derby, 2 Jackie Burke, 3 Woodpecker, 4 Hannibal, 5 Ted Turner, 6 Edinburgh, 7 Mahatma Gandhi, 8 Abraham, 9 Helen Mirren, 10 Calvary, 11 George Gissing, 12 Peter Abelard, 13 Gene Tunney, 14 Dale Evans, 15 Trombone, 16 Burkina Faso, 17 Vienna, 18 Vita Sackville-West, 19 Ellen MacArthur, 20 Fanny Burney.*

Entertainment

Your rating: ● **0-5** **Buy a TV** ● **6-10** **Keep at it** ● **11-15** **Join a quiz team** ● **16-20** **Enter a quiz show**

1. What was the title of the final ITV *Inspector Morse* drama?
2. With whom did the Eurythmics collaborate on the 1985 U.K. top ten hit *Sisters Are Doin' it For Themselves*?
3. Which *Star Wars: Episode 1* actress played a single mother in the 2000 film *Where the Heart Is*?
4. What was the name of Jimmy Nail's character in the eighties comedy drama series *Auf Wiedersehen, Pet*?
5. From which film was Destiny's Child's 2000 U.K. number one single *Independent Women* taken?
6. Which actor played Mike opposite Keanu Reeves' Scott in the 1991 film *My Own Private Idaho*?
7. Which naturalist presented the BBC 1 series *State of the Planet*?
8. The proceeds of which S Club 7 U.K. number one single benefited the 2000 Children in Need appeal?
9. Which comedy actress starred as relationship counsellor Kate in the BBC 1 sitcom *Kiss Me Kate*?
10. Which actress starred along with Lucy Liu and Drew Barrymore in the 2000 film remake of *Charlie's Angels*?
11. What was the name of Connie Booth's character in the sitcom *Fawlty Towers*?
12. Which teenage trio released their debut album, *One Touch*, in 2000, featuring the U.K. top ten hit *Overload*?
13. Which 1962 film featured John Wayne as General Sherman and Spencer Tracy's voice in its narration?
14. Which actor played lawyer John Close in the ITV drama series *Close & True*?
15. Which vocalist had a U.K. top five hit in 1996 with *Give Me a Little More Time*?
16. In which 2000 film did Robert De Niro star as an ex-cop recovering from a stroke?
17. Which character met a sudden death in the final episode of the sitcom *One Foot in the Grave*?
18. Which British group had a U.K. number one hit with *Start* in 1980?
19. Which character did Michael Caine play in the 1965 film *The Ipcress File*?
20. Which *Coronation Street* couple had a big win on the dogs in 2000?

ANSWERS: *1 The Remorseful Day, 2 Aretha Franklin, 3 Natalie Portman, 4 'Oz' Osbourne, 5 Charlie's Angels, 6 River Phoenix, 7 Sir David Attenborough, 8 Never Had a Dream Come True, 9 Caroline Quentin, 10 Cameron Diaz, 11 Polly Sherman, 12 Sugababes, 13 How the West Was Won, 14 Robson Green, 15 Gabrielle, 16 Flawless, 17 Victor Meldrew, 18 The Jam, 19 Harry Palmer, 20 Jack & Vera Duckworth*

General Knowledge

Your rating:
- 0-5 Join a library
- 6-10 Keep at it
- 11-15 Join a quiz team
- 16-20 Join Mensa

1. Which English actress won an Oscar for her portrayal of the Duchess of Brighton in *The VIPs*?
2. Who was assassinated while campaigning for the U.S. presidential nomination in 1968?
3. The film *The Fighting Prince of Donegal* is set during the reign of which English monarch?
4. What is the most common blood group in the world?
5. Which English novelist wrote *A Clockwork Orange*?
6. Of which U.S. state is Sacramento the capital?
7. What was the nickname of *Cheers* bar-owner Sam Malone?
8. Sabena is the national airline of which European country?
9. Which composer wrote the music for the songs *Smoke Gets in Your Eyes* and *Ol' Man River*?
10. Of which African country is Abuja the capital?
11. Who is the author of *Lost Boy* and *A Man Named Dave*?
12. Which American neurologist wrote *The Man who Mistook His Wife for a Hat* and *Awakenings*?
13. On which asteroid did NASA land an unmanned craft in 2001?
14. Which 18th-century political theorist wrote *Reflections on the Revolution in France*?
15. What was the real first name of American comedian Bud Abbott?
16. Which English novelist wrote *To the Lighthouse*?
17. Who did Telly Savalas play in the film *The Greatest Story Ever Told*?
18. Which Spanish surrealist artist painted *The Crucifixion* in 1951?
19. Which French nobleman wrote the novel *Justine*?
20. Which Italian conductor became principal conductor of the Berlin Philharmonic in 1989?

ANSWERS: *1 Dame Margaret Rutherford, 2 Robert Kennedy, 3 Elizabeth I, 4 O, 5 Anthony Burgess, 6 California, 7 Mayday, 8 Belgium, 9 Jerome Kern, 10 Nigeria, 11 Dave Pelzer, 12 Oliver Sacks, 13 Eros, 14 Edmund Burke, 15 William, 16 Virginia Woolf, 17 Pontius Pilate, 18 Salvador Dali, 19 Marquis de Sade, 20 Claudio Abbado.*

General Knowledge

Your rating: ● **0-5 Join a library** ● **6-10 Keep at it** ● **11-15 Join a quiz team** ● **16-20 Join Mensa**

1. Which English artist painted *Rain, Steam and Speed*?
2. Who said "Ask not what your country can do for you - ask what you can do for your country"?
3. Which film received 12 nominations for the 2001 Oscars?
4. What is the capital of Hungary?
5. Which American astronomer presented the TV series *Cosmos* and wrote the novel *Contact*?
6. In which country was the Nobel prize-winning nuclear physicist Ernest Rutherford born?
7. Which American author used the pen name Diedrich Knickerbocker?
8. What was the name of the garden in which Judas betrayed Jesus?
9. Which football team has signed a joint marketing deal with the New York Yankees baseball team?
10. Which singer had hits with *Private Dancer* and *What's Love Got to Do With It*?
11. During which period is the film *Thirteen Days* set?
12. Which Irish dramatist wrote *Juno and the Paycock*?
13. How many tries did England score in their 2001 Six Nations Championship victory over Italy?
14. Which American architect designed the Guggenheim Museum in New York City?
15. Who was the Greek goddess of the moon?
16. Which U.S. city is bisected by the Santa Monica mountains?
17. Which American author received a law degree from the University of Mississippi in 1981?
18. To which American comedian was Gracie Allen married?
19. Which small crustacean is known as a pill bug in America?
20. Who wrote the novel *Fathers and Sons*?

ANSWERS: *1 J M W Turner, 2 John F Kennedy, 3 Gladiator, 4 Budapest, 5 Carl Sagan, 6 New Zealand, 7 Washington Irving, 8 Gethsemane, 9 Manchester United, 10 Tina Turner, 11 Cuban Missile Crisis, 12 Sean O'Casey, 13 Ten, 14 Frank Lloyd Wright, 15 Selene, 16 Los Angeles, 17 John Grisham 18 George Burns, 19 Woodlouse, 20 Ivan Turgenev.*

General Knowledge

Your rating: ● 0-5 Join a library ● 6-10 Keep at it ● 11-15 Join a quiz team ● 16-20 Join Mensa

1. Which American singer-songwriter was born Robert Allen Zimmerman?
2. Where does the television programme name *Jackanory* come from?
3. Which comic police force did Mack Sennett create in his silent films?
4. Who was elected prime minister of Israel in 2001?
5. Which Irish novelist wrote *The Country Girls*?
6. Who is the traditional author of the Second Gospel?
7. What was the middle name of the poet W. H. Auden?
8. What name is given to the upper chamber of the British Parliament?
9. Who is the mother of Kate Hudson, who plays Penny Lane in the film *Almost Famous*?
10. What name is given to the traditional Japanese art of fencing with bamboo swords?
11. What was the profession of the hero in the 1941 film *Pimpernel Smith*?
12. Which poet and dramatist was murdered in a Deptford tavern in 1593?
13. Racing driver Dale Earnhardt was killed on the final lap of which well-known race in 2001?
14. Which tailless primate has slender and slow varieties?
15. What name is given to the lower house of the Manx Parliament?
16. Which U.S. pianist and bandleader wrote *Artistry in Rhythm*?
17. Which poet lived in Dove Cottage?
18. Which director made the films *Women in Love*, *The Boy Friend* and *Tommy*?
19. What sort of house has a name literally meaning in the Bengali style?
20. Which professional team golf event was first contested in 1927?

ANSWERS: *1 Bob Dylan, 2 A nursery rhyme, 3 Keystone Kops, 4 Ariel Sharon, 5 Edna O'Brien, 6 St Mark, 7 Hugh, 8 House of Lords, 9 Goldie Hawn, 10 Kendo, 11 Professor, 12 Christopher Marlowe, 13 Daytona 500, 14 Loris, 15 House of Keys, 16 Stan Kenton, 17 William Wordsworth, 18 Ken Russell, 19 Bungalow, 20 The Ryder Cup.*

Entertainment

Your rating: ● **0-5** **Buy a TV** ● **6-10** **Keep at it** ● **11-15** **Join a quiz team** ● **16-20** **Enter a quiz show**

1. What was the title of the Hindi movie quiz show shown on BBC2?
2. Which soul singer released an album entitled *Your Secret Love* in 1996?
3. Who directed the Hollywood satire *The Player*?
4. Who had a top ten hit single in 1982 with *Living On The Ceiling*?
5. Which *When Harry Met Sally* star played an heroic helicopter pilot in the film *Courage Under Fire*?
6. On which Saturday evening TV show did Rebel, Rio and Ace appear?
7. Which character was played by Helen Mirren in *Prime Suspect 5* on TV?
8. Which former member of the Go-Gos released an album entitled *A Woman And A Man* in 1996?
9. Who directed the 1982 film *Come Back to the 5 & Dime Jimmy Dean, Jimmy Dean*?
10. Which *Home and Away* character was played by Shane Ammann?
11. Who had a hit single in 1982 with *Say Hello Wave Goodbye*?
12. Which Dimbleby presented BBC 1's *Question Time*?
13. Who starred in the title role of Zeffirelli's 1996 screen version of *Jane Eyre*?
14. Which Sixties TV series starred David Jones, Peter Tork, Mickey Dolenz and Mike Nesmith?
15. Which US singer/songwriter released an album entitled *Baja Sessions* in 1996?
16. Who starred as Popeye Doyle in the film *The French Connection*?
17. Which sci-fi series followed Physics graduate Quinn Mallory's travels through a "wormhole" to parallel dimensions?
18. Who had a top ten hit in 1985 with *Say You, Say Me*?
19. Which 1996 film starred Bruce Willis as an assassin who tries to destroy two warring gangs of bootleggers?
20. Which occasional presenter of BBC 1's *Top of the Pops* hosted its spin-off Sunday afternoon Radio 1 show?

ANSWERS: *1 Bollywood or Bust!, 2 Luther Vandross, 3 Robert Altman, 4 Blancmange, 5 Meg Ryan, 6 Gladiators, 7 DS Jane Tennison, 8 Belinda Carlisle, 9 Robert Altman, 10 Curtis, 11 Soft Cell, 12 David, 13 Charlotte Gainsbourg, 14 The Monkees, 15 Chris Isaak, 16 Gene Hackman, 17 Sliders, 18 Lionel Richie, 19 Last Man Standing, 20 Jayne Middlemiss.*

General Knowledge

Your rating:
- 0-5 Join a library
- 6-10 Keep at it
- 11-15 Join a quiz team
- 16-20 Join Mensa

1. Which Roman general and statesman abandoned his wife Octavia to live with Cleopatra in Egypt?
2. The Needles can be found off the west coast of which British island?
3. Who reputedly showed that the rate of fall of a body is independent of its mass by dropping weights from the Leaning Tower of Pisa?
4. Which household appliance was pioneered by Elias Howe and redesigned by Isaac M. Singer in 1857?
5. Which meeting place for the College of Cardinals in the Vatican had its ceiling painted by Michelangelo?
6. Which alkaloid poison is derived from plants of the genus *Strychnos*?
7. By what name is the aquatic larva of frogs and toads known?
8. In the organisations known as MI-5 and MI-6, what do the initials MI stand for?
9. What was a galleon?
10. Which long-distance race is run over 26 miles 385 yards?
11. Which British field marshal became commander in chief of the British Expeditionary Force in 1915?
12. How is the Dog Star otherwise known?
13. Which British dramatist wrote *Separate Tables*?
14. Of which country was Jimmu the legendary first ruler?
15. Which British poet and dramatist wrote *The Beggar's Opera*?
16. Which Protestant reformer published an English translation of the Bible in 1535?
17. Of which South American country is Rosario a major city?
18. Which US novelist wrote *The Great Gatsby*?
19. What sort of creature is a porbeagle?
20. In 1987, which Indian cricketer became the first batsman to score 10,000 runs in Test cricket?

ANSWERS: *1 Mark Antony, 2 The Isle of Wight, 3 Galileo Galilei, 4 Sewing machine, 5 The Sistine Chapel, 6 Strychnine, 7 Tadpole, 8 Military Intelligence, 9 A ship, 10 Marathon, 11 Douglas Haig, 12 Sirius, 13 Sir Terence Rattigan, 14 Japan, 15 John Gay, 16 Miles Coverdale, 17 Argentina, 18 F. Scott Fitzgerald, 19 A shark, 20 Sunil Gavaskar.*

General Knowledge

Your rating:
- 0-5 Join a library
- 6-10 Keep at it
- 11-15 Join a quiz team
- 16-20 Join Mensa

1. George Stubbs is best known for his paintings of which animals?
2. Which Christian period of fasting begins on Ash Wednesday and lasts 40 days?
3. Which breed of short-haired tailless cat originated in the Isle of Man?
4. What was the ruling dynasty of Scotland from 1371 to 1714 and of England from 1603 to 1714?
5. Maoris make up about 10% of the population of which country?
6. What is a sitar?
7. Which nation did footballer Diego Maradona captain to win the 1986 World Cup?
8. Which member of the Beatles was married to Yoko Ono?
9. Which French patriot was known as the Maid of Orleans?
10. Which constellation of the zodiac is named after the Latin for lion?
11. Which Italian actress starred in the films *Two Women* and *Marriage Italian Style*?
12. Which artificial transuranic element is represented by the symbol Ha?
13. Who is the patron saint of Venice?
14. Of which African country is Maputo the capital?
15. With which sport was Australian Ken Rosewall associated?
16. Which Swiss psychiatrist gave his name to a personality test involving inkblots?
17. In which country can the dormant volcano Mount Popocatépetl be found?
18. What sort of creature is a markhor?
19. In which country is the tourist resort of Interlaken situated?
20. What sort of creature is a marabou?

ANSWERS: *1 Horses, 2 Lent, 3 Manx cat, 4 Stuarts, 5 New Zealand, 6 A musical instrument, 7 Argentina, 8 John Lennon, 9 Joan of Arc, 10 Leo, 11 Sophia Loren, 12 Hahnium, 13 St Mark, 14 Mozambique, 15 Tennis, 16 Hermann Rorschach, 17 Mexico, 18 A goat, 19 Switzerland, 20 A bird.*

General Knowledge

Your rating: ● 0-5 Join a library ● 6-10 Keep at it ● 11-15 Join a quiz team ● 16-20 Join Mensa

1. Which colour of rose represented the House of Lancaster in the Wars of the Roses?
2. In which Middle Eastern country is the Negev desert situated?
3. What sort of creature is a marlin?
4. What is the Scouts' motto?
5. In which Hampshire port can Nelson's flagship HMS Victory be found?
6. Who became principal conductor of the City of Birmingham Symphony Orchestra in 1980?
7. In which country is Port Said situated?
8. In 1949, which communist statesman proclaimed the establishment of the People's Republic of China?
9. How was the music hall singer and comedian Dame Grace Stansfield popularly known?
10. What is a maraca?
11. Which Indian statesman was the first governor general of Pakistan?
12. Which Australian novelist wrote the Booker Prize-winning novel *Schindler's Ark*?
13. Which all-girl group had their second number one hit single with *Say You'll Be There*?
14. Which French acrobat walked across a tightrope suspended over Niagara Falls in 1859?
15. What is the capital of Trinidad and Tobago?
16. Of which metal is galena the principal ore?
17. Who was president of the USA from 1909 to 1913?
18. The Galilean satellites are the four largest satellites of which planet?
19. Which British novelist wrote *Goodbye, Mr Chips*?
20. Which town in South Wales was formed by the amalgamation of Aberavon and Margam in 1921?

ANSWERS: *1 Red, 2 Israel, 3 A fish, 4 Be Prepared, 5 Portsmouth, 6 Simon Rattle, 7 Egypt, 8 Mao Tse-tung, 9 Gracie Fields, 10 A percussion instrument, 11 Mohammed Ali Jinnah, 12 Thomas Keneally, 13 The Spice Girls, 14 Charles Blondin, 15 Port-of-Spain, 16 Lead, 17 William Taft, 18 Jupiter, 19 James Hilton, 20 Port Talbot.*

Entertainment

Your rating: ● 0-5 Buy a TV ● 6-10 Keep at it ● 11-15 Join a quiz team ● 16-20 Enter a quiz show

1. Which former *Neighbours* and *Priscilla: Queen of the Desert* star played Rob McGregor in the TV series *Snowy River: the McGregor Saga*?
2. Which star of *Sex, Lies and Videotape* played a cop in the 1996 film *Two Days In The Valley*?
3. Which comedian was the host of *The A Force* on TV?
4. What was the title of Jamiroquai's first top ten single, which hit the charts in 1993?
5. Who starred as the wealthy NATO official in the film *Indiscreet*?
6. Which two pop megastars collaborated on the 1983 hit single *Say Say Say*?
7. Who starred as Gepetto in the 1996 film *The Adventures of Pinocchio*?
8. Hot House and My Little Friend were features of which Saturday evening TV show?
9. Which boy band released an album entitled *Rollercoaster* in 1996?
10. Which award-winning actor starred as surgeon Edgar Pascoe in the 1996 TV drama *The Fragile Heart*?
11. Which band had a top ten hit single in 1982 with *The Look of Love*?
12. Who played corrupt racist cop Charlie Wade in the 1996 film *Lone Star*?
13. Who starred as the womanising private eye in TV's *Sharman*?
14. Of which rock group is Evan Dando the lead singer?
15. Who played DI Charlie Scott in the TV drama *Thief Takers*?
16. Which rock group had a number one hit single in 1964 with *Little Red Rooster*?
17. Who starred as the 10-year-old child with the body of a 40-year-old man in the film *Jack*?
18. What did the initials of the cult TV programme TISWAS stand for?
19. Who has had number one hits as a member of the Housemartins and Beats International, and also as Fat Boy Slim?
20. Which Channel 4 fashion show was hosted by model Sophie Anderton?

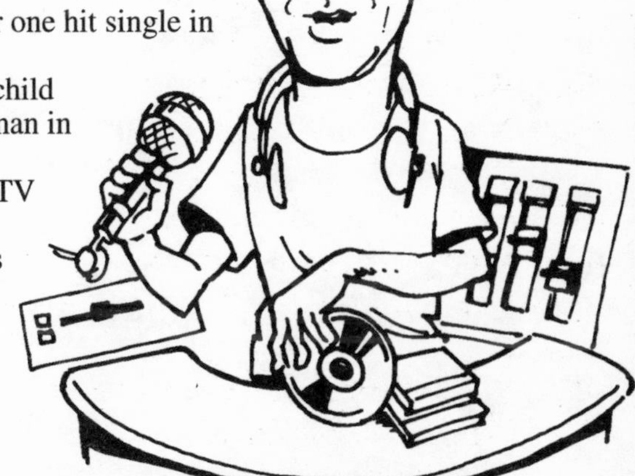

ANSWERS: *1 Guy Pearce, 2 James Spader, 3 Felix Dexter, 4 Too Young to Die, 5 Cary Grant, 6 Paul McCartney and Michael Jackson, 7 Martin Landau, 8 Noel's House Party, 9 Let Loose, 10 Nigel Hawthorne, 11 ABC, 12 Kris Kristofferson, 13 Clive Owen, 14 The Lemonheads, 15 Reece Dinsdale, 16 The Rolling Stones, 17 Robin Williams, 18 Today Is Saturday, Wear a Smile, 19 Norman Cook, 20 Desire.*

General Knowledge

Your rating: ● **0-5** **Join a library** ● **6-10** **Keep at it** ● **11-15** **Join a quiz team** ● **16-20** **Join Mensa**

1. What is the capital of Austria?
2. What sort of creature is a nuthatch?
3. Do stalactites grow upwards or downwards?
4. Which Italian composer wrote the operas *Rigoletto* and *Aida*?
5. What is the longest river in the Republic of Ireland?
6. Which British politician was leader of the Social Democratic Party from 1983 to 1987?
7. Which French author wrote *Around the World in Eighty Days*?
8. Which British decoration for "bravery...in the presence of the enemy" is represented by the initials VC?
9. Which Anglo-American poet, critic and dramatist wrote *The Waste Land* and *The Cocktail Party*?
10. Which British middle-distance runner won the gold medal in the 800m at the 1980 Olympic Games?
11. Which jazz singer was known as the *First Lady of Song*?
12. Which British dramatist wrote the comedies *Epsom Wells* and *The Virtuoso*?
13. Which European country was led by Enver Hoxha from 1946 to 1985?
14. In which country did Damon Hill clinch the Formula One World Championship in 1996?
15. What sort of creature is a Russian Blue?
16. Which French novelist wrote *La Fin de Chéri*?
17. Which organisation instigated the Aldermaston marches?
18. Which US novelist and essayist wrote *Myra Breckinridge*?
19. Of which African country is Yaoundé the capital?
20. Which first name did Madonna give her daughter?

ANSWERS: *1 Vienna, 2 A bird, 3 Downwards, 4 Giuseppe Verdi, 5 The River Shannon, 6 Dr David Owen, 7 Jules Verne, 8 Victoria Cross, 9 T. S. Eliot, 10 Steve Ovett, 11 Ella Fitzgerald, 12 Thomas Shadwell, 13 Albania, 14 Japan, 15 A cat, 16 Colette, 17 CND, 18 Gore Vidal, 19 Cameroon, 20 Lourdes.*

General Knowledge

Your rating: ● 0-5 Join a library ● 6-10 Keep at it ● 11-15 Join a quiz team ● 16-20 Join Mensa

1. Which popular US singer had hits with *Heartbeak Hotel*, *Hound Dog* and *Don't Be Cruel*?
2. What sort of creature is a cayman?
3. Of which country is Zagreb the capital?
4. Which London cricket ground is the headquarters of the Surrey County Cricket Club?
5. Which French philosopher wrote *Being and Nothingness* and *Nausea*?
6. Of which country did Nicolae Ceausescu become president in 1974?
7. What is the largest state of the USA?
8. Which specialist division of the British army is represented by the initials SAS?
9. To which group of islands does Sark belong?
10. Which dictator ruled over the Soviet Union from the 1920s until his death in 1953?
11. Who wrote the lyrics for the musicals *West Side Story* and *A Little Night Music*?
12. What was the name of the kingdom of the West Saxons, under which Anglo-Saxon England was united in the 9th century?
13. Which instrument is used in surveying to measure horizontal and vertical angles?
14. On which Hebridean island can Fingal's Cave be found?
15. Of which country is Bulawayo the second largest city?
16. Which deaf and blind woman wrote *The Story of My Life*, which was published in 1902?
17. What is the largest lake in Africa?
18. Which state of the USA has Montgomery as its capital?
19. Which British philanthropist founded St Christopher's Hospice in London in 1967?
20. What has been the name of Britain's royal family since 1917?

ANSWERS: *1 Elvis Presley, 2 A reptile, 3 Croatia, 4 The Oval, 5 Jean-Paul Sartre, 6 Romania, 7 Alaska, 8 Special Air Service, 9 The Channel Islands, 10 Joseph Stalin, 11 Stephen Sondheim, 12 Wessex, 13 A theodolite, 14 Staffa, 15 Zimbabwe, 16 Helen Keller, 17 Lake Victoria, 18 Alabama, 19 Dame Cicely Saunders, 20 The House of Windsor.*

General Knowledge

Your rating: ● **0-5 Join a library** ● **6-10 Keep at it** ● **11-15 Join a quiz team** ● **16-20 Join Mensa**

1. Which British poet wrote *Kubla Khan* and *The Rime of the Ancient Mariner*?
2. Which ringed planet is the second largest planet of the solar system?
3. What sort of creature is a cavy?
4. What is the name of the machine which selects the numbers of winning premium bonds?
5. In which continent can the Zambezi River be found?
6. Which daughter of Henry VIII and Anne Boleyn was the Queen of England from 1558 to 1603?
7. Of which country is Saskatchewan a province?
8. What was Australian tennis player Evonne Cawley's maiden name?
9. Which organisation is represented by the initials CBI?
10. Which country is associated with the alcoholic drink ouzo?
11. Which Essex town was known as Camulodunum to the Romans?
12. Who was president of Tanzania from 1964 to 1985?
13. Theravada is a conservative school of which religion?
14. Which U.S. general devised the European Recovery Programme for which he won a Nobel peace prize in 1953?
15. What sort of creature is a natterjack?
16. Which U.S. actress starred in the film *My Little Chickadee*?
17. Which French composer wrote *Trois morceaux en forme de poire*?
18. Which jockey won seven races on one day in 1996?
19. Which part of a flower produces pollen?
20. Which British dramatist wrote *The Merchant* and *Chips with Everything*?

ANSWERS: *1 Samuel Taylor Coleridge, 2 Saturn, 3 A rodent, 4 ERNIE, 5 Africa, 6 Elizabeth I, 7 Canada, 8 Goolagong, 9 Confederation of British Industry, 10 Greece, 11 Colchester, 12 Julius Nyerere, 13 Buddhism, 14 George C. Marshall, 15 A toad, 16 Mae West, 17 Erik Satie, 18 Frankie Dettori, 19 Stamen, 20 Arnold Wesker.*

Entertainment

Your rating: ● 0-5 Buy a TV ● 6-10 Keep at it ● 11-15 Join a quiz team ● 16-20 Enter a quiz show

1. Who directed the 1982 film *E.T. -The Extra-Terrestrial*?
2. Which *Dallas* character was played by Victoria Principal?
3. Which jazz singer is married to John Dankworth?
4. Which TV funnyman played Sir Toby Belch in Trevor Nunn's 1996 film version of *Twelfth Night*?
5. Which *Drop The Dead Donkey* star played Paul in the sitcom *Faith in the Future*?
6. Which pop group switched on Oxford Street's Christmas lights in 1996?
7. Who played Bick Benedict in the 1956 film *Giant*?
8. Which band had a top ten hit single in 1981 with *I Go To Sleep*?
9. Which *Trainspotting* star played a trumpet player in the film *Brassed Off*?
10. Which controversial newspaper columnist presented *Wanted* on TV?
11. Which singer and actress played the title role in the 1996 film musical *Evita*?
12. Which band had a top ten hit single in 1984 with *Heaven Knows I'm Miserable Now*?
13. What is the name of *Children in Need*'s mascot?
14. Which *Death Wish* actor played one of the heroic septet in *The Magnificent Seven*?
15. Which cook was the presenter of *TV Dinners*?
16. Who starred as Kathleen Riley in the 1987 film *Suspect*?
17. To which city's police force was DS Jane Tennison transferred in TV's *Prime Suspect 5*?
18. Which *Monty Python* star played Ratty in the 1996 film version of *The Wind In The Willows*?
19. What was the title of the Spice Girls' debut album?
20. Which singer starred as Joe E. Lewis in the 1957 film *The Joker Is Wild*?

ANSWERS: *1 Steven Spielberg, 2 Pam Ewing, 3 Cleo Laine, 4 Mel Smith, 5 Jeff Rawle, 6 The Spice Girls, 7 Rock Hudson, 8 The Pretenders, 9 Ewan McGregor, 10 Richard Littlejohn, 11 Madonna, 12 The Smiths, 13 Pudsey Bear, 14 Charles Bronson, 15 Hugh Fearnley-Whittingstall, 16 Cher, 17 Manchester's, 18 Eric Idle, 19 Spice, 20 Frank Sinatra.*

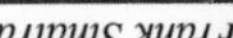

General Knowledge

Your rating: ● 0-5 Join a library ● 6-10 Keep at it ● 11-15 Join a quiz team ● 16-20 Join Mensa

1. Who directed the films *2001: A Space Odyssey* and *The Shining*?
2. Of which country was Charles Haughey prime minister?
3. How is Brazilian footballer Edson Arantes do Nascimento better known?
4. Of which country is Kuala Lumpur the capital?
5. Which units are used to measure the purity of gold?
6. What nationality was the composer Edvard Grieg?
7. Which state of the USA occupies a chain of over 20 volcanic islands in the Pacific Ocean?
8. Which U.S. actor starred in the films *Gone with the Wind* and *It Happened One Night*?
9. According to Greek mythology, which winged horse sprang from the blood of Medusa when she was beheaded by Perseus?
10. Which New Zealand detective-story writer penned several novels featuring Roderick Alleyn of Scotland Yard?
11. What sort of creature is a klipspringer?
12. Which Russian novelist and dramatist wrote *The Government Inspector* and *Dead Souls*?
13. In psychoanalysis, which part of the unconscious mind is governed by irrational instinctive forces?
14. Which metal is represented by the symbol Rh?
15. In which Devon port is The Royal Naval College situated?
16. Who was US president throughout World War I?
17. Which Italian poet wrote a series of love poems addressed to Laura which were known as the *Canzoniere*?
18. In which country can the Ellora Caves be found?
19. Which US political party was in power from 1791 to 1800?
20. Which German scholar wrote *Faust*, and *The Sorrows of Young Werther*?

ANSWERS: *1 Stanley Kubrick, 2 The Republic of Ireland, 3 Pele, 4 Malaysia, 5 Carats, 6 Norwegian, 7 Hawaii, 8 Clark Gable, 9 Pegasus, 10 Dame Ngaio Marsh, 11 An antelope, 12 Nikolai Gogol, 13 The id, 14 Rhodium, 15 Dartmouth, 16 Woodrow Wilson, 17 Petrarch, 18 India, 19 Federalist Party, 20 Goethe.*

General Knowledge

Your rating: ● 0-5 Join a library ● 6-10 Keep at it ● 11-15 Join a quiz team ● 16-20 Join Mensa

1. In which state of the USA is the fashionable resort of Palm Beach situated?
2. By what nickname was band leader Edward Kennedy Ellington usually known?
3. Which country's national anthem is often known as *La Marseillaise*?
4. Which British physicist and mathematician discovered the law of gravitation?
5. What sort of creature is a palomino?
6. Of which country is Peking the capital?
7. Which bluish-white metal is represented by the symbol Zn?
8. Which jazz pianist composed *Off Minor* and *Blue Monk*?
9. What is the capital of Brazil?
10. Which order of mammals includes kangaroos, wallabies, bandicoots and opossums?
11. Which lanthanide element is represented by the symbol Gd?
12. Which Italian film maker directed *La Strada* and *Amarcord*?
13. In which ocean are the Marshall Islands situated?
14. The Vedas are the basic scriptures of which religion?
15. Which US physician and paediatrician wrote *The Common Sense Book of Baby and Child Care*?
16. Which Swiss sculptor and painter created an abstract construction entitled *The Palace at 4 am*?
17. Which Dual Monarchy was established by the Ausgleich in 1867?
18. Which US novelist wrote *The Portrait of a Lady* and *The Ambassadors*?
19. Which birds are particularly susceptible to the disease psittacosis?
20. Which chancellor of the exchequer died in office in 1970?

ANSWERS: *1 Florida, 2 Duke, 3 France's, 4 Sir Isaac Newton, 5 A horse, 6 China, 7 Zinc, 8 Thelonious Monk, 9 Brasilia, 10 Marsupials, 11 Gadolinium, 12 Federico Fellini, 13 The Pacific Ocean, 14 Hinduism, 15 Benjamin Spock, 16 Alberto Giacometti, 17 Austria-Hungary, 18 Henry James, 19 Parrots, 20 Iain Macleod.*

General Knowledge

Your rating:
- **0-5** Join a library
- **6-10** Keep at it
- **11-15** Join a quiz team
- **16-20** Join Mensa

1. What does the acronym NATO stand for?
2. According to Arthurian legend who was the wife of King Arthur and lover of Lancelot?
3. Of which country did Bob Hawke become prime minister in 1983?
4. By what name was Zimbabwe known until 1979?
5. Which British novelist wrote *Pride and Prejudice*?
6. By what name are the 27 books that constitute the second major division of the Bible known?
7. Which British actor won an Academy Award for his performance in *The Bridge on the River Kwai*?
8. What is a monkey puzzle?
9. How many pairs of ribs usually make up the human rib-cage?
10. What nationality was the pioneering psychoanalyst Sigmund Freud?
11. Magnetite or lodestone is a form of which metal's oxide?
12. Which British fascist married Diana Mitford in 1936?
13. Which British composer wrote *Fantasia on a Theme by Thomas Tallis*?
14. How was jazz clarinetist and band leader Arthur Arshawsky better known?
15. Which national holiday is celebrated in the USA on the fourth Thursday in November?
16. Which river flows from the Belgian Ardennes to join the River Seine at Conflans?
17. What is the highest peak in North America?
18. In which country was Sir Yehudi Menuhin born?
19. To whom was the Earl of Snowdon married from 1960 to 1978?
20. What does a palynologist study?

***ANSWERS:** 1 North Atlantic Treaty Organisation, 2 Guinevere, 3 Australia, 4 Rhodesia, 5 Jane Austen, 6 The New Testament, 7 Sir Alec Guinness, 8 A tree, 9 Twelve, 10 Austrian, 11 Iron, 12 Sir Oswald Mosley, 13 Ralph Vaughan Williams, 14 Artie Shaw, 15 Thanksgiving Day, 16 The River Oise, 17 Mount McKinley, 18 The USA, 19 Princess Margaret, 20 Pollen.*

Entertainment

Your rating: ● **0-5** Buy a TV ● **6-10** Keep at it ● **11-15** Join a quiz team ● **16-20** Enter a quiz show

1. Which BBC 2 celebrity panel gameshow featured Phill Jupitus and Sean Hughes as team captains?
2. In 1983, which female vocalist released the album *She's So Unusual*, which featured four top five hit singles?
3. Who starred as the policeman martial arts expert in the 1996 film *The Glimmer Man*?
4. Who was the original presenter of the TV show *Question Time*?
5. Which British band failed to turn up to the 1996 MTV Awards ceremony despite winning the Best Group and Best Song prizes?
6. Who won a Best Actor Oscar in 1977 for his performance in *The Goodbye Girl*?
7. Who played Bill Porter in the BBC 1 sitcom *2 Point 4 Children*?
8. Who had a number one hit single in 1990 with *The Joker*?
9. Who starred in the title role of the 1996 film *Michael Collins*?
10. Which Seventies TV series was known as *My Partner the Ghost* in the US?
11. Which country/rock vocalist released an album in 1996 entitled *A Place In The World*?
12. Who played Des Barnes in *Coronation Street*?
13. Who starred as the nanny from hell in the 1992 film *The Hand That Rocks The Cradle*?
14. With which vocalist did UB40 collaborate on the 1990 top ten hit *I'll Be Your Baby Tonight*?
15. Who wrote the novel upon which the 1996 BBC series *The Tenant of Wildfell Hall* was based?
16. In which European city was the award-winning 1996 film *When The Cat's Away* set?
17. Which *Coronation Street* character was played by Pat Phoenix?
18. Which pop group's hits include *Tragedy*, *One For Sorrow* and *Better Best Forgotten*?
19. Which writer presented *The Mind Traveller* on TV?
20. What was the name of Phil Collins's 1996 album?

ANSWERS: *1 Never Mind The Buzzcocks, 2 Cyndi Lauper, 3 Steven Seagal, 4 Sir Robin Day, 5 Oasis, 6 Richard Dreyfuss, 7 Belinda Lang, 8 The Steve Miller Band, 9 Liam Neeson, 10 Randall and Hopkirk (Deceased), 11 Mary Chapin Carpenter, 12 Philip Middlemiss, 13 Rebecca DeMornay, 14 Robert Palmer, 15 Anne Brontë, 16 Paris, 17 Elsie Tanner, 18 Steps, 19 Oliver Sacks, 20 Dance Into The Light.*

General Knowledge

Your rating: ● **0-5** Join a library ● **6-10** Keep at it ● **11-15** Join a quiz team ● **16-20** Join Mensa

1. Which US swimmer won a record seven gold medals in the 1972 Munich Olympic Games?
2. In which London square is the National Gallery situated?
3. What sort of creature is a whelk?
4. Of what is linguistics the study?
5. The Seine, the Loire and the Rhône are the principal rivers of which country?
6. How is sodium chloride commonly known?
7. By what acronym is the Oxford Committee for Famine Relief better known?
8. What word describes the score in tennis when both players have a score of 40?
9. How many strings does a violin usually have?
10. In which German city were the trials of Nazi criminals held after World War II?
11. Landrace is a breed of which animal?
12. Which British astronomer was the first to realise that comets do not appear randomly but have periodic orbits?
13. Which British actress received an Emmy for her role in *Prime Suspect*?
14. Who was the second wife of Napoleon Bonaparte?
15. Of which country was Sir Sidney Holland prime minister from 1949 to 1957?
16. Which British novelist wrote *The Private Papers of Henry Ryecroft*?
17. What nationality was the middle-distance and long-distance runner Paavo Nurmi?
18. Which U.S. filmmaker directed the films *The Treasure of the Sierra Madre* and *Annie*?
19. What is the fourth book of the Old Testament?
20. Which Canadian-born supermodel succeeded Helena Bonham Carter as the Face of Yardley?

ANSWERS: 1 Mark Spitz, 2 Trafalgar Square, 3 A mollusc, 4 Language, 5 France, 6 Salt, 7 OXFAM, 8 Deuce, 9 Four, 10 Nuremberg, 11 Pig, 12 Edmund Halley, 13 Helen Mirren, 14 Marie Louise, 15 New Zealand, 16 George Gissing, 17 Finnish, 18 John Huston, 19 Numbers, 20 Linda Evangelista

General Knowledge

Your rating: ● **0-5 Join a library** ● **6-10 Keep at it** ● **11-15 Join a quiz team** ● **16-20 Join Mensa**

1. Which Irish dramatist wrote *Pygmalion* and *Man and Superman*?
2. What does the acronym NASA stand for?
3. Are protons positively or negatively charged?
4. Which volcano in Italy erupted in 79 AD, engulfing the towns of Herculaneum and Pompeii?
5. During which World War did Wilfred Owen write his poetry?
6. Which silvery-white reactive metal is represented by the symbol Mg?
7. Which political party did the Whigs become under Gladstone in the late 19th century?
8. Of which state of the USA is Nashville the capital?
9. With which sport is Barry Sheene associated?
10. In which former Yugoslav republic is the port of Split situated?
11. Which Czech author wrote the story *Metamorphosis* and the novel *The Trial*?
12. Which US actress starred in the films *Duel in the Sun* and *The Night of the Hunter*?
13. What sort of creature is a grackle?
14. Of which European country was Coimbra the capital from 1139 to 1260?
15. Which British sculptor is known for his Peter Pan in Kensington Gardens and the Edith Cavell memorial?
16. Which British cricketer became the first professional England captain in 1953?
17. Which ancient African city was said to have been founded by Dido?
18. What is the colloquial name for the Fasci di Combattimento, founded in 1919 by Mussolini?
19. What is the name of the equatorial belt of light variable winds within which the trade-wind zones converge?
20. Which British poet wrote the epic poem cycle *The Ring and the Book*?

ANSWERS: *1 George Bernard Shaw, 2 National Aeronautics and Space Administration, 3 Positively, 4 Vesuvius, 5 World War I, 6 Magnesium, 7 The Liberal Party, 8 Tennessee, 9 Motorcycling, 10 Croatia, 11 Franz Kafka, 12 Lillian Gish, 13 A bird, 14 Portugal, 15 Sir George Frampton, 16 Len Hutton, 17 Carthage, 18 Blackshirts, 19 Doldrums, 20 Robert Browning.*

General Knowledge

Your rating:
- 0-5 **Join a library**
- 6-10 **Keep at it**
- 11-15 **Join a quiz team**
- 16-20 **Join Mensa**

1. At which boxing weight was Joe Louis world champion?
2. How is halitosis commonly known?
3. What is the usual number of people in a jury?
4. Of which country was Valéry Giscard d'Estaing president from 1974 to 1981?
5. What sort of creature is a ray?
6. Which specialised agency of the United Nations is represented by the initials IMF?
7. Who was the wife of Louis XVI of France who was guillotined in 1793?
8. By what nickname was landscape gardener Lancelot Brown known?
9. Which resort on the Lancashire coast is famous for its Tower (modelled on the Eiffel Tower), Pleasure Beach, and illuminations?
10. With which sport is Stirling Moss associated?
11. What is the science of map and chart making known as?
12. In which Italian city is the Uffizi art gallery situated?
13. Which film producer and co-founder of MGM was born Samuel Goldfish?
14. Which hereditary military Japanese title was Tokugawa Keiki the last to have?
15. How is acetylsalicylic acid commonly known when in tablet form?
16. Who presented BBC TV's *Ski Sunday* for 19 years?
17. Which U.S. novelist and short-story writer wrote *The Case of Charles Dexter Ward*?
18. Who was the mother of Salome?
19. How is the eve of All Saints' Day commonly known?
20. Which punk rock group featured Joe Strummer, Mick Jones and Paul Simonon among its members?

ANSWERS: *1 Heavyweight, 2 Bad breath, 3 Twelve, 4 France, 5 A fish, 6 International Monetary Fund, 7 Marie Antoinette, 8 Capability, 9 Blackpool, 10 Motor racing, 11 Cartography, 12 Florence, 13 Samuel Goldwyn, 14 Shogun, 15 Aspirin, 16 David Vine, 17 H. P. Lovecraft, 18 Herodias, 19 Hallowe'en, 20 The Clash.*

Sports

Your rating:
- 0-5 Wooden spoon
- 6-10 Bronze medal
- 11-15 Silver medal
- 16-20 Gold medal

1. In which event did Britain win its only medal at the 1998 Winter Olympics?
2. Which number is in between five and one on a dart-board?
3. What nationality is 1996 Olympic men's 10,000m champion Haile Gebrselassie?
4. Which British football club won the Cup Winners' Cup in 1983?
5. For which rugby union club did Austin Healey leave Orrell?
6. Which nation does sprinter Frankie Fredericks represent?
7. Which boxer, known as the Fleetwood Assassin, won her claim for sex discrimination against the British Boxing Board of Control in 1998?
8. In which year did Nick Beal make his senior England rugby union debut, against Argentina?
9. At which 1999 Grand Prix did Michael Schmacher crash, breaking his leg?
10. Which club bought Kevin Campbell from Arsenal?
11. How many gold medals did Fanny Blankers-Koen win to become the 1948 Olympic Games' most successful female competitor?
12. Who became manager of the Republic of Ireland's soccer team in 1986?
13. How many players are there on each team in the traditional Scots game of shinty?
14. Who did Lennox Lewis beat to win the British heavyweight title in March 1991?
15. In which event did Duncan Goodhew win a gold medal at the 1980 Olympics?
16. Which French footballer scored twice in the 1998 World Cup Final?
17. Who did snooker's Nigel Bond lose to in the 1995 World Championship final?
18. Which British rugby union side did South Africa beat 18-0 in July 1998?
19. In which year did John Curry become the Olympic men's figure skating champion?
20. Which team won the UEFA Cup in 1994?

***ANSWERS:** 1 Four-man bobsleigh, 2 20, 3 Ethiopian, 4 Aberdeen, 5 Leicester, 6 Namibia, 7 Jane Couch, 8 1996, 9 British Grand Prix, 10 Nottingham Forest, 11 Four, 12 Jack Charlton, 13 12, 14 Gary Mason, 15 100m breast-stroke, 16 Zinedine Zidane, 17 Stephen Hendry, 18 England, 19 1976, 20 Inter Milan.*

General Knowledge

Your rating: ● 0-5 Join a library ● 6-10 Keep at it ● 11-15 Join a quiz team ● 16-20 Join Mensa

1. In which year did World War II end?
2. In which county is Ascot racecourse situated?
3. How is the Polish trade union Solidarnosc known in English?
4. In which country can the city of Bombay be found?
5. By what title is the chief law officer of the Crown in England and Wales known?
6. What is the capital of Paraguay?
7. What was the family name of the French emperors Napoleon I, Napoleon II, and Napoleon III?
8. Between which two European countries was South America divided during the 16th century?
9. Which former penal system for young offenders was named after a village near Rochester, Kent?
10. Using the tonic sol-fa system, what follows doh in the rising major scale?
11. What sort of creature is a frogmouth?
12. Who succeeded Cardinal Heenan as Archbishop of Westminster in 1976?
13. Which US novelist wrote *The Big Sleep* and *The Long Goodbye*, both featuring the detective Philip Marlowe?
14. What sort of creature is a chafer?
15. Which two countries were first to sign the Anti-Comintern Pact in 1936?
16. Which British Labour politician was minister of health from 1945 to 1951?
17. Which Italian film maker made *Blow-Up* and *Zabriskie Point*?
18. Which unit was defined in 1791 as one ten-millionth of the length of the quadrant of the earth's meridian through Paris?
19. According to the Old Testament, which son of David was famous for his wisdom as the third King of Israel?
20. Ko ji ki and Nihon Shoki are scriptures of which native Japanese religion?

ANSWERS: *1 1945, 2 Berkshire, 3 Solidarity, 4 India, 5 Attorney general, 6 Asunción, 7 Bonaparte, 8 Portugal and Spain, 9 Borstal, 10 Ray or re, 11 A bird, 12 Basil Hume, 13 Raymond Chandler, 14 A beetle, 15 Germany and Japan, 16 Aneurin Bevan, 17 Michelangelo Antonioni, 18 Metre, 19 Solomon, 20 Shinto.*

General Knowledge

Your rating:
- **0-5 Join a library**
- **6-10 Keep at it**
- **11-15 Join a quiz team**
- **16-20 Join Mensa**

1. Which nomadic people were ruled by Attila from 434 to 453 AD?
2. Which country was ruled by Ivan the Terrible?
3. With which sport is Ian Botham associated?
4. What is the natural satellite of the earth called?
5. What is the world's second largest ocean?
6. Of which former Yugoslavian republic is Ljubljana the capital?
7. In which African country is the town of Aswan situated?
8. Which political party did Clement Attlee represent on becoming British prime minister in 1945?
9. Which channel is situated between the coast of Hampshire and the Isle of Wight?
10. Which footballer captained the England team that won the World Cup in 1966?
11. Which Christian denomination developed out of the religious practices advocated by the Wesley brothers?
12. Which British novelist wrote *The Loneliness of the Long Distance Runner*?
13. Which American Sioux Indian chief led the massacre of General Custer and his men at the Little Bighorn?
14. Which footballer made a record £15 million move from Blackburn Rovers to Newcastle United in 1996?
15. Which French composer wrote the music to the opera *Carmen*?
16. Which metallic element is represented by the symbol Sb?
17. What is the name of the principal US opera company, which was founded in New York in 1883?
18. Which mythological daughter of Oedipus and Jocasta was the subject of a tragedy by Sophocles?
19. What was the first nuclear-powered submarine?
20. What is the chemical name for marsh gas?

ANSWERS: *1 The Huns, 2 Russia, 3 Cricket, 4 The moon, 5 The Atlantic, 6 Slovenia, 7 Egypt, 8 Labour, 9 The Solent, 10 Bobby Moore, 11 Methodism, 12 Alan Sillitoe, 13 Sitting Bull, 14 Alan Shearer, 15 Georges Bizet, 16 Antimony, 17 The Metropolitan Opera Association, 18 Antigone, 19 U.S.S. Nautilus, 20 Methane.*

General Knowledge

Your rating: ● **0-5** Join a library ● **6-10** Keep at it ● **11-15** Join a quiz team ● **16-20** Join Mensa

1. Which British actor and producer directed the films *Gandhi* and *Cry Freedom*?
2. Of which African country is Mogadishu the capital?
3. What does a botanist study?
4. What is the capital of El Salvador?
5. Who directed and starred in the film *Citizen Kane*?
6. In which English county are the resorts of Torquay and Paignton situated?
7. Which sort of sportsmen compete in the Tour de France?
8. What nationality was the painter Hieronymus Bosch?
9. In Greek legend, who cut the Gordian Knot?
10. From the hair of which sort of creatures is mohair manufactured?
11. Who was President of the USA from 1901 to 1909?
12. Which country claimed the area of Antarctica known as the Ross Dependency from 1923?
13. Which Soviet composer wrote the opera *War and Peace* and the ballet *Romeo and Juliet*?
14. Which legendary founders of Rome were twins who were suckled by a she-wolf?
15. What is the official language of the Coprincipality of Andorra?
16. Which Belgian novelist wrote detective stories featuring the Parisian commissaire de police, *Maigret*?
17. To which country do the Antipodes Islands belong?
18. Which German general was known as the *Desert Fox*?
19. Which US novelist wrote *Goodbye, Columbus* and *Portnoy's Complaint*?
20. Which Briton won his fourth gold medal in consecutive Olympics at Atlanta in 1996?

ANSWERS: *1 Sir Richard Attenborough, 2 Somalia, 3 Plants, 4 San Salvador, 5 Orson Welles, 6 Devon, 7 Cyclists, 8 Dutch, 9 Alexander the Great, 10 Goats, 11 Theodore Roosevelt, 12 New Zealand, 13 Sergei Prokofiev, 14 Romulus and Remus, 15 Catalan, 16 Georges Simenon, 17 New Zealand, 18 Erwin Rommel, 19 Philip Roth, 20 Steve Redgrave.*

Entertainment

Your rating:
- 0-5 Buy a TV
- 6-10 Keep at it
- 11-15 Join a quiz team
- 16-20 Enter a quiz show

1. Who played Helen Graham in the 1996 TV adaptation of *The Tenant of Wildfell Hall*?
2. Who had a top ten hit single in 1985 with the Billy Bragg song *A New England*?
3. In which country was the 1992 film musical *Sarafina!* set?
4. Who starred as Geordie country singer Jed Sheppard in TV's *Crocodile Shoes*?
5. Which Irish band released an album entitled *A Different Beat* in 1996?
6. Which 1996 film starred Stephen Baldwin and Laurence Fishburne as escaped convicts?
7. Which long-running Sixties pop music show was presented by Cathy McGowan?
8. Which band had a number one hit single in 1979 with *Walking On The Moon*?
9. Who starred as the dying gunfighter in the 1976 film *The Shootist*?
10. Who starred in the title role of the 1996 ITV adaptation of *Emma*?
11. Which techno band is led by singer Keith Flint?
12. Which animated sitcom featured the character Dolly Pond?
13. Who starred as Brian in Monty Python's *Life of Brian*?
14. The BBC2 drama series *The Crow Road* was adapted from a novel by which Scottish writer?
15. Which female vocalist had a top ten hit in 1964 with *I Just Don't Know What To Do With Myself*?
16. Who starred as the neurotic knife salesman in the film *The Fan*?
17. Which TV series starred Jack Klugman as a pathologist?
18. Who starred as Indiana Jones in *Indiana Jones and the Temple of Doom*?
19. Which former Take That star presented the 1996 MTV Awards?
20. What was the title of the 1998 thriller by director Brian De Palma which starred Nicolas Cage as a corrupt Atlantic City cop?

ANSWERS: *1 Tara Fitzgerald, 2 Kirsty MacColl, 3 South Africa, 4 Jimmy Nail, 5 Boyzone, 6 Fled, 7 Ready Steady Go!, 8 The Police, 9 John Wayne, 10 Kate Beckinsale, 11 The Prodigy, 12 Pond Life, 13 Graham Chapman, 14 Iain Banks, 15 Dusty Springfield, 16 Robert De Niro, 17 Quincy, 18 Harrison Ford, 19 Robbie Williams, 20 Snake Eyes.*

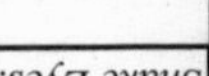

General Knowledge

Your rating:
- 0-5 Join a library
- 6-10 Keep at it
- 11-15 Join a quiz team
- 16-20 Join Mensa

1. Which Paris art gallery houses Leonardo da Vinci's *Mona Lisa*?
2. The Dolomites are a section of which mountain range?
3. Which British middle-distance runner won gold medals in the 1500m at the 1980 and 1984 Olympics?
4. What sort of creature is an asp?
5. In which country did the form of theatre known as Kabuki originate?
6. To which member of the Royal Family does the Duchy of Cornwall belong?
7. According to the Old Testament, who received the Ten Commandments on Mount Sinai?
8. In which London park can one find Speakers' Corner and the Serpentine boating lake?
9. What do the initials UHT stand for?
10. How was the Wild West showman William F. Cody better known?
11. In which sea can the vast sandbank Dogger Bank be found?
12. In England and Wales, which officer of the Crown is called in to inquire into the death of anyone who dies by an act of violence?
13. By what name is the SE coast of India between the Krishna Delta and Point Calimere usually known?
14. Which contemplative Roman Catholic religious order was founded in 1084 by St Bruno?
15. In the UK, which tax replaced profits tax in 1966?
16. Which Indonesian island is the largest of the Nusa Tenggara group?
17. What sort of plant is a saguaro?
18. In which city did the Peterloo Massacre take place?
19. Who was archbishop of Canterbury from 1070-1089?
20. In which ocean are the Line Islands situated?

ANSWERS: *1 The Louvre, 2 The Alps, 3 Sebastian Coe, 4 A snake, 5 Japan, 6 The Prince of Wales, 7 Moses, 8 Hyde Park, 9 Ultraheat-treated, 10 Buffalo Bill, 11 North Sea, 12 Coroner, 13 Coromandel Coast, 14 Carthusians, 15 Corporation tax, 16 Timor, 17 A cactus, 18 Manchester, 19 Lanfranc, 20 The Pacific Ocean.*

General Knowledge

Your rating: ● 0-5 Join a library ● 6-10 Keep at it ● 11-15 Join a quiz team ● 16-20 Join Mensa

1. Which unit of length is equal to 1760 yards?
2. The Mediterranean island of Corsica is a region of which country?
3. With which sport is W. G. Grace associated?
4. How is the International Criminal Police Organisation better known?
5. The St Bernard is a breed of which creature?
6. In which British city can the Isle of Dogs be found?
7. In which state of the USA are the ports of New Orleans and Baton Rouge situated?
8. Which subdivision of the Girl Guides Association is for girls aged between 7 and 10?
9. In the legal world, what does JP stand for?
10. Which Los Angeles suburb has been the centre of the US film industry since 1911?
11. Which official of the House of Lords summons members of the Commons by knocking on their door with his staff of office?
12. What is the capital of Costa Rica?
13. Who was the youngest daughter of Nicholas II of Russia?
14. Which British novelist wrote *Beau Geste*?
15. What sort of creature is a tinamou?
16. Who was the fourth wife of Henry VIII?
17. What is the largest of the Great Lakes?
18. What was the kingdom of the Serbs, Croats, and Slovenes formed in 1918 subsequently named?
19. Which golfing term describes a score of one stroke less than par on a particular hole?
20. At which Scottish resort was the famous Royal and Ancient Golf Club founded in 1754?

***ANSWERS:** 1 Mile, 2 France, 3 Cricket, 4 Interpol, 5 Dog, 6 London, 7 Louisiana, 8 Brownie Guides, 9 Justice of the peace, 10 Hollywood, 11 Black Rod, 12 San José, 13 Anastasia, 14 P. C. Wren, 15 A bird, 16 Anne of Cleves, 17 Lake Superior, 18 Yugoslavia, 19 Birdie, 20 St Andrews.*

General Knowledge

Your rating:
- **0-5 Join a library**
- **6-10 Keep at it**
- **11-15 Join a quiz team**
- **16-20 Join Mensa**

1. Which British dramatist, composer and actor wrote the play *Hay Fever* and the song *Mad Dogs and Englishmen*?
2. Which German composer wrote the opera *Fidelio*?
3. Which metal is the primary ingredient of the alloy bronze?
4. Which former peanut farmer was president of the USA from 1977 to 1981?
5. Which aviator brothers made the first powered and controlled flights on 17 December, 1903?
6. What sort of creature is a bull mastiff?
7. Which county has Exeter as its administrative centre?
8. Which English architect and scientist designed St Paul's Cathedral, where he is now buried?
9. Which science fiction writer and biochemist wrote the *Foundation Trilogy* and *I, Robot*?
10. Which French actress became one of the best-known sex symbols of the 1960s after her performance in the film *And God Created Woman*?
11. Which ancient city of Sumer is mentioned in Genesis as Abraham's homeland?
12. Of which US state is Helena the capital?
13. Which British cricketer captained England 27 times and played in 114 Test matches from 1950 to 1976?
14. Which Indian director helmed the films *Pather Panchali* and *The World of Apu*?
15. Which British show jumper won the European championships in 1961, 1967 and 1969?
16. Which Italian islet in the Tyrrhenian Sea features in the title of a novel by Dumas?
17. In which Italian port can the cathedral of San Lorenzo be found?
18. What sort of creature is a copperhead?
19. Which Irish author wrote *The Vicar of Wakefield* and *She Stoops to Conquer*?
20. Which jazz pianist is associated with *Take Five* and *Blue Rondo à la Turque*?

ANSWERS: *1 Noël Coward, 2 Ludwig van Beethoven, 3 Copper, 4 Jimmy Carter, 5 Orville and Wilbur Wright, 6 A dog, 7 Devon, 8 Sir Christopher Wren, 9 Isaac Asimov, 10 Brigitte Bardot, 11 Ur, 12 Montana, 13 Colin Cowdrey, 14 Satyajit Ray, 15 David Broome, 16 Monte Cristo, 17 Genoa, 18 A snake, 19 Oliver Goldsmith, 20 Dave Brubeck.*

Entertainment

Your rating:
- **0-5 Buy a TV**
- **6-10 Keep at it**
- **11-15 Join a quiz team**
- **16-20 Enter a quiz show**

1. Which comic actor made his directorial debut with the film *Harlem Nights*?
2. Which actor played former stripper Billy in TV's *Brazen Hussies*?
3. Which band had a number two hit single in 1979 with *Cool For Cats*?
4. In which country was the 1996 film *Mr Reliable* set?
5. Which Alex Haley saga about a black family was made into a successful Seventies TV series?
6. Which female vocalist recently released an album of remixes in 1996 entitled *Telegram*?
7. Which brothers starred as Jack and Frank in 1989's *The Fabulous Baker Boys*?
8. Which veteran broadcaster presented *Lives of Jesus* on TV?
9. Which US band had a top ten hit single in 1967 with *Daydream Believer*?
10. Who starred as the central character in the 1996 film *American Buffalo*?
11. Who starred in the title role of the 1996 period TV drama *Moll Flanders*?
12. Which group released an album entitled *Blue Is The Colour* in 1996?
13. Which character in BBC 1's *Hetty Wainthropp Investigates* was played by Dominic Monaghan?
14. Which film about the Boat Race was selected in 1996 for the 50th Royal Film Performance?
15. Which animated cartoon character always escaped the clutches of Wile E. Coyote?
16. Who had a top ten hit single in 1967 with *Waterloo Sunset*?
17. Who starred in the title role of the 1933 film *The Mummy*?
18. Which TV actors turned pop stars released an album entitled *Take Two* in 1996?
19. Which 1996 women's revenge comedy starred Diane Keaton, Goldie Hawn and Bette Midler?
20. Which BBC2 wine series was presented by Malcolm Gluck?

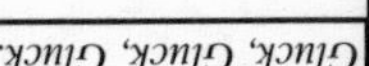

***ANSWERS:** 1 Eddie Murphy, 2 Robert Lindsay, 3 Squeeze, 4 Australia, 5 Roots, 6 Björk, 7 Jeff and Beau Bridges, 8 Mark Tully, 9 The Monkees, 10 Dustin Hoffman, 11 Alex Kingston, 12 The Beautiful South, 13 Geoffrey, 14 True Blue, 15 The Road Runner, 16 The Kinks, 17 Boris Karloff, 18 Robson and Jerome, 19 The First Wives Club, 20 Gluck, Gluck, Gluck.*

General Knowledge

Your rating: ● 0-5 Join a library ● 6-10 Keep at it ● 11-15 Join a quiz team ● 16-20 Join Mensa

1. Which US scientist invented the electric light bulb?
2. Of which ocean is the Coral Sea a section?
3. On which continent do aardvarks live in the wild?
4. In which London building are the British crown jewels kept?
5. Which British novelist wrote *A Clockwork Orange*?
6. Which county of SW England is known as Kernow in Celtic?
7. According to the Old Testament, in which garden were Adam and Eve created?
8. Which political party was led by Hugh Gaitskell from 1955 to 1963?
9. Which Soviet cosmonaut was the first person to orbit the earth?
10. Of which country is Burgundy a region?
11. Of which state of the USA is Columbia the capital?
12. Against which country did the UK wage the Cod Wars?
13. Which French poet and artist made his name with the novel *Les Enfants Terribles*?
14. In which year did the Spanish Civil War end?
15. Of which European country is St Stanislaw the patron saint?
16. What sort of creature is a stilt?
17. In which part of the body can the cochlea be found?
18. In Arthurian legend, which evil sorceress plotted the overthrow of her brother King Arthur?
19. Which word describes the reduction in the temperature of a liquid below its freezing point without its solidification?
20. Which Russian wrote *My Life in Art* and *An Actor Prepares*, which were later developed in the USA as "method" acting?

ANSWERS: *1 Thomas Edison, 2 The Pacific Ocean, 3 Africa, 4 The Tower of London, 5 Anthony Burgess, 6 Cornwall, 7 The Garden of Eden, 8 The Labour Party, 9 Yuri Gagarin, 10 France, 11 South Carolina, 12 Iceland, 13 Jean Cocteau, 14 1939, 15 Poland, 16 A bird, 17 The ear, 18 Morgan le Fay, 19 Supercooling, 20 Konstantin Stanislavsky.*

General Knowledge

Your rating: ● **0-5** Join a library ● **6-10** Keep at it ● **11-15** Join a quiz team ● **16-20** Join Mensa

1. Which British author wrote the *Just William* collection of stories?
2. What is the second largest city in Wales?
3. Who was vice president of the USA under Ronald Reagan?
4. What is the name of the implement used to hit the ball in a game of croquet?
5. Which piece of laboratory equipment did German chemist Robert Bunsen give his name to?
6. Which crooner who achieved worldwide fame during the 1930s and 1940s was born Harry Lillis Crosby?
7. Which football team did Matt Busby manage from 1946 to 1969?
8. On which island is the resort of Cowes situated?
9. Which 17th century British author wrote *The Pilgrim's Progress*?
10. A bunion can be found at the base of which digit?
11. Which European capital city is home to the Spanish Riding School?
12. Which British composer wrote the operas *Peter Grimes* and *Billy Budd*?
13. To which religion do the Sunnites belong?
14. Which Middlesex and England cricketer scored 18 centuries in the 1947 season?
15. Which small sultanate in NW Borneo has Bandar Seri Begawan as its capital?
16. Which canal builder constructed the Bridgewater Canal?
17. Which Hollywood actor starred in *The Virginian*, *The Westerner* and *High Noon*?
18. At which town was the first Scottish parliament held in 1326?
19. Who was the first president of Indonesia?
20. What was the family name of the dynasty which ruled Portugal from 1640 and Brazil from 1822 to 1889?

ANSWERS: *1 Richmal Crompton, 2 Swansea, 3 George Bush, 4 Mallet, 5 Bunsen burner, 6 Bing Crosby, 7 Manchester United, 8 The Isle of Wight, 9 John Bunyan, 10 The big toe, 11 Vienna, 12 Benjamin Britten, 13 Islam, 14 Denis Compton, 15 Brunei, 16 James Brindley, 17 Gary Cooper, 18 Stirling, 19 Sukarno, 20 Braganza or Braganza.*

General Knowledge

Your rating: ● **0-5** **Join a library** ● **6-10** **Keep at it** ● **11-15** **Join a quiz team** ● **16-20** **Join Mensa**

1. Which famous comet reappears every 76 years, its last appearance being in 1986?
2. Of which country is British Columbia the western most province?
3. How many people are needed to play the card game contract bridge?
4. Which device used for recording digital information is represented by the initials CD?
5. Which natural red dye is obtained from the dried bodies of certain Mexican insects?
6. On which river does Bristol lie?
7. Which British navigator discovered and charted New Zealand and the east coast of Australia in his ship the *Endeavour*?
8. Which British entrepreneur founded the Virgin record company in 1969 and later established an airline?
9. Which partnership wrote the comic operas *The Pirates of Penzance* and *The Yeomen of the Guard*?
10. Which instrument indicates the time by the direction or length of the shadow cast by an indicator mounted on a calibrated scale?
11. Which chalk escarpment extends NE from the Goring Gap, reaching 255 metres at Coombe Hill?
12. Which Italian nun was proclaimed patron saint of television in 1958?
13. Which Hollywood actress who starred in *Trading Places* became Lady Haden-Guest?
14. Which hard grey transition metal is represented by the symbol Cr?
15. Which British novelist wrote *Roderick Random* and *Peregrine Pickle*?
16. At which battle did Henry Tudor defeat Richard III, thereby ending the Wars of the Roses?
17. In which country did the Boxer Rising of 1900 take place?
18. Which British motor-racing driver was world champion in 1963 and 1965?
19. Which non-metallic element is represented by the symbol B?
20. Which Scottish philosopher and economist published *An Enquiry into the Nature and Causes of the Wealth of Nations* in 1776?

ANSWERS: *1 Halley's Comet, 2 Canada, 3 Four, 4 Compact disc, 5 Cochineal, 6 The River Avon, 7 Captain James Cook, 8 Richard Branson, 9 Gilbert and Sullivan, 10 Sundial, 11 The Chiltern Hills, 12 St Clare of Assisi, 13 Jamie Lee Curtis, 14 Chromium, 15 Tobias Smollett, 16 The Battle of Bosworth Field, 17 China, 18 Jim Clark, 19 Boron, 20 Adam Smith.*

Entertainment

Your rating: ● **0-5 Buy a TV** ● **6-10 Keep at it** ● **11-15 Join a quiz team** ● **16-20 Enter a quiz show**

1. Which popular science TV programme was first screened in 1957 and can still be seen on BBC1?
2. Who had a Christmas number one hit single in 1972 with *Long-Haired Lover from Liverpool*?
3. Which 1993 Merchant-Ivory film starred Anthony Hopkins and Emma Thompson as a butler and a housekeeper?
4. Who was named the 1996 BBC Sports Personality of the Year?
5. Who had a Christmas number one hit single in 1974 with *Lonely This Christmas*?
6. Who starred as Captain Jean-Luc Picard in the 1996 film *Star Trek: First Contact*?
7. Which satirical TV programme of the 1960s was familiarly known as *TW3*?
8. Which country music star released an album entitled *The Gift* in 1996?
9. Who starred as the orphaned teenager in the 1978 film *International Velvet*?
10. On which day of the week was *Breakfast with Frost* broadcast?
11. Which British animator won an Oscar for his 1993 short film *The Wrong Trousers*?
12. Who played Maxine Heavey in *Coronation Street*?
13. Which female vocalist released an album entitled *Stardust* in 1996?
14. Who starred as the attorney/matchmaker in the 1963 film *For Love Or Money*?
15. Who was Dick Martin's straight-man and co-host of TV's *Laugh-In*?
16. Which British singer connects the Seventies band Vinegar Joe and the Eighties band The Power Station?
17. Which 1996 Christmas film starred Arnold Schwarzenegger as a busy Minnesota businessman?
18. Which Friday-night Channel 4 show was written, shot and edited by its presenters from their Brixton bedsit?
19. Which 1996 Chris Rea album featured a collaboration with Shirley Bassey?
20. Which 1953 film starring Marilyn Monroe and Jane Russell featured the song *Diamonds Are a Girl's Best Friend*?

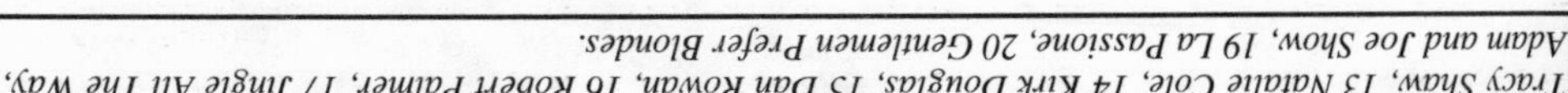

General Knowledge

Your rating:
- 0-5 Join a library
- 6-10 Keep at it
- 11-15 Join a quiz team
- 16-20 Join Mensa

1. What is the name of the sequel to Milton's *Paradise Lost*?
2. Which avant-garde New York rock group featured Lou Reed and John Cale?
3. Whose vice-president was Richard Nixon?
4. Of which group of islands is Espiritu Santo the largest?
5. What position would we call that of the Taoiseach?
6. Which British tennis-player won the 1994 Korean Open?
7. By what name do we know the spider *Latrodectus mactans*?
8. Who became Poet Laureate in 1999?
9. Which former Bishop of London has become a Roman Catholic priest?
10. In which African country is Abuja?
11. Goths were divided into Visigoths and which other group?
12. What was founded in 1920 as the second English garden city?
13. In Christianity and Judaism, what are the highest order of angels called?
14. Which poet won the 1948 Nobel prize for literature?
15. Which clan conspired with the English in the Glencoe massacre?
16. Where was the British Unknown Soldier buried in 1920?
17. Of what is stinkhorn a species?
18. Which incendiary liquid is a mixture of naphthenic and palmitic acids?
19. What is the oldest British university?
20. What is the hybrid between a blackberry and a raspberry called?

ANSWERS: *1 Paradise Regained, 2 Velvet Underground, 3 Dwight Eisenhower, 4 Vanuatu, 5 Prime Minister (of Ireland), 6 Jeremy Bates, 7 Black Widow, 8 Andrew Motion, 9 Dr Graham Leonard, 10 Nigeria, 11 Ostrogoths, 12 Welwyn Garden City, 13 Seraphim, 14 TS Eliot, 15 Campbells, 16 Westminster Abbey, 17 Fungus, 18 Napalm, 19 Oxford, 20 Loganberry.*

General Knowledge

Your rating: ● 0-5 Join a library ● 6-10 Keep at it ● 11-15 Join a quiz team ● 16-20 Join Mensa

1. At which sport was Australian Jack Brabham world champion in 1959, 1960 and 1966?
2. In which county is the city of Southampton situated?
3. Which French singer and actor was born Varenagh Aznavourian?
4. How is the clavicle commonly known?
5. What is the official currency unit of South Africa?
6. Auckland is the largest city of which country?
7. In Spain, what is equivalent to 100 céntimos?
8. Which green pigment present in organisms is capable of photosynthesis?
9. Which queen of Egypt was famous as the mistress of Julius Caesar and then of Mark Antony?
10. In which U.S. state was Muhammad Ali born in 1942?
11. Which insect transmits sleeping sickness?
12. Who was the father of Bonnie Prince Charlie?
13. Which British actress played elderly eccentrics in the films *Murder She Said* and *The VIPs*?
14. Of which African country is Luanda the capital?
15. Which South American soldier and statesman was Bolivia named in honour of?
16. Which river is known as Tevere in Italy?
17. In which African country is the port of Tobruk?
18. What is recorded by means of a sphygmomanometer?
19. What sort of creature is a slowworm?
20. Which British dramatist wrote *A Man For All Seasons*?

ANSWERS: *1 Motor-racing, 2 Hampshire, 3 Charles Aznavour, 4 Collar bone, 5 The rand, 6 New Zealand, 7 One peseta, 8 Chlorophyll, 9 Cleopatra, 10 Kentucky, 11 Tsetse fly, 12 James Edward Stuart, 13 Dame Margaret Rutherford, 14 Angola, 15 Simón Bolívar, 16 Tiber, 17 Libya, 18 Blood pressure, 19 A lizard, 20 Robert Bolt.*

General Knowledge

Your rating: ● **0-5** **Join a library** ● **6-10** **Keep at it**
● **11-15** **Join a quiz team** ● **16-20** **Join Mensa**

1. Which greenish poisonous halogen gas is represented by the symbol Cl?
2. Of which African country is Gaborone the capital?
3. Which pop singer famous for *Ziggy Stardust* was born David Jones?
4. Which county cricket team did Geoffrey Boycott play for from 1962 to 1986?
5. Which country was ruled by Kemal Atatürk from 1923 to 1938?
6. What sort of creature is a Bombay duck?
7. What is the name for the mass of nervous tissue that lies within the skull and is ensheathed by three membranes?
8. What is the capital of Bosnia and Hercegovina?
9. How many holes are in a standard tenpin bowling ball?
10. Which British explorer and journalist was sent by the New York Herald in 1871 to search for David Livingstone in Africa?
11. Of which African country is Kigali the capital?
12. In the world of broadcasting, what do the initials AM stand for?
13. Which Paris-born actress starred in *It Happened One Night*?
14. What sort of creature is a minivet?
15. According to Greek legend, which ferryman carried the souls of the dead over the Rivers Styx and Acheron?
16. Which English composer wrote the opera *Dido and Aeneas*?
17. Which state of the USA has Jackson as its capital?
18. Which transition metal is represented by the symbol Ti?
19. Which cold dry northerly wind is funnelled down the Rhône Valley in southern France to the Mediterranean Sea?
20. Who was president of the Soviet Union from 1984 to 1985?

ANSWERS: *1 Chlorine, 2 Botswana, 3 David Bowie, 4 Yorkshire, 5 Turkey, 6 A fish, 7 The brain, 8 Sarajevo, 9 Three, 10 Sir Henry Morton Stanley, 11 Rwanda, 12 Amplitude modulation, 13 Claudette Colbert , 14 A bird, 15 Charon, 16 Henry Purcell, 17 Mississippi, 18 Titanium, 19 The mistral, 20 Konstantin Chernenko.*

Entertainment

Your rating: ● **0-5** Buy a TV ● **6-10** Keep at it ● **11-15** Join a quiz team ● **16-20** Enter a quiz show

1. What was the title of the 1988 U.K. number one hit by Enya?
2. Which 2000 film featuring David Arquette and Oliver Platt was set in the world of wrestling?
3. Which *Star Trek* actor played disguise expert Paris in the Seventies TV series *Mission: Impossible*?
4. What was the title of the Backstreet Boys' fourth album, released in 2000?
5. Which actress starred in the title role of the 1985 film *Marie*?
6. Which *EastEnders*' character's business empire collapsed when he was declared bankrupt in 2000?
7. What was the title of Christina Aguilera's 2000 festive album release?
8. Who wrote the novel upon which the BBC 1 drama series *Take A Girl Like You* was based?
9. Which actor played *The Grinch* in the 2000 film of that name?
10. In which drama series did Michelle Collins play Kathy, a housewife-turned-armed robber?
11. Which children's TV character had the U.K. Christmas number one in 2000 with *Can We Fix It*?
12. Which TV family lived on a smallholding in Walnut Grove, Plum Creek, Minnesota?
13. Who directed and starred in the 1984 film *Harry & Son*?
14. Which flamboyant U.S. pianist successfully sued the Daily Mirror in 1959?
15. Which British actress played Woody Allen's wife in his 2000 film *Small Time Crooks*?
16. What was the Nashville Teens' biggest hit, which reached number six in the U.K. charts in 1964?
17. What was the venue for *Miss World 2000*, screened by Channel 5?
18. Which British group had a U.K. number one hit in 1963 with *Do You Love Me*?
19. Which 1984 film starred Jon Cryer and Demi Moore?
20. Which Beatles track provided Candy Flip with a 1990 U.K. top five single?

ANSWERS: *1 Orinoco Flow, 2 Ready to Rumble, 3 Leonard Nimoy, 4 Black & Blue, 5 Sissy Spacek, 6 Ian Beale's, 7 My Kind of Christmas, 8 Kingsley Amis, 9 Jim Carrey, 10 Daylight Robbery, 11 Bob the Builder, 12 The Ingalls of Little House on the Prairie, 13 Paul Newman, 14 Liberace, 15 Tracey Ullman, 16 Tobacco Road, 17 The Millennium Dome, 18 Brian Poole & the Tremeloes, 19 No Small Affair, 20 Strawberry Fields Forever.*

General Knowledge

Your rating: ● 0-5 Join a library ● 6-10 Keep at it ● 11-15 Join a quiz team ● 16-20 Join Mensa

1. Which Brazilian racing driver was killed at Imola in 1994?
2. What is the capital of Argentina?
3. Which novelist wrote *The Young Caesar* and *The Aerodrome*?
4. Who was the first female swimmer to win gold medals in three successive Olympics?
5. Which of the gifts brought by the Magi is also known as olibanum?
6. In which sport are Lonsdale Belts awarded?
7. Which film was advertised with the publicity line – "Weird is relative"?
8. Which American singer is known as the Queen of Soul?
9. Who was the king of the fairies in Shakespeare's *A Midsummer Night's Dream*?
10. Which Italian actress was born Sofia Scicolone?
11. Who played nurse Hilda Price in *General Hospital*?
12. Which well-known nursery rhyme was written by U.S. poet Sarah Josepha Hale in 1830?
13. Who played Cathy to Laurence Olivier's Heathcliff in the 1939 film *Wuthering Heights*?
14. Which British tennis player won the Copenhagen Open in 2001?
15. In which New Mexico city was the atomic bomb developed in the Manhattan Project?
16. Which canal extends 36 miles from Eastham on Merseyside?
17. Who is the heroine of *Far from the Madding Crowd* by Thomas Hardy?
18. Which English conductor founded the Academy of St Martin-in-the-Fields?
19. To which English king was Margaret of Anjou queen?
20. Which bird is known as a loon in North America?

ANSWERS: *1 Ayrton Senna, 2 Buenos Aires, 3 Rex Warner, 4 Dawn Fraser, 5 Frankincense, 6 Boxing, 7 The Addams Family, 8 Aretha Franklin, 9 Oberon, 10 Sophia Loren, 11 Linda Bellingham, 12 Mary Had a Little Lamb, 13 Merle Oberon, 14 Tim Henman, 15 Los Alamos, 16 Manchester Ship Canal, 17 Bathsheba Everdene, 18 Neville Marriner, 19 Henry VI, 20 Diver.*

General Knowledge

Your rating: ● **0-5 Join a library** ● **6-10 Keep at it** ● **11-15 Join a quiz team** ● **16-20 Join Mensa**

1. Which prayer is also called *Pater Noster* or *Our Father*?
2. Which American television series won eight Emmy Awards in 1995?
3. Which highly infectious disease of animals was discovered in Britain in 2001 for the first time in twenty years?
4. Marie Byrd Land is an unclaimed region of which continent?
5. Which Asian city hosted the 1988 Olympics?
6. In which country did frankfurters originate?
7. What nationality was the novelist Jeppe Aakjaer?
8. Of which country was General Franco head of state?
9. Which county is known as 'the Garden of England'?
10. On which river does Paris stand?
11. What was the title of the theme tune of *Minder*?
12. Which American dramatist wrote the play *Waiting for Lefty*?
13. Who played Lieutenant Norman Buntz in *Hill Street Blues*?
14. Which Japanese detective did Peter Lorre play in a series of films?
15. In which U.S. state is Kent State University?
16. Which French novelist wrote *Bonjour Tristesse*?
17. The film *Anne of the Indies* was about a female pirate known as what?
18. Which German astronomer discovered the three principles of planetary motion?
19. What was the first name of FBI agent Starling in the films *Silence of the Lambs* and *Hannibal*?
20. Which Disney film features the voices of John Goodman and

ANSWERS: *1 Lord's Prayer, 2 ER, 3 Foot-and-mouth, 4 Antarctica, 5 Seoul, 6 Germany, 7 Danish, 8 Spain, 9 Kent, 10 River Seine, 11 I Could Be So Good For You, 12 Clifford Odets, 13 Dennis Franz, 14 Mr Moto, 15 Ohio, 16 Françoise Sagan, 17 Captain Providence, 18 Johannes Kepler, 19 Clarice, 20 The Emperor's New Groove.*

General Knowledge

Your rating: ● 0-5 Join a library ● 6-10 Keep at it ● 11-15 Join a quiz team ● 16-20 Join Mensa

1. Which character in the Old Testament derived his strength from his long hair?
2. In which borough of New York City are Wall Street and Broadway?
3. What was the name of the bear in television's *The Life and Times of Grizzly Adams*?
4. What is the surname of the star of the sitcom *Ellen*?
5. Which former Wimbledon champion died of AIDS in 1993?
6. In which English county is Bodmin?
7. Which novel is subtitled *The Memoirs of a Woman of Pleasure*?
8. Which former world heavyweight boxing champion was known as 'Smokin' Joe'?
9. Who was the leader of the reggae group The Wailers?
10. What is the standard unit of currency of France?
11. Which French composer wrote the opera *Lakmé*?
12. Who played Juliet in John Gielgud's celebrated 1935 production of *Romeo and Juliet*?
13. Of which novel by Jane Austen is Anne Elliot the heroine?
14. Who led the British Labour Party from 1931 to 1935?
15. Which assault rifle adopted by the U.S. Army in 1967 is also called AR-15?
16. From which English king's visit did Bognor Regis derive its royal suffix?
17. Which 2001 film starred Kevin Spacey, Helen Hunt and Haley Joel Osment?
18. The title of the film *Fifteen Minutes* is a reference to a famous quote by Andy Warhol about what?
19. Which American dramatist wrote *Who's Afraid of Virginia Woolf*?
20. In which Scottish city is Marischal College?

ANSWERS: *1 Samson, 2 Manhattan, 3 Ben, 4 DeGeneres, 5 Arthur Ashe, 6 Cornwall, 7 Fanny Hill, 8 Joe Frazier, 9 Bob Marley, 10 Franc, 11 Leo Delibes, 12 Peggy Ashcroft, 13 Persuasion, 14 George Lansbury, 15 M16 rifle, 16 George V, 17 Pay It Forward, 18 Fame, 19 Edward Albee, 20 Aberdeen.*

Entertainment

Your rating:
- 0-5 Buy a TV
- 6-10 Keep at it
- 11-15 Join a quiz team
- 16-20 Enter a quiz show

1. Which 2000 film starring Val Kilmer was based around a expedition to Mars?
2. What was the name of Roddy McDowall's chimpanzee character in the TV series *The Planet of the Apes*?
3. Which British singer had a U.K. top five hit in 2000 with *Supreme*?
4. What condition does Dustin Hoffman's character suffer from in the 1988 film *Rain Man*?
5. Which soap celebrated its 40th birthday in December 2000?
6. Which children's TV characters had a U.K. top ten hit in 2000 with *Number 1*?
7. Which actress reprised her role as Cruella De Vil in the 2000 film sequel *102 Dalmatians*?
8. Which actor/comedian provided the narration for the TV series *The Wombles*?
9. Which 1990 film starred Tim Robbins as a Vietnam veteran?
10. In which year did Texas have a U.K. top ten hit with *I Don't Want A Lover*?
11. In which 2000 film did Johnny Depp appear as a gypsy called Cesar?
12. Which *EastEnders* character was sent to prison in 2000 for being in contempt of court?
13. Which British duo had a U.K. top five hit with *Sowing the Seeds of Love* in 1989?
14. Which 1988 Alan Parker film starred Gene Hackman and Willem Dafoe as FBI agents?
15. What nationality was *Emmerdale*'s Joe, who married Tricia in 2000 in order to escape deportation?
16. What was the title of Diana Ross' 1971 U.K. number one hit?
17. Who directed the 2000 film satire *Cecil B. Demented*?
18. What was the alter ego of *Wonder Woman* in the TV series?
19. Who won a Best Actor Oscar for his performance as reporter Mike Connor in the 1940 film *The Philadelphia Story*?
20. Which Australian singer had a 2000 U.K. top ten hit with *Please Stay*?

ANSWERS: *1 Red Planet, 2 Galen, 3 Robbie Williams, 4 Autism, 5 Coronation Street, 6 Tweenies, 7 Glenn Close, 8 Bernard Cribbins, 9 Jacob's Ladder, 10 1989, 11 The Man Who Cried, 12 Dot Cotton, 13 Tears For Fears, 14 Mississippi Burning, 15 Australian, 16 I'm Still Waiting, 17 John Waters, 18 Diana Prince, 19 James Stewart, 20 Kylie Minogue.*

General Knowledge

Your rating: • 0-5 Join a library • 6-10 Keep at it • 11-15 Join a quiz team • 16-20 Join Mensa

1. Which member of the Kennedy family drove his car off a bridge in 1969?
2. What is the profession of the character played by Bob Hope in the film *The Paleface*?
3. Which glamorous Hollywood couple announced their separation after 11 years of marriage in February 2001?
4. What nationality were most of the pop group Abba?
5. Which singer was billed as 'the Last of the Red Hot Mamas'?
6. In which English county is Mansfield?
7. Who created the blind detective Max Carrados?
8. In the Old Testament, who was the second son of Adam and Eve?
9. From which country does Frascati wine come?
10. In which English county is Looe?
11. Which English novelist wrote *The Children of the New Forest*?
12. What was the first Sunday newspaper published in Britain?
13. *Let the River Run* was the 1988 Oscar-winning song from which film?
14. On which Thomas Hardy novel is the film *The Claim* based?
15. Which fibrous protein is found in hair, nails, horns, hoofs and skin?
16. What was the first name of the founder of Lord's Cricket Ground?
17. Which chemical element has the symbol Se?
18. What was the occupation of *Clarence* in the 1988 sitcom?
19. Which English logician and philosopher wrote *The Principles of Mathematics* in 1903?
20. Against which king was the Rye House Plot directed?

ANSWERS: *1 Teddy Kennedy, 2 Dentist, 3 Tom Cruise and Nicole Kidman, 4 Swedish, 5 Sophie Tucker, 6 Nottinghamshire, 7 Ernest Bramah, 8 Abel, 9 Italy, 10 Cornwall, 11 Frederick Marryat, 12 The Observer, 13 Working Girl, 14 The Mayor of Casterbridge, 15 Keratin, 16 Thomas, 17 Selenium, 18 Removals man, 19 Bertrand Russell, 20 Charles II.*

General Knowledge

Your rating: ● 0-5 Join a library ● 6-10 Keep at it ● 11-15 Join a quiz team ● 16-20 Join Mensa

1. What name is given to the Saturday before Easter Sunday?
2. What nickname was given to any one of four large German guns produced by the Krupp works in World War I?
3. Who played *Little Lord Fauntleroy* in the 1921 film?
4. What is the name of the hero of *The Pilgrim's Progress*?
5. In which novel by George du Maurier does the character Svengali appear?
6. What part of an egg is also called deutoplasm?
7. Which singer picked up three awards at the 2001 Brits?
8. What relation is Smike to *Nicholas Nickleby* in the Dickens novel?
9. What is the first name of the star of the TV sitcom *Seinfeld*?
10. Which planet is known as the Red Planet?
11. Which island is also called Rapa Nui and Isla de Pascua?
12. Who played bashful bachelor David in the televison series *A Life of Bliss*?
13. Which actor plays William Forrester in the film *Finding Forrester*?
14. What name is given to a tree of the genus *Taxus*?
15. Which sparrow is also called a dunnock?
16. What is the only form of gambling permitted in the British armed forces?
17. Which actress became a star after playing an Amazon princess in 1932?
18. Which former Kent and England left-handed batsman took 1,018 first-class catches?
19. What is the name of Katharina's younger sister in Shakespeare's *The Taming of the Shrew*?
20. Of which U.S. state is Frankfort the capital?

ANSWERS: *1 Holy Saturday, 2 Big Bertha, 3 Mary Pickford, 4 Christian, 5 Trilby, 6 Yolk, 7 Robbie Williams, 8 Cousin, 9 Jerry, 10 Mars, 11 Easter Island, 12 George Cole, 13 Sean Connery, 14 Yew, 15 Hedge sparrow, 16 Bingo, 17 Katharine Hepburn, 18 Frank Woolley, 19 Bianca, 20 Kentucky.*

General Knowledge

Your rating: ● **0-5** **Join a library** ● **6-10** **Keep at it** ● **11-15** **Join a quiz team** ● **16-20** **Join Mensa**

1. Which atoll in the Marshall Islands gave its name to a form of swimwear?
2. In children's television programme *The Hoobs* what are Tiddlypeeps?
3. Which actor and rapper plays the title role in the film *The Legend of Bagger Vance*?
4. What is the first name of Dr Frankenstein in Mary Shelley's novel?
5. Which joint is formed by the meeting of the humerus, radius and ulna?
6. By what name was Haitian president François Duvalier known?
7. Who directed *Batman Forever*?
8. Dry ice is a solid form of which gas?
9. Which character in Greek mythology is also known as Ulysses?
10. Which Oscar-winning actor played Coach Boone in the film *Remember the Titans*?
11. To which Robert Louis Stevenson novel is *Catriona* the sequel?
12. Which state unilaterally declared independence from Nigeria in May 1967?
13. What is the subtitle of Dvorák's *Symphony No 9 in E minor*?
14. Which rugby team won the 2001 Tetley's Bitter Cup?
15. In which English county is the town of Bicester?
16. Which Irish novelist wrote *At Swim-Two-Birds*?
17. In the film *Men of Honour* Cuba Gooding Jnr plays what?
18. Which Hebrew prophet picked up the mantle as successor to Elijah?
19. John Dryden's *All For Love* is a reworking of which Shakespeare play?
20. Which U2 song won three Grammy awards in 2001?

ANSWERS: *1 Bikini, 2 Children, 3 Will Smith, 4 Victor, 5 Elbow, 6 Papa Doc, 7 Joel Schumacher, 8 Carbon dioxide, 9 Odysseus, 10 Denzel Washington, 11 Kidnapped, 12 Biafra, 13 From the New World, 14 Newcastle, 15 Oxfordshire, 16 Flann O'Brien, 17 A navy diver, 18 Elisha, 19 Antony and Cleopatra, 20 Beautiful Day.*

Entertainment

Your rating: ● **0-5 Buy a TV** ● **6-10 Keep at it** ● **11-15 Join a quiz team** ● **16-20 Enter a quiz show**

1. Which character's son returned to Weatherfield in the live episode celebrating *Coronation Street*'s 40th birthday in 2000?
2. Which British actor starred as a private-eye hired to find a long-lost daughter in the 1975 film *Peeper*?
3. Which five-times Olympic gold medallist was named BBC Sports Personality of the Year 2000?
4. Which boy band had a U.K. top five hit with *What Makes A Man* in 2000?
5. In which BBC 1 drama series did Amanda Burton star as pathologist Professor Sam Ryan?
6. Who played Ben Stiller's prospective father-in-law in the 2000 film *Meet the Parents*?
7. What was Lucy's married name in the classic sitcom *I Love Lucy*?
8. Which actor narrates the audio versions of the Harry Potter books?
9. Which 1976 film featured Dustin Hoffman and Roy Scheider as brothers?
10. Which 2000 album featured soul covers including Samantha Mumba's version of *Signed, Sealed, Delivered (I'm Yours)*?
11. Which 2000 film saw Arnold Schwarzenegger coming face to face with his clone?
12. With whom did Janet Jackson duet on the 1995 U.K. top five hit *Scream*?
13. Which actress played the title role in the 1972 film *Mary, Queen of Scots*?
14. What was the title of George McCraie's 1974 U.K. number one hit?
15. Which former *Big Brother* contestant presented the game show *Trust Me* on Channel 4?
16. Which former Beatle had a U.K. top five hit in 1972 with *Back Off Boogaloo*?
17. Which actor played the title role in the 2000 film version of *Hamlet*?
18. In the former detective drama series *Midnight Caller*, what was phone-in host Jack Killian's nickname?
19. Which country singer/songwriter released the album *Tomorrow's Sounds Today* in 2000?
20. In which city is the 1957 film *The Prince and the Showgirl* set?

ANSWERS: *1 Ken Barlow's, 2 Michael Caine, 3 Steve Redgrave, 4 Westlife, 5 Silent Witness, 6 Robert De Niro, 7 Ricardo, 8 Stephen Fry, 9 Marathon Man, 10 Motown Mania, 11 The 6th Day, 12 Michael Jackson, 13 Vanessa Redgrave, 14 Rock Your Baby, 15 Nick Bateman, 16 Ringo Starr, 17 Ethan Hawke, 18 Nighthawk, 19 Dwight Yoakam, 20 London.*

General Knowledge

Your rating:
- 0-5 Join a library
- 6-10 Keep at it
- 11-15 Join a quiz team
- 16-20 Join Mensa

1. Which queen was the daughter of Henry VIII and Anne Boleyn?
2. Who played a nun in the film *All About My Mother*?
3. Which British singer duetted with Eminem at the 2001 Grammy Awards?
4. Who became the youngest winner of a world-ranking snooker tournament when he won the 1993 U.K. championship?
5. By what first name was Emad Mohamed al-Fayed known?
6. What does the 'e' stand for in e-mail?
7. *The Roman Hat Mystery* was the first novel to feature which fictional detective?
8. By what name was Wild West gunfighter William H. Bonney known?
9. Which English novelist wrote *The Mill on the Floss*?
10. What is the nickname of the 13-ton bell in the clock tower of the Houses of Parliament?
11. Where was the television series *The Lotus Eaters* set?
12. Which king led England into the Hundred Years' War with France?
13. What was Ronnie Hilton's only number one hit in Britain?
14. Which South African political activist died from head injuries suffered in police custody in 1977?
15. *An Angel at My Table* is an autobiographical work by which New Zealand author?
16. What name is given to the first part of the small intestine?
17. Which was allegedly the favourite film of Joseph Stalin?
18. Who sculpted the statue of Peter Pan in Kensington Gardens?
19. Which U.S. author wrote *An Occurrence at Owl Creek Bridge*?
20. Which rare-earth metal has the chemical symbol Dy?

ANSWERS: *1 Elizabeth I, 2 Penelope Cruz, 3 Sir Elton John, 4 Ronnie O'Sullivan, 5 Dodi, 6 Electronic, 7 Ellery Queen, 8 Billy the Kid, 9 George Eliot, 10 Big Ben, 11 Crete, 12 Edward III, 13 No Other Love, 14 Stephen Biko, 15 Janet Frame, 16 Duodenum, 17 Volga Volga, 18 Sir George Frampton, 19 Ambrose Bierce, 20 Dysprosium.*

General Knowledge

Your rating:
- **0-5 Join a library**
- **6-10 Keep at it**
- **11-15 Join a quiz team**
- **16-20 Join Mensa**

1. Which English composer wrote five *Pomp and Circumstance* marches?
2. What was the name of the pet space monkey in *Lost In Space*?
3. Which football team beat Birmingham City on penalties to win the 2001 Worthington Cup?
4. After whom is the month July named?
5. Which Irish poet wrote *The Lake Isle of Innisfree*?
6. What name is given to any muscle with two heads?
7. In which country is Graham Greene's novel *The Comedians* set?
8. What nickname was given to the bicycle designed by James Starley in 1870?
9. Which great Australian batsman died in 2001 at the age of 92?
10. What name for a tea container is a corruption of the Malay weight kati?
11. What was the top grossing film in 1998 in America?
12. Which port is the capital of Spain's Biscay (or Vizcaya) province?
13. Who led a rebellion against Henry VI in 1450?
14. Which actor received an Academy Fellowship at the 2001 BAFTAs?
15. What does someone suffering from dysphagia have difficulty doing?
16. Which cartoon character created by Chic Young married Dagwood Bumstead?
17. Who is the native referred to in the title of Thomas Hardy's *The Return of the Native*?
18. Who was the first athlete to win two Olympic marathons?
19. Which boxer became the oldest-ever world heavyweight champion in 1994?
20. Who wrote the lyrics of the song *Three Coins in a Fountain*?

ANSWERS: *1 Sir Edward Elgar, 2 The Bloop, 3 Liverpool, 4 Julius Caesar, 5 W B Yeats, 6 Biceps, 7 Haiti, 8 Penny-farthing, 9 Sir Donald Bradman, 10 Caddy, 11 Saving Private Ryan, 12 Bilbao, 13 Jack Cade, 14 Albert Finney, 15 Swallowing, 16 Blondie, 17 Clym Yeobright, 18 Abebe Bikila, 19 George Foreman, 20 Sammy Cahn.*

General Knowledge

Your rating:
- 0-5 Join a library
- 6-10 Keep at it
- 11-15 Join a quiz team
- 16-20 Join Mensa

1. Which screen legend played Bottom in a 1935 film version of *A Midsummer Night's Dream*?
2. In which English city is the National Railway Museum?
3. Which Charles Dickens novel is dedicated to Thomas Carlyle?
4. How many feet are there in a yard?
5. Which winter sports event combines cross-country skiing and rifle shooting?
6. What was U.S. president Eisenhower's first name?
7. What were *The Zoo Gang* on television?
8. In which European country is the resort of Biarritz?
9. What does the abbreviation FBI stand for?
10. Which channel between Spain and Africa connects the Mediterranean Sea with the Atlantic Ocean?
11. Which film actor died on 2 February 1996?
12. Which American poet wrote the verse collection *Leaves of Grass*?
13. What name is given to the fatty substance released by sebaceous glands?
14. Which team did England beat in Sven-Göran Eriksson's first game as England coach?
15. What is a jingling Johnny?
16. Which American football legend was called the 'Gipper'?
17. What sort of creature is Akela in Rudyard Kipling's *The Jungle Book*?
18. Which star of the film *Billy Elliot* won the Best Actor award at the 2001 BAFTAs?
19. Which group picked up the 2001 Brit Awards for Best British Group and Best British Album?
20. What sort of creature is a whydah?

ANSWERS: *1 James Cagney, 2 York, 3 Hard Times, 4 Three, 5 Biathlon, 6 Dwight, 7 French Resistance fighters, 8 France, 9 Federal Bureau of Investigation, 10 Strait of Gibraltar, 11 Gene Kelly, 12 Walt Whitman, 13 Sebum, 14 Spain, 15 A musical instrument, 16 George Gipp, 17 Wolf, 18 Jamie Bell, 19 Coldplay, 20 A bird.*

Sports

Your rating: ● 0-5 Wooden spoon ● 6-10 Bronze medal ● 11-15 Silver medal ● 16-20 Gold medal

1. Who captained the Continental European team to victory in the inaugural golf competition for the trophy that bears his name?
2. Which Japanese city hosted the 1998 Winter Olympics?
3. Who was the first man to win both the 200m and 400m gold medals at the same Olympic Games?
4. Butch Harmon and David Leadbetter are top coaches in which sport?
5. Where does the Great North Run half-marathon begin?
6. Which U.S. tennis player triumphed in the women's singles and doubles competitions at the Sydney Olympics, adding two gold medals to her trophy cabinet?
7. Which football team plays at Carrow Road?
8. What number shirt does a hooker traditionally wear in rugby union?
9. Who beat Jim Courier in the final to win Wimbledon in 1993?
10. On which course did Nick Faldo win the British Open in 1990?
11. Which team won the 2000 Worthington Cup?
12. How many tries did England score in their 80-23 win over Italy in February 2001?
13. Which country won seven gold medals in boxing at the 1992 Olympics?
14. Who was the European footballer of the year in 1968?
15. Which golfer won the U.S. Open in 1994 and 1997?
16. Which boxer took 243 seconds to dispose of British champion Julius Francis in a much-hyped fight in January 2000?
17. Who won the gold medal in the 100m breaststroke event at the 1988 Olympics?
18. Which British stadium hosted the final of the 1976 European Cup?
19. What is the value of the brown ball in snooker?
20. What nationality is footballer Paolo Di Canio?

***ANSWERS:** 1 Severiano Ballesteros, 2 Nagano, 3 Michael Johnson, 4 Golf, 5 Newcastle, 6 Venus Williams, 7 Norwich City, 8 2, 9 Pete Sampras, 10 St Andrews, 11 Leicester City, 12 10, 13 Cuba, 14 George Best, 15 Ernie Els, 16 Mike Tyson, 17 Adrian Moorhouse, 18 Hampden Park, 19 Four, 20 Italian.*

General Knowledge

Your rating:
- 0-5 Join a library
- 6-10 Keep at it
- 11-15 Join a quiz team
- 16-20 Join Mensa

1. Which American comedienne married Desi Arnaz in 1940?
2. What name is given to the promontory of basalt columns on the coast of Antrim in Northern Ireland?
3. What was the family business in the television series *The Brothers*?
4. Who won the first Grand Prix of the 2001 Formula 1 season in Melbourne?
5. Which acute respiratory disease is also called pertussis?
6. What is the surname of the members of The Bee Gees?
7. What is the surname of the character played by Colin Firth in the film *Bridget Jones's Diary*?
8. Which tower in Chicago became the world's tallest building in 1973?
9. What name was given to a chair that was carried on poles?
10. Who was known as the 'Maid of Orléans'?
11. Who wrote *The Moon and Sixpence*?
12. Which American engineer invented the cotton gin?
13. In the Old Testament, which military commander under King David killed Absalom?
14. Which 2001 film starred Juliette Binoche, Leslie Caron, Johnny Depp and Dame Judi Dench?
15. What name is given to a holy war waged on behalf of Islam as a religious duty?
16. Which animal was called camelopardalis or spotted camel by the Romans?
17. Which Jane Austen novel begins "It is a truth universally acknowledged that a single man in possession of a good fortune must be in want of a wife"?
18. Which Russian dramatist wrote *The Seagull*?
19. On which river does Cheltenham stand?
20. Which American Beat poet wrote *Howl*?

ANSWERS: *1 Lucille Ball, 2 Giant's Causeway, 3 Haulage, 4 Michael Schumacher, 5 Whooping cough, 6 Gibb, 7 Darcy, 8 Sears Tower, 9 Sedan chair, 10 Joan of Arc, 11 W Somerset Maugham, 12 Eli Whitney, 13 Joab, 14 Chocolat, 15 Jihad, 16 Giraffe, 17 Pride and Prejudice, 18 Anton Chekhov, 19 River Chelt, 20 Allen Ginsberg.*

General Knowledge

Your rating: ● 0-5 Join a library ● 6-10 Keep at it ● 11-15 Join a quiz team ● 16-20 Join Mensa

1. Which cartoonist created the schoolgirls of St Trinian's?
2. What is kept in television's *Veronica's Closet*?
3. Which pop star visited Britain in 2001 to address the Oxford Union on the subject of child welfare?
4. Which Welsh actor married Elizabeth Taylor twice?
5. Which king did caricaturist James Gillray portray as Farmer George?
6. In which U.S. state is Wichita?
7. What nationality is Corelli in the novel *Captain Corelli's Mandolin*?
8. For what sort of seafood is Whitstable famous?
9. Which English engineer and pilot invented the jet engine?
10. How many pieces of silver did Judas receive for betraying Jesus?
11. In which historical period was the televison series *By the Sword Divided* set?
12. Which English novelist wrote *Cold Comfort Farm*?
13. Who did Greg Rusedski defeat in the final of the 2001 Sybase Open?
14. Which English mountaineer was the first man to climb the Matterhorn?
15. What is the capital of Canada's Yukon Territory?
16. Which German city was formerly called Karl-Marx-Stadt?
17. In the film *Back to the Future III* Marty goes on a mission to which year?
18. Which American novelist wrote *The Age of Innocence*?
19. What is the name of Viola's twin brother in Shakespeare's *Twelfth Night*?
20. Which former manager of Wolverhampton Wanderers died in 2001 at the age of 85?

ANSWERS: *1 Ronald Searle, 2 Lingerie, 3 Michael Jackson, 4 Richard Burton, 5 George III, 6 Kansas, 7 Italian, 8 Oysters, 9 Sir Frank Whittle, 10 Thirty, 11 The Civil War, 12 Stella Gibbons, 13 Andre Agassi, 14 Edward Whymper, 15 Whitehorse, 16 Chemnitz, 17 1885, 18 Edith Wharton, 19 Sebastian, 20 Stan Cullis.*

General Knowledge

Your rating:
- **0-5** Join a library
- **6-10** Keep at it
- **11-15** Join a quiz team
- **16-20** Join Mensa

1. Which British novelist wrote *Room at the Top*?
2. Who narrated the film *The Swiss Family Robinson*?
3. Which member of the *Beyond the Fringe* team is a medical doctor?
4. From which lake was Donald Campbell's *Bluebird* raised in 2001?
5. Which metal is added to copper to make brass?
6. Triton is the largest known satellite of which planet?
7. Who was the first presenter of television's *Busman's Holiday*?
8. What do the letters D.C. stand for in Washington, D.C.?
9. Which radio soap opera celebrated its 50th anniversary in 2001?
10. Who directed the Oscar-winning film *Annie Hall*?
11. What type of car was Miriam in the TV series *Lovejoy*?
12. Which German composer wrote *A German Requiem*?
13. In Greek mythology, which race of creatures were part horse and part man?
14. Which country ended the Australian cricket team's run of 16 successive wins in 2001?
15. What sort of blood cells are also called leucocytes?
16. Which chemical element was discovered by Hennig Brand in the 17th century?
17. What type of building provides refuge from a flood in the film *When Tomorrow Comes*?
18. Which U.S. folk singer wrote *Where Have All the Flowers Gone* and *Kisses Sweeter Than Wine*?
19. In art, what name is given to a depiction of the Virgin Mary supporting the body of the dead Christ?
20. Which motor race takes its name from the Italian for 'thousand miles'?

ANSWERS: *1 John Braine, 2 Orson Welles, 3 Jonathan Miller, 4 Coniston Water, 5 Zinc, 6 Neptune, 7 Julian Pettifer, 8 District of Columbia, 9 The Archers, 10 Woody Allen, 11 A Morris Minor, 12 Johannes Brahms, 13 Centaurs, 14 India, 15 White blood cells, 16 Phosphorus, 17 A church, 18 Pete Seeger, 19 Pieta, 20 Mille Miglia.*

Entertainment

Your rating: ● 0-5 **Buy a TV** ● 6-10 **Keep at it** ● 11-15 **Join a quiz team** ● 16-20 **Enter a quiz show**

1. Who starred in the lead role of BBC 1's *Hetty Wainthropp Investigates*?
2. Who had a U.K. top ten hit single in 1965 with *We Gotta Get Out Of This Place*?
3. Who starred as the likeable con artist in the 1973 film *Paper Moon*?
4. From which sitcom was *Robin's Nest* a spin-off?
5. Who recorded the albums *Crocodile Shoes* and *Crocodile Shoes II*?
6. Which *Godfather* star appeared in the 1996 film *The Island Of Dr Moreau*?
7. Which *Our Friends In The North* star played Mr Knightley in the 1996 ITV adaptation of *Emma*?
8. Which dance act had a U.K. number one hit single in 1990 with *The Power*?
9. Who starred as Deloris in the 1992 film *Sister Act*?
10. What is the name of Bart's saxophone-playing sister in TV's *The Simpsons*?
11. What was the first name of TV's *Inspector Morse*?
12. Which Latin crooner released an album entitled *Tango* in 1996?
13. Which US actress played Kitty Kiernan in the film *Michael Collins*?
14. Who was the man with the scores on BBC 2's *Shooting Stars*?
15. Who had a U.K. number one hit single in 1985 with *Nineteen*?
16. Who starred as Ariane in the 1957 film *Love In The Afternoon*?
17. Which French footballer supplied his analysis of 1998 World Cup matches for BBC 1?
18. Which singing sisters released an album in 1996 entitled *Alisha Rules The World*?
19. The TV series *The Prince and the Pauper* was based on a story by which US author?
20. Which controversial British filmmaker directed the 1996 film *The Pillow Book*?

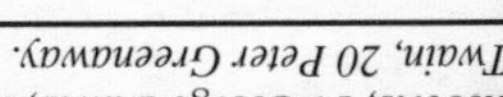

ANSWERS: *1 Patricia Routledge, 2 The Animals, 3 Ryan O'Neal, 4 Man About the House, 5 Jimmy Nail, 6 Marlon Brando, 7 Mark Strong, 8 Snap, 9 Whoopi Goldberg, 10 Lisa, 11 Endeavour, 12 Julio Iglesias, 13 Julia Roberts, 14 George Dawes, 15 Paul Hardcastle, 16 Audrey Hepburn, 17 David Ginola, 18 Alisha's Attic, 19 Mark Twain, 20 Peter Greenaway.*

General Knowledge

Your rating:
- **0-5 Join a library**
- **6-10 Keep at it**
- **11-15 Join a quiz team**
- **16-20 Join Mensa**

1. What is the largest desert in the world?
2. Which radioactive metallic element is represented by the symbol U?
3. A system of what sort of writing was devised by Sir Isaac Pitman?
4. What sort of creature is a black widow?
5. Backgammon is a board game for how many players?
6. In which Caribbean country is the port and tourist resort of Montego Bay?
7. In which state of the USA is San Diego situated?
8. Which British detective writer created the characters Hercule Poirot and Miss Marple?
9. Of which country was Menachem Begin prime minister from 1977 to 1983?
10. Which silvery-white metal is represented by the symbol Sn?
11. According to the Old Testament, who was the elder brother of Moses?
12. Which moor in northern Scotland was the scene, in 1746, of the last land battle to be fought in Britain?
13. Which Australian tennis player won the women's singles at Wimbledon in 1963, 1965 and 1970?
14. Which African country was known as Upper Volta until 1984?
15. Which British novelist wrote *The Citadel* and *The Judas Tree*?
16. Which Irish criminal collaborated with William Hare in the murder of at least 15 people and the digging up of corpses?
17. In which county is the city of St Albans situated?
18. Which British middle-distance runner set new world records for the mile and the 2000m in 1985?
19. Which U.S. Beat poet wrote *Howl*?
20. Which soldier and statesman was Lord Protector of the Commonwealth from 1653 to 1658?

ANSWERS: *1 The Sahara, 2 Uranium, 3 Shorthand, 4 A spider, 5 Two, 6 Jamaica, 7 California, 8 Dame Agatha Christie, 9 Israel, 10 Tin, 11 Aaron, 12 Culloden Moor, 13 Margaret Court, 14 Burkina Faso, 15 A. J. Cronin, 16 William Burke, 17 Hertfordshire, 18 Steve Cram, 19 Allen Ginsberg, 20 Oliver Cromwell.*

General Knowledge

Your rating: ● 0-5 Join a library ● 6-10 Keep at it ● 11-15 Join a quiz team ● 16-20 Join Mensa

1. Which chemical element is represented by the symbol Si?
2. In which Californian city can the Golden Gate Bridge be found?
3. From which country does Edam cheese originate?
4. Which British novelist wrote *Lord of the Flies*?
5. Which US novelist wrote *The Grapes of Wrath* and *Of Mice and Men*?
6. Which island country in the West Indies did the USA invade in 1983?
7. What is the first name of the Princess Royal?
8. What peak on the French-Italian border is the highest mountain in the Alps?
9. What nationality was the composer Johann Sebastian Bach?
10. What is measured in amperes?
11. Which German philosopher wrote *The Phenomenology of Mind*?
12. Which British portrait and landscape painter is famous for his *Blue Boy* and the *Harvest Wagon*?
13. Which king of Lydia was famous for his wealth?
14. What sort of creature is a bullhead?
15. Which wartime poet died of blood poisoning in 1915?
16. Of which African country is Bujumbura the capital?
17. Which part of the body is inflamed when one is suffering from gingivitis?
18. Which branch of Christianity was founded by Mary Baker Eddy?
19. Which Spanish director's films include *Un Chien andalou* and *That Obscure Object of Desire*?
20. Which British writer wrote the Booker Prize-winning novel *Hotel du Lac*?

ANSWERS: *1 Silicon, 2 San Francisco, 3 The Netherlands, 4 William Golding, 5 John Steinbeck, 6 Grenada, 7 Anne, 8 Mont Blanc, 9 German, 10 Electric current, 11 Hegel, 12 Thomas Gainsborough, 13 Croesus, 14 A fish, 15 Rupert Brooke, 16 Burundi, 17 The gums, 18 Christian Science, 19 Luis Buñuel, 20 Anita Brookner.*

General Knowledge

Your rating: ● 0-5 Join a library ● 6-10 Keep at it ● 11-15 Join a quiz team ● 16-20 Join Mensa

1. Which spirit is usually distilled from grain flavoured with juniper berries?
2. What is the capital of Cuba?
3. How was jazz musician John Birks Gillespie better known?
4. What sort of creature is a crane?
5. Followers of which religion worship in a synagogue?
6. Of which country is Tripoli the capital?
7. Which Welsh actor and star of *Who's Afraid of Virginia Woolf* married Elizabeth Taylor twice?
8. In which West Midlands city was a cathedral opened in 1962 retaining the ruins of the original cathedral bombed in 1940?
9. Which French naval officer and underwater explorer is famous for such films as *The Silent World* and *The Living Sea*?
10. How are the respiratory organs of aquatic animals usually known?
11. Who was the President of the USA from 1923 to 1929?
12. Which republic on the north coast of South America was once known as Dutch Guiana?
13. Which British sportsman is the only man to have been world champion in both motorcycling and motor-racing?
14. Who was chancellor of West Germany from 1969 to 1974?
15. Which Polish astronomer formulated the modern heliocentric theory of the solar system?
16. Sphalerite is the principal ore of which metal?
17. Which German composer wrote the choral works *A German Requiem* and the *Alto Rhapsody*?
18. How is the cachalot otherwise known?
19. Which Bradford-born novelist wrote *Room at the Top* and *Life at the Top*?
20. Which Welsh buccaneer was knighted in 1674 and made lieutenant general of Jamaica?

ANSWERS: *1 Gin, 2 Havana, 3 Dizzy Gillespie, 4 A bird, 5 Judaism, 6 Libya, 7 Richard Burton, 8 Coventry, 9 Jacques Cousteau, 10 Gills, 11 Calvin Coolidge, 12 Suriname, 13 John Surtees, 14 Willy Brandt, 15 Nicolaus Copernicus, 16 Zinc, 17 Johannes Brahms, 18 Sperm whale, 19 John Braine, 20 Sir Henry Morgan.*

Entertainment

Your rating: ● **0-5 Buy a TV** ● **6-10 Keep at it** ● **11-15 Join a quiz team** ● **16-20 Enter a quiz show**

1. In which country was the 1996 film *The Last Of The High Kings* set?
2. Which Hollywood star was reunited with an elephant she had met seven years previously in the 1996 TV programme *In the Wild*?
3. Which song did Elaine Paige and Barbara Dickson take to the U.K. number one spot in 1985?
4. Who won a Best Supporting Actor Oscar for his performance in the 1966 film *The Fortune Cookie*?
5. Who starred as TV's *Rumpole of the Bailey*?
6. Which saxophonist was nicknamed "Bird"?
7. Which *Speed* star played a criminal in the 1996 film *Feeling Minnesota*?
8. What was the revamped version of the ITV game show *Strike It Lucky* called?
9. Which '80s band's singer and guitarist were taken to court by drummer Mike Joyce who claimed they swindled him out of thousands of pounds?
10. Who presented Channel 4's *Gazzetta Football Italia*?
11. Who released an album entitled *The Day* in 1996, which included guest performances from Mariah Carey, Eric Clapton and Stevie Wonder?
12. Which *EastEnders* character was played by Martine McCutcheon?
13. Which Scottish actor starred as a Franciscan monk in *The Name of the Rose*?
14. Who had a U.K. number one hit single in 1979 with *Ring My Bell*?
15. Which sci-fi TV series featured Jerry Doyle as Security Chief Garibaldi?
16. Who directed the 1996 film *Kansas City*?
17. Who starred in the title role of TV's *The Fall and Rise of Reginald Perrin*?
18. Which housewives' favourite released an album in 1996 entitled *Summer of '78*?
19. Which *Cracker* creator wrote the screenplay to the 1996 drama-documentary *Hillsborough*?
20. With whom did Luther Vandross duet on the 1992 and 1995 U.K. top ten hit *The Best Things in Life Are Free*?

ANSWERS: *1 Ireland, 2 Goldie Hawn, 3 I Know Him So Well, 4 Walter Matthau, 5 Leo McKern, 6 Charlie Parker, 7 Keanu Reeves, 8 Michael Barrymore's Strike It Rich, 9 Morrissey and Johnny Marr of The Smiths, 10 James Richardson, 11 Babyface, 12 Tiffany Mitchell, 13 Sean Connery, 14 Anita Ward, 15 Babylon 5, 16 Robert Altman, 17 Leonard Rossiter, 18 Barry Manilow, 19 Jimmy McGovern, 20 Janet Jackson.*

General Knowledge

Your rating:
- 0-5 Join a library
- 6-10 Keep at it
- 11-15 Join a quiz team
- 16-20 Join Mensa

1. Of which country is Sumatra the second largest island?
2. In which sphere of Olympic events did Nadia Comaneci win several gold medals?
3. What sort of creature is a corncrake?
4. What do the initials BBC stand for?
5. In which Central American country was the Aztec empire centred?
6. Which yellow solid substance is represented by the chemical symbol S?
7. What nationality was the navigator Christopher Columbus?
8. Of which country is Brisbane the third largest city?
9. What sort of creature is a constrictor?
10. From which tree are cocoa and chocolate derived?
11. Who was conductor of the BBC Symphony Orchestra (1930-1949) and the London Philharmonic Orchestra (1949-1957)?
12. Which alkaloid extracted from deadly nightshade is used during anaesthesia to decrease lung secretions?
13. Monégasque is a mixture of which two languages?
14. Naevus is the medically correct term for which area of darkly pigmented skin?
15. Which inlet of the Tasman Sea was the site of Captain Cook's first landing in Australia?
16. Which Germanic god of war gave his name to "Tuesday"?
17. In which state of the USA is the Mojave Desert situated?
18. Plato's *Phaedo* is an account of the death of which Athenian philosopher?
19. Who was the England football coach for one match in 1999 between the reigns of Glenn Hoddle and Kevin Keegan?
20. Which country won the 1999 Eurovision Song Contest?

ANSWERS: *1 Indonesia, 2 Gymnastics, 3 A bird, 4 British Broadcasting Corporation, 5 Mexico, 6 Sulphur, 7 Italian, 8 Australia, 9 Snake, 10 Cacao tree, 11 Sir Adrian Boult, 12 Atropine, 13 French and Italian, 14 A mole, 15 Botany Bay, 16 Tyr, 17 California, 18 Socrates, 19 Howard Wilkinson, 20 Sweden.*

General Knowledge

Your rating:
- **0-5 Join a library**
- **6-10 Keep at it**
- **11-15 Join a quiz team**
- **16-20 Join Mensa**

1. In which principality is Monte Carlo situated?
2. Of which country did P. W. Botha become president in 1984?
3. Which religion was established by Mohammed?
4. What is the official name of the centigrade temperature scale?
5. What type of vehicle was a penny-farthing?
6. Across which continent does the Andes mountain system extend?
7. What is the capital of Poland?
8. How many signs of the zodiac are there?
9. Of which natural phenomena are cirrus, altostratus and stratocumulus examples?
10. Who recorded the albums *Forgiven Not Forgotten* and *Talk on Corners*?
11. Which island is the largest and most northerly of the Inner Hebrides group?
12. Which Russian composer wrote the tone poem *In the Steppes of Central Asia*?
13. In which Irish county is the town of Clonmel?
14. Which middle-distance runner fell in the 1984 Olympic 3,000m after a clash with Zola Budd?
15. In which ocean is the Bismarck Archipelago situated?
16. Who won the women's singles title at Wimbledon in 1996?
17. According to the Old Testament, which son of Nebuchadnezzar was the last King Of Babylon?
18. Which French sculptor is famous for *The Kiss*, which can be seen in the Tate Gallery?
19. Which country won the 1999 Cricket World Cup?
20. What was the surname of the family in *Only Fools and Horses*?

ANSWERS: *1 Monaco, 2 South Africa, 3 Islam, 4 Celsius scale, 5 Bicycle, 6 South America, 7 Warsaw, 8 Twelve, 9 Clouds, 10 The Corrs, 11 Skye, 12 Aleksandr Borodin, 13 Tipperary, 14 Mary (Dekker) Slaney, 15 The Pacific Ocean, 16 Steffi Graf, 17 Belshazzar, 18 Auguste Rodin, 19 Australia, 20 Trotter.*

General Knowledge

Your rating:
- 0-5 Join a library
- 6-10 Keep at it
- 11-15 Join a quiz team
- 16-20 Join Mensa

1. How is the vegetable zucchini otherwise known?
2. Mandarin and Cantonese are dialects of which language?
3. Which reddish-brown metal is represented by the symbol Cu?
4. Which comedy writer, actor and director is famous for the films *Blazing Saddles* and *The Producers*?
5. In which county is the resort of Bournemouth?
6. In which state of the USA is the city of Cleveland situated?
7. In which Italian city can the Bridge of Sighs be found?
8. Which force occurring on a liquid makes it behave as if the surface has an elastic skin?
9. Which 19th century British engineer is famous for the construction of the Clifton Suspension Bridge?
10. Of which island group is Stanley the capital?
11. Which English lawyer, scholar and martyr wrote *Utopia*?
12. Which railway runs the 9335 km from Moscow to Vladivostok?
13. Which rock group played to a record 250,000 fans at Knebworth House in 1996?
14. Which sculptor is famous for his gigantic heads of U.S. presidents at Mount Rushmore National Memorial?
15. What sort of creature is a tope?
16. Who was the first woman MP to sit in the House of Commons?
17. Which suburb of Birmingham was founded as a model factory and village by George Cadbury?
18. Which U.S. film actress was known as the "It" girl?
19. Who became Roman emperor following the murder of his nephew Caligula in 41 AD?
20. How is the anaesthetic trichloromethane more commonly known?

ANSWERS: *1 Courgette, 2 Chinese, 3 Copper, 4 Mel Brooks, 5 Dorset, 6 Ohio, 7 Venice, 8 Surface tension, 9 Isambard Kingdom Brunel, 10 The Falkland Islands, 11 Sir Thomas More, 12 Trans-Siberian Railway, 13 Oasis, 14 Gutzon Borglum, 15 A shark, 16 Nancy Astor, 17 Bournville, 18 Clara Bow, 19 Claudius, 20 Chloroform.*

Entertainment

Your rating: ● **0-5 Buy a TV** ● **6-10 Keep at it** ● **11-15 Join a quiz team** ● **16-20 Enter a quiz show**

1. Which US vocalist released a live album entitled *Across America* in 1997?
2. Who directed the 1988 film *The Last Temptation of Christ*?
3. Which duo had a Christmas U.K. number one hit single in 1982 with *Save Your Love*?
4. Who played Cruella de Vil in the 1997 live-action version of *101 Dalmatians*?
5. Which comedienne got her big break appearing alongside Lenny Henry and David Copperfield in the TV series *Three of a Kind*?
6. Which song did both Madonna and Mike Flowers Pops release as a single in late 1996?
7. Who starred in the title role of the 1969 film *Midnight Cowboy*?
8. Which *Inspector Morse* star starred as Colin Worsfold in the 1997 comedy-drama *Gobble*?
9. Who had a Christmas U.K. number one hit single in 1987 with *Always on my Mind*?
10. What was the title of the claymation series about Stone-Age dwellers which appeared on BBC 2 in 1997?
11. Which choirboy released an album entitled *The Choirboy's Christmas* in 1996?
12. Which *Pulp Fiction* actress starred in Ted Demme's 1996 film *Beautiful Girls*?
13. Which actor played Trigger in *Only Fools and Horses* and Owen Newitt in *The Vicar of Dibley*?
14. Which US vocalist released an album entitled *This Is The Time - The Christmas Album* in 1996?
15. Which *Brookside* character was played by Vince Earl?
16. Who starred as Wyatt Earp in the 1957 film *Gunfight At The O.K. Corral*?
17. Which football pundit presented *The Football Millionaires*; a 1999 BBC 1 documentary featuring David Beckham and other highly-paid players?
18. During which war was the TV series *Tenko* set?
19. Which Oscar-winning actress directed the 1996 film *Home For The Holidays*?
20. Who starred as boxer Bobby Carr in the 1996 TV drama *Respect*?

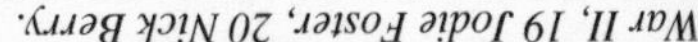

ANSWERS: *1 Art Garfunkel, 2 Martin Scorsese, 3 Renee and Renato, 4 Glenn Close, 5 Tracy Ullman, 6 Don't Cry For Me Argentina, 7 Jon Voight, 8 Kevin Whately, 9 Pet Shop Boys, 10 Gogs, 11 Anthony Way, 12 Uma Thurman, 13 Roger Lloyd Pack, 14 Michael Bolton, 15 Ron Dixon, 16 Burt Lancaster, 17 Alan Hansen, 18 World War II, 19 Jodie Foster, 20 Nick Berry.*

General Knowledge

Your rating: ● 0-5 Join a library ● 6-10 Keep at it ● 11-15 Join a quiz team ● 16-20 Join Mensa

1. In Roman Catholic doctrine, what is the name of the state in which souls are purified after death to make them fit for heaven?
2. Which Buckinghamshire country house has been the official country residence of British prime ministers since 1921?
3. Which Manchester United footballer played for England 106 times and scored a record 49 goals?
4. How is the study of the movements and positions of heavenly bodies in relation to their presumed influence upon human affairs usually known?
5. According to Greek mythology, what was the name of the ship that Jason took on the quest of the Golden Fleece?
6. Which ceremonial arch stands at the centre of the Étoile at the top of the Champs Elysée in Paris?
7. With which U.S. sport was Babe Ruth associated?
8. What nationality was the artist Henri Toulouse-Lautrec?
9. What sort of alloy is melted to form a joint between other metals?
10. What is the official language of Argentina?
11. Which West Yorkshire town is situated at the confluence of the Rivers Colne and Holme?
12. Which system of treating illness was developed by Samuel Hahnemann, based on the principle of "like cures like"?
13. What is the highest mountain in Ireland?
14. Which Act established the Hanoverian succession to the English throne?
15. Of which US state is Carson City the capital?
16. What sort of creature is a thickhead?
17. Who was the third wife of Henry VIII of England?
18. Which African country partly consists of the former republic of Tanganyika and the island of Zanzibar?
19. Which US actor starred in the films *Little Caesar* and *Double Indemnity*?
20. With which branch of science was Edwin Powell Hubble associated?

ANSWERS: *1 Purgatory, 2 Chequers, 3 Bobby Charlton, 4 Astrology, 5 The Argo, 6 Arc de Triomphe, 7Baseball, 8 French, 9 Solder, 10 Spanish, 11 Huddersfield, 12 Homeopathy, 13 Carrantuohill, 14 The Act of Settlement, 15 Nevada, 16 A bird, 17 Jane Seymour, 18 Tanzania, 19 Edward G. Robinson, 20 Astronomy.*

General Knowledge

Your rating: • 0-5 Join a library • 6-10 Keep at it • 11-15 Join a quiz team • 16-20 Join Mensa

1. In which continent can Lake Titicaca be found?
2. In which county is the town of Cheltenham situated?
3. Which sport is played for the Ryder Cup?
4. With whom did Marx collaborate on *The Communist Manifesto* of 1848?
5. Which metal is represented by the symbol Na?
6. Which noble gas is represented by the symbol Ar?
7. In which state of the USA are the Twin Cities of Minneapolis and St Paul situated?
8. How is the Totalizator system of betting usually referred to?
9. Which former Soviet town was the site of the explosion of a nuclear reactor in 1986?
10. Of which county is Chelmsford the administrative centre?
11. Which U.S. industrialist founded the oil-refining company Standard Oil in 1870?
12. Which river flows from the Adirondack Mountains to New York Bay?
13. Which German physicist discovered X-rays while professor at the University of Würzburg, Bavaria?
14. Which former boxer lit the Olympic Flame at Atlanta in 1996?
15. Which three European nations are known as the Low Countries?
16. The Thar Desert is situated along the border of which two countries?
17. What is the name for the fluid that remains after blood has been allowed to clot?
18. On which gulf is the Italian resort of Amalfi situated?
19. Which British music-hall comedian was known as "the prime minister of mirth"?
20. Which French composer wrote the *Symphonie Fantastique* and *Le Carnaval romain*?

ANSWERS: *1 South America, 2 Gloucestershire, 3 Golf, 4 Engels, 5 Sodium, 6 Argon, 7 Minnesota, 8 The Tote, 9 Chernobyl, 10 Essex, 11 John D. Rockefeller, 12 The Hudson River, 13 Roentgen, 14 Muhammad Ali, 15 The Netherlands, Belgium and Luxembourg, 16 India and Pakistan, 17 Serum, 18 The Gulf of Salerno, 19 Sir George Robey, 20 Hector Berlioz.*

General Knowledge

Your rating: ● **0-5** Join a library ● **6-10** Keep at it ● **11-15** Join a quiz team ● **16-20** Join Mensa

1. With which sport is Gary Sobers associated?
2. In which University can the Bodleian Library be found?
3. What sort of creature is a minnow?
4. Which specialised agency of the United Nations is represented by the initials WHO?
5. Who was the Greek god of war, identified by the Romans with Mars?
6. Of which European country is Tirana the capital?
7. In which year did World War I start?
8. According to the Old Testament, at which Turkish mountain did Noah's ark come to rest after the flood?
9. In which city is the Bolshoi Ballet based?
10. Which chess piece is usually represented by a horse's head?
11. Which British feminist author wrote the novel *The Life and Loves of a She-Devil*?
12. Which channel separates the island of Anglesey from the mainland of NW Wales?
13. Who was the Animals bass player, who discovered Jimi Hendrix?
14. The Merino is a breed of which animal?
15. Which New Zealand-born cartoonist created the character Colonel Blimp?
16. What is the capital of the state of Western Australia?
17. Which French novelist fled to England after defending Dreyfus in an open letter called *J'accuse*?
18. What is the state capital of Kansas?
19. Which British actor starred in the films *Dr Crippen* and *Cul de Sac*?
20. On which river does the town of Merthyr Tydfil stand?

ANSWERS: *1 Cricket, 2 Oxford University, 3 A fish, 4 World Health Organisation, 5 Ares, 6 Albania, 7 1914, 8 Mount Ararat, 9 Moscow, 10 The knight, 11 Fay Weldon, 12 Menai Strait, 13 Chas Chandler, 14 Sheep, 15 Sir David Low, 16 Perth, 17 Émile Zola, 18 Topeka, 19 Donald Pleasence, 20 River Taff.*

Entertainment

Your rating:	● 0-5 Buy a TV	● 6-10 Keep at it
	● 11-15 Join a quiz team	● 16-20 Enter a quiz show

1. Who was the host of *The Alphabet Game* on TV?
2. Which alter-ego of Steve Coogan released an album entitled *Phenomenon* in 1997?
3. Who starred as Harry Palmer in the 1967 film *Funeral in Berlin*?
4. Who starred as Gordon Brittas in the TV sitcom *The Brittas Empire*?
5. Which band had a U.K. top ten hit single in 1976 with *Daddy Cool*?
6. Which actress played Kathleen Quigley in the 1997 film *Some Mother's Son*?
7. Which 1970s sci-fi TV series centred on the activities of the anti-alien organisation SHADO?
8. Which band had a U.K. top ten hit single in 1982 with *It Started With A Kiss*?
9. Who starred as Betty Lou in the 1927 film *It*?
10. Who starred as euthanasia campaigner Derek Humphry in the 1997 TV docu-drama *Goodbye My Love*?
11. Which former member of The Byrds released an album entitled *Live From Mars* in 1997?
12. Who directed, co-produced and starred in the 1997 film *The Mirror Has Two Faces*?
13. Which quiz show was originally based on the US series *College Bowl*?
14. Which band had a U.K. top ten hit single in 1981 with *Just Can't Get Enough*?
15. Who starred as Lenny Bruce in the 1974 film *Lenny*?
16. Who played the evil Mrs Danvers in the 1997 TV adaptation of *Rebecca*?
17. Which 1997 Barry Levinson film featured Robert De Niro as a Catholic priest?
18. Which *Big Breakfast* presenter hosted *The 1999 Brit Awards*?
19. Who played the effeminate Molina in the 1985 film *Kiss of the Spider Woman*?
20. Which *EastEnders* character was played by Paul Bradley?

ANSWERS: *1 Andrew O'Connor, 2 Tony Ferrino, 3 Michael Caine, 4 Chris Barrie, 5 Boney M, 6 Helen Mirren, 7 UFO, 8 Hot Chocolate, 9 Clara Bow, 10 Robert Lindsay, 11 Roger McGuinn, 12 Barbra Streisand, 13 University Challenge, 14 Depeche Mode, 15 Dustin Hoffman, 16 Diana Rigg, 17 Sleepers, 18 Johnny Vaughan, 19 William Hurt, 20 Nigel Bates.*

General Knowledge

Your rating: ● 0-5 Join a library ● 6-10 Keep at it ● 11-15 Join a quiz team ● 16-20 Join Mensa

1. Which city is the capital of the Spanish region of Catalonia?
2. What is the minimum number of sides that a polygon can have?
3. Who became president of the Palestine Liberation Organisation in 1968?
4. Which Greek epic poet is the presumed author of the *Iliad* and *Odyssey*?
5. In which U.S. city can the White House and the Smithsonian Institution be found?
6. What sort of creature is a borzoi?
7. What was the name of the former policy of racial segregation in South Africa, which was introduced in 1948?
8. Which city is every Muslim expected to visit at least once in his or her lifetime, being the birthplace of Mohammed?
9. By which acronym were the Australian and New Zealand Army Corps which served in World War I known?
10. Which actress and singer partnered Fred Astaire in many film musicals, including *Top Hat*, *Swing Time* and *Follow the Fleet*?
11. Which wood means "wood of life" in Latin?
12. How was Ho Chi Minh City known until 1976?
13. What does the acronym UNESCO stand for?
14. Of which African country is Lilongwe the capital?
15. Which British author wrote the gothic novel *The Castle of Otranto*?
16. Of which Canadian province is Halifax the capital?
17. Which international Roman Catholic organisation means "God's work" in Latin?
18. Which Greek mathematician is famous for his geometry book *Elements*?
19. Which British composer wrote the World War I song *Keep the Home Fires Burning*?
20. Which flying mammals belong to the order *Chiroptera*?

ANSWERS: *1 Barcelona, 2 Three, 3 Yasser Arafat, 4 Homer, 5 Washington, DC, 6 A dog, 7 Apartheid, 8 Mecca, 9 Anzac, 10 Ginger Rogers, 11 Lignum vitae, 12 Saigon, 13 United Nations Educational, Scientific and Cultural Organisation, 14 Malawi, 15 Horace Walpole, 16 Nova Scotia, 17 Opus Dei, 18 Euclid, 19 Ivor Novello, 20 Bats.*

General Knowledge

Your rating:
- **0-5 Join a library**
- **6-10 Keep at it**
- **11-15 Join a quiz team**
- **16-20 Join Mensa**

1. What is the main artery of the human body called?
2. Of which country is Bern the capital?
3. With which sport is Sugar Ray Robinson associated?
4. Which bony structures grow from the heads of deer?
5. What is the longest river in South America?
6. Which singer had a hit with *Rock Around the Clock*, backed by the Comets?
7. In the U.K., which government department is responsible for immigration, race relations and prisons?
8. In which European country is the port of Bilbao?
9. Which U.S. actor starred in the films *The Graduate* and *Midnight Cowboy*?
10. How many legs do arachnids have?
11. *The Disasters of War* and *Maja Clothed* are works by which Spanish painter?
12. What was the name of the ruling dynasty of France from 987 to 1328?
13. Who won the men's singles title at Wimbledon in 1996?
14. In which Irish county can the town of Castlebar be found?
15. Which British novelist wrote *The Darling Buds of May*?
16. What is the name for the sterile offspring of a female ass and a male horse?
17. Which English political philosopher wrote *Leviathan*?
18. The name of which constellation near Orion means 'Great Dog' in Latin?
19. Which grandson of Sigmund Freud was a Liberal MP?
20. How are the Friendly Islands otherwise known?

ANSWERS: *1 The aorta, 2 Switzerland, 3 Boxing, 4 Antlers, 5 The River Amazon, 6 Bill Haley, 7 The Home Office, 8 Spain, 9 Dustin Hoffman, 10 Eight, 11 Goya, 12 Capetians, 13 Richard Krajicek, 14 Mayo, 15 H. E. Bates, 16 Hinny, 17 Thomas Hobbes, 18 Canis Major, 19 Clement Freud, 20 Tonga.*

General Knowledge

Your rating:
- **0-5 Join a library**
- **6-10 Keep at it**
- **11-15 Join a quiz team**
- **16-20 Join Mensa**

1. Who succeeded Edward Heath as leader of the Conservative Party in 1975?
2. In which state of the USA is the city of Memphis situated?
3. Which rock group's members have included Mick Jagger, Keith Richards and Bill Wyman?
4. Which British general commanded British, German and Dutch forces to victory at Waterloo in 1815?
5. What is the capital of the Republic of Ireland?
6. Which legendary Greek hero killed the Minotaur of Crete with the help of Ariadne?
7. What is the highest mountain in the British Isles?
8. According to Arthurian legend, which wizard assisted Arthur and his father, Uther Pendragon?
9. How many different suits are in a standard pack of playing cards?
10. In which state of the USA is the original Disneyland, which opened in 1955?
11. Which English Civil War soldier became Cromwell's son-in-law in 1646?
12. Which Liberal prime minister held together a cabinet which included Lloyd George, Asquith and Churchill?
13. Which U.S. novelist wrote *Breakfast at Tiffany's*?
14. Which British poet and essayist wrote *Cautionary Tales*?
15. What sort of creature is a wapiti?
16. To what did Cape Kennedy change its name in 1973?
17. Which crude drug is prepared from the dried leaves of foxglove plants?
18. With which brass instrument was Bix Beiderbecke associated?
19. Which city on the River Avon was an early Roman centre known as Aquae Sulis?
20. What sort of fortune-telling cards are made up of the Greater Arcana and the Lesser Arcana?

ANSWERS: *1 Margaret Thatcher, 2 Tennessee, 3 The Rolling Stones, 4 The Duke of Wellington, 5 Dublin, 6 Theseus, 7 Ben Nevis, 8 Merlin, 9 Four, 10 California, 11 Henry Ireton, 12 Sir Henry Campbell-Bannerman, 13 Truman Capote, 14 Hilaire Belloc, 15 A deer, 16 Cape Canaveral, 17 Digitalis, 18 Cornet, 19 Bath, 20 Tarot.*

Entertainment

Your rating: ● **0-5** **Buy a TV** ● **6-10** **Keep at it** ● **11-15** **Join a quiz team** ● **16-20** **Enter a quiz show**

1. Who presented the consumer TV panel game *All Over The Shop*?
2. Which actress played Paul Newman's wife in the 1958 film *Cat on a Hot Tin Roof*?
3. Which band released an album entitled *Glow* in 1997?
4. Who played Nancy in the 1997 film *Flirting With Disaster*?
5. Who was the presenter of TV's *Pet Power*?
6. Which British rock group had a U.K. hit with *The Theme From M*A*S*H (Suicide Is Painless)*?
7. Who starred in the title role of the 1974 film *The Gambler*?
8. Which political party did TV interviewer Brian Walden represent as an MP for 13 years?
9. Which 1997 F. Gary Gray film co-starred Queen Latifah as one of four cleaners who become armed robbers?
10. Which Sir Walter Scott hero appeared on our TV screens in a 1997 adaptation starring Steven Waddington?
11. Which soul duo had a U.K. top ten hit single in 1988 with *Teardrops*?
12. Which *Pulp Fiction* star played June in the 1990 film *Henry & June*?
13. Who starred as forensic pathologist Dr Iain McCallum in ITV's *McCallum*?
14. Which *Back To The Future* star played a psychic investigator in the 1997 film *The Frighteners*?
15. Who starred as TV's *Dixon of Dock Green*?
16. Which one-time punk heroes released an album entitled *Written In Red* in 1997?
17. Who directed the 1938 film *The Lady Vanishes*?
18. Which *Peak Practice* character was played on TV by Adrian Lukis?
19. Which *Brookside* character was played on TV by John Burgess?
20. Which actor starred as an attorney framed for the murder of his ex-mistress in the film *Enemy of the State*?

ANSWERS: *1 Paul Ross, 2 Elizabeth Taylor, 3 Reef, 4 Patricia Arquette, 5 Anthea Turner, 6 Manic Street Preachers, 7 James Caan, 8 The Labour Party, 9 Set It Off, 10 Ivanhoe, 11 Womack and Womack, 12 Uma Thurman, 13 John Hannah, 14 Michael J. Fox, 15 Jack Warner, 16 The Stranglers, 17 Alfred Hitchcock, 18 Dr David Shearer, 19 David Crosbie, 20 Will Smith.*

General Knowledge

Your rating: ● 0-5 Join a library ● 6-10 Keep at it ● 11-15 Join a quiz team ● 16-20 Join Mensa

1. In which ocean can the Bay of Bengal be found?
2. Which mysterious phenomenon is represented by the initials ESP?
3. Which resort on the French Riviera is famous for its annual film festival?
4. With which sport is Jack Dempsey associated?
5. Of which African country is Alexandria the second largest city?
6. Which U.S. political party has been led by F. D. Roosevelt, J. F. Kennedy and Jimmy Carter?
7. Which British doctor and middle-distance runner was the first man to run a mile in under 4 minutes?
8. Which Japanese city was largely destroyed by the first atomic bomb to be used in warfare?
9. What is the capital of Thailand?
10. Which French existentialist wrote the novels *The Outsider*, *The Plague* and *The Rebel*?
11. Who was the father of King Rehoboam of Judah?
12. Which state of the USA has Madison as its capital?
13. By which acronym is the International Association of Poets, Playwrights, Editors, Essayists, and Novelists known?
14. Which British architect designed the Crystal Palace for the Great Exhibition of 1851?
15. Which British cricketer, known as 'Lol', was at the centre of the bodyline controversy of 1932-33?
16. Which South African novelist wrote *Cry, the Beloved Country*?
17. Which Mexican poet and diplomat wrote the poem *Piedra de Sol*?
18. Which Portuguese archipelago has Funchal as its capital?
19. How many goals did England score against Holland in their Euro 96 group match?
20. Which severe viral disease was named after the Nigerian village in which it was first described in 1969?

ANSWERS: *1 The Indian Ocean, 2 Extrasensory perception, 3 Cannes, 4 Boxing, 5 Egypt, 6 Democratic Party, 7 Roger Bannister, 8 Hiroshima, 9 Bangkok, 10 Albert Camus, 11 Solomon, 12 Wisconsin, 13 PEN, 14 Sir Joseph Paxton, 15 Harold Larwood, 16 Alan Paton, 17 Octavio Paz, 18 Madeira Islands, 19 Four, 20 Lassa fever.*

General Knowledge

Your rating: ● **0-5 Join a library** ● **6-10 Keep at it** ● **11-15 Join a quiz team** ● **16-20 Join Mensa**

1. In which unitary council is Weston-super-Mare?
2. Which sporting organisation is represented by the initials MCC?
3. What is the capital of Algeria?
4. The Mahabharata and the Ramayana are holy texts of which religion?
5. What is the deepest adult male singing voice?
6. Which group of Spanish islands includes Lanzarote and Tenerife?
7. According to the New Testament, which Apostle had a vision while travelling to Damascus, which led to his conversion?
8. Who was the principal Roman sea god, identified with the Greek Poseidon?
9. Which state of the USA has Sacramento as its capital?
10. In which county is Trowbridge?
11. By what name were the four hundred Church of England clergy who refused to swear allegiance to William III known?
12. What is the largest city in the Canary Islands?
13. Which French painter and sculptor initiated Fauvism in the early 1900s?
14. Which French novelist wrote *Les Liaisons dangereuses*?
15. Which organ is inflamed when suffering from the disease nephritis?
16. How many players are there in a netball team?
17. Which British author wrote *The Railway Children*?
18. Which Roman emperor murdered his wife Octavia in order to marry Poppaea?
19. Which Canadian actor starred in the film *East of Eden* and the TV series *Dr Kildare*?
20. Which port was the capital of Nigeria before Abuja?

ANSWERS: *1 North Somerset, 2 Marylebone Cricket Club, 3 Algiers, 4 Hinduism, 5 Bass, 6 The Canary Islands, 7 St Paul, 8 Neptune, 9 California, 10 Wiltshire, 11 Nonjurors, 12 Las Palmas, 13 Henri Matisse, 14 Pierre Choderlos de Laclos, 15 Kidney, 16 Seven, 17 Edith Nesbit, 18 Nero, 19 Raymond Massey, 20 Lagos.*

General Knowledge

Your rating:
- **0-5 Join a library**
- **6-10 Keep at it**
- **11-15 Join a quiz team**
- **16-20 Join Mensa**

1. What was the name of the ship that carried the Pilgrim Fathers to America?
2. How is deoxyribonucleic acid better known?
3. Of which country is the Algarve the most southerly province?
4. How many players in a basketball side can be on the court at the same time?
5. Which island state in the West Indies has Bridgetown as its capital?
6. Of which country did Hirohito become emperor in 1926?
7. According to the chronicler Roger of Wendover, which English woman rode naked through the market place of Coventry?
8. From 1510 to 1961, the Indian state of Goa was an overseas territory of which European country?
9. Which term describes the time taken for half the atoms in a sample of a radioactive isotope to decay?
10. Which disaster started in Pudding Lane and is commemorated by Sir Christopher Wren's Monument of 1671?
11. Matabeleland is an area of which African country?
12. Which annual international festival of opera is held near Lewes, East Sussex?
13. On which river does Norwich lie?
14. Which U.S. dramatist wrote *The Little Foxes*?
15. Which Russian physiologist is famous for his demonstration of the conditioned reflex?
16. Which French Franciscan friar and diplomat was known as the Éminence Grise?
17. Which French physician and astrologer became famous for the prophecies he made in *Centuries*?
18. Which Dutch dancer was executed as a German spy in World War I?
19. Which Japanese director's films include *Seven Samurai* and *Ran*?
20. What is the SI unit of work or energy named after a 19th century British physicist?

ANSWERS: *1 The Mayflower, 2 DNA, 3 Portugal, 4 Five, 5 Barbados, 6 Japan, 7 Lady Godiva, 8 Portugal, 9 Half-life, 10 The Great Fire of London, 11 Zimbabwe, 12 Glyndebourne, 13 The River Wensum, 14 Lillian Hellman, 15 Pavlov, 16 Père Joseph, 17 Nostradamus, 18 Mata Hari, 19 Akira Kurosawa, 20 Joule.*

Entertainment

Your rating: ● **0-5** Buy a TV ● **6-10** Keep at it ● **11-15** Join a quiz team ● **16-20** Enter a quiz show

1. Which *Changing Rooms* host became the presenter of BBC 1's *Summer Holiday* in 1999?
2. Which 1999 film attempted to lift the lid off club and drug youth culture?
3. Which Seventies U.S. drama series starred Karl Malden and Michael Douglas as police detectives?
4. Which U.S. group released *Californication* in 1999, their first album for four years?
5. Who starred in and directed the 1977 film *Grand Theft Auto*?
6. What was the title of the BBC 1 series in which Philippa Forrester and vet Mark Evans joined animal behaviourists trying to cure problem pets?
7. Which group had U.K. top ten hits with *The Crunch* and *Clouds Across the Moon*?
8. Which actress played the police chief investigating the disappearance of a three-year-old boy in the 1999 film *The Deep End of the Ocean*?
9. Which 1999 BBC 2 documentary series followed the work of Iolo Williams, RSPB species officer?
10. Which ex-Beatle told us to *Back Off Boogaloo* in 1972?
11. Which 1964 romantic comedy about the relationship between a screenwriter and his secretary starred William Holden and Audrey Hepburn?
12. Which *Emmerdale* character married Roy Glover in 1999?
13. Which U.S. actor had two U.K. top ten hits in 1987, with *Respect Yourself* and *Under the Boardwalk*?
14. In which 1999 film starring Jamie Lee Curtis did Donald Sutherland appear as a sea captain?
15. Which John Le Carré hero was played by Alec Guinness in the Seventies TV spy thriller *Tinker, Tailor, Soldier, Spy*?
16. What was the title of Gay Dad's 1999 debut album?
17. Which actress starred as the mother of a satanically possessed infant in the 1975 film *I Don't Want to Be Born*?
18. In which part of Britain did *Coronation Street*'s Platts, Websters and Battersbys spend their holidays in 1999?
19. Which 1998 film starred Sandra Bullock as a young mother who finds out on a TV talk show that her best friend is having an affair with her husband?
20. Which pop band took part in a live TV request show in 1999, entitled *Just for You*?

ANSWERS: *1 Carol Smillie, 2 Human Traffic, 3 The Streets of San Francisco, 4 Red Hot Chili Peppers, 5 Ron Howard, 6 Barking Mad, 7 Rah Band, 8 Whoopi Goldberg, 9 Birdman, 10 Ringo Starr, 11 Paris When It Sizzles, 12 Kelly Windsor, 13 Bruce Willis, 14 Virus, 15 George Smiley, 16 Leisurenoise, 17 Joan Collins, 18 Wales, 19 Hope Floats, 20 Boyzone.*

General Knowledge

Your rating: ● 0-5 Join a library ● 6-10 Keep at it ● 11-15 Join a quiz team ● 16-20 Join Mensa

1. Which British electrical engineer produced colour-television pictures in 1928?
2. Of which Welsh island is Beaumaris the chief town?
3. What was the nationality of the philosopher Immanuel Kant?
4. What sort of creature is a chiffchaff?
5. What is the capital of Greece?
6. Which game is played with rackets and a shuttlecock?
7. According to the Old Testament, which founder of the Hebrew nation was commanded by God to sacrifice his son Isaac?
8. Of which Mediterranean island is Palermo the capital?
9. Which event in Scottish athletics involves carrying a 4 to 5 metre-long tree trunk vertically and throwing it forward?
10. Which study of the behaviour and flow of air around objects is important in vehicle design?
11. Which market town is the administrative centre of West Sussex?
12. What is the capital of the Dominican Republic?
13. What sort of creature is a molly?
14. Which British novelist wrote the popular thriller *Bulldog Drummond*?
15. In which year did Heathrow Airport open to passengers?
16. Which German film actress and singer starred in *The Blue Angel* and *Blonde Venus*?
17. Which Italian political theorist wrote *The Prince*?
18. Of which African republic is Bamako the capital?
19. With which instrument was jazz musician Art Tatum associated?
20. Which British field marshal was deputy commander of NATO forces from 1951 to 1958?

ANSWERS: *1 John Logie Baird, 2 Anglesey, 3 German, 4 A bird, 5 Athens, 6 Badminton, 7 Abraham, 8 Sicily, 9 Caber tossing, 10 Aerodynamics, 11 Chichester, 12 Santo Domingo, 13 A fish, 14 Sapper, 15 1946, 16 Marlene Dietrich, 17 Niccolò Machiavelli, 18 Mali, 19 Piano, 20 Montgomery.*

General Knowledge

Your rating: • 0-5 Join a library • 6-10 Keep at it • 11-15 Join a quiz team • 16-20 Join Mensa

1. According to legend, what was the capital of King Arthur's kingdom?
2. What is the largest city of Brazil?
3. Which vehicle was invented by the architect Joseph Hansom?
4. In general, which are bigger, African elephants or Indian elephants?
5. Which U.S. city is the location of John F. Kennedy International Airport?
6. Which substance found in coffee and tea acts as a stimulant?
7. What do the initials CND stand for?
8. Which legendary Trojan leader was the hero of Virgil's *Aeneid*?
9. What is the lowest temperature that can theoretically be attained?
10. Which British novelist wrote *David Copperfield* and *Bleak House*?
11. According to Greek legend, which daughter of Tyndareus married Agamemnon?
12. Which Swedish director made the films *Autumn Sonata* and *Fanny and Alexander*?
13. How many points does a star of David possess?
14. How is lignite commonly known?
15. Which French dramatist wrote *Tartuffe* and *Le Misanthrope*?
16. What sort of creature is a Clydesdale?
17. Which Indian cricketer was the youngest player to have scored 2,000 runs and taken 200 wickets in Test matches?
18. Of which country is Lake Taupo (or Taupomoana) the largest lake?
19. Which Austrian composer wrote the operas *Wozzeck* and *Lulu*?
20. What does the acronym COBOL stand for?

ANSWERS: *1 Camelot, 2 São Paulo, 3 Hansom cab, 4 African elephants, 5 New York City, 6 Caffeine, 7 Campaign for Nuclear Disarmament, 8 Aeneas, 9 Absolute zero, 10 Charles Dickens, 11 Clytemnestra, 12 Ingmar Bergman, 13 Six, 14 Brown coal, 15 Molière, 16 A horse, 17 Kapil Dev, 18 New Zealand, 19 Alban Berg, 20 Common business oriented language.*

General Knowledge

Your rating:
- **0-5 Join a library**
- **6-10 Keep at it**
- **11-15 Join a quiz team**
- **16-20 Join Mensa**

1. Which National Park contains the mountain ridge Cader Idris?
2. Of which country is Karachi the largest city?
3. According to the Old Testament, who killed his younger brother Abel?
4. Which nationalist movement is represented by the initials ANC?
5. What is the capital of Spain?
6. Which British general founded the Boy Scouts?
7. Who was the Greek god of love?
8. Which island group includes Majorca and Ibiza?
9. Of which vegetable is the Savoy a variety?
10. With which sport is Severiano Ballesteros associated?
11. What does the acronym UNICEF stand for?
12. What sort of creature is a sidewinder?
13. Which French film maker directed and acted in *Monsieur Hulot's Holiday*?
14. What is the capital of Chile?
15. Of which U.S. state is Dover the capital?
16. Which German novelist wrote *All Quiet on the Western Front*?
17. What nationality was the philosopher Kierkegaard?
18. Which transition metal is represented by the symbol Co?
19. Which British dramatist wrote *The Shoemaker's Holiday*?
20. Which instrument did jazz band leader Lionel Hampton popularise?

ANSWERS: *1 Snowdonia, 2 Pakistan, 3 Cain, 4 African National Congress, 5 Madrid, 6 Lord Baden-Powell, 7 Eros, 8 The Balearic Islands, 9 Cabbage, 10 Golf, 11 United Nations International Children's Emergency Fund, 12 A snake, 13 Jacques Tati, 14 Santiago, 15 Delaware, 16 Erich Maria Remarque, 17 Danish, 18 Cobalt, 19 Thomas Dekker, 20 The vibraphone.*

Sports

Your rating: ● 0-5 Wooden spoon ● 6-10 Bronze medal ● 11-15 Silver medal ● 16-20 Gold medal

1. Who won the men's race in the 1998 London Marathon?
2. What is the name of rugby union club Gloucester's home ground?
3. Which field event title did Jan Zelezny successfully defend at the 1996 Olympic Games?
4. Who knocked France out of the 1986 World Cup?
5. In which year did basketball's Michael Jordan become the NBA's leading scorer for a record tenth time?
6. In which field event did Bob Beamon set a world record at the 1968 Olympic Games that held for 23 years?
7. What was heavyweight boxer Rocky Marciano's nickname?
8. Which club won the League Cup in four successive seasons during the 1980s?
9. In which year did Mary Rand win the Olympic long jump and come second in the pentathlon?
10. Who captured his second major of 1998 in winning the Open at Royal Birkdale?
11. Which World Championship snooker venue is in Sheffield, England?
12. Which rugby union club did Jonathan Sleightholme leave to join Northampton?
13. Which team were captained by Ferenc Puskas at the 1954 football World Cup?
14. Which swimming event did John Naber become the first person to complete in less than two minutes in 1976?
15. Which British driver won the 1989 and 1992 Brazilian Grands Prix?
16. How many players does a beach volleyball team have?
17. Which German player was European Footballer of the Year in 1981?
18. How many caps did rugby union's Gavin Hastings win for Scotland between 1986 and 1995?
19. Why was Rhodesia banned from the 1972 Olympic Games?
20. Which Italian footballer for Sheffield Wednesday famously pushed over referee Paul Alcock in 1998?

***ANSWERS:** 1 Abel Anton, 2 Kingsholm, 3 Javelin, 4 West Germany, 5 1998, 6 Long jump, 7 The Brockton Blockbuster, 8 Liverpool, 9 1964, 10 Mark O'Meara, 11 Crucible Theatre, 12 Bath, 13 Hungary, 14 200m backstroke, 15 Nigel Mansell, 16 Two, 17 Karl-Heinz Rummenigge, 18 61, 19 Because of its apartheid policies, 20 Paulo Di Canio.*

General Knowledge

Your rating:
- 0-5 Join a library
- 6-10 Keep at it
- 11-15 Join a quiz team
- 16-20 Join Mensa

1. Who was the leader of the Labour Party from 1980 to 1983?
2. Which Caribbean country was ruled by Dr Francois Duvalier from 1957 to 1971?
3. Which U.S. novelist wrote *Catch-22*?
4. How is milk sugar otherwise known?
5. What was the forename of Napoleon Bonaparte's first wife?
6. What is the second largest continent in the world?
7. A deficiency of which protein hormone causes the symptoms of diabetes mellitus?
8. Which member of The Beatles released the solo albums *All Things Must Pass* and *Extra Texture*?
9. What is the capital of Egypt?
10. What sort of plant is an ink cap?
11. Which Dublin-born artist painted *Study after Velásquez*?
12. Who was British prime minister from 1923 to 1924, 1924 to 1929, and 1935 to 1937?
13. Of which country is Manama the capital?
14. Which nation gave the Statue of Liberty to America in 1884?
15. On which river does the city of Londonderry lie?
16. Which Greek tragic dramatist wrote *Seven against Thebes* and *Prometheus Bound*?
17. Which German publisher of guidebooks wrote his first guide in 1829?
18. What sort of creature is an Affenpinscher?
19. Patagonia is formed from parts of which two South American countries?
20. Which British yachtsman was the first to sail round the world singlehanded?

ANSWERS: *1 Michael Foot, 2 Haiti, 3 Joseph Heller, 4 Lactose, 5 Joséphine, 6 Africa, 7 Insulin, 8 George Harrison, 9 Cairo, 10 A mushroom, 11 Francis Bacon, 12 Stanley Baldwin, 13 Bahrain, 14 France, 15 River Foyle, 16 Aeschylus, 17 Karl Baedecker, 18 A dog, 19 Argentina and Chile, 20 Sir Francis Chichester.*

General Knowledge

Your rating: ● **0-5 Join a library** ● **6-10 Keep at it** ● **11-15 Join a quiz team** ● **16-20 Join Mensa**

1. Which measurement of intellectual ability is represented by the initials IQ?
2. Which British fighter pilot served in the RAF during World War II despite having lost his legs in an accident in 1931?
3. In which country is the city of Chihuahua?
4. What nationality was the painter and etcher Rembrandt?
5. Which French chemist and microbiologist was the first to produce an effective rabies vaccine?
6. In Greek mythology, which brother of Prometheus was forced to support the sky?
7. What is the capital of Turkey?
8. In which state of the USA is the city of Chicago?
9. Which country's presidents have resided at the Palais de l'Élysée since 1873?
10. In which ocean are the Seychelles and Madagascar?
11. Which US actor starred in the films *Public Enemy* and *The Roaring Twenties*?
12. Which British novelist wrote *The Dressmaker* and *Injury Time*?
13. Which section of the Mediterranean Sea contains the Cyclades and the Dodecanese islands?
14. Which type of insects may belong to the genus *Aedes*?
15. Who succeeded Sir Keith Joseph as secretary of state for education and science in 1987?
16. According to Virgil, who killed herself after being abandoned by her lover Aeneas?
17. Which Italian author wrote the libretti for Mozart's operas *The Marriage of Figaro* and *Don Giovanni*?
18. Of which country is Sarawak a state?
19. Which English monarch summoned the Long Parliament in 1640?
20. Which US president approved the dropping of atom bombs on Japan?

ANSWERS: *1 Intelligence quotient, 2 Sir Douglas Bader, 3 Mexico, 4 Dutch, 5 Louis Pasteur, 6 Atlas, 7 Ankara, 8 Illinois, 9 France, 10 The Indian Ocean, 11 James Cagney, 12 Beryl Bainbridge, 13 Aegean Sea, 14 Mosquitoes, 15 Kenneth Baker, 16 Dido, 17 Lorenzo Da Ponte, 18 Malaysia, 19 Charles I, 20 Harry S. Truman.*

General Knowledge

Your rating:
- **0-5 Join a library**
- **6-10 Keep at it**
- **11-15 Join a quiz team**
- **16-20 Join Mensa**

1. What sort of creature is an impala?
2. The name of which tuned percussion instrument means 'bell play' in German?
3. Which U.S. novelist wrote *A Farewell to Arms* and *The Old Man and the Sea*?
4. Of which country is Nassau the capital?
5. What do the initials GNP stand for?
6. In which continent is the vast Gobi Desert situated?
7. What sort of creature is a flounder?
8. In which Italian city can La Scala opera house be found?
9. What is the capital of Iraq?
10. According to the New Testament, who baptised Jesus?
11. Which breed of dog is named after a character in Sir Walter Scott's novel *Guy Mannering*?
12. Of which country is Phnom Penh the capital?
13. Which battle was made famous by Tennyson's poem *The Charge of the Light Brigade*?
14. What is the largest natural lake in Wales?
15. Which avant-garde U.S. composer wrote *Imaginary Landscape No 4* for 12 randomly tuned radio sets?
16. What is the largest island of the Canadian Arctic?
17. Against which monarch did Jack Cade lead a Kentish rebellion in 1450?
18. Which U.S. novelist wrote *The Call of the Wild*?
19. In which state of the USA is Jefferson City situated?
20. Which stringed musical instrument is named after the Greek wind god Aeolus?

ANSWERS: *1 An antelope, 2 Glockenspiel, 3 Ernest Hemingway, 4 The Bahamas, 5 Gross National Product, 6 Asia, 7 A fish, 8 Milan, 9 Baghdad, 10 John the Baptist, 11 Dandie Dinmont terrier, 12 Cambodia, 13 The Battle of Balaclava, 14 Lake Bala, 15 John Cage, 16 Baffin Island, 17 Henry VI, 18 Jack London, 19 Missouri, 20 Aeolian harp.*

Entertainment

Your rating: ● **0-5** Buy a TV ● **6-10** Keep at it ● **11-15** Join a quiz team ● **16-20** Enter a quiz show

1. Which chat show host presented the 1999 British Academy Television Awards as well as winning in the Best Light Entertainment Performance category?
2. Which Scottish rock band released their second album, *The Man Who*, in 1999?
3. Which country's tourist industry was investigated by the 1999 BBC 1 documentary series *Tourist Trouble*?
4. Which Hollywood star played Hollywood star Anna Scott in the 1999 film *Notting Hill*?
5. Which *Monty Python* member wrote and starred in the Seventies spoof comedy series *Ripping Yarns*?
6. Which tubular bells-playing musician released an album entitled *Guitars* in 1999?
7. In which 1991 film, featuring Harvey Keitel as a detective, did Demi Moore and Bruce Willis both appear?
8. Which scientific anniversary was marked by Channel 4 in 1999 by a documentary series, *The Baby Makers*?
9. What was the title of Kenny Thomas' 1991 U.K. top five hit?
10. In which *Pygmalion*-esque 1999 film did a high school sports hero transform a nerd into a prom queen?
11. What was the title of the 1999 ITV drama in which John Thaw played cosmetic surgeon Joe MacConnell?
12. Which dried fruit provided a U.K. top five hit in 1971 for Titanic?
13. In which 1968 film did Julie Christie and Richard Chamberlain play an unhappily-married couple?
14. What was Kate's occupation in the BBC 1 sitcom *Kiss Me Kate*?
15. Which band motored into the U.K. top five in 1967 with *Paper Sun* and *Hole in My Shoe*?
16. Which actor was Oscar-nominated in 1999 for his role as Bill Paxton's older brother in the film *A Simple Plan*?
17. Who was the host of the quiz show *Sale of the Century*?
18. What was the title of the album released by Moby in 1999?
19. Which former footballer presented ITV's *Guinness World Records*?
20. What was the title of Boyzone's greatest hits album, released in 1999?

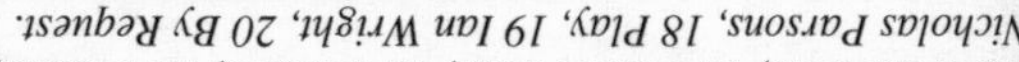

ANSWERS: *1 Michael Parkinson, 2 Travis, 3 Britain's, 4 Julia Roberts, 5 Michael Palin, 6 Mike Oldfield, 7 Mortal Thoughts, 8 The 21st birthday of the first test-tube baby, Louise Brown, 9 Thinking About Your Love, 10 She's All That, 11 Plastic Man, 12 Sultana, 13 Petulia, 14 Therapist, 15 Traffic, 16 Billy Bob Thornton, 17 Nicholas Parsons, 18 Play, 19 Ian Wright, 20 By Request.*

General Knowledge

Your rating:
- **0-5** Join a library
- **6-10** Keep at it
- **11-15** Join a quiz team
- **16-20** Join Mensa

1. What is Macgillicuddy's Reeks?
2. At which Surrey racecourse are the Derby and the Oaks run?
3. Which science-fiction author wrote *Fahrenheit 451*?
4. Which muscular tube, also known as the gullet, runs from the pharynx to the stomach?
5. Of which country is Bergen the second largest city?
6. The name of which constellation of the zodiac means 'bull' in Latin?
7. Which British novelist wrote *The Time Machine*?
8. On which river is Hampton Court situated?
9. What sort of creature is a chameleon?
10. What is the capital of Sweden?
11. Of which country is Mount Logan the highest mountain?
12. Which noble gas is represented by the symbol Kr?
13. Which British director won the Palme d'Or at Cannes for his film *Secrets and Lies*?
14. On which river can Lake Constance be found?
15. Which Polish-born British novelist wrote *Nostromo* and *Lord Jim*?
16. Which psychiatrist wrote *The Divided Self* and *Knots*?
17. Which British chemist gave his name to a miner's safety lamp which he invented in 1815?
18. Which English king was a leader of the third crusade?
19 What sort of creature is a Moorish idol?
20. Which king of France was known as Coeur-de-Lion?

ANSWERS: *1 A mountain range (in Kerry), 2 Epsom, 3 Ray Bradbury, 4 Oesophagus, 5 Norway, 6 Taurus, 7 H. G. Wells, 8 The Thames, 9 A lizard, 10 Stockholm, 11 Canada, 12 Krypton, 13 Mike Leigh, 14 The Rhine, 15 Joseph Conrad, 16 R. D. Laing, 17 Sir Humphry Davy, 18 Richard I, 19 A fish, 20 Louis VIII.*

General Knowledge

Your rating: ● 0-5 Join a library ● 6-10 Keep at it
● 11-15 Join a quiz team ● 16-20 Join Mensa

1. With which musical instrument was Italian virtuoso Niccolò Paganini associated?
2. Which *Dirty Harry* star became mayor of Carmel, California in 1986?
3. How is the city of Constantinople known today?
4. Which county cricket team's ground is situated at Hove?
5. According to the Old Testament, who were the first two human beings?
6. What do the initials CIA stand for?
7. Which Czech-born tennis player was Wimbledon singles champion in 1976, 1979 and 1982-86?
8. Which branch of medicine is concerned with the problems of infants and children?
9. Which Brazilian city is overlooked by Sugar Loaf Mountain and a giant figure of Christ?
10. Which children's writer invented the fictional schools of St Clare's and Mallory Towers?
11. By what name is 6 June 1944 better known?
12. To which Celtic paradise was King Arthur taken after his final battle?
13. Who was the German director of the films *The Enigma of Kaspar Hauser* and *Wozzeck*?
14. Of which African republic is Antananarivo the capital?
15. Which Singapore-born novelist created the character Simon Templar in *Enter the Saint*?
16. Which British conductor founded the London Philharmonic Orchestra?
17. Which order was founded by St Ignatius Loyola in 1533 to propagate the Roman Catholic faith?
18. Which British poet and critic wrote a series of detective stories as Nicholas Blake?
19. Who was the first vice president and the second president of the USA?
20. In which Irish county is Blarney Castle situated?

ANSWERS: *1 The violin, 2 Clint Eastwood, 3 Istanbul, 4 Sussex, 5 Adam and Eve, 6 Central Intelligence Agency, 7 Martina Navratilova, 8 Paediatrics, 9 Rio de Janeiro, 10 Enid Blyton, 11 D-Day, 12 Avalon, 13 Werner Herzog, 14 Madagascar, 15 Leslie Charteris, 16 Sir Thomas Beecham, 17 Jesuits, 18 C. Day Lewis, 19 John Adams, 20 Cork.*

General Knowledge

Your rating: ● 0-5 Join a library ● 6-10 Keep at it ● 11-15 Join a quiz team ● 16-20 Join Mensa

1. What nationality is the composer Karlheinz Stockhausen?
2. Which British novelist wrote *Watership Down* and *The Plague Dogs*?
3. Which river flows mainly northeast from Staffordshire through Nottingham?
4. What do the initials GMT stand for?
5. What is the Latin name for the constellation Great Bear?
6. What are kelp, laver and sea lettuce examples of?
7. According to the New Testament, who was the mother of Jesus Christ?
8. In which state of the USA is the city of Seattle?
9. Which British landscape painter won a gold medal in France for his *Haywain*?
10. Which Canadian city was the venue for the 1976 Olympics?
11. According to the New Testament, which town was the birthplace of Jesus?
12. Which British poet wrote *A Shropshire Lad*?
13. In which state of the USA is the city of Chattanooga?
14. Which German novelist wrote *Steppenwolf* and *The Glass Bead Game*?
15. Cheddar Gorge is located in which range of hills?
16. Which famous U.S. magician and escapologist was born Erich Weiss?
17. Which award is given for the fastest seaborne crossing of the Atlantic?
18. Which sort of insects does the adjective formic relate to?
19. Which Russian composer wrote *Scheherazade* and *The Golden Cockerel*?
20. Which French postimpressionist painted *The Card Players,* which is displayed in the Louvre?

ANSWERS: *1 German, 2 Richard Adams, 3 The River Trent, 4 Greenwich Mean Time, 5 Ursa Major, 6 Seaweed, 7 Mary, 8 Washington, 9 John Constable, 10 Montreal, 11 Bethlehem, 12 A. E. Housman, 13 Tennessee, 14 Hermann Hesse, 15 The Mendip Hills, 16 Harry Houdini, 17 Blue Riband of the Atlantic, 18 Ants, 19 Rimsky-Korsakov, 20 Paul Cézanne.*

Entertainment

Your rating: ● **0-5** **Buy a TV** ● **6-10** **Keep at it** ● **11-15** **Join a quiz team** ● **16-20** **Enter a quiz show**

1. Who introduced the acts competing for the *Record of the Year 2000* on ITV?
2. What was the title of the 2001 U.K. number one hit by Rui Da Silva featuring Cassandra?
3. Which actor was the subject of *The BBC and BAFTA Tribute* in 2000 after receiving a knighthood earlier in the year?
4. In which 2000 film did Nicolas Cage star as a wealthy stockbroker who finds himself in a parallel life?
5. Which former soap actor played Eddie Scrooge in ITV's contemporary version of *A Christmas Carol* in 2000?
6. Which group were deprived of a possible U.K. number one in 2001 after some stores began selling their single *It's the Way You Make Me Feel* a week early?
7. Which actor's TV roles have included Eddie Yeats in *Coronation Street*, Onslow in *Keeping Up Appearances* and Twiggy in *The Royle Family*?
8. In which U.S. state was the 1980 John Travolta film *Urban Cowboy* set?
9. Which sitcom's cast, including Jennifer Saunders and Joanna Lumley, appeared in the comedy pilot *Mirrorball*?
10. With whom did Queen collaborate on the 1981 U.K. number one hit *Under Pressure*?
11. Which 2000 film version of a children's cartoon series featured the evil Lawrence III?
12. Which *Emmerdale* character ended his stag night by being tied to a telegraph pole wearing his underwear and dog collar?
13. Which British group had a U.K. top ten hit with *Sale of the Century* in 1996?
14. Which 1974 film directed by, and starring, Sidney Poitier, also featured Bill Cosby and Richard Pryor?
15. Which U.S. girl group had a 1974 U.K. number one hit with *When Will I See You Again*?
16. Which British comic actor played the title role in the 2000 film *Merlin: The Return*?
17. Which member of *The Goodies* appeared in the Eighties sitcom *Me and My Girl*?
18. What was the title of the 2001 U.K. top five hit by Fragma featuring Maria Rubia?
19. In which African country was the 1988 film *A World Apart* set?
20. Which awards ceremony was hosted by Jonathan Ross in late 2000?

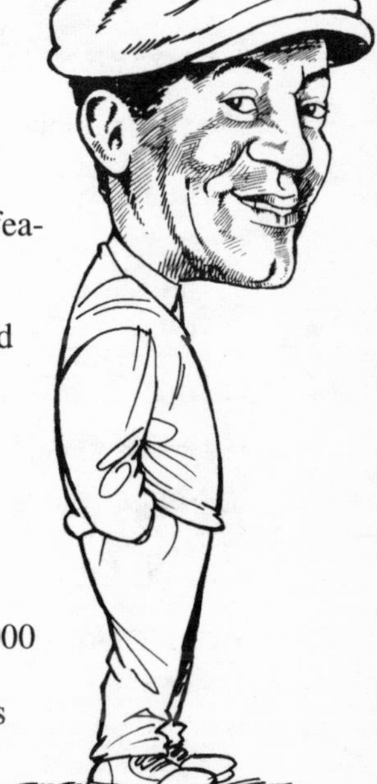

ANSWERS: *1 Denise Van Outen, 2 Touch Me, 3 Michael Caine, 4 The Family Man, 5 Ross Kemp, 6 Steps, 7 Geoffrey Hughes, 8 Texas, 9 Absolutely Fabulous', 10 David Bowie, 11 Pokemon the Movie 2000, 12 Ashley, 13 Sleeper, 14 Uptown Saturday Night, 15 Three Degrees, 16 Rik Mayall, 17 Tim Brooke-Taylor, 18 Everytime You Need Me, 19 South Africa, 20 The British Comedy Awards 2000.*

General Knowledge

Your rating: • 0-5 Join a library • 6-10 Keep at it • 11-15 Join a quiz team • 16-20 Join Mensa

1. Which American dramatist wrote *The Crucible*?
2. By what name is nacre popularly known?
3. Where was the children's TV show *Words and Pictures* set?
4. What name is given to a stand or support for utensils before or on a fire?
5. Which British naval explorer landed at Botany Bay in 1770?
6. In which war was the Battle of the Brandywine fought?
7. What is the name of the pig in the story *Charlotte's Web*?
8. What sort of creature is a Gila monster?
9. Of which salad plant are cos and iceberg varieties?
10. Of which organ is the medulla oblongata a part?
11. What was the first programme to appear on Channel Four?
12. Which French painter founded Cubism with Pablo Picasso?
13. What sort of creature is a trogon?
14. Which motoring organisation agreed to pay £20 million after it was caught plagiarising Ordnance Survey maps?
15. What is the SI unit of frequency?
16. Which German poet wrote *The Ship of Fools*?
17. Who won a Best Song Oscar for the film *Philadelphia*?
18. In the Stations of the Cross, what number is the picture in which Jesus dies on the cross?
19. What name is given to a Hindu of the highest caste?
20. Which English art critic coined the term Post-Impressionism?

ANSWERS: *1 Arthur Miller, 2 Mother-of-pearl, 3 A public library, 4 Trivet, 5 Captain James Cook, 6 American War of Independence, 7 Wilbur, 8 A lizard, 9 Lettuce, 10 The brain, 11 Countdown, 12 Georges Braque, 13 A bird, 14 The AA, 15 Hertz, 16 Sebastian Brant, 17 Bruce Springsteen, 18 Twelve, 19 Brahman, 20 Roger Fry.*

General Knowledge

Your rating: ● **0-5** Join a library ● **6-10** Keep at it ● **11-15** Join a quiz team ● **16-20** Join Mensa

1. Which 19th-century French educator developed a system of writing for the blind?
2. What was the name given to the series of disputes over fishing between Britain and Iceland?
3. Which American trombonist and bandleader disappeared on a flight in 1944?
4. After appearing together in which film did Tom Hanks and Rita Wilson get married?
5. Which creature has between 14 and 177 pairs of legs?
6. Of which country was Bob Hawke prime minister?
7. In which city was actor Kenneth Branagh born?
8. Which comedy duo caused an outcry with a sketch about microwaving a cat?
9. Which method of execution was abolished by the Roman emperor Constantine?
10. Which song from *The Wizard of Oz* was voted the best song of the 20th century by the U.S. music establishment?
11. What was the name of the song chosen as the U.K. entry for the 2001 Eurovision Song Contest?
12. Which American poet wrote the verse collections *A Boy's Will* and *North of Boston*?
13. *Villette* is based on the experiences of Charlotte Bronte as a governess in which foreign city?
14. Which spy was released in 2001 after serving 19 years for betraying secrets during the Cold War?
15. The former duchy of Brabant is divided between which two countries?
16. Which 15-year-old U.S. gymnast won five medals at the Barcelona Olympics?
17. In which country was *Braveheart* mostly filmed?
18. Of which element is tritium a radioactive isotope?
19. Which 3rd-century Roman martyr was condemned to be killed by a squad of archers?
20. Who succeeded to the U.S. presidency on the death of Zachary Taylor?

ANSWERS: *1 Louis Braille, 2 The 'Cod Wars', 3 Glenn Miller, 4 Volunteers, 5 Centipede, 6 Australia, 7 Belfast, 8 Hale and Pace, 9 Crucifixion, 10 Over the Rainbow, 11 No Dream Impossible, 12 Robert Frost, 13 Brussels, 14 Geoffrey Prime, 15 Belgium and the Netherlands, 16 Shannon Miller, 17 Ireland, 18 Hydrogen, 19 Saint Sebastian, 20 Millard Fillmore.*

General Knowledge

Your rating:
- 0-5 Join a library
- 6-10 Keep at it
- 11-15 Join a quiz team
- 16-20 Join Mensa

1. Which leading flat jockey was imprisoned for tax evasion in 1987?
2. In which of his own films does Wes Craven appear as Fred the janitor?
3. Which member of the Royal Family was fined for driving her Bentley at 93 mph in 2001?
4. How many years are there in a century?
5. Which Conservative politician married Jennie Jerome in 1874?
6. In which English county is the town of Braintree?
7. Which *Jaws* actor plays the captain of *SeaQuest DSV* on television?
8. What nationality is the former racing driver and constructor Sir Jack Brabham?
9. Which of the Mitford sisters married Oswald Mosley?
10. What name is given to a large landed estate in Spanish America?
11. In which century was the diary of Samuel Pepys first published?
12. Which Scottish golfer won the British Open five times in the first decade of the 20th century?
13. Who wrote the novels *Tropic of Cancer* and *Tropic of Capricorn*?
14. Which 2001 film starred Keanu Reeves, James Spader and Marisa Tomei?
15. What name is given to the mark under the c in words such as façade and Français?
16. Which former West German chancellor was born Herbert Frahm?
17. Which poet wrote the verse collection *A Martian Sends a Postcard Home*?
18. Who was allowed to help Jesus to carry the cross?
19. Which Second Division team reached the 2000/01 F.A. Cup semi-finals by beating Leicester City?
20. Which very hard metal has the chemical symbol Ta?

ANSWERS: *1 Lester Piggott, 2 Scream, 3 The Princess Royal, 4 100, 5 Randolph Churchill, 6 Essex, 7 Roy Scheider, 8 Australian, 9 Diana, 10 Hacienda, 11 19th, 12 James Braid, 13 Henry Miller, 14 The Watcher, 15 Cedilla, 16 Willy Brandt, 17 Craig Raine, 18 Simon of Cyrene, 19 Wycombe Wanderers, 20 Tantalum.*

Entertainment

Your rating: ● 0-5 Buy a TV ● 6-10 Keep at it ● 11-15 Join a quiz team ● 16-20 Enter a quiz show

1. Which actor played Jeremy Stickles in the 2000 BBC 1 dramatisation of *Lorna Doone*?
2. Which US actress/singer scored a U.K. number one hit with *Love Don't Cost a Thing* in 2001?
3. Which *Star Trek: the Next Generation* actor played Ebenezer Scrooge in a 2000 TV movie version of *A Christmas Carol*?
4. Which 2000 film by M. Night Shyamalan starred Bruce Willis as a security guard who escapes a fatal train derailment?
5. Which Seventies drama series starring Edward Woodward as a newspaper reporter provided a depressing vision of the future?
6. Which Eighties sci-fi series provided the title of a 2001 U.K. top five hit by Feeder?
7. Who directed the *Lethal Weapon* series of films?
8. What was the title of Roachford's 1989 U.K. top five hit?
9. In which country is the 2000 film *Saltwater* set?
10. Which *Coronation Street* character married Emma Taylor on Christmas Eve 2000?
11. Who played *Calamity Jane* in the 1953 film musical of the same name?
12. Which female vocalist had a U.K. top five hit in 1989 with *The Best*?
13. Which 1992 film featured James Belushi and Cybill Shepherd as husband and wife?
14. Which Hollywood actor made an appearance in BBC 2's *The Last Fast Show Ever*?
15. Which glamrock group had a U.K. number one hit in 1973 with *See My Baby Jive*?
16. In which 2000 film did Winona Ryder appear as a former victim of demonic possession?
17. Which Sixties sitcom starring Arthur Lowe was a spin-off from *Coronation Street*?
18. Which British group had a 2001 U.K. top ten hit with *Inner Smile*?
19. What was the name of Arnold Schwarzenegger's character in the 1987 film *Predator*?
20. Which BBC 1 drama, based on *Don Quixote*, starred Colin Firth in the title role?

ANSWERS: *1 Martin Clunes, 2 Jennifer Lopez, 3 Patrick Stewart, 4 Unbreakable, 5 1990, 6 Buck Rogers, 7 Richard Donner, 8 Cuddly Toy, 9 Ireland, 10 Curly Watts, 11 Doris Day, 12 Tina Turner, 13 Once Upon a Crime, 14 Johnny Depp, 15 Wizzard, 16 Lost Souls, 17 Pardon the Expression, 18 Texas, 19 Dutch, 20 Donovan Quick.*

General Knowledge

Your rating: ● 0-5 Join a library ● 6-10 Keep at it ● 11-15 Join a quiz team ● 16-20 Join Mensa

1. Which German motor manufacturer was set up in 1937 to produce a 'people's car'?
2. The River Tamar forms a historic boundary between which two counties?
3. What is the profession of Nick in the sitcom *Beast*?
4. Who played Sally Bowles in the film *Cabaret*?
5. Which fish is smoked and sold as finnan haddie?
6. Of which country has Juan Carlos been king since 1975?
7. Which E.M. Forster novel centres on the relationship between the Schlegels and the Wilcoxes?
8. Which classic children's story was written by Louisa M. Alcott?
9. What name is given to the national religious folk cult of Haiti?
10. Which substance gives tea its colour and astringency?
11. The film *Jerry Maguire* featured which sport?
12. Which 16th-century English composer wrote the 40-part *Spem in alium*?
13. What is the chief river of Ghana?
14. Which 2001 film about the Cuban missile crisis starred Kevin Costner?
15. Of which organisation was Oliver Tambo president general from 1969 to 1991?
16. Which U.S. shot-putter developed the style in which the putter turns 180 degrees?
17. In which country did television's *Reilly - Ace of Spies* operate?
18. Which epic poem by Dante begins on Good Friday in 1300?
19. Which 19th-century British philosopher wrote the essay *On Liberty*?
20. Who was the first direct descendant of Queen Elizabeth II not to bear a royal title?

ANSWERS: *1 Volkswagen, 2 Devon and Cornwall, 3 Vet, 4 Liza Minnelli, 5 Haddock, 6 Spain, 7 Howards End, 8 Little Women, 9 Voodoo, 10 Tannin, 11 American football, 12 Thomas Tallis, 13 Volta, 14 Thirteen Days, 15 African National Congress, 16 Parry O'Brien, 17 Russia, 18 The Divine Comedy, 19 John Stuart Mill, 20 Peter Phillips.*

General Knowledge

Your rating:

- **0-5** Join a library
- **6-10** Keep at it
- **11-15** Join a quiz team
- **16-20** Join Mensa

1. Which Canadian singer recorded the albums *Blue* and *Miles of Aisles*?
2. What number was *The Prisoner* in the television series of that name?
3. Which Irish adventurer attempted to steal the crown jewels from the Tower of London in 1671?
4. Who was sacked as manager of Tottenham Hotspur in 2001?
5. Which device in a jet engine provides extra thrust for takeoff or supersonic flight?
6. Of which U.S. state is Tallahassee the capital?
7. Who won Best Score Oscars for *Star Wars* and *ET*?
8. In geometry, what name is given to a straight line that touches a curve at one point?
9. What was the first single by Hear'Say, the group created by the *Popstars* TV series?
10. Which South African language is also called Cape Dutch?
11. The title of the TV series *Triangle* described the route between Gothenburg, Rotterdam and which English port?
12. Which Shakespeare play is about one of King Priam's sons?
13. What is the name of the petrol-thickening jelly used in incendiary bombs and flame-throwers?
14. Which golfer became the oldest winner in the history of the European tour when he won the 2001 Madeira Island Open?
15. What sort of creature is a tanager?
16. Which French author was born François-Marie Arouet?
17. Who provided the voice for Jessica Rabbit in the film *Who Framed Roger Rabbit*?
18. Which South African dramatist wrote the play *No-Good Friday*?
19. Which Welsh rugby player scored in every possible way in their 2001 Six Nations win against France?
20. Agate is a semiprecious variety of what form of quartz?

ANSWERS: *1 Joni Mitchell, 2 Six, 3 Colonel Blood, 4 George Graham, 5 Afterburner, 6 Florida, 7 John Williams, 8 Tangent, 9 Pure and Simple, 10 Afrikaans, 11 Felixstowe, 12 Troilus and Cressida, 13 Napalm, 14 Des Smyth, 15 A bird, 16 Voltaire, 17 Kathleen Turner, 18 Athol Fugard, 19 Neil Jenkins, 20 Chalcedony.*

General Knowledge

Your rating:
- 0-5 Join a library
- 6-10 Keep at it
- 11-15 Join a quiz team
- 16-20 Join Mensa

1. Which narcotic drug obtained from opium is used in medicine for the relief of severe pain?
2. Which child star was born Joe Yule?
3. What is the longest river in Europe?
4. Who was the first bowler to take 500 wickets in Test cricket?
5. Which English novelist wrote *She* and *Queen Sheba's Ring*?
6. From which character in Greek mythology do we get the word tantalise?
7. Who played *Edward VII* in the 1975 TV series?
8. For which film did Jessica Tandy win a Best Actress Oscar?
9. What name is given to the natural environment of an organism?
10. Which fish gets its name from its long whisker-like barbels?
11. Michael Barrymore was formerly what to Shirley Bassey and others?
12. Which team game was originally called Mintonette?
13. In Greek mythology, which merman is traditionally shown blowing on a conch shell?
14. Which *This Life* actor starred in the TV drama series *Teachers*?
15. Tammany Hall is the executive committee of which U.S. political party in New York?
16. Which Italian physicist gave his name to the SI unit of electromotive force?
17. Which director released the album *You Made Me Love You*?
18. By what name was the Russian city of Volgograd known from 1925 to 1961?
19. What form of Indian cookery takes its name from the cylindrical clay oven used?
20. Which American novelist wrote *Player Piano* and *Breakfast of Champions*?

ANSWERS: *1 Morphine, 2 Mickey Rooney, 3 The Volga, 4 Courtney Walsh, 5 H Rider Haggard, 6 Tantalus, 7 Timothy West, 8 Driving Miss Daisy, 9 Habitat, 10 Catfish, 11 Hairdresser, 12 Volleyball, 13 Triton, 14 Andrew Lincoln, 15 Democratic Party, 16 Alessandro Volta, 17 Orson Welles, 18 Stalingrad, 19 Tandoori, 20 Kurt Vonnegut Jr.*

Entertainment

Your rating: ● **0-5** Buy a TV ● **6-10** Keep at it ● **11-15** Join a quiz team ● **16-20** Enter a quiz show

1. Which comedian starred in the BBC 1 collection of sketches *In Pieces*?
2. Which sportz-metal band hit the UK number one spot in 2001 with *Rollin'*?
3. Which famous Flowerpot Men returned to TV in 2001, this time in full colour and without strings?
4. Who directed the 2000 action film *Crouching Tiger, Hidden Dragon*?
5. Which actor played Indian reporter Hari Kumar in the Eighties TV drama *The Jewel in the Crown*?
6. What was the title of the U.K. debut single by Spooks, which hit the top ten in 2001?
7. Which 1979 film starred Charles Bronson as an FBI agent and Rod Steiger as a Mafia boss?
8. Which ITV drama series starred Peter Davison and Amanda Redman as husband and wife?
9. Which U.S. band had a U.K. top five hit with *E-Bow the Letter* in 1996?
10. Which 2000 film featured Kim Basinger as the aunt of a little girl who can perform miracles?
11. What was the title of the BBC 1 comedy drama which starred Billy Connolly as Kingdom Swann, Edwardian photographer?
12. What was the title of Sonia's debut single, which hit the U.K. number one spot in 1989?
13. Which horror film actor played Prince Prospero in 1964's *The Masque of the Red Death*?
14. Which former *EastEnder* starred as single mum Abby in the BBC 1 drama series *2,000 Acres of Sky*?
15. Which U.S. vocalist had a U.K. top five hit in 1976 with *Theme From Mahogany (Do You Know Where You're Going To)*?
16. Which 2000 film set in an American high school was based on a novel by Dostoevsky?
17. What did Del and Raquel name their son in the sitcom *Only Fools and Horses*?
18. Which girl group had a 2001 U.K. top ten hit with *All Hooked Up*?
19. Which future James Bond star appeared as French anthropologist Pommier in the 1985 film *Nomads*?
20. Which decade was revisited by Channel 4 in its follow-up to the series *The 1900s House*?

ANSWERS: *1 Lenny Henry, 2 Limp Bizkit, 3 Bill and Ben, 4 Ang Lee, 5 Art Malik, 6 Things I've Seen, 7 Love and Bullets, 8 At Home With the Braithwaites, 9 REM, 10 Bless the Child, 11 Gentlemen's Relish, 12 You'll Never Stop Me Loving You, 13 Vincent Price, 14 Michelle Collins, 15 Diana Ross, 16 Crime + Punishment in Suburbia, 17 Damien, 18 All Saints, 19 Pierce Brosnan, 20 The 1940s (The 1940s House).*

General Knowledge

Your rating: ● 0-5 Join a library ● 6-10 Keep at it ● 11-15 Join a quiz team ● 16-20 Join Mensa

1. Which prolific U.S. inventor invented the electric light bulb?
2. Whose first film appearance was as second welder in the 1957 film *Time Lock*?
3. Which film was named Best Picture at the 2001 Oscars?
4. In which constellation are the stars Castor and Pollux?
5. Which country singer and actor married Julia Roberts in 1993?
6. On which Japanese port was the second atom bomb dropped in 1945?
7. What is the middle name of American author Dean R. Koontz?
8. What title is given to the prime minister of Germany?
9. Which Swedish tennis player won five successive Wimbledon men's singles titles?
10. Of which county is Kingston-upon-Thames the administrative centre?
11. To which film was *The Jewel of the Nile* a sequel?
12. Which Russian-born U.S. novelist wrote *The Fountainhead*?
13. General Sani Abacha became president of which African country in 1993?
14. Which pilot flew the first British Concorde in 1969?
15. Who wrote *The Unbearable Lightness of Being*?
16. Which Italian actor starred in *A Fistful of Dollars* and *Lucky Luciano*?
17. What relation was novelist Isabel Allende to the overthrown Chilean president Salvador Allende?
18. By what name was Haitian president Jean-Claude Duvalier known?
19. Which 2001 film starred Robert De Niro and Kelsey Grammer?
20. What is the technical name for weakening of the bones?

ANSWERS: *1 Thomas Edison, 2 Sean Connery, 3 Gladiator, 4 Gemini, 5 Lyle Lovett, 6 Nagasaki, 7 Ray, 8 Chancellor, 9 Bjorn Borg, 10 Surrey, 11 Romancing the Stone, 12 Ayn Rand, 13 Nigeria, 14 Brian Trubshaw, 15 Milan Kundera, 16 Gian Maria Volonte, 17 Niece, 18 Baby Doc, 19 15 Minutes, 20 Osteoporosis.*

General Knowledge

Your rating: ● 0-5 Join a library ● 6-10 Keep at it ● 11-15 Join a quiz team ● 16-20 Join Mensa

1. Which comic strip features Snoopy, Charlie Brown and Linus?
2. Which jazz musician is the subject of the novel *Young Man with a Horn* by Dorothy Baker?
3. Which title was conferred on Princess Anne in 1987?
4. In which European country is the port La Coruña?
5. Which athletics field event was formerly known as the hop, step and jump?
6. What does IVF stand for?
7. Whose was the only voice heard in the Mel Brooks film *Silent Movie*?
8. Which 2001 film starred Sandra Bullock, Michael Caine and William Shatner?
9. In the Old Testament, which miraculous food sustained the Israelites in the wilderness?
10. What name is given to an abscess at the root of an eyelash?
11. Who wrote *The Cat in the Hat*?
12. Which Shakespeare play features Ferdinand, the king of Navarre?
13. Who won a Best Actor Oscar for his performance in *Gladiator*?
14. Which community for homeless boys was founded by Father Edward Flanagan in Nebraska in 1917?
15. What was the pen name of the author John Griffith Chaney?
16. Abigail was one of the wives of which Biblical king of Israel?
17. Who was the first contestant to be evicted from the *Big Brother* house in the 2001 series?
18. Which gas is synthesised using the Haber-Bosch process?
19. By what name is the central keep of the Tower of London known?
20. Which British author created the detective Albert Campion?

ANSWERS: *1 Peanuts, 2 Bix Beiderbecke, 3 Princess Royal, 4 Spain, 5 Triple jump, 6 In vitro fertilisation, 7 Marcel Marceau, 8 Miss Congeniality, 9 Manna, 10 Stye, 11 Dr Seuss, 12 Love's Labours Lost, 13 Russell Crowe, 14 Boys Town, 15 Jack London, 16 David, 17 Penny, 18 Ammonia, 19 The White Tower, 20 Margery Allingham.*

General Knowledge

Your rating: ● **0-5** **Join a library** ● **6-10** **Keep at it** ● **11-15** **Join a quiz team** ● **16-20** **Join Mensa**

1. Which bridge was re-erected as a tourist attraction at Lake Havasu City in Arizona?
2. Which former pop star starred in the TV series *Budgie*?
3. Which university won the 2001 Boat Race?
4. With which sport is Kareem Abdul-Jabbar associated?
5. Which German city was the venue for the trials of Nazi war criminals after World War II?
6. How many inches are there in a foot?
7. Which film had the publicity line - "In space no-one can hear you scream"?
8. What name is given to the removal or reduction of parts of a plant or tree?
9. Which country did England's cricket team beat 2-1 in a Test series in 2001?
10. What is Scotland's third largest city?
11. What is the name of the language used in the Anthony Burgess novel *A Clockwork Orange*?
12. Which French monarch was known as the Sun King?
13. Of which newspaper was Ben Bradlee executive editor from 1968 to 1991?
14. Which veteran singer-songwriter won the Oscar for Best Original Song at the 2001 Oscars?
15. What sort of glassware has a name meaning 'a thousand flowers' in Italian?
16. Which English runner won the 800m at the 1924 and 1928 Olympics?
17. In which TV series did the character Frasier first appear?
18. What name is given to a star that explodes and increases in brightness by a million times or more?
19. With what sort of books is author Louis L'Amour chiefly associated?
20. Which Essex town was called Caesaromagus by the Romans?

ANSWERS: *1 London Bridge, 2 Adam Faith, 3 Cambridge, 4 Basketball, 5 Nuremberg, 6 Twelve, 7 Alien, 8 Pruning, 9 Sri Lanka, 10 Aberdeen, 11 Nadsat, 12 Louis XIV, 13 Washington Post, 14 Bob Dylan, 15 Millefiori, 16 Doug Lowe, 17 Cheers, 18 Supernova, 19 Westerns, 20 Chelmsford.*

Sports

Your rating: ● 0-5 Wooden spoon ● 6-10 Bronze medal ● 11-15 Silver medal ● 16-20 Gold medal

1. Which South American country knocked Great Britain out of the Davis Cup world group in July 2000?
2. Which British golfer lost in a play-off for the 1995 U.S. Open title to Steve Elkington?
3. Who won the F.A. Cup in 2000?
4. In which country is the Magny-Cours motor racing circuit?
5. What nationality is 1976 Olympic Games double gold medallist Alberto Juantorena?
6. Which driver achieved his first victory in 123 races at the 2000 German Grand Prix?
7. Which jockey rode Troy to victory in the 1979 Derby?
8. Who was the first player to reach 1000 points in Tests in rugby union?
9. Which sport is often called the noble art?
10. Who won the 100m at the 1996 Olympics?
11. Which country did Britain's men beat by half a point to win athletics' European Cup at Gateshead in July 2000?
12. Wayne Gretzky is a legend in which sport?
13. Which country won the 1970 football World Cup?
14. Who did the Newcastle Falcons beat in the Tetleys Bitter Cup Final in February 2001?
15. What is the minimum number of darts required to finish from a 501 start?
16. Which British football manager was born in Glasgow in 1941?
17. In which month is Royal Ascot traditionally held?
18. Former middle-distance runner Steve Ovett was born in which year?
19. How many pieces does a player start a game of chess with?
20. Which legendary cricketer had a Test batting average of 99.94?

ANSWERS: *1 Ecuador, 2 Colin Montgomerie, 3 Chelsea, 4 France, 5 Cuban, 6 Rubens Barrichello, 7 Willie Carson, 8 Neil Jenkins, 9 Boxing, 10 Donovan Bailey, 11 Germany, 12 Ice hockey, 13 Brazil, 14 Harlequins, 15 9, 16 Alex Ferguson, 17 June, 18 1955, 19 16, 20 Don Bradman.*

General Knowledge

Your rating:
- 0-5 Join a library
- 6-10 Keep at it
- 11-15 Join a quiz team
- 16-20 Join Mensa

1. Which British athlete won the women's long jump at the 1964 Olympics?
2. Who wrote *The Thirty-Nine Steps*?
3. Which English king abdicated in 1936?
4. Who won a Best Actress Oscar for her performance in *Erin Brockovich*?
5. How many millimetres are there in a kilometre?
6. In which U.S. state is Napa Valley?
7. Where was the actor Andrew Sachs born?
8. What was the name of the Lone Ranger's horse?
9. Which actress starred in *The Night of the Hunter* and *The Whales of August*?
10. How many cards does each player have in a game of whist?
11. Which religious group featured in the film *Witness*?
12. Which French actor starred in the Hollywood films *Algiers* and *Gaslight*?
13. With which boy band is Ritchie Neville a singer?
14. Which English poet wrote *Stone and Flower* and *Farewell Happy Fields*?
15. In radio, what does AM stand for?
16. Which U.S. nuclear-powered submarine was the first vessel to circumnavigate the world underwater?
17. How many films did Fred Astaire make with Ginger Rogers?
18. Whitefish Bay is the southeastern arm of which of the Great Lakes?
19. Which star of *Fawlty Towers* presented *The Human Face* on TV?
20. What was the real first name of the spy Kim Philby?

ANSWERS: *1 Mary Rand, 2 John Buchan, 3 Edward VIII, 4 Julia Roberts, 5 One million, 6 California, 7 Germany, 8 Silver, 9 Lillian Gish, 10 Thirteen, 11 The Amish, 12 Charles Boyer, 13 5ive, 14 Kathleen Raine, 15 Amplitude modulation, 16 Triton, 17 11, 18 Lake Superior, 19 John Cleese, 20 Harold*

General Knowledge

Your rating: ● 0-5 Join a library ● 6-10 Keep at it ● 11-15 Join a quiz team ● 16-20 Join Mensa

1. Which international environmental pressure group was founded in British Columbia in 1971?
2. What name is given to tissue damage caused by exposure to extreme cold?
3. Which 2001 film set in Mexico starred Penelope Cruz and Matt Damon?
4. Who sailed around the world in *Gipsy Moth IV*?
5. Which collection of fairy tales includes *Hansel and Gretel* and *Rumpelstiltskin*?
6. Who was elected President of France in 1995?
7. Which Russian novelist wrote *And Quiet Flows the Don*?
8. Which lighthouse was one of the Seven Wonders of the World?
9. In which English county is Burton upon Trent?
10. Who served three terms as Lord Mayor of London between 1397 and 1420?
11. Which system of healing is based on the belief that disease results from a lack of normal nerve function?
12. Who presented the quiz show *3-2-1*?
13. Which dancer and choreographer died in 2001 at the age of 102?
14. What is the only seal that feeds on penguins?
15. Which English dramatist wrote *The Lady's Not for Burning*?
16. In which English county is the town of Chippenham?
17. Who provided the voice of the dragon in the Disney film *Mulan*?
18. The Fédération Colombophile Internationale is the world governing body of which sport?
19. Which English novelist wrote *New Grub Street*?
20. Who was the first prime minister to use Chequers as his country residence?

ANSWERS: 1 *Greenpeace*, 2 *Frostbite*, 3 *All the Pretty Horses*, 4 *Sir Francis Chichester*, 5 *Grimm's Fairy Tales*, 6 *Jacques Chirac*, 7 *Mikhail Sholokhov*, 8 *Pharos of Alexandria*, 9 *Staffordshire*, 10 *Dick Whittington*, 11 *Chiropractic*, 12 *Ted Rogers*, 13 *Dame Ninette de Valois*, 14 *Leopard seal*, 15 *Christopher Fry*, 16 *Wiltshire*, 17 *Eddie Murphy*, 18 *Pigeon racing*, 19 *George Gissing*, 20 *David Lloyd George*.

General Knowledge

Your rating: ● 0-5 Join a library ● 6-10 Keep at it ● 11-15 Join a quiz team ● 16-20 Join Mensa

1. Which scavenging doglike mammal has striped, spotted and brown varieties?
2. Who made up *The Odd Couple* with Jack Lemmon?
3. Which country was the first to use 'gunboat diplomacy'?
4. A portrait of which American president was sold for $20 million in March 2001?
5. Which Scottish village hosts the best-known Highland Games?
6. What sort of creature is a cockatoo?
7. Who wrote an autobiography entitled *Is It Me*?
8. Of which Asian country is Tamil Nadu a state?
9. Which supposedly magical word was used by Gnostics in the 2nd century?
10. How many players are there is a volleyball team?
11. Which 19th-century British artist painted *Christ in the House of His Parents*?
12. Who connects *Star Trek* and *T J Hooker* on TV?
13. Which American author wrote *The Holcroft Covenant* and *The Icarus Agenda*?
14. In what year did the English Civil War end?
15. Which African lake is the second deepest in the world?
16. In Arthurian legend, which knight of the Round Table was the son of King Lot?
17. In which country is the Shakespeare play *A Midsummer Night's Dream* set?
18. Of which Himalayan kingdom is Thimbu or Thimphu the capital?
19. Which American astronomer predicted the existence of a planet beyond Neptune?
20. Of which Irish county is Mullingar the county town?

ANSWERS: *1 Hyena, 2 Walter Matthau, 3 Germany, 4 George Washington, 5 Braemar, 6 A parrot, 7 Terry Wogan, 8 India, 9 Abracadabra, 10 Six, 11 Sir John Everett Millais, 12 William Shatner, 13 Robert Ludlum, 14 1651, 15 Lake Tanganyika, 16 Gawain, 17 Greece, 18 Bhutan, 19 Percival Lowell, 20 Westmeath.*

Entertainment

Your rating:
- **0-5 Buy a TV**
- **6-10 Keep at it**
- **11-15 Join a quiz team**
- **16-20 Enter a quiz show**

1. Which comedian played a drugs baron in the Lynda La Plante TV drama *Supply and Demand*?
2. Who won a Best Actor Oscar for his performance in the 1967 film *In the Heat of the Night*?
3. Which Radio One DJ narrated the Channel 4 series *Classic Trains*?
4. Which Scandinavian band had a U.K. top ten hit single in 1991 with *Joyride*?
5. Which actor played The Director in the film *Beyond The Clouds*?
6. Who starred on TV as *The Bionic Woman*?
7. Which trouser-splitting '60s star collaborated with Marc Almond on a 1997 album entitled *Legend*?
8. Who played Jesus in the 1965 film *The Greatest Story Ever Told*?
9. Who starred as Father Peter in BBC 1's *Ballykissangel*?
10. Who had a U.K. number one hit single in 1960 with *Tell Laura I Love Her*?
11. Which actor played Irish bridge-building engineer Colonel Patterson in the film *The Ghost And The Darkness*?
12. Which Sixties TV adventure series starring Richard Basehart and David Hedison was set aboard an atomic submarine?
13. Who directed the 1980 film *The Great Rock 'N' Roll Swindle*?
14. Who had a U.K. top ten hit single in 1992 with *Tears In Heaven*?
15. Who starred in the title role of the 1997 film *The Preacher's Wife*?
16. Who presented TV's *Put it to the Test*?
17. Which British band released an album entitled *Razorblade Suitcase* in 1997?
18. What is the name of Bart's favourite clown in the animated TV series *The Simpsons*?
19. Which 1997 film, starring Geoffrey Rush, told the true story of eccentric Australian concert pianist David Helfgott?
20. Which footballer won the BBC's 1998 Sports Personality of the Year Award at the 45th *Sports Review of the Year*?

ANSWERS: *1 Freddie Starr, 2 Rod Steiger, 3 John Peel, 4 Roxette, 5 John Malkovich, 6 Lindsay Wagner, 7 P. J. Proby, 8 Max Von Sydow, 9 Stephen Tompkinson, 10 Ricky Valance, 11 Val Kilmer, 12 Voyage to the Bottom of the Sea, 13 Julien Temple, 14 Eric Clapton, 15 Whitney Houston, 16 Carol Vorderman, 17 Bush, 18 Krusty, 19 Shine, 20 Michael Owen.*

General Knowledge

Your rating:
- 0-5 Join a library
- 6-10 Keep at it
- 11-15 Join a quiz team
- 16-20 Join Mensa

1. At which Swiss resort is the Cresta Run located?
2. What is the classical literary language of the Hindu scriptures?
3. How many cents are in a U.S. dollar?
4. Of which country is Antwerp the main port?
5. What sort of creature is an anaconda?
6. Which starchy foodstuff is the main ingredient of the Japanese drink saké?
7. Which New Zealand soprano sang at the wedding of the Prince and Princess of Wales, and was made a DBE in 1982?
8. In 1979, Greenland gained self-government under the sovereignty of which European country?
9. What is defined by Ohm's law as the ratio of the potential difference between the ends of a conductor to the current flowing through it?
10. In which Bosnian city was Francis Ferdinand assassinated in 1914, precipitating World War I?
11. Which Italian racing motorcyclist won a record 15 world championship titles between 1966 and 1975?
12. Which Canadian island is known as "the graveyard of the Atlantic"?
13. Which British novelist wrote *The Mysteries of Udolpho*?
14. Which British composer wrote the opera *Troilus and Cressida*?
15. What was the name for the legislative assembly of the German Empire and the Weimar Republic?
16. Who was the vice president of the USA from 1969 to 1973?
17. Of which country is Dhaka the capital?
18. Who was the last king of Italy?
19. Which disease is prevented by the Sabin vaccine?
20. What sort of creature is a tamarin?

ANSWERS: *1 St Moritz, 2 Sanskrit, 3 One hundred, 4 Belgium, 5 A snake, 6 Rice, 7 Dame Kiri Te Kanawa, 8 Denmark, 9 Resistance, 10 Sarajevo, 11 Giacomo Agostini, 12 Sable Island, 13 Ann Radcliffe, 14 Sir William Walton, 15 Reichstag, 16 Spiro Agnew, 17 Bangladesh, 18 Umberto II, 19 Polio, 20 A monkey.*

General Knowledge

Your rating:
- 0-5 Join a library
- 6-10 Keep at it
- 11-15 Join a quiz team
- 16-20 Join Mensa

1. Which U.S. composer wrote the music to *West Side Story*?
2. In which county can Eton College be found?
3. What is the name for a straight line that touches a curve at only one point?
4. Which British author wrote the children's classic *Alice's Adventures in Wonderland*?
5. What is the official language of the Republic of San Marino?
6. On which river does Nottingham stand?
7. Which Australian feminist wrote *The Female Eunuch*?
8. Which silvery-white metal is represented by the symbol Al?
9. Which international environmental pressure group was founded in 1971 to protest against nuclear tests in the Aleutian Islands?
10. In which European country is the port of Piraeus?
11. What was the name of the Danish princess who married Edward VII when he was the Prince of Wales?
12. Who was director general of the BBC from 1927 to 1938?
13. Which Irish monk founded the monastery at Lindisfarne?
14. What is the name of both the third largest city in Spain and the third largest city in Venezuela?
15. Which US explorer was the first to reach the North Pole?
16. Of which African republic was Hastings Banda president?
17. Which British aeronautical engineer is best known for his invention in 1943 of a bouncing bomb?
18. What sort of creature is a greylag?
19. On which Mediterranean island is the volcano Mount Etna?
20. Which unit of power is represented by the letter W?

ANSWERS: *1 Leonard Bernstein, 2 Berkshire, 3 Tangent, 4 Lewis Carroll, 5 Italian, 6 The River Trent, 7 Germaine Greer, 8 Aluminium, 9 Greenpeace, 10 Greece, 11 Alexandra, 12 John Reith, 13 St Aidan, 14 Valencia, 15 Robert Peary, 16 Malawi, 17 Sir Barnes Wallis, 18 A goose, 19 Sicily, 20 Watt.*

General Knowledge

Your rating: ● **0-5** Join a library ● **6-10** Keep at it ● **11-15** Join a quiz team ● **16-20** Join Mensa

1. According to legend, which king of Wessex burnt a peasant housewife's cakes?
2. At which Maryland retreat of the U.S. president did Sadat and Begin agree to a framework for establishing peace in the Middle East?
3. Against which country did England fight the Battle of Agincourt?
4. With which sport is David Gower associated?
5. Which U.S. actress starred in the films *Platinum Blonde* and *Bombshell*?
6. The storming of which Paris fortress on 14th July 1789 was regarded as the beginning of the French Revolution?
7. Which brothers wrote the collection of fairy tales called *Kinder und Hausmärchen*?
8. Which country formed the Benelux customs union with Belgium and the Netherlands in 1948?
9. Which 11-a-side field game is started with a bully-off in the centre of the field?
10. Of which country is Beirut the capital?
11. Which French novelist wrote *Bonjour Tristesse*?
12. At which London theatre did Lilian Baylis establish an opera and ballet company in 1931?
13. Which House of Representatives committee was established in 1935 to investigate subversive organisations in the USA?
14. Which U.S. general commanded the Seventh Army in Sicily and the Third Army in France in World War II?
15. What sort of creature is a remora?
16. Which pupil of Aristotle was king of Macedon from 336 to 323 BC?
17. What is the capital of Florida?
18. What sort of creature is a barbastelle?
19. Of which country was Alfonso XIII king from 1886 to 1931?
20. Which U.S. director made the films *The Wild Bunch* and *Straw Dogs*?

ANSWERS: *1 Alfred the Great, 2 Camp David, 3 France, 4 Cricket, 5 Jean Harlow, 6 The Bastille, 7 The brothers Grimm, 8 Luxembourg, 9 Hockey, 10 The Lebanon, 11 Françoise Sagan, 12 Sadler's Wells Theatre, 13 The Un-American Activities Committee, 14 George Patton, 15 A fish, 16 Alexander the Great, 17 Tallahassee, 18 A bat, 19 Spain, 20 Sam Peckinpah.*

Entertainment

Your rating: ● **0-5 Buy a TV** ● **6-10 Keep at it** ● **11-15 Join a quiz team** ● **16-20 Enter a quiz show**

1. What was the name of the girl group who were Britain's entry in the 1999 *Eurovision Song Contest*?
2. Which British band had a 1999 U.K. hit with *Canned Heat*, taken from their album, *Synkronized*?
3. In which 1999 film did Keanu Reeves star as computer nerd Thomas and his alter-ego, Neo?
4. What was the title of the Seventies series starring Derek Farr and Patricia Hayes, about the inhabitants of a London lodging house pre-World War II?
5. What was the title of Baz Luhrmann's 1999 U.K. number one hit?
6. Which actress played the girl in the 1937 film *One Hundred Men and a Girl*?
7. What was the name of the pathologist played by Amanda Burton in the BBC 1 crime drama series *Silent Witness*?
8. Who had three U.K. top ten hits in 1964 with *Hold Me*, *Together* and *Somewhere*?
9. Who wrote the semi-autobiographical novel upon which the 1999 film *Other Voices, Other Rooms*, was based?
10. Which ITV drama series, created by former *Coronation Street* producer Brian Park, was set in Larkhall women's prison?
11. What was the title of the 1968 U.K. number one hit for Love Affair?
12. Which famous U.S. novelist wrote and directed the 1984 film *Runaway*?
13. Which 1999 fly-on-the-wall ITV documentary followed the work of the PDSA veterinary charity at the New Cross clinic in London?
14. Which British group had U.K. top ten hits in 1982 with *Ghosts* and *I Second That Emotion*?
15. Which *Pulp Fiction* actress starred in the 1999 film *American Perfekt*?
16. Which actor starred as the director of operations of a SAS-style unit in the TV drama series *The Sandbaggers*?
17. Which Texan band had a 1999 U.K. top five single with *Kiss Me*?
18. Which 1973 film starred Barbra Streisand and Robert Redford as lovers who meet on a college campus of the late 1930s?
19. Which comedy panel gameshow had Jonathan Ross as its host and Phill Jupitus and Julian Clary as its team captains?
20. Which 1973 film starring Al Pacino was based on the true story of a New York policeman who helped to expose departmental corruption in the force?

ANSWERS: *1 Precious, 2 Jamiroquai, 3 The Matrix, 4 London Belongs to Me, 5 Everybody's Free (To Wear Sunscreen), 6 Deanna Durbin, 7 Professor Sam Ryan, 8 P.J. Proby, 9 Truman Capote, 10 Bad Girls, 11 Everlasting Love, 12 Michael Crichton, 13 The People's Vet, 14 Japan, 15 Amanda Plummer, 16 Roy Marsden, 17 Sixpence None the Richer, 18 The Way We Were, 19 It's Only TV, But I Like It, 20 Serpico.*

General Knowledge

Your rating: ● 0-5 Join a library ● 6-10 Keep at it ● 11-15 Join a quiz team ● 16-20 Join Mensa

1. Which British statesman founded the Metropolitan Police in 1829?
2. In which state of the USA is the city of Las Vegas situated?
3. Which noble gas is represented by the symbol Ne?
4. Who is the patron saint of Ireland?
5. What sort of creature is a mastiff?
6. Which 17th century mausoleum in Agra was constructed from pure white Makrana marble?
7. How is light amplification by stimulated emission of radiation better known?
8. Who began the Reformation in 1517 by nailing his 95 theses on the door of the Wittenberg castle church?
9. Which British hospital reformer was the first woman to receive the Order of Merit?
10. The name of which intellectual and cultural movement that began in Italy in the 14th century means 'rebirth' in French?
11. Who was the last Anglo-Saxon King of England?
12. Which US composer wrote the songs *Swanee River* and *Beautiful Dreamer*?
13. What sort of creature is a firebrat?
14. According to Greek legend, which nymph was deprived of speech leaving her able to repeat only the final words of others?
15. What is the largest of the Swedish islands?
16. Which Russian tsar was the subject of a play by Pushkin, on which Mussorgsky based a famous opera?
17. Which Anglican churchman was nicknamed the 'Gloomy Dean'?
18. Which US chess player became an International Grandmaster at 15 and world champion in 1972?
19. Which strait connects the Sea of Marmara with the Aegean Sea?
20. Which Italian poet wrote *The Divine Comedy*?

ANSWERS: *1 Sir Robert Peel, 2 Nevada, 3 Neon, 4 St Patrick, 5 A dog, 6 The Taj Mahal, 7 Laser, 8 Martin Luther, 9 Florence Nightingale, 10 Renaissance, 11 Harold II, 12 Stephen Foster, 13 An insect, 14 Echo, 15 Gotland, 16 Boris Godunov, 17 William Inge, 18 Bobby Fischer, 19 Dardanelles, 20 Dante Alighieri.*

General Knowledge

Your rating:
- **0-5 Join a library**
- **6-10 Keep at it**
- **11-15 Join a quiz team**
- **16-20 Join Mensa**

1. The name of which constellation of the zodiac means 'archer' in Latin?
2. What nationality was the jazz guitarist Django Reinhardt?
3. Which Scottish lake is famous for its reported sightings of a monster?
4. By what name are the followers of Sun Myung Moon's Unification Church usually known?
5. On which Mediterranean island did the Mafia criminal organisation originate?
6. After which French novelist is "sadism" named?
7. What do the initials UFO stand for?
8. Which tax system is represented by the initials PAYE?
9. According to classical mythology, how many horns does a unicorn have?
10. Which scientific term describes the bending of a beam of light as it passes from one medium to another?
11. Which French director's films include *Alphaville* and *A bout de souffle*?
12. On which river is the Grand Coulee Dam?
13. Which political party was founded in 1926 by Eamon De Valera from moderate Sinn Féin members?
14. Which English general defeated Charles I at Naseby as commander in chief of the New Model Army?
15. What is the largest type of penguin?
16. Which German composer wrote the operas *Orfeo ed Euridice* and *Alceste*?
17. Which soft silvery metal is represented by the symbol In?
18. Which US president issued the Emancipation Proclamation of 1863?
19. Which word describes the chemical decomposition of a substance by passing an electric current through it?
20. On which estuary does the port of Immingham lie?

ANSWERS: *1 Sagittarius, 2 Belgian, 3 Loch Ness, 4 Moonies, 5 Sicily, 6 Marquis de Sade, 7 Unidentified flying object, 8 Pay As You Earn, 9 One, 10 Refraction, 11 Jean-Luc Godard, 12 Columbia River, 13 Fianna Fáil, 14 Thomas Fairfax, 15 The emperor penguin, 16 Christoph Gluck, 17 Indium, 18 Abraham Lincoln, 19 Electrolysis, 20 The Humber estuary.*

General Knowledge

Your rating:
- 0-5 Join a library
- 6-10 Keep at it
- 11-15 Join a quiz team
- 16-20 Join Mensa

1. Which street in the centre of the financial district of New York is synonymous with the stock exchange?
2. What do the initials VHF stand for?
3. What sort of creature is an ibis?
4. Of which Himalayan country is Kathmandu the capital?
5. Ascorbic acid is an alternative name for which vitamin?
6. Which language is spoken by the Walloons of Belgium?
7. By what name are the ceremonial yeoman warders at the Tower of London known?
8. What is the name for the structure which connects a foetus to the placenta in the womb?
9. Which city developed from the Roman fort of Mancunium?
10. What does the abbreviation YHA stand for?
11. In which country is the volcano Mount Ruapehu?
12. Which British chemist and physicist gave his name to a unit of electrical capacitance?
13. Which French playwright wrote *Hotel Paradiso* and *A Flea in Her Ear*?
14. What sort of creature is a Falabella?
15. What was the first name of former foreign secretary Lord Carrington?
16. What is the capital of Ghana?
17. In which Elizabethan theatre, in Southwark, were most of Shakespeare's plays first produced?
18. Who starred in the films *The Prisoner of Zenda* and *Sinbad the Sailor*?
19. What nationality was the artist Max Ernst?
20. In which country are the Western and Eastern Ghats mountain ranges situated?

ANSWERS: *1 Wall Street, 2 Very High Frequency, 3 A bird, 4 Nepal, 5 Vitamin C, 6 French, 7 Beefeaters, 8 Umbilical cord, 9 Manchester, 10 Youth Hostels Association, 11 New Zealand, 12 Michael Faraday, 13 Georges Feydeau, 14 A pony, 15 Peter, 16 Accra, 17 The Globe Theatre, 18 Douglas Fairbanks Jr, 19 German, 20 India.*

Entertainment

Your rating: ● **0-5** Buy a TV ● **6-10** Keep at it ● **11-15** Join a quiz team ● **16-20** Enter a quiz show

1. In which ITV police drama series did Robson Green star as DI Dave Creegan?
2. Which 1999 film starred Christopher Lloyd as a shape-shifting alien?
3. Which London duo released their second album, *Vertigo*, in 1999, featuring the U.K. hit song *If Everybody Looked the Same*?
4. Which actor played manipulative uncle Alex Kyle in the 1999 ITV drama series *An Evil Streak*?
5. Which actor played drifter Francis Phelan in the 1987 film *Ironweed*?
6. Which Seventies series about women on a sales promotion team featured Anna Carteret and Floella Benjamin?
7. Which song was a U.K. hit for Elvis Presley in 1964 and for ZZ Top in 1992?
8. Which Rodgers and Hammerstein musical was adapted into an animated film in 1999?
9. Which character, played by George Clooney, left the Channel 4 U.S. medical drama *ER* in 1999?
10. Which rap group asked us to *Walk This Way* in 1986?
11. Which daytime TV duo hosted the 1999 *British Soap Awards*?
12. Which artist was played by Kirk Douglas in the 1956 film *Lust For Life*?
13. Which female vocal group claimed they were *Born Too Late* in 1958?
14. Which actor played *Captain Jack* in the 1999 film written by Jack Rosenthal?
15. Which Seventies comedy series set amongst executives in a toy factory starred Dinsdale Landen and Terence Alexander?
16. Which Macunian band, the forerunner of New Order, was captured in live performance on the 1999 album *Preston, February 28, 1980*?
17. Which G.K. Chesterton character did Alec Guinness play in the 1954 film of the same name?
18. Which *Emmerdale* character died in 1999 after a fall from a cliff-top in suspicious circumstances?
19. Which ex-Spice Girl's debut solo album was entitled *Schizophonic*?
20. Which comedian presented *Unzipped* on Channel 4 in 1999, investigating celebrity scandals?

ANSWERS: *1 Touching Evil, 2 My Favourite Martian, 3 Groove Armada, 4 Trevor Eve, 5 Jack Nicholson, 6 Send in the Girls, 7 Viva Las Vegas, 8 The King and I, 9 Dr Doug Ross, 10 Run DMC, 11 Richard Madeley & Judy Finnigan, 12 Vincent Van Gogh, 13 The Poni-Tails, 14 Bob Hoskins, 15 Devenish, 16 Joy Division, 17 Father Brown, 18 Rachel Hughes, 19 Geri Halliwell, 20 Graham Norton.*

General Knowledge

Your rating:
- 0-5 Join a library
- 6-10 Keep at it
- 11-15 Join a quiz team
- 16-20 Join Mensa

1. With which sport is Sir Stanley Matthews associated?
2. Of which county is Taunton the administrative centre?
3. Which gas makes up approximately 78% of the earth's atmosphere?
4. Which two countries compete for cricket's Ashes?
5. By what name are the 21 books of the New Testament that were written as letters collectively known?
6. Which government office is represented by the initials HMSO?
7. Which communist guerillas fought the government of South Vietnam during the Vietnam War?
8. What is the name for the flap of cartilage at the root of the tongue which prevents food from entering the windpipe?
9. Which famous art gallery on Millbank, London was built in 1897 with the financial support of a sugar merchant?
10. Who advocated a policy of appeasement towards the fascist powers as prime minister of Britain from 1937-40?
11. Which head of the Soviet secret police force was executed for conspiracy in 1953?
12. Who became king of the Scots after killing Macbeth?
13. What sort of creature is a fritillary?
14. Which town is the administrative centre of East Sussex?
15. Who was head of RAF Fighter Command during the Battle of Britain?
16. Who wrote *Gone With The Wind*?
17. Which lyricist collaborated with Richard Rodgers on the musicals *Oklahoma!* and *The Sound of Music*?
18. The hull of which Tudor warship was lifted in 1982 and placed in dry-dock in Portsmouth?
19. Which French novelist wrote *Indiana*?
20. Of which U.S. state is Annapolis the capital?

ANSWERS: *1 Football, 2 Somerset, 3 Nitrogen, 4 England and Australia, 5 Epistles, 6 Her Majesty's Stationery Office, 7 Viet Cong, 8 Epiglottis, 9 The Tate Gallery, 10 Neville Chamberlain, 11 Beria, 12 Malcolm III, 13 A butterfly, 14 Lewes, 15 Hugh Dowding, 16 Margaret Mitchell, 17 Oscar Hammerstein II, 18 Mary Rose, 19 George Sand, 20 Maryland.*

General Knowledge

Your rating:
- 0-5 Join a library
- 6-10 Keep at it
- 11-15 Join a quiz team
- 16-20 Join Mensa

1. Which Russian novelist wrote *Dr Zhivago*?
2. Which stadium was the site of the 1948 Olympics?
3. Which Swedish actress starred in *Casablanca* and *Gaslight*?
4. What is the largest continent in the world?
5. In Roman numerals, which letter represents 500?
6. In which US city is Staten Island situated?
7. Spaghetti, lasagne and tagliatelle are varieties of which Italian food?
8. Which British novelist wrote *Of Human Bondage* and *The Moon and Sixpence*?
9. Which member of the Beatles was born Richard Starkey?
10. In which university city can the Ashmolean Museum be found?
11. What is the highest mountain in Africa?
12. Of which English county is Winchester the administrative centre?
13. Which Danish composer and conductor developed the principle of progressive tonality?
14. Which canal connects the Red Sea to the Mediterranean Sea?
15. According to the New Testament, who was the first person to see Jesus after the resurrection?
16. Which organ is supplied with blood by the renal artery?
17. Which U.S. novelist wrote *The Maltese Falcon* and *The Thin Man*?
18. Which King of the Scots defeated the English forces at Bannockburn in 1314?
19. Which German philosopher wrote *Thus Spake Zarathustra*?
20. Which British actress won an Oscar for her performance in the film *A Passage to India*?

ANSWERS: *1 Boris Pasternak, 2 Wembley, 3 Ingrid Bergman, 4 Asia, 5 D, 6 New York City, 7 Pasta, 8 W. Somerset Maugham, 9 Ringo Starr, 10 Oxford, 11 Mount Kilimanjaro, 12 Hampshire, 13 Carl Nielsen, 14 Suez Canal, 15 Mary Magdalene, 16 The kidney, 17 Dashiell Hammett, 18 Robert the Bruce, 19 Nietzsche, 20 Dame Peggy Ashcroft.*

General Knowledge

Your rating: ● 0-5 Join a library ● 6-10 Keep at it ● 11-15 Join a quiz team ● 16-20 Join Mensa

1. Which U.S. tennis player won the men's singles title at Wimbledon in 1974 and 1982?
2. What sort of creature is a bullfinch?
3. With which sport is Sir Donald Bradman associated?
4. Of which US state is Santa Fe the capital?
5. At what sort of Spanish spectator sport would one find matadors and picadors?
6. Which Australian city is famous for its Harbour Bridge and Opera House?
7. What is the closest planet to the sun?
8. What nationality was the pioneer psychoanalyst Carl Gustav Jung?
9. Which author founded Jersey's Zoological Park?
10. Which former husband of Mia Farrow was the conductor of the London Symphony Orchestra from 1969 to 1979?
11. In the Christian calendar, what is the first day of Lent?
12. What is the capital of Mexico?
13. In which ocean does the Republic of Nauru lie?
14. Which cross between a raspberry and a blackberry was first grown in California in 1881?
15. Of which U.S. state is Montgomery the capital?
16. Which Italian composer wrote the operas *Orfeo* and *The Coronation of Poppea*?
17. Which king of Spain sent the Spanish Armada to invade England in 1588?
18. Which French poet wrote *Les Illuminations*?
19. How is the insect *Musca domestica* commonly known?
20. Which German family of arms manufacturers developed the World War I artillery piece known as Big Bertha?

ANSWERS: *1 Jimmy Connors, 2 A bird, 3 Cricket, 4 New Mexico, Bullfighting, 6 Sydney, 7 Mercury, 8 Swiss, 9 Gerald Durrell, 10 André Previn, 11 Ash Wednesday, 12 Mexico City, 13 Pacific Ocean, 14 Loganberry, 15 Alabama, 16 Monteverdi, 17 Philip II, 18 Arthur Rimbaud, 19 Housefly, 20 Krupp.*

Entertainment

Your rating: ● 0-5 Buy a TV ● 6-10 Keep at it ● 11-15 Join a quiz team ● 16-20 Enter a quiz show

1. Which *Coronation Street* businessman faced a blackmail attempt in 1999 which threatened his marriage?
2. Which U.S. boy band had a 1999 U.K. number one hit with *I Want It That Way*?
3. In which 1999 BBC 1 drama did Paul Nicholls play Daniel, an actor cast as Jesus in a village play?
4. Which 1999 thriller starred Alessandro Nivola, Reese Witherspoon and Josh Brolin?
5. Which actress starred as the title character, an unmarried mother, in the Seventies comedy series *Miss Jones and Son*?
6. Which northern band released an album entitled *Magic Hour* in 1999?
7. Which actor starred as a former FBI man turned southern sheriff in the 1986 film *Raw Deal*?
8. Which duo had a U.K. number one hit in 1992 with *Ebeneezer Goode*?
9. Which actress starred as Sarah opposite Ben Affleck's Ben in the 1999 film *Forces of Nature*?
10. Which 1999 psychological ITV drama starred Caroline Goodall as a lawyer representing her husband after his arrest for murder?
11. Who directed the 1999 black comedy film *Parting Shots*, starring Chris Rea and Joanna Lumley, among others?
12. What was the title of the 1994 U.K. top five hit by former *Big Breakfast* puppets Zig and Zag?
13. Which 1959 film starred Frank Sinatra as the commander of a British-American task force in Burma during World War II?
14. In which 1999 BBC 2 series did an amply-proportioned US chef and his diminutive British counterpart find culinary links between their two countries?
15. Which British duo had U.K. top five hits in the Eighties with *Only You*, *Don't Go* and *Nobody's Diary*?
16. Which actor played *Twin Dragons* in the Hong Kong action adventure movie?
17. Which actor played the lead role in the Seventies TV production *Will Shakespeare*?
18. Which band released their first studio album for five years in 1999, *Viva El Amor*?
19. Which actor played heavyweight boxing champion Jack Johnson in the 1970 film about his life, *The Great White Hope*?
20. Which pop star was the focus of a 1999 Channel 4 documentary film by Molly Dineen?

ANSWERS: *1 Mike Baldwin, 2 Backstreet Boys, 3 The Passion, 4 Best Laid Plans, 5 Paula Wilcox, 6 Cast, 7 Arnold Schwarzenegger, 8 Shamen, 9 Sandra Bullock, 10 Trust, 11 Michael Winner, 12 Them Girls Them Girls, 13 Never So Few, 14 Big Kevin, Little Kevin, 15 Yazoo, 16 Jackie Chan, 17 Tim Curry, 18 The Pretenders, 19 James Earl Jones, 20 Geri Halliwell*

General Knowledge

Your rating:
- **0-5** Join a library
- **6-10** Keep at it
- **11-15** Join a quiz team
- **16-20** Join Mensa

1. Which form of transport was invented by Sir Christopher Cockerell?
2. In which county is the city of Truro?
3. What do the initials CID stand for?
4. During which war was the Battle of the Bulge fought?
5. Which U.S. city is home to Coney Island?
6. Which Irish novelist wrote *Dracula*?
7. Which cricket ground is the headquarters of the Marylebone Cricket Club?
8. Does Antarctica surround the North Pole or the South Pole?
9. Which political party has been led by Disraeli, Churchill and Macmillan?
10. What sort of creature is an adder?
11. Who was Queen of the Netherlands from 1948 to 1980?
12. Which British jockey was champion jockey 26 times between 1925 and 1953?
13. Which Middle East federation is represented by the initials UAE?
14. Which twin heroes of classical mythology were transformed into the Gemini constellation?
15. Of the four main islands of Japan, which is the smallest?
16. What is the name for the marks which appear on the body of a living person resembling Christ's wounds from the crucifixion?
17. What is the chief mountain system of Mexico?
18. Which Greek island was the birthplace of the mathematician and philosopher Pythagoras?
19. What sort of creature is a merganser?
20. Which Polish novelist wrote the historical epic *Quo Vadis*?

ANSWERS: *1 Hovercraft, 2 Cornwall, 3 Criminal Investigation Department, 4 World War II, 5 New York City, 6 Bram Stoker, 7 Lord's, 8 South Pole, 9 The Conservative Party, 10 A snake, 11 Juliana, 12 Sir Gordon Richards, 13 United Arab Emirates, 14 Castor and Pollux, 15 Shikoku, 16 Stigmata, 17 Sierra Madre, 18 Samos, 19 A duck, 20 Henryk Sienkiewicz.*

General Knowledge

Your rating: ● **0-5** Join a library ● **6-10** Keep at it ● **11-15** Join a quiz team ● **16-20** Join Mensa

1. Which Italian composer wrote the operas *Tosca* and *Madame Butterfly*?
2. Which Swedish tennis player won the men's singles at Wimbledon in 1980 for the fifth consecutive year?
3. Which ancient forest of Nottinghamshire is famous for its associations with Robin Hood?
4. According to Greek legend, which son of Daedalus was killed when the sun melted his wings?
5. Which comic fat boy of Greyfriars School was created by the British writer Frank Richards?
6. Which English poet wrote *The Canterbury Tales*?
7. Through which US state does the San Andreas Fault run?
8. Which peninsula does Denmark share with Germany?
9. Which natural phenomena are measured by the Richter scale?
10. Which Russian dramatist wrote *The Seagull* and *Uncle Vanya*?
11. Of which Central American Republic is Tegucigalpa the capital?
12. Which Italian composer wrote the one-act opera *Cavalleria Rusticana*?
13. Yell and Unst are part of which group of islands?
14. Who had a U.K. hit in 1976 with *Tonight's the Night*, shortly after leaving The Faces?
15. To which king of France was Marie Antoinette married?
16. Which British novelist wrote *Tristram Shandy*?
17. Which British chemist was the originator of the modern atomic theory of matter?
18. Which prime minister became 1st Earl of Beaconsfield?
19. Which borough of Greater London was created in 1965 from parts of Kent, including Orpington and Penge?
20. Which French director's films include *Jules et Jim* and *Love on the Run*?

ANSWERS: *1 Puccini, 2 Bjorn Borg, 3 Sherwood Forest, 4 Icarus, 5 Billy Bunter, 6 Geoffrey Chaucer, 7 California, 8 Jutland, 9 Earthquakes, 10 Anton Chekov, 11 Honduras, 12 Pietro Mascagni, 13 The Shetland Islands, 14 Rod Stewart, 15 Louis XVI, 16 Laurence Sterne, 17 John Dalton, 18 Benjamin Disraeli, 19 Bromley, 20 François Truffaut.*

General Knowledge

Your rating: ● **0-5** Join a library ● **6-10** Keep at it ● **11-15** Join a quiz team ● **16-20** Join Mensa

1. The island of Corfu is part of which country?
2. Who was president of the USA from 1945 to 1953?
3. In which county is the resort of Southend-on-Sea?
4. What sort of creature is a shih-tzu?
5. Which national cricket team was captained by Sir Don Bradman?
6. Which organisation is represented by the initials UN?
7. What sort of creature is a stickleback?
8. What was the nickname of German World War I air ace Manfred von Richthofen?
9. What is the capital of Canada?
10. Which British Grand Prix driver was world champion in 1969, 1971 and 1973?
11. Which two states of the USA are divided by the Mason-Dixon line?
12. According to the Old Testament, who was the first of the Hebrew prophets and the last of the "judges"?
13. Which female tennis player won the Italian Open for the fourth time in succession in 1996?
14. Which German composer wrote the *Spring Symphony*?
15. Who was prime minister of Canada from 1968 to 1979 and from 1980 to 1984?
16. Which poet, whose works include *Sea Fever*, became poet laureate in 1930?
17. Which legendary courtier was seated beneath a sword suspended by a single hair?
18. Which is the larger of the two principle islands of New Zealand?
19. Which British cricketer was the first bowler to take 300 Test wickets?
20. Which Hollywood actor starred in *The Glenn Miller Story* and *Shenandoah*?

ANSWERS: *1 Greece, 2 Harry S. Truman, 3 Essex, 4 A dog, 5 Australia, 6 United Nations, 7 A fish, 8 The Red Baron, 9 Ottawa, 10 Jackie Stewart, 11 Pennsylvania and Maryland, 12 Samuel, 13 Conchita Martinez, 14 Robert Schumann, 15 Pierre Trudeau, 16 John Masefield, 17 Damocles, 18 South Island, 19 Freddy Trueman, 20 James Stewart.*

Sports

Your rating: ● **0-5 Wooden spoon** ● **6-10 Bronze medal** ● **11-15 Silver medal** ● **16-20 Gold medal**

1. Which British cyclist crashed out of the 1998 Tour de France whilst wearing the Yellow Jersey?
2. Which cricketer captained Yorkshire from 1971 to 1978?
3. Which club signed Alan Kennedy from Newcastle United?
4. Which rugby union club side did Phil de Glanville captain in the 1995 Pilkington Cup final?
5. Which jockey rode Mark of Esteem to victory in the 1996 2000 Guineas?
6. In which year did Torvill and Dean use Ravel's Bolero for their winning Olympic free-dance?
7. Who became manager of Liverpool in 1959?
8. At which year's Olympic Games did Leon and Michael Spinks both win gold medals?
9. Who won the gold medal in the javelin event at the 1995 World Athletics Championship?
10. Which Spanish football team won the European Cup for the first time in 32 years in 1998?
11. Who became the first European Open snooker champion by beating Terry Griffiths?
12. Who knocked Tim Henman out of the men's singles at Wimbledon in 1998 and 1999?
13. Which U.S. golfer won the British Open in 1970?
14. What is the name of rugby union side Richmond's home ground?
15. What is the nickname of Bristol City football club?
16. In which year were the summer Olympic Games held in Seoul?
17. At which cycling event did Chris Boardman become Olympic champion in 1992?
18. Which club bought David Batty from Newcastle United in 1998?
19. Which team won 15 of the 16 Formula 1 Grands Prix in 1988?
20. In which event did Carl Lewis win a fourth consecutive Olympic gold medal in 1996?

ANSWERS: *1 Chris Boardman, 2 Geoffrey Boycott, 3 Liverpool, 4 Bath, 5 Frankie Dettori, 6 1984, 7 Bill Shankly, 8 1976, 9 Jan Zelezny, 10 Real Madrid, 11 John Parrott, 12 Pete Sampras, 13 Jack Nicklaus, 14 The Madejski Stadium, 15 The Robins, 16 1988, 17 4,000m individual pursuit, 18 Leeds United, 19 McLaren, 20 Long jump.*

General Knowledge

Your rating: ● 0-5 Join a library ● 6-10 Keep at it ● 11-15 Join a quiz team ● 16-20 Join Mensa

1. In which Kent cathedral was Thomas Becket martyred?
2. In which parts of the body are varicose veins usually found?
3. Of which African country is Addis Ababa the capital?
4. What sort of creature is a barracuda?
5. Which British dramatist and novelist wrote *Peter Pan*?
6. Which Austrian city was the birthplace of Mozart?
7. Which Welsh poet wrote *Under Milk Wood*?
8. What was the nickname of U.S. astronaut Edwin Aldrin?
9. In which European country can the Cantabrian Mountains be found?
10. On which day of the week does Pancake Day fall?
11. Who became the first president of India in 1950?
12. In Greek mythology, who was the twin sister of Apollo?
13. Which French author wrote *Locus Solus*?
14. Which British dramatist wrote *The Tragedy of Jane Shore*?
15. What sort of creature is a krait?
16. What was the capital of South Yemen?
17. Which Italian artist painted the *Vision of St Eustace*?
18. The former kingdom of Barotseland is part of which country?
19. Who became the first chancellor of the Federal Republic of Germany in 1949?
20. In which northwest English town was the first British nuclear submarine built?

ANSWERS: *1 Canterbury, 2 Legs, 3 Ethiopia, 4 A fish, 5 Sir James Barrie, 6 Salzburg, 7 Dylan Thomas, 8 Buzz, 9 Spain, 10 Tuesday, 11 Rajendra Prasad, 12 Artemis, 13 Raymond Roussel, 14 Nicholas Rowe, 15 A snake, 16 Aden, 17 Pisanello, 18 Zambia, 19 Konrad Adenauer, 20 Barrow-in-Furness.*

General Knowledge

Your rating: ● **0-5** **Join a library** ● **6-10** **Keep at it** ● **11-15** **Join a quiz team** ● **16-20** **Join Mensa**

1. What is the largest of the Balearic Islands?
2. What was the nickname of the U.S. lawman James Butler Hickok?
3. At which racecourse near Liverpool is the Grand National run?
4. In Greek legend, which Cretan monster had a bull's head and a man's body?
5. Which churchman was president of Cyprus from 1960 to 1974?
6. What is the name for the goatskin pouch worn in traditional Highland dress?
7. Which Royal Gardens near Richmond were the site of the first botanic garden in 1759?
8. Which small country between Switzerland and Austria has Vaduz as its capital?
9. Which unit used to measure the power of a lens is equal to the reciprocal of its focal length in metres?
10. Which Scottish port between the mouths of the Rivers Don and Dee is known as the 'Granite City'?
11. Which British actor starred as Sir Thomas More in the 1966 film *A Man for All Seasons*?
12. Which theatre was founded in Paris in 1680?
13. Which Irish writer wrote the novel *Good Behaviour*?
14. Which British poet and critic wrote the verse satire Absalom and Achitopel?
15. Which Peruvian diplomat became U.N. secretary-general in 1982?
16. What is the name for a line on a map which joins points of equal temperature?
17. What is the largest of the Shetland Islands?
18. Which Irish novelist wrote *Uncle Silas* and *In a Glass Darkly*?
19. Which word describes plants that can live for many years?
20 Which lanthanide element is represented by the symbol Eu?

ANSWERS: *1 Majorca, 2 Wild Bill Hickok, 3 Aintree, 4 Minotaur, 5 Archbishop Makarios III, 6 Sporran, 7 Kew Gardens, 8 Liechtenstein, 9 Dioptre, 10 Aberdeen, 11 Paul Scofield, 12 Comedie Française, 13 Molly Keane, 14 John Dryden, 15 Javier Perez de Cuellar, 16 Isotherm, 17 Mainland, 18 Sheridan Le Fanu, 19 Perennials, 20 Europium.*

General Knowledge

Your rating: ● 0-5 Join a library ● 6-10 Keep at it ● 11-15 Join a quiz team ● 16-20 Join Mensa

1. Which river rises in the Wicklow Mountains and flows through Dublin to Dublin Bay?
2. In which country was surrealist painter Joan Miro born?
3. Which London cemetery contains the graves of Karl Marx and George Eliot?
4. In Greek legend, which king of Thebes killed his father and married his mother?
5. Which measure is equal to one sixtieth of a degree, in geometry?
6. Which acting school is represented by the acronym RADA?
7. In which ocean do the Isles of Scilly lie?
8. Which Soviet secret police force replaced the MGB in 1954?
9. Glaucoma is a disease of which organ?
10. Which snooker player was known as 'Hurricane'?
11. Which U.S. physicist was awarded the 1960 Nobel Prize for his invention of the bubble chamber?
12. What sort of creature is a skimmer?
13. Which Russian composer wrote the opera *Ivan Susanin (A Life for the Tsar)*?
14. In which U.S. state is the city of Key West?
15. Which Japanese general and prime minister was executed as a war criminal after World War II?
16. Which British economist wrote the *General Theory of Employment, Interest and Money*?
17. What is the name for an integer that is equal to the sum of all its factors (except itself)?
18. What is the longest nerve in the body?
19. Which British novelist wrote *A High Wind in Jamaica*?
20. Which French painter was known as *Le Douanier*?

ANSWERS: *1 The River Liffey, 2 Spain, 3 Highgate Cemetery, 4 Oedipus, 5 Minute, 6 The Royal Academy of Dramatic Art, 7 The Atlantic Ocean, 8 KGB, 9 The eye, 10 Alex Higgins, 11 Donald Glaser, 12 A bird, 13 Mikhail Glinka, 14 Florida, 15 Hideki Tojo, 16 John Maynard Keynes, 17 Perfect number, 18 The sciatic nerve, 19 Richard Hughes, 20 Henri Rousseau.*

Entertainment

Your rating: ● **0-5 Buy a TV** ● **6-10 Keep at it** ● **11-15 Join a quiz team** ● **16-20 Enter a quiz show**

1. Which actor played the half-vampire martial arts expert *Blade* in the 1998 film of the same name?
2. Which actress played Harriet Smith, the British ambassador to Ireland, in the BBC 1 series *The Ambassador*?
3. Which Scottish band released an album entitled *The Hush* in 1999?
4. In which 1978 film did Goldie Hawn play a librarian who suffers attempts on her life by a group plotting to assassinate the Pope?
5. Which British actress's life was depicted by Keeley Hawes and Amanda Redman in the 1999 ITV drama *The Blonde Bombshell*?
6. Which Brixton-based DJ combo scored a U.K. top five hit with *Red Alert*, and released their debut album, *Remedy*, in 1999?
7. What was the title of the 1999 BBC 1 variety show hosted by comedians Gareth Hale and Norman Pace?
8. Which actor starred as Ray, a man with nightmarish neighbours in the 1989 film *The 'Burbs*?
9. What was the title of the 1993 U.K. top five single by Jamaican group Inner Circle?
10. Which Scottish actor played the undertaker in the TV comedy *Dad's Army*?
11. Which 1999 slasher film sequel starred Jennifer Love Hewitt as a college student trying to escape from an oil-skin-wearing killer?
12. What was the title of the Channel 5 celebrity-based motoring series presented by Henry Cole?
13. Which Seventies group's U.K. hits included *In the Summertime*, *Baby Jump* and *Lady Rose*?
14. Which 1987 film set in the Sixties starred Jodie Foster and Tim Robbins as Linda and Harry, residents of the Bronx?
15. Which U.S. ventriloquist, along with Chuck Wood and Ted E. Bare, hosted a chat show series on ITV?
16. Who directed and starred as a journalist in the 1999 film *True Crime*?
17. Which 1999 ITV documentary series followed the progress of six aspiring young actors hoping to find fame in Hollywood?
18. Which British singer starred in, and released a soundtrack album from the 1999 film *Swing*?
19. Which actor was Captain Ahab in the 1956 film version of *Moby Dick*?
20. Which 1970 TV comedy about a working-class couple made stars of Paula Wilcox and Richard Beckinsale?

ANSWERS: *1 Wesley Snipes, 2 Pauline Collins, 3 Texas, 4 Foul Play, 5 Diana Dors, 6 Basement Jaxx, 7 h&p@bbc, 8 Tom Hanks, 9 Sweat (A La La La La Long), 10 John Laurie, 11 I Still Know What You Did Last Summer, 12 Stars and Cars, 13 Mungo Jerry, 14 Five Corners, 15 David Strassman (Strassman), 16 Clint Eastwood, 17 Desperately Seeking Stardom, 18 Lisa Stansfield, 19 Gregory Peck, 20 The Lovers.*

General Knowledge

Your rating:
- **0-5** Join a library
- **6-10** Keep at it
- **11-15** Join a quiz team
- **16-20** Join Mensa

1. Who married Queen Victoria in 1840?
2. Is the Isle of Man part of the United Kingdom?
3. Which British author wrote *Charlie and the Chocolate Factory*?
4. In which continent can the Republic of Sierra Leone be found?
5. In which year did Hong Kong return to Chinese control?
6. Of which state of the USA is Richmond the capital?
7. From which country does Parmesan cheese come?
8. Which art form was Henry Moore famous for?
9. What do the initials PSBR stand for?
10. Of which state of the USA is Boston the capital?
11. Which U.S. aviator made the first solo nonstop flight across the Atlantic Ocean?
12. In which city did the July Revolution of 1830 take place?
13. At which battle was Richard III killed?
14. The name of which method of painting means ‘fool the eye’ in French?
15. Which river rises in South Africa and flows generally northeast through Mozambique to the Indian Ocean?
16. Which kingdom of Anglo-Saxon England was ruled by Penda and Offa?
17. Of which African country is Gabarone the capital?
18. Which infectious disease of rabbits was introduced to the UK as a pest-control measure in the 1950s?
19. Which English physician and humanist founded the Royal College of Physicians in 1518?
20. Which Norwegian seaport is the largest town north of the Arctic Circle?

ANSWERS: *1 Prince Albert, 2 No, 3 Roald Dahl, 4 Africa, 5 1997, 6 Virginia, 7 Italy, 8 Sculpture, 9 Public Sector Borrowing Requirement, 10 Massachusetts, 11 Charles Lindbergh, 12 Paris, 13 The Battle of Bosworth Field, 14 Trompe l'oeil, 15 The Limpopo River, 16 Mercia, 17 Botswana, 18 Myxomatosis, 19 Thomas Linacre, 20 Tromsø.*

General Knowledge

Your rating:
- 0-5 Join a library
- 6-10 Keep at it
- 11-15 Join a quiz team
- 16-20 Join Mensa

1. What nationality was the composer Franz Schubert?
2. Siamese, Persian and Abyssinian are breeds of which animal?
3. Which British novelist wrote *The Lord of the Rings*?
4. Who directed the films *Psycho*, *The Birds* and *Strangers on a Train*?
5. Which Test cricket team did Viv Richards captain?
6. Which two countries are divided by the thirty-eighth parallel?
7. What is the chief religion of India?
8. What sort of creature is a shrike?
9. What is the only common metal that is liquid at room temperature?
10. Who was the first man to walk on the moon?
11. Which area separates the North and South Downs?
12. What is the nontechnical name for the scapula?
13. What was Richard Nixon's middle name?
14. Which Flemish geographer gave his name to a map projection used in all British Ordnance Survey maps?
15. Who wrote the operas *Cosi fan tutte* and *The Magic Flute*?
16. With which game was Victor Korchnoi associated?
17. In which city is the Brandenburg Gate?
18. Which soprano was known as the 'Swedish nightingale'?
19. The sackbut was the old English name for which musical instrument?
20. Which English city was known as Lindum Colonia under the Romans?

ANSWERS: *1 Austrian, 2 Cat, 3 J. R. R. Tolkien, 4 Sir Alfred Hitchcock, 5 West Indies, 6 North and South Korea, 7 Hinduism, 8 A bird, 9 Mercury, 10 Neil Armstrong, 11 The Weald, 12 Shoulder blade, 13 Milhous, 14 Mercator, 15 Mozart, 16 Chess, 17 Berlin, 18 Jenny Lind, 19 The trombone, 20 Lincoln.*

General Knowledge

Your rating:
- **0-5 Join a library**
- **6-10 Keep at it**
- **11-15 Join a quiz team**
- **16-20 Join Mensa**

1. Which British novelist wrote *Jane Eyre*?
2. Which reddish-brown liquid element is represented by the symbol Br?
3. How many lines are in a limerick?
4. Which major New York street is the site of most of the leading commercial theatres?
5. Which statesman established a socialist government in Cuba in 1959?
6. Which Russian novelist wrote *War and Peace*?
7. In which U.S. state is Honolulu?
8. In which sport would you find a gully, fine leg and extra cover?
9. How is myopia better known?
10. How many symphonies did Beethoven complete?
11. Who was Moses's elder brother, who built the golden calf?
12. What sort of creature is a flycatcher?
13. Which Basque town, virtually destroyed by German planes in the Spanish Civil War, was immortalised in a Picasso painting?
14. Which Trotskyist faction was expelled from the Labour Party in 1986?
15. What is the largest of the Great Lakes?
16. In which country is the town of Eilat?
17. With which apostle is the symbol of two crossed keys associated?
18. In which city did Anne Frank hide from the Nazis?
19. Which king was married to Caroline of Brunswick?
20. Who created James Bond?

ANSWERS: *1 Charlotte Brontë, 2 Bromine, 3 Five, 4 Broadway, 5 Fidel Castro, 6 Leo Tolstoy, 7 Hawaii, 8 Cricket, 9 Shortsightedness, 10 Nine, 11 Aaron, 12 A bird, 13 Guernica, 14 Militant Tendency, 15 Lake Superior, 16 Israel, 17 St Peter, 18 Amsterdam, 19 George IV, 20 Ian Fleming.*

Entertainment

Your rating: ● **0-5** **Buy a TV** ● **6-10** **Keep at it** ● **11-15** **Join a quiz team** ● **16-20** **Enter a quiz show**

1. Which 1957 musical film about an American film producer in Paris who falls in love with a beautiful Russian starred Fred Astaire and Cyd Charisse?
2. Which comedian/actor starred as a singing travel agent in the 1999 BBC 1 comedy drama *The Man*?
3. Electronic were formed by members of which two other groups?
4. In which 1999 film did Nicolas Cage star as a private eye who embarks on an investigation of the Hollywood porn industry?
5. Which comedy duo hosted the Saturday night game show *Families At War*?
6. Which band released an album in 1999 entitled *The Unauthorised Biography of Reinhold Messner*?
7. Which 1999 ITV drama starred Robson Green as former footballer Michael Flynn?
8. Which ex-*EastEnder* had a *Perfect Moment* at the top of the U.K. charts in 1999?
9. Which Eighties period drama serial about a group of travelling film showmen featured Bob Hoskins and Frances de la Tour?
10. Which actor starred as the cop Mason Storm in the 1990 film *Hard to Kill*?
11. Which actor, who starred in TV's *Hornblower*, also played Pip in BBC 2's 1999 adaptation of Dickens' *Great Expectations*?
12. Which group had two U.K. top five hits in the Sixties with *He's In Town* and *Poor Man's Son*?
13. In which 1999 film did Paul Newman and Kevin Costner star as father and son?
14. Which shopping-based fashion series was formerly presented by Liza Tarbuck on Channel 4?
15. What was the title of Donna Summer's 1977 U.K. number one hit?
16. In which 1984 Tony Richardson film did Rob Lowe and Jodie Foster star as brother and sister?
17. Which young cook appeared fully clothed in BBC 2's *The Naked Chef*?
18. Which song provided a U.K. number eleven hit for both Sister Sledge in 1984 and Maureen in 1990?
19. Which Bernardo Bertolucci film starred David Thewlis as a concert-pianist and Thandie Newton as his cleaner?
20. What type of firm operated from *77 Sunset Strip* in the U.S. TV series?

ANSWERS: *1 Silk Stockings, 2 Lenny Henry, 3 The Smiths & New Order (Johnny Marr & Bernard Sumner), 4 8MM, 5 Vic Reeves & Bob Mortimer, 6 Ben Folds Five, 7 Rhinoceros, 8 Martine McCutcheon, 9 Flickers, 10 Steven Seagal, 11 Ioan Gruffudd, 12 Rockin' Berries, 13 Message in a Bottle, 14 She's Gotta Have It, 15 I Feel Love, 16 The Hotel New Hampshire, 17 Jamie Oliver, 18 Thinking of You, 19 Besieged, 20 Firm of private detectives.*

General Knowledge

Your rating:
- 0-5 Join a library
- 6-10 Keep at it
- 11-15 Join a quiz team
- 16-20 Join Mensa

1. Who wrote *Twenty Thousand Leagues Under the Sea*?
2. How many attempts is a competitor allowed at a particular height in the high jump?
3. What sort of creature is a storm petrel?
4. Of which African country is Harare the capital?
5. Which legendary Greek king of Ithaca was the hero of Homer's Odyssey?
6. What do the initials RAF stand for?
7. Of which US state is Augusta the capital?
8. Which science-fiction writer wrote *The War of the Worlds*?
9. What is the largest city in Scotland?
10. How many tentacles does an octopus have?
11. Which sister of Emperor Augustus married Mark Antony?
12. What is the largest lake in the British Isles?
13. Which aviator and entrepreneur produced the film *Scarface*?
14. Who won the women's race in the 1996 London Marathon?
15. In computer terminology, what do the initials OCR represent?
16. Who was the first American to orbit the earth?
17. Which Japanese novelist wrote *Confessions of a Mask*?
18. Who succeeded to the U.S. presidency after Kennedy's assassination?
19. What is the highest mountain entirely in Italy?
20. Who was the last Danish King of England?

ANSWERS: *1 Jules Verne, 2 Three, 3 A bird, 4 Zimbabwe, 5 Odysseus, 6 Royal Air Force, 7 Maine, 8 H. G. Wells, 9 Glasgow, 10 Eight, 11 Octavia, 12 Lough Neagh, 13 Howard Hughes, 14 Liz McColgan, 15 Optical character recognition, 16 John Glenn, 17 Yukio Mishima, 18 Lyndon Johnson, 19 Gran Paradiso, 20 Hardecanute.*

General Knowledge

Your rating: ● 0-5 Join a library ● 6-10 Keep at it ● 11-15 Join a quiz team ● 16-20 Join Mensa

1. Which British novelist wrote *Tom Brown's Schooldays*?
2. Which ancient city's Hanging Gardens were one of the Seven Wonders of the World?
3. Which Italian city is famous for the Rialto Bridge and St Mark's Square?
4. Which child star of the 1930s won a special Academy Award in 1934?
5. Which French fashion designer was famous for his New Look and the H-line?
6. What sort of creature is a kookaburra?
7. Which acute form of pneumonia is caused by the bacterium *Legionella pneumophila*?
8. Which French poet and dramatist wrote the novel *Les Misérables*?
9. With which sport is Jack Nicklaus associated?
10. What was Pope John Paul II's native country?
11. Which U.S. film producer and animator was responsible for *Snow White and the Seven Dwarfs* and *Pinocchio*?
12. Which prime minister secured passage of a bill that conferred the title Empress of India on Queen Victoria?
13. Which village at the NE tip of Scotland is the site of the house of 16th-century Dutch immigrant John de Groot?
14. Which famous megalithic structure is the focus of a cluster of ceremonial sites on Salisbury Plain, Wiltshire?
15. Which British aviator established several long-distance records with her solo flights in the 1930s?
16. Which king abdicated in 1936 because of objections to his liaison with Mrs Wallis Simpson?
17. Which 1852 Harriet Beecher Stowe bestseller greatly stimulated anti-slavery feeling?
18. What is the name for an industry in which the market is supplied by one supplier?
19. Which Swiss national hero was ordered to shoot an apple from his son's head?
20. What sort of creature is a mullet?

ANSWERS: *1 Thomas Hughes, 2 Babylon, 3 Venice, 4 Shirley Temple, 5 Christian Dior, 6 A bird, 7 Legionnaires' disease, 8 Victor Hugo, 9 Golf, 10 Poland, 11 Walt Disney, 12 Benjamin Disraeli, 13 John O' Groats, 14 Stonehenge, 15 Amy Johnson, 16 Edward VIII, 17 Uncle Tom's Cabin, 18 Monopoly, 19 William Tell, 20 A fish.*

General Knowledge

Your rating: ● 0-5 Join a library ● 6-10 Keep at it ● 11-15 Join a quiz team ● 16-20 Join Mensa

1. How is the tibia better known?
2. The port of Le Havre lies at the mouth of which river?
3. What was the honourable way of death for Japanese samurai who wished to avoid shame?
4. Which Roman goddess became identified with the Greek Aphrodite as goddess of love?
5. Of what sort of creatures are Aberdeen Angus a breed?
6. Which field event in athletics involves throwing a 2kg circular object?
7. Which U.S. novelist wrote *The Naked Lunch*?
8. In which county is Gatwick airport?
9. Of which country was Robert Mugabe prime minister from 1980 to 1987?
10. Which Hungarian composer wrote the operetta *The Merry Widow*?
11. Elvers are the young of which fish?
12. Who became poet laureate in 1984?
13. What is measured in ohms?
14. Which Hancock was the star of *Hancock's Half Hour*?
15. What is the capital of Vietnam?
16. What is the name for the official reports of debates in the UK parliament?
17. What sort of creature is a Rottweiler?
18. Which composer wrote *The Messiah* ?
19. Which British dramatist wrote *Rosencrantz and Guildenstern Are Dead*?
20. In what part of the body would one find the metacarpals and phalanges?

ANSWERS: *1 Shin bone, 2 River Seine, 3 Hara-kiri, 4 Venus, 5 Cattle, 6 Discus, 7 William Burroughs, 8 West Sussex, 9 Zimbabwe, 10 Franz Lehar, 11 The eel, 12 Ted Hughes, 13 Electrical resistance, 14 Tony Hancock, 15 Hanoi, 16 Hansard, 17 A dog, 18 Handel, 19 Tom Stoppard, 20 The hand*

Entertainment

Your rating: ● **0-5 Buy a TV** ● **6-10 Keep at it** ● **11-15 Join a quiz team** ● **16-20 Enter a quiz show**

1. Which band released an album entitled *Maybe You've Been Brainwashed Too* in 1999?
2. Which 1969 film comedy about a 19th-century teenage highwayman starred John Hurt in the title role?
3. Whose walk from Edinburgh Observatory to Greenwich Observatory was covered by the BBC2 travel series *As the Crow Flies*?
4. Which 1999 film starred Robert Carlyle and Jonny Lee Miller as 18th century highwaymen and Liv Tyler as the love interest?
5. Which 1999 ITV comedy drama about the reforming of an Eighties New Romantic band starred Martin Clunes and Neil Morrissey?
6. Which Welsh band released an album entitled *Equally Cursed and Blessed* in 1999?
7. Which actor played Jan Schlictmann, a lawyer fighting for compensation for leukaemia-stricken families, in the film *A Civil Action*?
8. Which actress starred as Jinx Kingsley in the 1999 BBC 1 Minette Walters crime thriller *The Dark Room*?
9. Which 15-year-old U.S. singer/songwriter released her debut album, *From in the Shadows*, in 1999?
10. Which Sixties BBC science programme featured Raymond Baxter as its commentator?
11. Which English actor played Chopin in the 1991 film *Impromptu*?
12. What was the only U.K. hit for Levert, which reached the top ten in 1987?
13. Which musical instrument was the focus of a 1999 film featuring Samuel L. Jackson and Greta Scacchi, which followed its story from 17th century Italy to modern Canada?
14. Which song provided top ten hits for Jimmy Parkinson, the Platters and Freddie Mercury?
15. Who won an Oscar for Best Actor for his role as Father Flanagan in the 1938 film *Boys Town*?
16. Which 1999 BBC 1 wildlife series investigated the extraordinary abilities of animals?
17. Who took a *Walk On the Wild Side* in the top ten in 1973?
18. Which *Scream* creator provided the screenplay for the sci-fi thriller *The Faculty*?
19. Which comedy actor was the star of the Seventies TV series *Life Begins at Forty*?
20. What was the title of Steve Harley's 1999 album, which was recorded at London's Jazz Cafe?

ANSWERS: *1 New Radicals, 2 Sinful Davey, 3 Janet Street-Porter's, 4 Plunkett and Macleane, 5 Hunting Venus, 6 Catatonia, 7 John Travolta, 8 Dervla Kirwan, 9 Shelby Starner, 10 Eye on Research, 11 Hugh Grant, 12 Casanova, 13 Violin (The Red Violin), 14 The Great Pretender, 15 Spencer Tracy, 16 SuperNatural, 17 Lou Reed, 18 Kevin Williamson, 19 Derek Nimmo, 20 Stripped to the Bare Bones.*

General Knowledge

Your rating:
- 0-5 Join a library
- 6-10 Keep at it
- 11-15 Join a quiz team
- 16-20 Join Mensa

1. Which hard silvery metal is represented by the symbol Ni?
2. Which tree provides the main food-source for koalas?
3. Of which former Soviet republic is Tbilisi the capital?
4. Which Spanish novelist wrote *Don Quixote*?
5. Which U.S. airbase near Newbury was the first UK site for cruise missiles?
6. Which annual British dog show first took place in London in 1886?
7. Who became chancellor of West Germany in 1982?
8. In which county can the town of Watford be found?
9. Which Czech tennis player won the men's title at the U.S. Open in 1985 and 1986?
10. In Greek legend, which monstrous dog guarded the entrance to the underworld?
11. What is the largest Atlantic port in Europe?
12. Which Italian composer wrote the opera *Lucia di Lammermoor*?
13. What is the capital of Nicaragua?
14. Who was appointed chancellor of Germany after Hitler's death?
15. Which British historian wrote *The Origins of the Second World War*?
16. Who became prime minister of Canada in 1984?
17. Which French tennis player won her first Wimbledon singles title in 1919?
18. Which building was designed by Joseph Paxton to house the Great Exhibition of 1851?
19. Which British writer created the mild-mannered detective Albert Campion?
20. What sort of creature is an anole?

ANSWERS: *1 Nickel, 2 Eucalyptus, 3 Georgia, 4 Miguel de Cervantes, 5 Greenham Common, 6 Cruft's, 7 Helmut Kohl, 8 Hertfordshire, 9 Ivan Lendl, 10 Cerberus, 11 Rotterdam, 12 Donizetti, 13 Managua, 14 Karl Dönitz, 15 A. J. P. Taylor, 16 Brian Mulroney, 17 Suzanne Lenglen, 18 Crystal Palace, 19 Margery Allingham, 20 A lizard.*

General Knowledge

Your rating: ● **0-5** **Join a library** ● **6-10** **Keep at it** ● **11-15** **Join a quiz team** ● **16-20** **Join Mensa**

1. In which city were the 1980 Summer Olympics held?
2. Which hexagonal, accordion-like musical instrument was invented by Sir Charles Wheatstone?
3. What is the longest river in Scotland?
4. Which fortress on the north bank of the Thames held such famous prisoners as Lady Jane Grey and Anne Boleyn?
5. The Galapagos Islands are part of which South American country?
6. Which actress starred in the films *National Velvet* and *Cleopatra*?
7. As part of which group did Pete Townshend become famous for smashing his guitars?
8. In which country did Robert Clive help to establish British supremacy?
9. Who became president of the National Union of Mineworkers in 1981?
10. Which British novelist wrote *Little Lord Fauntleroy*?
11. Who directed the films *The Fallen Idol* and *The Third Man*?
12. Which colonel led the military regime that seized power in Greece in 1967?
13. Mount Hermon is on the border between which two countries?
14. Which Anglo-Saxon thegn led a raid on Peterborough Abbey in 1070?
15. Which British writer penned *The Anathemata*?
16. Which pope caused controversy with his failure to condemn fascism during World War II?
17. Who was the last Emperor of Russia?
18. Which British novelist wrote A Man from the North and *The Old Wives' Tale*?
19. At which French Riviera resort can the Promenade des Anglais be found?
20. In which U.S. state is the city of Omaha?

ANSWERS: *1 Moscow, 2 Concertina, 3 The Tay, 4 The Tower of London, 5 Ecuador, 6 Elizabeth Taylor, 7 The Who, 8 India, 9 Arthur Scargill, 10 Frances Hodgson Burnett, 11 Sir Carol Reed, 12 George Papadopoulos, 13 Syria and Lebanon, 14 Hereward the Wake, 15 David Jones, 16 Pius XII, 17 Nicholas II, 18 Arnold Bennett, 19 Nice, 20 Nebraska.*

General Knowledge

Your rating: ● 0-5 Join a library ● 6-10 Keep at it ● 11-15 Join a quiz team ● 16-20 Join Mensa

1. Which European country colonised Martinique in 1635?
2. Which Labour MP renounced his peerage in 1963 and won a by-election at Chesterfield in 1984?
3. Are anodes positive or negative?
4. Of which country is Reykjavik the capital?
5. Which U.S. novelist created the character *Tarzan of the Apes*?
6. Which Finnish composer wrote *Finlandia*?
7. Which U.S. singer became famous for the song *Mammy*?
8. What sort of creature is a martin?
9. According to the Old Testament, who was the youngest son of Jacob and Rachel?
10. Which French fashion designer took over Dior's fashion house in 1957?
11. At which French city was Joan of Arc tried and burned in 1431?
12. Who did Cicero describe as "the father of history"?
13. What sort of creature is a kob?
14. Which U.S. novelist wrote *The Sound and the Fury*?
15. Who was prime minister of Australia from 1968 to 1971?
16. What is the chief river in Burma?
17. Tobermory is the chief town of which Scottish island?
18. Which Hungarian composer achieved international recognition with his *Psalmus Hungaricus*?
19. Which British lexicographer wrote *Rasselas* in a week to pay for his mother's funeral?
20. Which French mathematician discovered the first transcendental number in 1873?

ANSWERS: *1 France, 2 Tony Benn, 3 Positive, 4 Iceland, 5 Edgar Rice Burroughs, 6 Jean Sibelius, 7 Al Jolson, 8 A bird, 9 Benjamin, 10 Yves Saint-Laurent, 11 Rouen, 12 Herodotus, 13 An antelope, 14 William Faulkner, 15 Sir John Grey Gorton, 16 The Irrawaddy River, 17 Mull, 18 Zoltan Kodaly, 19 Samuel Johnson, 20 Charles Hermite.*

Entertainment

Your rating: ● **0-5** **Buy a TV** ● **6-10** **Keep at it** ● **11-15** **Join a quiz team** ● **16-20** **Enter a quiz show**

1. Which Scottish estate was the setting for the BBC 1 series *Monarch of the Glen*?
2. Which U.S. country singer released the acoustic album *Little Sparrow* in 2001?
3. Who was the presenter of Channel 4's *Time Team*?
4. Which Oscar-winning actor was *Cast Away* in the 2000 film?
5. Which former musical quiz show was presented by both Tom O'Connor and Lionel Blair?
6. Which U.S. singer had a U.K. top five hit in 2001 with *Pop Ya Colla*?
7. Which legendary British actor played Prince Feisal, leader of an Arab revolt, in the 1962 film *Lawrence of Arabia*?
8. In which country was the BBC 1 historical drama *Rebel Heart* set?
9. Which U.S. group had a U.K. number one hit with *Use It Up and Wear It Out* in 1980?
10. Which 2000 film starred Morgan Freeman as a police officer and Gene Hackman as a lawyer?
11. Which British group had a 1990 U.K. top five hit with *I'm Free*?
12. Which 1991 film featured a family of giant beetles disguised as humans in order to save the Brazilian rain forest?
13. Which 2001 ITV series revealed the process involved in the formation of a manufactured music group?
14. What was the title of Wet Wet Wet's second number one single, which reached the top of the U.K. charts in 1992?
15. Which 2000 British film featured Ben Kingsley and Ian McShane as gangsters?
16. Which original *Star Trek* character was played by DeForest Kelley?
17. Which Donna Summer song provided Martine McCutcheon with a 2001 U.K. top ten hit?
18. Which U.S. comic actor played a Russian circus musician in the 1984 film *Moscow on the Hudson*?
19. Which Channel 4 comedy series was set in a northern nightclub owned by wheelchair-bound Brian Potter?
20. Which girl band had a 2001 U.K. number one hit with *Whole Again*?

ANSWERS: *1 Glenbogle, 2 Dolly Parton, 3 Tony Robinson, 4 Tom Hanks, 5 Name That Tune, 6 Usher, 7 Alec Guinness, 8 Ireland, 9 Odyssey, 10 Under Suspicion, 11 Soup Dragons, 12 Meet the Applegates, 13 Popstars, 14 Goodnight Girl, 15 Sexy Beast, 16 Dr Leonard McCoy (Bones), 17 On the Radio, 18 Robin Williams, 19 Peter Kay's Phoenix Nights, 20 Atomic Kitten.*

General Knowledge

Your rating: ● 0-5 Join a library ● 6-10 Keep at it ● 11-15 Join a quiz team ● 16-20 Join Mensa

1. Which creatures does an ornithologist study?
2. What name is given to goods thrown overboard to lighten a ship in distress?
3. Which football team did Alf Garnett support?
4. In which European country is the city of Verona?
5. Who recorded the albums *Look Sharp*, *Jumpin' Jive* and *Night and Day*?
6. What is the full name of the disease known as flu?
7. Which film portrayed the life of Fanny Brice?
8. Which British author wrote a series of novels set in Barsetshire?
9. What name is given to a dome-shaped dwelling made from blocks of snow?
10. What name is given to the carved and painted poles erected by Native American tribes?
11. Which chieftain united the Gauls against Julius Caesar in 52 BC?
12. Of which country was Daniel Ortega head of state?
13. What is the name of the gang William is a member of in stories by Richmal Crompton?
14. What was the name of the motorist whose beating at the hands of the LAPD led to five days of rioting in 1992?
15. Which lyricist wrote the words to *On the Sunny Side of the Street* and *The Way You Look Tonight*?
16. What is the second period of the Palaeozoic Era called?
17. Who played eight members of the same family in *Kind Hearts and Coronets*?
18. On which Shakespeare play is Akira Kurosawa's film *Ran* based?
19. What was the first name of actor Lon Chaney?
20. Which character in Greek mythology sacrificed his daughter Iphigeneia?

ANSWERS: *1 Birds, 2 Jetsam, 3 West Ham United, 4 Italy, 5 Joe Jackson, 6 Influenza, 7 Funny Girl, 8 Anthony Trollope, 9 Igloo, 10 Totem poles, 11 Vercingetorix, 12 Nicaragua, 13 The Outlaws, 14 Rodney King, 15 Dorothy Fields, 16 Ordovician Period, 17 Alec Guinness, 18 King Lear, 19 Alonso, 20 Agamemnon.*

General Knowledge

Your rating:
- 0-5 Join a library
- 6-10 Keep at it
- 11-15 Join a quiz team
- 16-20 Join Mensa

1. Which famous first-class train was inaugurated in 1883, running from Paris to the Black Sea?
2. After whom is the Harvard lampoon Worst Actress of the Year Award named?
3. What name is given to the breakdown of sugar to alcohol by the action of yeast?
4. Which comedian hosted the 2001 Oscars?
5. Who played Sir Thomas More in the 1966 film *A Man for All Seasons*?
6. Which author wrote *The Shining*, *Misery* and *The Green Mile*?
7. Who was the first chairman of TV's *What's My Line*?
8. What is the largest city in Nevada?
9. What was the surname of the American engineer after whom a fairground big wheel is named?
10. Which Italian composer wrote the opera *Aida*?
11. Who wrote the novel *Room at the Top*?
12. Which author wrote *Cakes and Ale* and *The Moon and Sixpence*?
13. By what name was 16th-century Italian artist Paolo Caliari known?
14. Which driver halted Michael Schumacher's run of six successive victories by winning the 2001 Brazilian Grand Prix?
15. Of which county in Northern Ireland is Enniskillen the county town?
16. Which king was the subject of Shakespeare's first history play?
17. Which Michael Caine film ends with a bus on the edge of a cliff?
18. In which African country did the Mau Mau operate in the 1950s?
19. In which African country is the city of Fez?
20. Which Italian dramatist won the Nobel prize for literature in 1997?

ANSWERS: *1 Orient Express, 2 Natalie Wood, 3 Fermentation, 4 Steve Martin, 5 Paul Scofield, 6 Stephen King, 7 Eamonn Andrews, 8 Las Vegas, 9 Ferris, 10 Giuseppe Verdi, 11 John Braine, 12 W Somerset Maugham, 13 Paolo Veronese, 14 David Coulthard, 15 Fermanagh, 16 King John, 17 The Italian Job, 18 Kenya, 19 Morocco, 20 Dario Fo.*

General Knowledge

Your rating: ● 0-5 Join a library ● 6-10 Keep at it ● 11-15 Join a quiz team ● 16-20 Join Mensa

1. Which film dog was played by a male collie called Pal?
2. What was the first novel by John Grisham?
3. What is the name of Fred Flintstone's wife?
4. Which golfer added the Players Championship, the so-called 'fifth major', to his collection of titles in March 2001?
5. Who played the young starlet in the 1933 film *King Kong*?
6. Which former Labour MP bought the *Daily Mirror* in 1984?
7. In which novel do the characters divide into hunters and fire-keepers?
8. Who won a Best Actor Oscar for *Patton*?
9. Who directed the films *Taxi Driver*, *Raging Bull* and *Goodfellas*?
10. Which veteran British comedian is idolised in Albania?
11. The cast of which TV series were reunited to make *Mirrorball*?
12. Which character in Greek mythology was able to charm all living things with his lyre playing?
13. What is the first novel in Paul Scott's *Raj Quartet*?
14. Which film directed by Ang Lee was named Best Foreign Film at the 2001 Oscars?
15. What was the nickname of American gangster Charles Arthur Floyd?
16. Which French dramatist wrote *A Flea in Her Ear*?
17. Who played Will Scarlett in the film *Robin Hood - Prince of Thieves*?
18. Which French racing driver was world champion in 1985, 1986, 1989 and 1993?
19. Which American orchestra did Eugene Ormandy conduct from 1936 to 1980?
20. Which important fuel gas has the chemical formula C3 H8?

ANSWERS: *1 Lassie, 2 A Time to Kill, 3 Wilma, 4 Tiger Woods, 5 Fay Wray, 6 Robert Maxwell, 7 Lord of the Flies, 8 George C Scott, 9 Martin Scorsese, 10 Sir Norman Wisdom, 11 Absolutely Fabulous, 12 Orpheus, 13 The Jewel in the Crown, 14 Crouching Tiger, Hidden Dragon, 15 Pretty Boy, 16 Georges Feydeau, 17 Christian Slater, 18 Alain Prost, 19 Philadelphia Orchestra, 20 Propane.*

Sports

Your rating: ● **0-5** **Wooden spoon** ● **6-10** **Bronze medal**
● **11-15** **Silver medal** ● **16-20** **Gold medal**

1. Which cyclist won Great Britain's first gold medal at the Sydney Olympics?
2. A professional boxer between 140-147 pounds fights in which weight division?
3. Which tennis player won the French Open in 1991 and 1992?
4. In which sport would the Nottingham Panthers play the Sheffield Steelers?
5. What colour ring on an archery target is worth seven points?
6. Which country did New Zealand beat in their successful defence of the America's Cup in 2000?
7. In which event did Mary Peters win gold at the 1972 Olympics?
8. What nationality is top rugby league player Iestyn Harris?
9. Which Everton player scored the only goal of the 1995 F.A. Cup Final?
10. In 1977 Janet Guthrie became the first woman to qualify for what?
11. In the summer of 2000, which cricket side was beaten by England in a Test series for the first time in 31 years?
12. Who refereed the 2001 Worthington Cup Final between Birmingham City and Liverpool?
13. A professional boxer between 112 and 118 pounds fights in which weight division?
14. Which horse won the Grand National in 1994?
15. Which number lies between 20 and 12 on a dart-board?
16. In January 2000, who became the youngest Briton and the fifth-youngest person of all time to be chosen as a Formula 1 driver?
17. Who was the first batsman to score his 100th first-class century during a Test match?
18. Who became Britain's most expensive goal-keeper in May 2000?
19. What is the maximum length in inches of a baseball bat?
20. In which sport do England and Scotland compete for the Calcutta Cup?

ANSWERS: *1 Jason Queally, 2 Welterweight, 3 Jim Courier, 4 Ice hockey, 5 Red, 6 Italy, 7 Pentathlon, 8 Welsh, 9 Paul Rideout, 10 Indianapolis 500, 11 West Indies, 12 David Elleray, 13 Bantamweight, 14 Minnehoma, 15 5, 16 Jenson Button, 17 Geoff Boycott, 18 Fabien Barthes, 19 42, 20 Rugby union.*

General Knowledge

Your rating: ● 0-5 Join a library ● 6-10 Keep at it ● 11-15 Join a quiz team ● 16-20 Join Mensa

1. Which singer-songwriter recorded the album *Tapestry* in 1971?
2. Who wrote the autobiography *Angela's Ashes*?
3. Which Hollywood actor played a cocaine trafficker in the 2001 film *Blow*?
4. Which country held the crew of a U.S. spy plane after it made an emergency landing in 2001?
5. In computing, what does the abbreviation AI stand for?
6. Which Scottish novelist wrote *Ivanhoe*?
7. The film *Lust for Life* concerned the life of which artist?
8. Of which U.S. state is Montpelier the capital?
9. What name is given to the Japanese art of paper folding?
10. Which Australian-born actor wrote *My Wicked, Wicked Ways*?
11. Who took over from Julie Walters as the mother of Adrian Mole on TV?
12. Which series of novels by James Fenimore Cooper includes *The Last of the Mohicans*?
13. Who won the Best Supporting Actress Oscar for her performance in *Pollock* at the 2001 Oscars?
14. Which poet wrote the lyric drama *Prometheus Unbound*?
15. What is the trade name of the antidepressant drug fluoxetine?
16. Which American talk show host was born Lawrence Harvey Zeiger in 1933?
17. Which TV series was set in Royston Vasey?
18. With which king is the Authorised Version of the Bible associated?
19. Which English admiral was known as 'Old Grog'?
20. What term for an unconventional individual is named after a 19th-century American lawyer who failed to brand his cattle?

ANSWERS: *1 Carole King, 2 Frank McCourt, 3 Johnny Depp, 4 China, 5 Artificial intelligence, 6 Sir Walter Scott, 7 Van Gogh, 8 Vermont, 9 Origami, 10 Errol Flynn, 11 Lulu, 12 The Leatherstocking Tales, 13 Marcia Gay Harden, 14 Percy Bysshe Shelley, 15 Prozac, 16 Larry King, 17 The League of Gentlemen, 18 James I, 19 Edward Vernon, 20 Maverick.*

General Knowledge

Your rating: ● 0-5 Join a library ● 6-10 Keep at it ● 11-15 Join a quiz team ● 16-20 Join Mensa

1. Which flower is used as a symbol of remembrance for the dead of the World Wars?
2. For which novel did Kingsley Amis win the Booker Prize?
3. What is the diameter of a compact disc in centimetres?
4. Which former captain became England's leading run-scorer in Test cricket in 1993?
5. How many horses finished the 2001 Grand National?
6. Which chesspiece is also called a castle?
7. Which disease did *The Singing Detective* have?
8. What name is given to the amount a borrower is charged for a loan, usually expressed as a percentage?
9. In which Jules Verne novel does Captain Nemo appear?
10. Which former England coach left Southampton to become manager of Tottenham Hotspur in 2001?
11. Where was the film *Purely Belter* set?
12. Which British dramatist wrote *Look Back in Anger* and *The Entertainer*?
13. Who directed the *Carry On* series of films?
14. Who won the Best Supporting Actor Oscar for his performance in *Traffic* at the 2001 Oscars?
15. Who was principal conductor of the Hallé Orchestra until his death in 1970?
16. Which passenger ship was sunk by a German U-boat on May 7 1915?
17. Which was the second film in which Clint Eastwood played Harry Callaghan?
18. Who is the only woman to have been chosen as a running mate in a U.S. presidential election?
19. What is the real first name of blues guitarist B B King?
20. Which 2001 film starred Robert De Niro and Cuba Gooding Jr?

ANSWERS: *1 Poppy, 2 The Old Devils, 3 12 cm, 4 Graham Gooch, 5 Four, 6 Rook, 7 Psoriasis, 8 Interest, 9 Twenty Thousand Leagues Under the Sea, 10 Glenn Hoddle, 11 Newcastle, 12 John Osborne, 13 Gerald Thomas, 14 Benicio Del Toro, 15 Sir John Barbirolli, 16 The Lusitania, 17 Magnum Force, 18 Geraldine Ferraro, 19 Riley, 20 Men of Honour.*

General Knowledge

Your rating: ● 0-5 Join a library ● 6-10 Keep at it ● 11-15 Join a quiz team ● 16-20 Join Mensa

1. Which poet is best known for his *Elegy Written in a Country Churchyard*?
2. Which film star is an international bridge player?
3. Who succeeded Richard Nixon as U.S. President?
4. Which singer and actress starred in the film *The Wedding Planner*?
5. Of which U.S. state is Denver the capital?
6. Which French city in the Côte d'Or department is famous for its mustard?
7. Who went *Full Circle* around the world on television?
8. With which sport is Ivan Mauger associated?
9. Which Oscar-winning film was the directorial debut of Robert Redford?
10. Which device was first used for capital punishment in New York in 1890?
11. What was the first full-length film by Walt Disney?
12. Which comic strip detective was created by Chester Gould in 1931?
13. What was the adopted name of Canadian-born beauty expert Florence Nightingale Graham?
14. Which team beat Tottenham Hotspur in the 2000/01 F.A. Cup semi-finals?
15. What is the lightest metal?
16. Which composer wrote the opera *Elektra*?
17. What nationality is the author Margaret Atwood?
18. What name for the devil means 'light-bearer' in Latin?
19. Which forename is shared by Prince Andrew and Prince Harry?
20. Which French-born actress won an Oscar for *It Happened One Night*?

ANSWERS: *1 Thomas Gray, 2 Omar Sharif, 3 Gerald Ford, 4 Jennifer Lopez, 5 Colorado, 6 Dijon, 7 Michael Palin, 8 Speedway, 9 Ordinary People, 10 Electric chair, 11 Snow White, 12 Dick Tracy, 13 Elizabeth Arden, 14 Arsenal, 15 Lithium, 16 Richard Strauss, 17 Canadian, 18 Lucifer, 19 Albert, 20 Claudette Colbert.*

Entertainment

Your rating: ● **0-5** Buy a TV ● **6-10** Keep at it ● **11-15** Join a quiz team ● **16-20** Enter a quiz show

1. Which city was the setting for the Channel 4 comedy drama series *Sex and the City*, starring Sarah Jessica Parker?
2. In which 2000 film did Michael Douglas play a judge turned drugs 'czar'?
3. Which actress played Edie Pegden in the TV sit-com *Last of the Summer Wine*?
4. Which song by British band Toploader reached the U.K. top ten in 2001 after being released for the third time?
5. Which actor played the first black U.S. president in the 1972 film *The Man*?
6. Which British female vocalist had a U.K. top five hit in 1985 with *That Ole Devil Called Love*?
7. In which 2000 film did Helen Hunt and Haley Joel Osment star as mother and son?
8. Which actor played US President Josiah Bartlet in the Channel 4 drama series *The West Wing*?
9. Which U.S. group had a U.K. number one hit in 1970 with *The Tears of a Clown*?
10. Which 1961 film, starring Margaret Rutherford as Miss Marple, was adapted from the Agatha Christie novel *4.50 from Paddington*?
11. Which ITV comedy drama series starred Ardal O'Hanlon as magazine journalist Eamon?
12. With whom did UB40 collaborate on the 1990 U.K. top ten hit *I'll Be Your Baby Tonight*?
13. Which actress starred as a Brazilian chef in the 1999 film *Woman on Top*?
14. Which comedy writer was behind series such as *Butterflies*, *Luv* and *Bread*?
15. Which U.S. band had a 2001 U.K. top five hit with *Loco*?
16. Which member of the team played King Arthur in 1975's *Monty Python and the Holy Grail*?
17. Which BBC 1 fly-on-the-wall documentary series followed a team of U.S. lawyers and their clients in Massachusetts?
18. Who had a 2001 U.K. top five hit with *Teenage Dirtbag*?
19. Which member of Blue Watch became a dad to baby Eve in the 2001 series of *London's Burning*?
20. Which actor starred as advertising executive Nick Marshall in the 2000 film *What Women Want*?

ANSWERS: *1 New York, 2 Traffic, 3 Thora Hird, 4 Dancing in the Moonlight, 5 James Earl Jones, 6 Alison Moyet, 7 Pay It Forward, 8 Martin Sheen, 9 Smokey Robinson & the Miracles, 10 Murder She Said, 11 Big Bad World, 12 Robert Palmer, 13 Penelope Cruz, 14 Carla Lane, 15 Fun Lovin' Criminals, 16 Graham Chapman, 17 Boston Law, 18 Wheatus, 19 Geoffrey Pearce, 20 Mel Gibson.*

General Knowledge

Your rating: • 0-5 Join a library • 6-10 Keep at it • 11-15 Join a quiz team • 16-20 Join Mensa

1. Which American actor starred in *High Noon* and *Mr Deeds Goes to Town*?
2. With which radio station is TV's Alan Partridge associated?
3. Who replaced Peter Gabriel as lead singer of Genesis in 1975?
4. Which team won the 2000/01 Scottish Premier League title?
5. Of which African country is Lusaka the capital?
6. Which common wild plant gets its name from the French for lion's tooth?
7. Which chef presented a *Seafood Lovers' Guide* on TV?
8. What name was given to the load line on a ship's hull, introduced in 1876?
9. Who succeeded Harold Wilson as prime minister in 1976?
10. Which city will host the 2002 Commonwealth Games?
11. Who wrote the novel *National Velvet*?
12. Which Essex town was sacked by the Iceni led by Boudicca in 60 A.D.?
13. What name is given to a negatively charged particle that is a constituent of all atoms?
14. In which French city was Joan of Arc burned at the stake?
15. For which gemstones is the Australian mining town of Coober Pedy famous?
16. Which American novelist wrote *Imaginary Friends* and *Foreign Affairs*?
17. *The Day of the Jackal* centres on the attempted assassination of which leader?
18. Which British boxer lost his world title to Marco Antonio Barrera in 2001?
19. Who was producer of the *Star Wars* and *Indiana Jones* series of films?
20. Which German tennis player won five successive Grand Slam tournaments in the 1980s?

ANSWERS: *1 Gary Cooper, 2 Radio Norwich, 3 Phil Collins, 4 Celtic, 5 Zambia, 6 Dandelion, 7 Rick Stein, 8 Plimsoll line, 9 James Callaghan, 10 Manchester, 11 Enid Bagnold, 12 Colchester, 13 Electron, 14 Rouen, 15 Opals, 16 Alison Lurie, 17 General De Gaulle, 18 Naseem Hamed, 19 George Lucas, 20 Steffi Graf.*

General Knowledge

Your rating: ● **0-5 Join a library** ● **6-10 Keep at it** ● **11-15 Join a quiz team** ● **16-20 Join Mensa**

1. Which Roman emperor ordered the building of a wall between Solway Firth and the Tyne?
2. What is the name of the cat in *The Simpsons*?
3. In the Old Testament, who was the twin brother of Jacob?
4. Which former member of the *Goons* died in 2001 at the age of 79?
5. How many heads of U.S. presidents are carved into Mount Rushmore?
6. Which American author wrote *The Turn of the Screw*?
7. What is the surname of the sisters in the Jane Austen novel *Sense and Sensibility*?
8. What sort of creature is a kite?
9. Who has become the first man to hold all of golf's Major titles at the same time?
10. Which London street is synonymous with private medicine?
11. Which American author created the detective Philip Marlowe?
12. Which opera by Donizetti was based on a novel by Sir Walter Scott?
13. What name is given to a boundary between air masses having different temperature and humidity?
14. Which horse won the 2001 Grand National?
15. What was the name of Dustin Hoffman's character in *The Graduate*?
16. Which English dramatist wrote *Hobson's Choice*?
17. Which Monty Python star sang the theme song for *One Foot in the Grave*?
18. According to legend, at whom did Peeping Tom peep?
19. Who wrote the novel *Jane Eyre*?
20. Which Irish monk founded the monastery at Lindisfarne?

ANSWERS: *1 Hadrian, 2 Snowball, 3 Esau, 4 Sir Harry Secombe, 5 Four, 6 Henry James, 7 Dashwood, 8 A bird, 9 Tiger Woods, 10 Harley Street, 11 Raymond Chandler, 12 Lucia di Lammermoor, 13 Front, 14 Red Marauder, 15 Benjamin Braddock, 16 Harold Brighouse, 17 Eric Idle, 18 Lady Godiva, 19 Charlotte Brontë, 20 St Aidan.*

General Knowledge

Your rating: ● 0-5 Join a library ● 6-10 Keep at it ● 11-15 Join a quiz team ● 16-20 Join Mensa

1. Which English swimmer won the 100m breaststroke at the Seoul Olympics?
2. Who wrote the novel *Mary Barton*?
3. What does the *Ugly Duckling* grow into in Hans Christian Andersen's fairy tale?
4. Which 2001 film starred Renée Zellweger in the title role?
5. With which singing group did Diana Ross find fame?
6. Which chesspiece can only move diagonally?
7. Which word connects the cab company in *Taxi* and the dessert company in *The Fall and Rise of Reginald Perrin*?
8. In which Tennessee city is the Country and Western Music Hall of Fame?
9. What is the name of the five-sided building that houses the head-quarters of the U.S. armed forces?
10. Which pianist and singer was born Nathaniel Adams Coles?
11. Who played *Harry O* on television?
12. Which French monarch was married to Marie-Antoinette?
13. Who wrote the short story collection *Guys and Dolls*?
14. Which country beat American Samoa by a world record score of 31-0 in a World Cup qualifying game in 2001?
15. What is the shallowest of the Great Lakes?
16. Which American composer wrote the opera *Nixon in China*?
17. Who wrote the war-time trilogy *Sword of Honour*?
18. Which 60s group had hits with *White Rabbit* and *Somebody to Love*?
19. Which U.S. novelist wrote *The Accidental Tourist*?
20. What is the stage name of Marshall Bruce Mathers III?

ANSWERS: *1 Adrian Moorhouse, 2 Elizabeth Gaskell, 3 A swan, 4 Bridget Jones's Diary, 5 The Supremes, 6 Bishop, 7 Sunshine, 8 Nashville, 9 The Pentagon, 10 Nat King Cole, 11 David Janssen, 12 Louis XVI, 13 Damon Runyon, 14 Australia, 15 Lake Erie, 16 John Adams, 17 Evelyn Waugh, 18 Jefferson Airplane, 19 Anne Tyler, 20 Eminem.*

Entertainment

Your rating: ● **0-5** **Buy a TV** ● **6-10** **Keep at it** ● **11-15** **Join a quiz team** ● **16-20** **Enter a quiz show**

1. Which group were *Prolonging the Magic* with their 1999 album?
2. Which U.S. actor was *The Landlord* in the 1970 film?
3. Which BBC 1 documentary series followed the exploits of Alun Jenkins, head of the exclusive dating agency, The Executive Club?
4. Which band had a 1999 hit with *Electricity*, the first single taken fom their album, *Head Music*?
5. In which fictional Yorkshire town was ITV's *Where the Heart Is* set?
6. Who directed the film *eXistenZ*, starring Jude Law and Jennifer Jason Leigh?
7. Which band's tracks were covered by various artists on the 1999 album, *Burning London*?
8. What was the title of the 1999 ITV thriller which starred Pete Postlethwaite as detective John McKeown?
9. Which actor played drug kingpin Nino Brown in the 1991 film *New Jack City*?
10. What was the name of the character played by McLean Stevenson in the TV series *M*A*S*H*?
11. What was the title of Survivor's 1982 U.K. number one hit?
12. In which 1999 film did Val Kilmer play Mira Sorvino's blind masseur?
13. Which BBC 1 documentary series followed the work of environmental health officers in London's Borough of Haringey?
14. Which male vocalist had U.K. top ten hits in the Sixties with *Marcheta*, *Mexicali Rose* and *Wimoweh*?
15. In which Channel 4 comedy series did Michael J. Fox star as Mike, the deputy Mayor of New York City?
16. Which actress was *Joan of Arc* in the 1948 film?
17. Which song provided U.K. top ten hits for Michael Jackson in 1972 and Marti Webb in 1985?
18. Which Black Country comedian embarked on a third series of his eclectic chat show in 1999?
19. Which actress played the oppressive mother of Adam Sandler's college football hero in the 1999 film *The Waterboy*?
20. What was the title of the Seventies TV series which featured stories about the Royal Flying Corps of World War I?

ANSWERS: *1 Cake, 2 Beau Bridges, 3 The Matchmaker, 4 Suede, 5 Skelthwaite, 6 David Cronenberg, 7 The Clash's, 8 Butterfly Collectors, 9 Wesley Snipes, 10 Colonel Blake, 11 Eye of the Tiger, 12 At First Sight, 13 A Life of Grime, 14 Karl Denver, 15 Spin City, 16 Ingrid Bergman, 17 Ben, 18 Frank Skinner (The Frank Skinner Show), 19 Kathy Bates, 20 Wings.*

General Knowledge

Your rating:
- 0-5 Join a library
- 6-10 Keep at it
- 11-15 Join a quiz team
- 16-20 Join Mensa

1. Which country's ruling regime from 1933 to 1945 was known as the Third Reich?
2. Of which group of islands is Alderney the third largest?
3. What sort of creature is a saluki?
4. Which novelist wrote *Frankenstein: the Modern Prometheus*?
5. Which organ of the body is infected by pyelitis?
6. Which city on the River Arno is famous for its Leaning Tower?
7. Which international Christian organisation was founded in 1865 in London by William Booth?
8. Which Marxist theorist directed the Red Army to victory as war commissar during the civil war of 1918 to 1920?
9. Which Berkshire village is associated with protest marches organised by CND from 1958 to 1963?
10. Which military parade is held on the Horse Guards parade ground in London, on the sovereign's official birthday?
11. With which composer did W.S. Gilbert collaborate on 14 popular operas?
12. Which U.S. president was assassinated by John Wilkes Booth?
13. Which British actress starred in the films *The Prime of Miss Jean Brodie* and *A Private Function*?
14. What is the capital of Peru?
15. Which day precedes Good Friday?
16. Which principal Roman god was identified with the Greek Zeus?
17. Which athletics event involves throwing an iron or brass sphere as far as possible?

18 Which British telephone service for the suicidal and despairing was started in 1953 by the Rev Chad Varah?

19. Which style of design takes its name from the 1925 Esposition Internationale des Arts Décoratifs et Industriels Modernes?
20. What is the largest glacier in Switzerland?

ANSWERS: *1 Germany, 2 The Channel Islands, 3 A dog, 4 Mary Shelley, 5 The kidney, 6 Pisa, 7 Salvation Army, 8 Leon Trotsky, 9 Aldermaston, 10 Trooping the Colour, 11 Arthur Sullivan, 12 Abraham Lincoln, 13 Maggie Smith, 14 Lima, 15 Maundy Thursday, 16 Jupiter, 17 Shot put, 18 The Samaritans, 19 Art Deco, 20 Aletsch Glacier.*

General Knowledge

Your rating: ● 0-5 Join a library ● 6-10 Keep at it ● 11-15 Join a quiz team ● 16-20 Join Mensa

1. Which constellation lies on the zodiac between Aries and Aquarius?
2. In which ocean do the Pitcairn Islands lie?
3. Which English-born U.S. film actor starred in *The Philadelphia Story* and *North By Northwest*?
4. Which Dutch postimpressionist painter cut off part of his own left ear?
5. Which incompetent police force featured in the silent film comedies produced by Mack Sennett?
6. What is the name for the strong fibrous tissue that joins one bone to another at a joint?
7. What do the initials RNLI stand for?
8. In which state of the USA is the Grand Canyon situated?
9. How is the scapula otherwise known?
10. Of which county is Shrewsbury the administrative centre?
11. Which Spanish novelist wrote *Guzman de Alfarache*?
12. Of which Pacific country is Port Moresby the capital?
13. Which legendary chief of the Onondaga tribe was the subject of a poem by Longfellow?
14. Which general was president of the USA from 1869 to 1877?
15. Which style of 13th century music means 'old art' in Latin?
16. What sort of creature is an alewife?
17. With which musical instrument was Austrian child prodigy Fritz Kreisler associated?
18. Which Soviet astronomer was the first to observe volcanic activity on the moon?
19. Who replaced Terry Venables as England football coach?
20. Which British essayist and poet wrote the tragedy *Cato*?

ANSWERS: *1 Pisces, 2 The Pacific, 3 Cary Grant, 4 Vincent Van Gogh, 5 Keystone Kops, 6 Ligament, 7 Royal National Lifeboat Institution, 8 Arizona, 9 Shoulder blade, 10 Shropshire, 11 Mateo Aleman, 12 Papua New Guinea, 13 Hiawatha, 14 Ulysses S. Grant, 15 Ars antiqua, 16 A fish, 17 The violin, 18 Nikolai Kozirev, 19 Glenn Hoddle, 20 Joseph Addison.*

General Knowledge

Your rating: ● **0-5** Join a library ● **6-10** Keep at it ● **11-15** Join a quiz team ● **16-20** Join Mensa

1. Which city is the administrative centre of Merseyside?
2. Which organ of the body forms and secretes bile?
3. Is the Tropic of Cancer north or south of the equator?
4. Which poisonous element is represented by the symbol As?
5. Of which European country is Kraków the third largest city?
6. Who was the first American in space?
7. Which country did the Thirteen Colonies become in 1776?
8. Which animal has the longer gestation period, an elephant or a rat?
9. In which county is the town of Sheerness?
10. Which Russian poet and novelist wrote *Eugene Onegin* and *Boris Godunov*?
11. What sort of creature is a pratincole?
12. What is the capital of South Australia?
13. Which U.S. dramatist wrote *Waiting For Lefty*?
14. What is a Pirani gauge used to measure?
15. Ádi Granth are the sacred canonical scriptures of which religion?
16. Of which country is Pusan the second largest city?
17. In Greek mythology, which king of Cyprus made an ivory statue and fell in love with it?
18. In which country was film director Otto Preminger born?
19. Of which U.S. state is Lincoln the capital?
20. What is the name for the point in the orbit of the moon which is nearest the earth?

ANSWERS: *1 Liverpool, 2 The liver, 3 North, 4 Arsenic, 5 Poland, 6 Alan Shepard, 7 The USA, 8 An elephant, 9 Kent, 10 Pushkin, 11 A bird, 12 Adelaide, 13 Clifford Odets, 14 Low gas pressures, 15 Sikhism, 16 South Korea, 17 Pygmalion, 18 Austria, 19 Nebraska, 20 Perigee.*

Entertainment

Your rating: ● **0-5 Buy a TV** ● **6-10 Keep at it** ● **11-15 Join a quiz team** ● **16-20 Enter a quiz show**

1. Which character married Peggy Mitchell in *EastEnders* in 1999?
2. In which 1988 film did Sean Penn and Robert Duvall star as Danny McGavin and Bob Hodges, members of the gang crime division of the LAPD?
3. Which *Coronation Street* couple, who separated 10 years previously, decided to give their relationship another try in 1999?
4. Which Irish band returned to the music scene in 1999 with a single entitled *Promises*, taken from the album *Bury the Hatchet*?
5. Who wrote the play upon which the 1999 film *An Ideal Husband* was based?
6. Which actor played the adult *Merlin* in the 1999 epic fantasy adventure on Channel 4?
7. What was the title of Reef's 1999 album, the follow-up to 1997's *Glow*?
8. Which Gerry Anderson puppet series featured the adventures of a submarine of the future?
9. Which actress played the title role in the 1940 film *Kitty Foyle*?
10. What was the title of the ITV drama sequel to 1998's *Coming Home*, which was based on the book by Rosamunde Pilcher?
11. Who were *Under the Moon of Love* at number one in 1976?
12. Which 1999 film directed by Todd Solondz featured the lives of various dysfunctional individuals?
13. Which occasional ITV show, featuring a celebrity audience, was boxer Lennox Lewis a subject of in 1999?
14. What were the titles of the two U.K. number one hits by Jimmy Young in 1955?
15. Which actor played the leading role of Theophilus North in the 1988 film *Mr. North*?
16. Which 1999 ITV drama series imagined what would happen to the survivors if the Earth was hit by a meteor?
17. Who were on the *Road to Nowhere* in the top ten in 1985?
18. In which 1999 film did Anne Heche play a lawyer and Jada Pinkett play a reporter?
19. What was the name of Alf Garnett's wife, played by Dandy Nichols, in the comedy series *Till Death Us Do Part*?
20. Which legendary producer released a soundtrack album in 1999 entitled *Playing By Heart*, inspired by the work of jazz trumpeter Chet Baker?

ANSWERS: *1 Frank Butcher, 2 Colors, 3 Ken Barlow and Deirdre Rachid, 4 The Cranberries, 5 Oscar Wilde, 6 Sam Neill, 7 Rides, 8 Stingray, 9 Ginger Rogers, 10 Nancherrow, 11 Showaddywaddy, 12 Happiness, 13 An Audience With..., 14 Unchained Melody & The Man From Laramie, 15 Anthony Edwards, 16 The Last Train, 17 Talking Heads, 18 Return to Paradise, 19 Else, 20 John Barry.*

General Knowledge

Your rating: ● 0-5 Join a library ● 6-10 Keep at it ● 11-15 Join a quiz team ● 16-20 Join Mensa

1. Which Czech-born British publisher founded Pergamon Press?
2. With which art form is Donatello associated?
3. Which British novelist wrote *Brighton Rock*?
4. Of which country was David Ben-Gurion the first prime minister?
5. Which team did Johann Cruyff captain to the final of the 1974 World Cup?
6. What is the sterile offspring of a female horse and a male ass known as?
7. Of which vegetable is kohlrabi a variety?
8. By what name are the New Testament accounts of Christ's life ascribed to Matthew, Mark, Luke and John collectively known?
9. What is the English name for the Irish county of Dún Na Ngall?
10. In Greek mythology, which son of Zeus was the messenger of the gods?
11. What does the Tibetan word 'yeti' mean?
12. Which Russian novelist wrote *The Lower Depths*?
13. Which leading member of the Bloomsbury group wrote *Eminent Victorians*?
14. Which silvery-white element is represented by the symbol Te?
15. In which resort was the National Library of Wales established in 1911?
16. Which British physicist shared the 1933 Nobel Prize with Schrödinger?
17. Which Italian anatomist gave his name to the canal connecting the ear and throat?
18. What was the name of the raft on which Thor Heyerdahl travelled from Peru to the Tuamota islands in 1947?
19. Which civil engineer is best known for his construction of the suspension bridge over the Menai Strait?
20. Who opened the first birth-control clinic in Britain in 1921?

ANSWERS: *1 Robert Maxwell, 2 Sculpture, 3 Graham Greene, 4 Israel, 5 The Netherlands, 6 A mule, 7 Cabbage, 8 The Gospels, 9 Donegal, 10 Hermes, 11 Snowman, 12 Maxim Gorky, 13 Lytton Strachey, 14 Tellurium, 15 Aberystwyth, 16 Paul Dirac, 17 Eustachio, 18 Kon-Tiki, 19 Thomas Telford, 20 Marie Stopes.*

General Knowledge

Your rating:
- 0-5 Join a library
- 6-10 Keep at it
- 11-15 Join a quiz team
- 16-20 Join Mensa

1. What sort of animal is a Pomeranian?
2. Of which country is Helsinki the capital?
3. What is the highest British decoration for civilian bravery?
4. According to the New Testament, who baptised Christ?
5. Sicily is the largest island in which sea?
6. How is the plastic polyvinyl chloride commonly known?
7. What sort of precious stone is the Koh-i-noor?
8. Who was the first leader of communist Russia?
9. Which Russian composer wrote the operas *Swan Lake* and *The Nutcracker*?
10. Which statesman was the first to use the term Iron Curtain?
11. What is the art of combining two or more melodic lines simultaneously in music?
12. Which English poet was appointed Dean of St Paul's in 1621?
13. Who was King of Wessex from 802 to 839 AD?
14. Who became U.S. president after Lincoln's assassination?
15. Which gas makes up approximately 98% of the atmosphere of Venus?
16. In Greek legend, which dryad was the wife of Orpheus?
17. What is the capital of Liberia?
18. What is the largest living lizard?
19. Which British novelist wrote *The Cruel Sea*?
20. Which Soviet marshal commanded all Warsaw Pact forces in Europe from 1955 to 1960?

ANSWERS: *1 A dog, 2 Finland, 3 George Cross, 4 John the Baptist, 5 The Mediterranean, 6 PVC, 7 Diamond, 8 Lenin, 9 Tchaikovsky, 10 Winston Churchill, 11 Counterpoint, 12 John Donne, 13 Egbert, 14 Andrew Johnson, 15 Carbon dioxide, 16 Eurydice, 17 Monrovia, 18 Komodo dragon, 19 Nicholas Monsarrat, 20 Ivan Koniev.*

General Knowledge

Your rating: ● **0-5 Join a library** ● **6-10 Keep at it** ● **11-15 Join a quiz team** ● **16-20 Join Mensa**

1. Which U.S. actor starred in *Chinatown* and *The Witches of Eastwick*?
2. At which city in the northwest of France is a 24-hour motor race held annually?
3. What sort of creature is a quail?
4. Who was the chief author of the U.S. Declaration of Independence?
5. In which country can the Bog of Allen be found?
6. What does the acronym GATT stand for?
7. Which political party, founded in 1925, is dedicated to the achievement of Welsh independence?
8. Which England cricket captain was involved in a controversy over umpiring in Pakistan in 1987?
9. Which film production company was founded by Louis B. Mayer and Samuel Goldwyn in 1924?
10. What sort of creatures do entomologists study?
11. Which Greek physician compiled the first pharmacopoeia?
12. Which port is the largest town of the Outer Hebrides?
13. What sort of creature is a mugger?
14. Which golfer won the U.S. Masters at Augusta in 1996?
15. Which Irish-American novelist wrote *The Ginger Man*?
16. Which king of England married Isabella of France in 1308?
17. What does the acronym EFTA stand for?
18. Which French painter made the first non-narrative film, *Le Ballet mécanique*?
19. What is the capital of the Côte d'Ivoire?
20. Which Rugby League player and novelist wrote *This Sporting Life*?

ANSWERS: *1 Jack Nicholson, 2 Le Mans, 3 A bird, 4 Thomas Jefferson, 5 The Republic of Ireland, 6 General Agreement on Tariffs and Trade, 7 Plaid Cymru, 8 Mike Gatting, 9 MGM, 10 Insects, 11 Pedanius Dioscorides, 12 Stornoway, 13 A crocodile, 14 Nick Faldo, 15 J. P. Donleavy, 16 Edward II, 17 European Free Trade Association, 18 Fernand Léger, 19 Abidjan, 20 David Storey.*

Entertainment

Your rating:
- ● 0-5 Buy a TV
- ● 6-10 Keep at it
- ● 11-15 Join a quiz team
- ● 16-20 Enter a quiz show

1. What was the title of Alvin Stardust's only U.K. number one single, which topped the charts in 1974?
2. What was the title of the Seventies BBC series originally presented by Melvyn Bragg, in which new paperback books were reviewed?
3. Which classic soul singer released *Come 2 My House* in 1999, a jazz-funk album produced by Prince and featuring a cameo from Queen Latifah?
4. Who wrote and directed the 1991 film *The People Under the Stairs*?
5. At which Hampshire police station was the ITV documentary series *Cop Shop* set?
6. Which British rock group marked the 20th anniversary of the release of their debut single in 1999 with a new album, *What Are You Going To Do With Your Life?*?
7. Which presenter took over from Barry Norman as the host of BBC 1's *Film* review show?
8. Which 1999 film starring Brendan Fraser and Alicia Silverstone followed the story of a family emerging from 35 years spent in a nuclear bunker?
9. What was the name of the dance troupe which featured on the *Kenny Everett Video Show*?
10. Which actress played Brooke Shields' mother in the 1978 film *Pretty Baby*?
11. What was the title of the fifth album by Orbital, released in 1999?
12. Which 1999 BBC 1 documentary series traced the history of British TV comedy?
13. Which actress played Odessa the maid to Sissy Spacek's upper-middle-class housewife in the 1990 film *The Long Walk Home*?
14. Which song provided U.K. top five hits for both the Mindbenders in 1966 and Phil Collins in 1988?
15. Who directed the film *Tea With Mussolini*?
16. What was Soft Cell's only U.K. number one hit?
17. Which actress played Sharon alongside David Duchovny's Randy in the 1991 film about religious fanaticism, *The Rapture*?
18. Which character, who left in disgrace after an affair with Ricky Butcher, returned to *EastEnders* in 1999?
19. Which group had a U.K. top five hit in 1991 with *The Whole of the Moon*?
20. Which actor played Ilya Kuryakin in the TV series *The Man From UNCLE*?

ANSWERS: *1 Jealous Mind, 2 Read All About It, 3 Chaka Khan, 4 Wes Craven, 5 Gosport, 6 Echo & the Bunnymen, 7 Jonathan Ross, 8 Blast From the Past, 9 Hot Gossip, 10 Susan Sarandon, 11 The Middle of Nowhere, 12 Laughter in the House: The Story of British Sitcom, 13Whoopi Goldberg , 14 A Groovy Kind of Love, 15 Franco Zeffirelli, 16 Tainted Love, 17 Mimi Rogers, 18 Natalie Price, 19 Waterboys, 20 David McCallum.*

General Knowledge

Your rating: ● 0-5 Join a library ● 6-10 Keep at it ● 11-15 Join a quiz team ● 16-20 Join Mensa

1. Who directed the films *Annie Hall* and *Hannah and Her Sisters*?
2. Which poet published his *Poems, Chiefly in the Scottish Dialect* in 1786?
3. Of which U.S. state is Atlanta the capital?
4. The Anschluss of 1938 signalled the union of Germany with which country?
5. What is the title of the spiritual ruler of Tibet?
6. What sort of creature is a Clydesdale?
7. Which British novelist wrote *A Town Like Alice*?
8. Ozone is a form of which gas?
9. Scapa Flow is a section of which ocean?
10. Which country's representative assembly is called the Dáil Éireann?
11. Which English architect designed the Queen's House, Greenwich?
12. Which African country was known as Dahomey until 1975?
13. *Anopheles* is a genus of which insects?
14. Which vegetable comes from the plant *Ipomoea batatas*?
15. Which Scottish literary critic and judge was editor of the Edinburgh Review until 1829?
16. Which South African novelist wrote *The Hunter and the Whale*?
17. Which London borough was created in 1965 from the former boroughs of Bethnal Green, Stepney and Poplar?
18. Who was president of the USA from 1885 to 1889 and from 1893 to 1897?
19. Which Lebanese mystic and poet wrote *The Prophet*?
20. What is the capital of Senegal?

***ANSWERS:** 1 Woody Allen, 2 Robert Burns, 3 Georgia, 4 Austria, 5 Dalai Lama, 6 Horse, 7 Nevil Shute, 8 Oxygen, 9 The Atlantic, 10 Republic of Ireland, 11 Inigo Jones, 12 People's Republic of Benin, 13 Mosquitoes, 14 Sweet potato, 15 Lord Francis Jeffrey, 16 Sir Laurens Van der Post, 17 Tower Hamlets, 18 Stephen Grover Cleveland, 19 Kahlil Gibran, 20 Dakar.*

General Knowledge

Your rating:
- 0-5 Join a library
- 6-10 Keep at it
- 11-15 Join a quiz team
- 16-20 Join Mensa

1. Which Spanish surrealist painter wrote the autobiographical *Diary of a Genius*?
2. Which Frankenstein actor was born William Pratt?
3. What sort of creature is a red admiral?
4. What was the venue of the Olympic Games from 776 BC until at least 261 AD?
5. Which unit of water-depth is equal to six feet?
6. Which French composer wrote the opera *Pelléas et Mélisande*?
7. With which instrument was jazz musician Miles Davis associated?
8. In which county is the fishing port of St Ives?
9. Of which political party was Roy Jenkins leader from 1982 to 1983?
10. What sort of creature is a fennec?
11. Which pope's election at the Council of Constance ended the Great Schism?
12. In Greek mythology, how were Clotho, Lachesis and Atropos collectively known?
13. Which horse won the 1996 Grand National?
14. What is the largest national park of New Zealand?
15. Which lyricist collaborated with Frederick Loewe on the musicals *Brigadoon*, *My Fair Lady* and *Camelot*?
16. Which transition metal is represented by the symbol Sc?
17. Which Flemish painter also served as diplomatic envoy of Philip the Good, Duke of Burgundy?
18. Which English poet wrote *To his Coy Mistress*?
19. In which country is the Qattara Depression?
20. Which U.S. physicist constructed the first laser in 1953?

ANSWERS: *1 Salvador Dali, 2 Boris Karloff, 3 A butterfly, 4 Olympia, Greece, 5 Fathom, 6 Claude Debussy, 7 The trumpet, 8 Cornwall, 9 The Social Democratic Party, 10 A fox, 11 Martin V, 12 The Fates, 13 Rough Quest, 14 Fiordland, 15 Alan Jay Lerner, 16 Scandium, 17 Jan van Eyck, 18 Andrew Marvell, 19 Egypt, 20 Charles Townes.*

General Knowledge

Your rating:
- **0-5 Join a library**
- **6-10 Keep at it**
- **11-15 Join a quiz team**
- **16-20 Join Mensa**

1. Which prickly nocturnal creatures belong to the subfamily *Erinaceinae*?
2. Which US actor co-starred with Paul Newman in *Butch Cassidy and the Sundance Kid*?
3. Which sort of enclosed single-seater chair was carried on poles by two men?
4. Which Soviet chess player was world champion from 1975 until his defeat by Kasparov in 1985?
5. On which river does St Louis, Missouri lie?
6. Which unit of area is equal to 100 ares?
7. Of which country was Farouk I king from 1936 to 1952?
8. Who is the patron saint of England?
9. A thoroughbred is a breed of which animal?
10. Which halogen gas is represented by the symbol F?
11. In a water polo game, how many players are allowed in the pool at one time?
12. Of which country is Doha the capital?
13. On what day of the year is Lady Day celebrated?
14. In which river do the Thousand Islands lie?
15. Who wrote a series of novels featuring the detective Lord Peter Wimsey?
16. What sort of creature is a Gila monster?
17. Who was general secretary of the Transport and General Workers' Union from 1968 to 1978?
18. Which town is revered by both Jews and Muslims as the burial place of Abraham?
19. Which British tribe rebelled against Roman rule under Boadicea?
20. Which Irish dramatist wrote *Love and a Bottle*?

ANSWERS: *1 Hedgehogs, 2 Robert Redford, 3 Sedan chair, 4 Anatoly Karpov, 5 Mississippi, 6 Hectare, 7 Egypt, 8 St George, 9 Horse, 10 Fluorine, 11 Fourteen, 12 Qatar, 13 March the 25th, 14 St Lawrence River, 15 Dorothy L. Sayers, 16 A lizard, 17 Jack Jones, 18 Hebron, 19 Iceni, 20 George Farquhar.*

Entertainment

Your rating: ● **0-5** Buy a TV ● **6-10** Keep at it ● **11-15** Join a quiz team ● **16-20** Enter a quiz show

1. Which British band scored a 1999 U.K. top five hit with *Tender*?
2. Which BBC 1 comedy series was set in a remote RAF early-warning station in Scotland?
3. In which country was the 1999 foreign film *Central Station* set?
4. Which veteran DJ discovered the *Sounds of the Suburbs* of Britain on Channel 4?
5. Which American rock group released an album entitled *Summerteeth* in 1999?
6. What was the name of Leslie Nielsen's character in the *Naked Gun* movies?
7. What was the title of the 1979 BBC costume drama set in Cornwall?
8. Which former Japan singer released his first solo album for 12 years, *Dead Bees On A Cake*, in 1999?
9. Which *London's Burning* actor appeared in *Coronation Street* as Sharon Gaskell's two-timing fiance Ian Bentley?
10. Which successful children's cartoon series about a gang of babies was the source of a 1999 film?
11. Which British soul singer had a 1999 U.K. top ten hit with *My Love*?
12. Which 1999 Channel 4 series examined the best acts of all time in six music genres?
13. Which 1987 film starred Anne Bancroft as New York writer Helene Hanff and Anthony Hopkins as Frank Doel, an antiquarian bookseller in London?
14. Which actor starred as Marshall in the ITV drama series *Wonderful You*?
15. Which British/Canadian group had top ten hits in the Eighties with *Vienna*, *All Stood Still* and *Dancing With Tears In My Eyes*?
16. What sort of creature was *Mighty Joe* in the Disney film?
17. Which TV series of the early Eighties starred Susannah York and Ralph Bates as a middle-class couple coming to terms with divorce?
18. What was the title of the Temperance Seven's 1961 U.K. number one hit?
19. Which 1999 BBC 2 documentary series explored the role of regulation enforcers within particular organisations?
20. Which 1940 Oscar-nominated film starred Bette Davis as a plantation-owner's wife who murders her lover?

ANSWERS: *1 Blur, 2 All Along the Watchtower, 3 Brazil, 4 John Peel, 5 Wilco, 6 Lt. Frank Drebin, 7 Penmarric, 8 David Sylvian, 9 Jonathan Guy Lewis, 10 Rugrats (The Rugrats Movie), 11 Kele Le Roc, 12 Top Ten, 13 84 Charing Cross Road, 14 Greg Wise, 15 Ultravox, 16 A giant gorilla, 17 Second Chance, 18 You're Driving Me Crazy, 19 Internal Affairs, 20 The Letter.*

General Knowledge

Your rating:
- 0-5 Join a library
- 6-10 Keep at it
- 11-15 Join a quiz team
- 16-20 Join Mensa

1. By what name was Cambodia formerly known?
2. Which British snooker player won the world professional championship in 1981, 1983 and 1984?
3. Which member of the Beatles was assassinated in 1980?
4. Which British humorist wrote *Three Men in a Boat*?
5. What nationality was the composer Franz Joseph Haydn?
6. From 1884 the Watch Tower Bible and Tract Society became the legal publishing agency of which religious movement?
7. Which gas is represented by the symbol He?
8. To what did heavyweight boxer Cassius Clay change his name?
9. With which type of silent acting is Marcel Marceau associated?
10. Which Scottish missionary and explorer discovered the Victoria Falls and Lake Nyasa?
11. Who was British home secretary from 1979 to 1983?
12. Which king of France was married to Mary, Queen of Scots?
13. Which British novelist wrote *The Towers of Trebizond*?
14. Who replaced Paul Keating as Australian prime minister?
15. In which ocean are the Midway Islands?
16. Which brittle grey-white metalloid is represented by the symbol Ge?
17. Which British chemist, independently of Carl Scheele, discovered oxygen?
18. What was the supreme court of France from the 12th century until the French Revolution?
19. Which sea channel between Denmark and Sweden links the Kattegat and the Baltic Sea?
20. What sort of creature is a francolin?

ANSWERS: *1 Kampuchea, 2 Steve Davis, 3 John Lennon, 4 Jerome K. Jerome, 5 Austrian, 6 Jehovah's Witnesses, 7 Helium, 8 Muhammad Ali, 9 Mime, 10 David Livingstone, 11 William Whitelaw, 12 Francis II, 13 Dame Rose Macaulay, 14 John Howard, 15 Pacific, 16 Germanium, 17 Joseph Priestley, 18 Parlement, 19 The Sound, 20 A partridge.*

General Knowledge

Your rating:
- 0-5 Join a library
- 6-10 Keep at it
- 11-15 Join a quiz team
- 16-20 Join Mensa

1. Which German novelist wrote *The Tin Drum*?
2. Which Apollo mission made the first manned lunar landing?
3. The Costa Brava is a coastal region of which country?
4. What sort of creature is a parakeet?
5. Which U.S. general directed the recapture of the southwest Pacific in World War II?
6. Which method of heat transfer within a fluid is by means of motion of the fluid?
7. Which order of friars was founded in 1209 by St Francis of Assisi?
8. What sort of creatures are measured in hands?
9. Which star of *Gentlemen Prefer Blondes* married Arthur Miller?
10. Of which U.S. state is Columbus the capital?
11. Which channel separates the mainland of South America from Tierra del Fuego?
12. With which instrument is jazz musician Humphrey Lyttelton associated?
13. Which sort of radiation lies between infrared rays and radio waves in the electromagnetic spectrum?
14. Which US novelist wrote *The Man with the Golden Arm*?
15. Which music-hall comedian starred in the films *Oh Mr Porter!* and *Ask a Policeman*?
16. What is the capital of the U.S. state of Illinois?
17. Which Spanish Jesuit missionary was known as the Apostle of the Indies?
18. The tomb of Catherine of Aragon can be found in the cathedral of which city?
19. Which Irish diplomat was chairman of Amnesty International from 1961 to 1975?
20. Who wrote the lyrics for the musical *Heathcliff*?

ANSWERS: *1 Günter Grass, 2 Apollo 11, 3 Spain, 4 A parrot, 5 Douglas MacArthur, 6 Convection, 7 Franciscans, 8 Horses, 9 Marilyn Monroe, 10 Ohio, 11 Strait of Magellan, 12 The trumpet, 13 Microwaves, 14 Nelson Algren, 15 Will Hay, 16 Springfield, 17 St Francis Xavier, 18 Peterborough, 19 Sean MacBride, 20 Sir Tim Rice.*

General Knowledge

Your rating:
- 0-5 Join a library
- 6-10 Keep at it
- 11-15 Join a quiz team
- 16-20 Join Mensa

1. What is the official residence of the president of the USA?
2. With which instrument was jazz musician Charlie Parker associated?
3. In 1215, which Great Charter was sealed at Runnymede by King John of England?
4. What is ikebana?
5. Which British science-fiction writer penned the novel *The Day of the Triffids*?
6. Which constellation lies on the zodiac between Libra and Leo?
7. What are the two official languages of Gibraltar?
8. Which English poet wrote *Paradise Lost*?
9. Which type of fired clay means ‘baked earth’ in Italian?
10. In Greek mythology, which daughter of Zeus fled to Troy with Paris?
11. Which English dramatist wrote the political satire *A Game at Chess*?
12. Who was president of Egypt from 1956 to 1970?
13. What sort of plants are studied by a mycologist?
14. In the French Republican calendar, how long did a décade represent?
15. Which two countries fought the Battle of the Nile on 1 August 1798?
16. To which genus of plants does the Eurasian bindweed belong?
17. In which Irish mountains does the River Liffey rise?
18. Who introduced the philosophical concept of mimesis?
19. Which British inventor became general surveyor of roads in 1827?
20. What sort of creature is a karakul?

ANSWERS: *1 The White House, 2 The saxophone, 3 The Magna Carta, 4 Japanese flower arrangement, 5 John Wyndham, 6 Virgo, 7 English and Spanish, 8 John Milton, 9 Terracotta, 10 Helen, 11 Thomas Middleton, 12 Gamal Abdel Nasser, 13 Fungi, 14 Ten days, 15 Britain and France, 16 Convolvulus, 17 The Wicklow Mountains, 18 Aristotle, 19 John McAdam, 20 A sheep.*

Entertainment

Your rating: ● **0-5** Buy a TV ● **6-10** Keep at it ● **11-15** Join a quiz team ● **16-20** Enter a quiz show

1. Which actor starred as a TV newsman-turned-adventurer in the 1975 film *The Passenger*?
2. Which controversial Channel 4 drama series focussed on the lives of three gay men living in Manchester?
3. Which Pet Shop Boys song provided a U.K. hit for East 17 in 1993?
4. What was the title of the Seventies TV drama series starring Phyllis Calvert and Penelope Keith which featured the private problems of the writer of a woman's page?
5. Which band scored a U.K. top five hit with *Just Looking* in 1999?
6. Which actor played two brothers in the 1982 film *The Man From Snowy River*?
7. Which sitcom veteran played family friend Arthur Capstick in the BBC 1 comedy series *Mrs Merton and Malcolm*?
8. Which folk/dance crossover artist released her second album, *Central Reservation*, in 1999?
9. Who presented the BBC 1 spin-off *Holiday on a Shoestring*?
10. In which 1999 film do two teenagers get transported into the world of a black-and-white Fifties sitcom?
11. Which male vocalist had U.K. number one hits in the Sixties with *I Remember You*, *Lovesick Blues* and *Wayward Wind*?
12. In the second series of which BBC 1 police drama was Pc Terry Sydenham, played by Paul Nicholls, murdered?
13. Which 1954 film starred Jane Wyman as a blind woman and Rock Hudson as the rich playboy responsible both for her blindness and its cure?
14. In which Channel 4 series did U.S. satirist Michael Moore investigate corporate crime?
15. Which actor starred as doctor *Patch Adams* in the film of the same name?
16. Which song provided U.K. number one hits for Tab Hunter in 1957 and Donny Osmond in 1973?
17. Which planet were the family of the future on their way to colonise before their spacecraft was shipwrecked in the Sixties U.S. TV series *Lost in Space*?
18. Which child performer played *Little Miss Broadway* in the 1938 film?
19. Which Chinese city's crime problems were explored in a 1999 Channel 4 documentary series?
20. What was the title of the 1964 U.K. number one hit by Billy J. Kramer and the Dakotas?

ANSWERS: *1 Jack Nicholson, 2 Queer as Folk, 3 West End Girls, 4 Kate, 5 The Stereophonics, 6 Kirk Douglas, 7 Brian Murphy, 8 Beth Orton, 9 Craig Doyle, 10 Pleasantville, 11 Frank Ifield, 12 City Central, 13 Magnificent Obsession, 14 Michael Moore - The Awful Truth, 15 Robin Williams, 16 Young Love, 17 Alpha Centauri, 18 Shirley Temple, 19 Shanghai's (Shanghai Vice), 20 Little Children.*

General Knowledge

Your rating: ● **0-5** Join a library ● **6-10** Keep at it ● **11-15** Join a quiz team ● **16-20** Join Mensa

1. Which member of the royal family is the international president of the Worldwide Fund for Nature?
2. Soweto forms a suburb of which South African city?
3. The Adriatic Sea is an arm of which body of water?
4. Which word describes the sale of a public corporation to the private sector?
5. Which slow-moving reptiles belong to the family *Testudinidae*?
6. In which county can Clacton-on-Sea be found?
7. What is the official currency unit of Switzerland?
8. Which Wiltshire town developed around the workshops of the Great Western Railway?
9. Which artist achieved notoriety with paintings of soup cans and portraits of Marilyn Monroe?
10. Which green pigment absorbs the light which is essential for photosynthesis?
11. Who wrote the librettos for Verdi's *Otello* and *Falstaff*?
12. Which British poet is known for his *Poems on Several Occasions*?
13. At which California city is the annual Tournament of Roses held?
14. What is a piddock?
15. What is the name of the world's highest active volcano?
16. Which British tennis player was the world singles table-tennis champion in 1929?
17. Which Scottish-born U.S. industrialist founded the Keystone Bridge company in 1865?
18. What is the name for the point in the orbit of the moon when it is furthest from the earth?
19. Which Polish composer wrote *Threnody for the Victims of Hiroshima*?
20. What sort of creature is a prion?

ANSWERS: *1 The Duke of Edinburgh, 2 Johannesburg, 3 The Mediterranean Sea, 4 Privatisation, 5 Tortoises, 6 Essex, 7 The Swiss franc, 8 Swindon, 9 Andy Warhol, 10 Chlorophyll, 11 Arrigo Boito, 12 Matthew Prior, 13 Pasadena, 14 A mollusc, 15 Cotopaxi, 16 Fred Perry, 17 Andrew Carnegie, 18 Apogee, 19 Penderecki, 20 A bird.*

General Knowledge

Your rating: ● 0-5 Join a library ● 6-10 Keep at it ● 11-15 Join a quiz team ● 16-20 Join Mensa

1. In which state of the USA is Death Valley?
2. Which Russian composer wrote *Pictures at an Exhibition*?
3. Who was the second wife of Henry VIII?
4. Can penguins fly?
5. Of which country is Asuncion the capital?
6. Which U.S. boxer was the first to beat Muhammad Ali professionally?
7. Which British ice-dance champions won an Olympic gold medal in 1984?
8. Which state was founded by the English Quaker William Penn?
9. Who was British prime minister from 1955 to 1957?
10. What sort of creature is a mustang?
11. Which apostle was the son of Zebedee and the brother of John?
12. Which Italian dynasty ruled Mantua from 1328 to 1707?
13. Who was king of Romania from 1914 to 1927?
14. Which Russian novelist wrote *Oblomov*?
15. Of which country was Paul Henri Spaak the first socialist prime minister?
16. In which cathedral can the tomb of St Swithin be found?
17. Which German composer wrote the operas *Cardillac* and *Mathis der Maler*?
18. Which U.S. inventor patented the vulcanisation process of rubber in 1844?
19. What sort of creature is a chuckwalla?
20. What was the Roman name for the Scottish tribes living north of the Antonine Wall?

ANSWERS: *1 California, 2 Modest Mussorgsky, 3 Anne Boleyn, 4 No, 5 Paraguay, 6 Joe Frazier, 7 Torvill and Dean, 8 Pennsylvania, 9 Anthony Eden, 10 A horse, 11 St James, 12 Gonzaga, 13 Ferdinand, 14 Ivan Goncharov, 15 Belgium, 16 Winchester Cathedral, 17 Paul Hindemith, 18 Charles Goodyear, 19 A lizard, 20 Picts.*

General Knowledge

Your rating: ● **0-5** Join a library ● **6-10** Keep at it ● **11-15** Join a quiz team ● **16-20** Join Mensa

1. In the New Testament, how many Apostles were chosen by Jesus?
2. In World War II, which three countries were known as the Axis Powers?
3. In which county can the Forest of Dean be found?
4. In Greek mythology, who was Apollo's father?
5. What is the official language of Costa Rica?
6. Who edited the last volume of *Das Kapital* after Marx's death?
7. What sort of creature is a plover?
8. Which swinging device is used to regulate clock mechanisms?
9. What is the largest living species of ape?
10. Which Liberal prime minister resigned in 1885 after failing to save Gordon from Khartoum?
11. Which Czech composer wrote the opera *Jenufa*?
12. Who was the only president of the German Democratic Republic?
13. Which Soviet cosmonaut was the first woman to walk in space?
14. What is the fifth book of the Old Testament?
15. Which star of the silent film *Polyanna* married Douglas Fairbanks?
16. Who was the Roman god of doors, thresholds, and beginnings?
17. Which former hurling star became prime minister of Ireland in 1966?
18. What sort of creature is a devil's coach-horse?
19. Which British poet and novelist wrote *Image of a Society*?
20. Which French city lies at the confluence of the Rivers Rhône and Saône?

ANSWERS: *1 Twelve, 2 Germany, Italy and Japan, 3 Gloucestershire, 4 Zeus, 5 Spanish, 6 Friedrich Engels, 7 A bird, 8 Pendulum, 9 Gorilla, 10 Gladstone, 11 Leos Janacek, 12 Wilhelm Pieck, 13 Svetlana Savitskaya, 14 Deuteronomy, 15 Mary Pickford, 16 Janus, 17 Jack Lynch, 18 A beetle, 19 Roy Fuller, 20 Lyons.*

Sports

Your rating:
- 0-5 Wooden spoon
- 6-10 Bronze medal
- 11-15 Silver medal
- 16-20 Gold medal

1. Which England cricketer made his maiden Test century in the fifth Test against the West Indies in 1998?
2. Which martial art literally means 'empty hand'?
3. Which football team's ground is called Roots Hall?
4. What are represented by the five rings of the Olympic flag?
5. What colour jacket is traditionally given to the winners of the U.S. Masters golf competition?
6. How many points did rugby union's Jonathan Webb score for England in the 1992 Five Nations Championship?
7. Who was the first person to run a mile in under four minutes?
8. Which German skier became the first skier ever to retain an Olympic downhill title in 1998?
9. How many Grand Prix wins did Italian Formula 1 driver Alberto Ascari notch up between 1951 and 1955?
10. What colour ball is worth five points in snooker?
11. Which goalkeeper won 125 caps for England?
12. Who is the only woman to have trained two Grand National-winning horses?
13. Who scored two penalties in the 1994 F.A. Cup final?
14. Which English swimmer won a 1998 Commonwealth gold for the 200m butterfly in a new Games record time?
15. How many world title fights did boxer Muhammad Ali contest under his original name Cassius Clay?
16. Which Northern Ireland international was voted European Footballer of the Year in 1968?
17. In which year did rugby union's Kyran Bracken make his England debut, against New Zealand?
18. In which event did Mary Peters win an Olympic gold medal in 1972?
19. Which football team are known as the 'Dons'?
20. In which year did badminton make its Olympic debut?

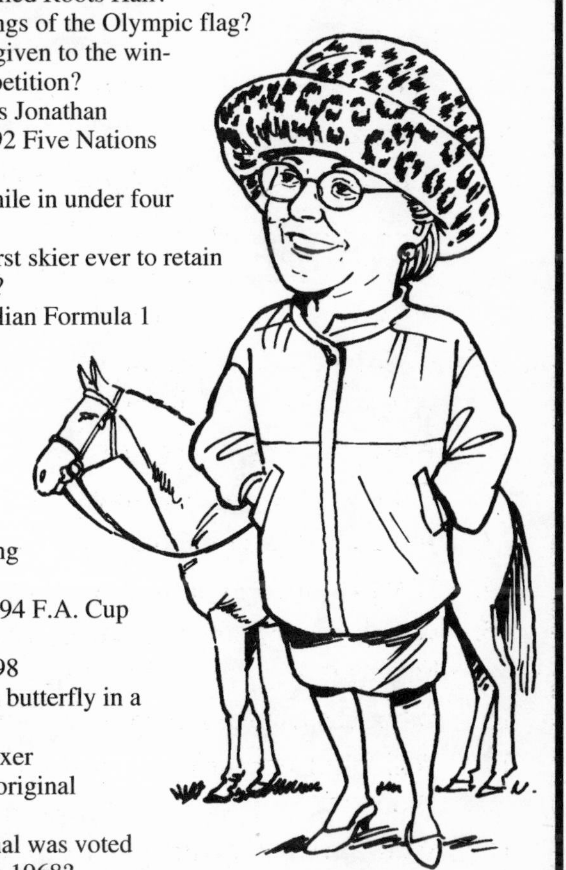

ANSWERS: *1 Mark Ramprakash, 2 Karate, 3 Southend United's, 4 The continents, 5 Green, 6 67, 7 Roger Bannister, 8 Katja Seizinger, 9 13, 10 Blue, 11 Peter Shilton, 12 Jenny Pitman, 13 Eric Cantona, 14 James Hickman, 15 One, 16 George Best, 17 1993, 18 Pentathlon, 19 Wimbledon, 20 1992.*

General Knowledge

Your rating:
- **0-5 Join a library**
- **6-10 Keep at it**
- **11-15 Join a quiz team**
- **16-20 Join Mensa**

1. Which famous writing sisters lived in Haworth Parsonage, Yorkshire?
2. What is the longest river in Africa?
3. Which U.S. scientist experimented with electricity by flying a kite during a thunderstorm?
4. What is the official language of Austria?
5. Which treatment for mental disorders is represented by the initials ECT?
6. In which part of the body would one find the palate?
7. Which legendary king of Phrygia turned everything he touched to gold?
8. With which instrument is jazz musician Stephane Grappelli associated?
9. Who became Home Secretary in the Cabinet reshuffle after the General Election of 2001?
10. Which country's seat of government is The Hague?
11. Which French composer wrote *Boléro*?
12. The Cotswold Hills are situated mainly in which county?
13. Which dictator ruled Spain from 1939 until his death in 1975?
14. What is measured in pascals?
15. Which fruit comes from the tree *Citrus paradisi*?
16. What is the Islamic name for God?
17. Which biblical character slayed Goliath?
18. What sort of creature is an iguana?
19. Which famous Scottish king killed Duncan I in battle?
20. In which South American country is the port of Fray Bentos?

ANSWERS: *1 The Brontë sisters, 2 The Nile, 3 Benjamin Franklin, 4 German, 5 Electroconvulsive therapy, 6 The mouth, 7 Midas, 8 The violin, 9 David Blunkett, 10 The Netherlands, 11 Maurice Ravel, 12 Gloucestershire, 13 Franco, 14 Pressure, 15 Grapefruit, 16 Allah, 17 David, 18 A lizard, 19 Macbeth, 20 Uruguay.*

General Knowledge

Your rating: • **0-5** Join a library • **6-10** Keep at it • **11-15** Join a quiz team • **16-20** Join Mensa

1. Of which South American country was Juan Perón president?
2. Who became principal conductor of the City of Birmingham Symphony Orchestra in 1980?
3. Which German Jewish girl wrote a famous diary while hiding from the Nazis in Amsterdam?
4. What sort of creature is an Appaloosa?
5. Of which island is Palermo the capital?
6. In the New Testament, which apostle denied Christ three times?
7. What is a nimbostratus?
8. Which U.S. actress starred in *Jezebel* and *All About Eve*?
9. Which British novelist and dramatist wrote *An Inspector Calls*?
10. Which ragtime pianist wrote *The Entertainer* and *Maple Leaf Rag*?
11. In which country did Carnatic music originate?
12. To which French town was the papacy removed in 1309?
13. What does the acronym 'quango' stand for?
14. What is bladderwrack?
15. Who discovered the binomial theorem in 1676?
16. What is the main river of British Columbia?
17. Which Swiss philanthropist shared the first Nobel Peace Prize in 1901?
18. With which musical instrument was jazz musician Buddy Bolden associated?
19. The Adullamites were a group of disaffected MPs of which political party?
20. Which Scots poet wrote *Lament for the Makaris*?

ANSWERS: *1 Argentina, 2 Simon Rattle, 3 Anne Frank, 4 A horse, 5 Sicily, 6 Peter, 7 A cloud, 8 Bette Davis, 9 J. B. Priestley, 10 Scott Joplin, 11 India, 12 Avignon, 13 Quasi-autonomous non-governmental organisation, 14 A type of seaweed, 15 Sir Isaac Newton, 16 Fraser River, 17 Jean Henri Dunant, 18 The cornet, 19 The Liberal Party, 20 William Dunbar.*

General Knowledge

Your rating: ● 0-5 Join a library ● 6-10 Keep at it ● 11-15 Join a quiz team ● 16-20 Join Mensa

1. Which film actor starred in *Rebel without a Cause*, *East of Eden* and *Giant*?
2. Of which religion are Brahma, Vishnu, and Shiva the principal gods?
3. What sort of creature is a fulmar?
4. In which county is the resort of Torquay?
5. Which contagious disease is caused by the bacterium *Bacillus anthracis*?
6. Which royal house succeeded the Tudors in 1603?
7. Which Irish county is situated between Galway Bay and the Shannon estuary?
8. Who wrote *Rebecca* and *My Cousin Rachel*?
9. In which mountain range is K2 situated?
10. What is the largest island of Western Samoa?
11. In which European country is the town of Worms?
12. Which Nigerian dramatist and poet wrote *The Lion and the Jewel*?
13. Which Italian heavyweight boxing champion acted in the film *On the Waterfront*?
14. With which instrument is French musician Paul Tortelier associated?
15. What sort of creature is a fer-de-lance?
16. Which Spanish general led a successful coup in 1923?
17. Who was Emperor of Japan from 1867 to 1912?
18. In which state of the USA is the village of Wounded Knee?
19. Which U.S. comedian died in 1996 at the age of 100?
20. Which British composer wrote the *Capriol Suite*?

ANSWERS: *1 James Dean, 2 Hinduism, 3 A bird, 4 Devon, 5 Anthrax, 6 Stuarts, 7 Clare, 8 Dame Daphne Du Maurier, 9 The Karakoram Range, 10 Savai'i, 11 Germany, 12 Wole Soyinka, 13 Primo Carnera, 14 The cello, 15 A snake, 16 Miguel Primo de Rivera, 17 Mutsuhito, 18 South Dakota, 19 George Burns, 20 Peter Warlock.*

Entertainment

Your rating: ● **0-5** **Buy a TV** ● **6-10** **Keep at it** ● **11-15** **Join a quiz team** ● **16-20** **Enter a quiz show**

1. Which pop star presented BBC 1's talent show series *Get Your Act Together*?
2. Which female vocalist had U.K. top ten hits in the Eighties with *Love Resurrection, All Cried Out* and *That Ole Devil Called Love*?
3. Which British actor made his U.S. film debut as an Irish servant in 1916 Philadelphia in the 1967 Walt Disney film *The Happiest Millionaire*?
4. Which real-life Dublin criminal was played by Ken Stott in the 1999 BBC 1 drama *Vicious Circle*?
5. What was the title of Jennifer Rush's 1985 U.K. number one single?
6. For their performances in which 1999 film did James Coburn win an Oscar and Nick Nolte an Oscar nomination?
7. Which Seventies documentary series followed a group of volunteers who lived in a simulated Iron Age settlement for a year, cut off from the modern world apart from the presence of the camera crew?
8. Which band released an album entitled *Apple Venus Volume 1* in 1999, their first for seven years?
9. Which actor played the heroic African adventurer Allan Quatermain in the 1985 film version of *King Solomon's Mines*?
10. Which 1999 ITV comedy series set in Luton in 1976 followed the struggles of six teenagers and their parents?
11. What was the title of the third album by dance act Underworld, released in 1999?
12. Which film starring Meg Ryan and Tom Hanks was a remake of 1940's *The Shop Around the Corner*, in which James Stewart and Margaret Sullavan took the lead roles?
13. What was the title of the first television agony column, presented in the Fifties by South African actress Edana Romney?
14. Which London-based guitar band released their third album, *Revelations*, in 1999?
15. Which actor played James Bond in the 1974 film *The Man With the Golden Gun*?
16. What was the name of the women's football team in the BBC 1 drama series *Playing the Field*?
17. Which Australian vocalist was the U.K.'s entrant in the 1996 Eurovision Song Contest, and had a number one with her song *Ooh Aah...Just a Little Bit*?
18. Which 1999 World War II film set in the Pacific featured Sean Penn, George Clooney, Nick Nolte and Woody Harrelson?
19. Which actor played harbourmaster Mike Nicholls in the BBC 1 drama series *Harbour Lights*?
20. Which vocalist had U.K. top ten hits in 1986 with *Addicted to Love* and *I Didn't Mean To Turn You On*?

ANSWERS: *1 Ronan Keating, 2 Alison Moyet, 3 Tommy Steele, 4 Martin Cahill, 5 The Power of Love, 6 Affliction, 7 Living in the Past, 8 XTC, 9 Richard Chamberlain, 10 Days Like These, 11 Beaucoup Fish, 12 You've Got Mail, 13 Is This Your Problem?, 14 Gene, 15 Roger Moore, 16 Castlefield Blues, 17 Gina G, 18 The Thin Red Line, 19 Nick Berry, 20 Robert Palmer.*

General Knowledge

Your rating:
- **0-5 Join a library**
- **6-10 Keep at it**
- **11-15 Join a quiz team**
- **16-20 Join Mensa**

1. Mount Everest is part of which mountain system?
2. Which Soviet leader signed a major arms limitation treaty with President Reagan in 1987?
3. In which year did Sir Yehudi Menuhin die?
4. What is the capital of Argentina?
5. Which crystalline hydrocarbon is used to make mothballs?
6. What sort of creature is a chub?
7. What nationality was the explorer Fridtjof Nansen?
8. With which instrument is jazz musician Benny Goodman associated?
9. Which city is known as Napoli in Italian?
10. What sort of creature is a funnel weaver?
11. Who was prime minister of the Union of South Africa from 1924 to 1939?
12. Of which country is Dakar the capital?
13. Which road was built about 312 BC between Rome and Capua by the statesman Appius Claudius?
14. What sort of creature is a Russian Blue?
15. Which US composer wrote *Central Park in the Dark*?
16. Which British soldier recounted his exploits in the book *The Seven Pillars of Wisdom?*
17. Which Grand Prince of Muscovy was crowned tsar in 1547?
18. In which year was football's World Cup first held?
19. The BCG vaccine gives partial protection against which disease?
20. Which British philosopher was awarded the Nobel Prize for Literature in 1950?

ANSWERS: *1 The Himalayas, 2 Mikhail Gorbachev, 3 1999, 4 Buenos Aires, 5 Naphthalene, 6 A fish, 7 Norwegian, 8 The clarinet, 9 Naples, 10 A spider, 11 James Hertzog, 12 Senegal, 13 The Appian Way, 14 A cat, 15 Charles Ives, 16 T. E. Lawrence, 17 Ivan the Terrible, 18 1930, 19 Tuberculosis, 20 Bertrand Russell.*

General Knowledge

Your rating:
- 0-5 Join a library
- 6-10 Keep at it
- 11-15 Join a quiz team
- 16-20 Join Mensa

1. Which term is used to describe a number of universities in the northeast USA of high academic and social prestige?
2. Beachy Head is on the coast of which county?
3. Which U.S. actor co-starred with Katherine Hepburn in nine films?
4. Who was chancellor of the exchequer from 1983 to 1989?
5. What do the initials NSPCC stand for?
6. In which European country is the seaport of Ostend?
7. Who became the first Norman King of England in 1066?
8. Who was the Roman goddess of the hearth?
9. Which religion, based on the Four Noble Truths, has more than 500 million followers?
10. What is the capital of Cuba?
11. Which volcanic island is the largest of the Bismarck Archipelago?
12. Holbein the Younger was court painter for which English king?
13. Which French anthropologist wrote *From Honey to Ashes?*
14. Which Pulp star was arrested on suspicion of causing actual bodily harm at the 1996 Brit Awards?
15. In Greek mythology, who was the mother of Apollo and Artemis?
16. Which chemical element is represented by the symbol Se?
17. Who was the supreme god in Babylonian mythology?
18. Hydrochloric acid is a solution of which gas?
19. Who was prime minister of New Zealand from 1972 to 1974?
20. Which British poet wrote *The Wreck of the Deutschland*?

ANSWERS: *1 Ivy League, 2 East Sussex, 3 Spencer Tracy, 4 Nigel Lawson, 5 National Society for the Prevention of Cruelty to Children, 6 Belgium, 7 William the Conqueror, 8 Vesta, 9 Buddhism, 10 Havana, 11 New Britain, 12 Henry VIII, 13 Lévi-Strauss, 14 Jarvis Cocker, 15 Leto, 16 Selenium, 17 Marduk, 18 Hydrogen chloride, 19 Norman Kirk, 20 Gerard Manley Hopkins.*

General Knowledge

Your rating: ● **0-5** Join a library ● **6-10** Keep at it ● **11-15** Join a quiz team ● **16-20** Join Mensa

1. Who became prime minister of a coalition government in Britain in 1940?
2. What is the name for the close-grained white tissue which forms the tusks of elephants?
3. Which island in San Francisco Bay was the site of a notorious maximum security prison?
4. What do the initials PLO stand for?
5. In which county can Watford and Stevenage be found?
6. Which British novelist wrote *A Room with a View*?
7. Do stalagmites grow upwards or downwards?
8. Albuquerque is the largest city of which US state?
9. What sort of creature is a natterjack?
10. What sort of fruit comes from the tree *Prunus domestica*?
11. What do the initials LPG stand for?
12. Who played British missionary Gladys Aylward in the 1958 film *The Inn of the Sixth Happiness*?
13. Which Roman emperor began the construction of the Colosseum in Rome?
14. Who wrote *Lady Chatterley's Lover*?
15. Which British novelist wrote a series of novels set in the imaginary county of Barsetshire?
16. To which republic do the Gilbert Islands belong?
17. Which king of England was married to Margaret of Anjou?
18. Who wrote *Confessions of an English Opium Eater*?
19. Which Japanese island is separated from Honshu by the Tsugaru Strait?
20. Which unit, equal to 1 gram per 9000 metres, is used to measure the fineness of materials?

ANSWERS: *1 Winston Churchill, 2 Ivory, 3 Alcatraz, 4 Palestine Liberation Organisation, 5 Hertfordshire, 6 E. M. Forster, 7 Upwards, 8 New Mexico, 9 A toad, 10 Plum, 11 Liquefied Petroleum Gas, 12 Ingrid Bergman, 13 Vespasian, 14 D. H. Lawrence, 15 Anthony Trollope, 16 Kiribati, 17 Henry VI, 18 Thomas De Quincey, 19 Hokkaido, 20 Denier.*

Entertainment

Your rating: ● **0-5 Buy a TV** ● **6-10 Keep at it** ● **11-15 Join a quiz team** ● **16-20 Enter a quiz show**

1. Which *EastEnders* couple tied the knot in 1999 in a spur-of-the-moment ceremony?
2. Which female duo had a U.K. number one hit in 1992 with *Stay*?
3. In which 1982 film did Charlton Heston play Silas McGee, a disreputable Scottish miner?
4. What was the name of the original family of Channel 5's *Family Affairs*, seven of whom were killed in a huge explosion in 1999?
5. Which song provided a U.K. top ten hit for Elvis Presley in 1969 and the Fine Young Cannibals in 1986?
6. Which actress played Stella in the 1999 film *How Stella Got Her Groove Back*?
7. In what type of institution was the sitcom *The Brittas Empire* set?
8. Which legendary rocker's work from 1953 to 1955 was reprised on the 1999 double album *Sunrise*?
9. Which actor played Henry Turner in the 1991 film *Regarding Henry*?
10. Which actor played Sir Percy Blakeney, the 18th century English aristocrat with a secret identity, in the 1999 BBC 1 adaptation of *The Scarlet Pimpernel*?
11. In 1999, which New York group celebrated their first U.K. number one single since 1980 with *Maria*?
12. Which 1999 Italian film featured the talents of Roberto Benigni as director, co-writer and star?
13. Which seaside town provided the final resting place for Tiffany Mitchell's ashes in *EastEnders*?
14. Which US rock artist released a self-titled album in 1999 featuring the tracks *It All Comes True* and *Days of Farewell*?
15. Which long-running medical drama following a young surgeon in a university hospital was entitled *Medical Center* in the U.S.?
16. Which 1987 film starred Warren Beatty and Dustin Hoffman as untalented singer/songwriters?
17. Which U.S. actress played Carrie, a New York journalist, in Channel 4's controversial comedy-drama series *Sex and the City*?
18. Which song provided U.K. hits for Earth Wind and Fire in 1978 and Black Box in 1990?
19. Which 1999 ITV series tracked down the most disaster-prone people in the country?
20. What was the title of Denise La Salle's 1985 U.K. top ten hit?

ANSWERS: *1 Terry Raymond and Irene Hills, 2 Shakespears' Sister, 3 Mother Lode, 4 The Harts, 5 Suspicious Minds, 6 Angela Bassett, 7 A leisure centre, 8 Elvis Presley's, 9 Harrison Ford, 10 Richard E. Grant, 11 Blondie, 12 Life is Beautiful, 13 Peacehaven, 14 John Mellencamp, 15 Calling Doctor Gannon, 16 Ishtar, 17 Sarah Jessica Parker, 18 Fantasy, 19 Britain's Worst, 20 My Toot Toot.*

General Knowledge

Your rating:
- 0-5 Join a library
- 6-10 Keep at it
- 11-15 Join a quiz team
- 16-20 Join Mensa

1. Of which country was Ferdinand Marcos president from 1965 to 1986?
2. Andrés Segovia helped revive the popularity of which instrument?
3. Which royal was married to Lord Snowdon from 1960 to 1978?
4. With which sport was Rocky Marciano associated?
5. Which U.S. Black civil-rights leader was assassinated by James Earl Ray in 1968?
6. At which racecourse is the flat race known as the Oaks run?
7. Lady Emma Hamilton was the mistress of which British admiral?
8. What is the capital of New Zealand?
9. Which sport is played in the Davis Cup?
10. Which Bohemian folk dance is characterised by three steps and a hop?
11. What is the shortest book of the Old Testament?
12. Who was the president of France throughout the First World War?
13. Which Austrian composer wrote the song cycle *Kindertotenlieder*?
14. Who is the author of the autobiographical *Rogue Trader*?
15. Which British artist painted *Mares and Foals in a Landscape*?
16. Which English king was murdered in Pontefract Castle?
17. Who was poet laureate from 1968 to 1972?
18. Which unit of weight for precious stones is equal to two milligrams?
19. In which English county can Maiden Castle be found?
20. Which nocturnal mammal gets its name from the Afrikaans for earth pig?

ANSWERS: *1 The Philippines, 2 The guitar, 3 Princess Margaret, 4 Boxing, 5 Martin Luther King, 6 Epsom, 7 Nelson, 8 Wellington, 9 Tennis, 10 Polka, 11 The Book of Obadiah, 12 Raymond Poincaré, 13 Gustav Mahler, 14 Nick Leeson, 15 George Stubbs, 16 Richard II, 17 Cecil Day Lewis, 18 Point, 19 Dorset, 20 Aardvark.*

General Knowledge

Your rating:
- **0-5 Join a library**
- **6-10 Keep at it**
- **11-15 Join a quiz team**
- **16-20 Join Mensa**

1. Which Austrian psychiatrist wrote *The Interpretation of Dreams*?
2. The Niagara Falls can be found on the border between which two countries?
3. What is the name for an area within a desert where water is available for vegetation and human use?
4. Who directed *2001: A Space Odyssey* and *Lolita*?
5. What sort of creature is a ptarmigan?
6. Which secret racist society is known by the initials KKK?
7. Of which African country is Mogadishu the capital?
8. What sort of creature is a taipan?
9. Of which U.S. state is Des Moines the capital?
10. What is the largest of the Society Islands?
11. In Greek legend, who killed the many-headed Hydra?
12. Which English puritan sect led by John Lilburne were active from 1647 to 1649?
13. Who was director of the Victoria and Albert Museum from 1974 to 1987?
14. Which country achieved independence in 1965 with Sir Dawda Jawara as prime minister?
15. Which U.S. poet wrote *The British Prison Ship*?
16. Which British novelist wrote *Strangers and Brothers*?
17. What is a gamelan?
18. What was the name of the ruling dynasty of Scotland from 1371 to 1714?
19. Which former Conservative MP is the author of *A Woman's Place*?
20. Which reactive metal is represented by the symbol Sr?

ANSWERS: *1 Sigmund Freud, 2 USA and Canada, 3 Oasis, 4 Stanley Kubrick, 5 A bird, 6 Ku Klux Klan, 7 Somalia, 8 A snake, 9 Iowa, 10 Tahiti, 11 Heracles, 12 The Levellers, 13 Sir Roy Strong, 14 Gambia, 15 Philip Freneau, 16 C. P. Snow, 17 A type of percussion orchestra, 18 Stuart, 19 Edwina Currie, 20 Strontium.*

General Knowledge

Your rating:
- 0-5 Join a library
- 6-10 Keep at it
- 11-15 Join a quiz team
- 16-20 Join Mensa

1. Which river rises in the Cotswolds and flows through Oxford, Reading and London?
2. How many balls are on the table at the start of a snooker game?
3. Which Irving Berlin musical was based on the life of sharpshooter Annie Oakley?
4. What sort of creature is a snipe?
5. Of which country is Tripoli the capital?
6. Which U.S. novelist wrote *Little Women*?
7. Which alkaloid poison is derived from plants of the genus *Strychnos*?
8. Which organisation was formed in the USA in 1934 to help alcoholics to help themselves?
9. How is US comedian Leslie Townes Hope better known?
10. The storming of the Bastille was a feature of which country's revolution?
11. Which composer wrote 12 symphonies and *Bachianas Brasileiras*?
12. Who was president of Ghana from 1960 to 1966?
13. Of which constellation is Aldebaran the brightest star?
14. In Thailand, which monetary unit is equal to 100 satang?
15. Of which U.S. state is Charleston the capital?
16. Who wrote the *Essays of Elia*?
17. 'Wing chun' is a style of which martial art?
18. Which US novelist wrote *Burr* and *Lincoln*?
19. The Alcock Convention of 1869 was a treaty between which two countries?
20. How is the snow leopard otherwise known?

ANSWERS: *1 The Thames, 2 Twenty two, 3 Annie Get Your Gun, 4 A bird, 5 Libya, 6 Louisa May Alcott, 7 Strychnine, 8 Alcoholics Anonymous, 9 Bob Hope, 10 France, 11 Heitor Villa-Lobos, 12 Kwame Nkrumah, 13 Taurus, 14 Baht, 15 West Virginia, 16 Charles Lamb, 17 Kung fu, 18 Gore Vidal, 19 Britain and China, 20 Ounce.*

Entertainment

Your rating: ● **0-5 Buy a TV** ● **6-10 Keep at it** ● **11-15 Join a quiz team** ● **16-20 Enter a quiz show**

1. Which actor played Detective Chief Inspector Ross Tanner in the crime drama series *Second Sight*?
2. Which British female vocalist had a 2001 U.K. top five hit with *Here With Me*?
3. Which former Goon fronted the surreal Sixties comedy sketch show *It's a Square World*?
4. Which 1973 film featured Jack Nicholson as a sailor escorting a thief to naval prison?
5. Which ITV comedy series set in the 1970s featured Slade's Noddy Holder as headmaster Neville Holder?
6. Which U.S. duo had U.K. top ten hits in the Seventies with *Amateur Hour* and *Beat the Clock*?
7. Which 2000 film by Michael Winterbottom was based on Thomas Hardy's novel *The Mayor of Casterbridge*?
8. Which actress played Pandora Braithwaite in the BBC 1 adaptation of *Adrian Mole The Cappuccino Years*?
9. Which U.S. male vocalist had U.K. top ten hits in the Nineties with *I Wonder Why* and *You're All That Matters to Me*?
10. Which two actors played *The Last Hard Men* in the 1976 film of that name?
11. Which BBC 1 comedy series set in a toy company starred Pauline Quirke and Robert Daws?
12. What was the debut single of the Pet Shop Boys, which hit the U.K. number one spot in 1985?
13. Who played actor Max Schreck in the 2000 film *Shadow of the Vampire*?
14. Which science fiction series of the Sixties featured Oliver Reed as scientist Dr Richard Franklin?
15. What was the title of the 2001 U.K. top five hit by Jakatta?
16. Which 1990 film starred Gene Hackman and Anne Archer as a deputy district attorney and his key witness?
17. Which *Coronation Street* character discovered the existence of his 12-year-old son in 2001?
18. Which legendary actor and dancer's first screen appearance came in 1933's *Dancing Lady*, in which he played himself?
19. Who had a 2001 U.K. top five hit with *Ms Jackson*?
20. Which 2000 film earned Goldie Hawn's daughter Kate Hudson an Oscar nomination?

ANSWERS: *1 Clive Owen, 2 Dido, 3 Michael Bentine, 4 The Last Detail, 5 The Grimleys, 6 Sparks, 7 The Claim, 8 Helen Baxendale, 9 Curtis Stigers, 10 Charlton Heston & James Coburn, 11 Office Gossip, 12 West End Girls, 13 Willem Dafoe, 14 R3, 15 American Dream, 16 Narrow Margin, 17 Mike Baldwin, 18 Fred Astaire, 19 Outkast, 20 Almost Famous.*

General Knowledge

Your rating:
- 0-5 Join a library
- 6-10 Keep at it
- 11-15 Join a quiz team
- 16-20 Join Mensa

1. Which actress starred in the films *Body Heat*, *Romancing the Stone* and *Peggy Sue Got Married*?
2. What is the surname of *Lucky Jim* in the novel by Kingsley Amis?
3. Who wrote *The Tale of Jeremy Fisher*?
4. What name is given to a Muslim place of worship?
5. What is the only venomous snake found wild in the British Isles?
6. Which English king succeeded Henry III?
7. In which TV show was the clapometer first used?
8. Who wrote *The Satanic Verses*?
9. What was the pen name of American author Samuel Langhorne Clemens?
10. Which actor won an Oscar for his performance in *Reversal of Fortune*?
11. In which TV series for children did the Soup Dragon appear?
12. Which sea lies between the Italian mainland and the islands of Sicily, Sardinia and Corsica?
13. What is the name of the Earl of Wessex's film company?
14. Which American hurdler was undefeated in 107 meetings between 1977 and 1987?
15. In which U.S. state are the Adirondack Mountains?
16. Which French priest founded the Lazarists?
17. Who played Norma Desmond in *Sunset Boulevard*?
18. Which poet is the subject of the poem *Adonais* by Percy Bysshe Shelley?
19. What nationality is the actress Liv Ullmann?
20. Which Shakespeare play is subtitled *What You Will*?

ANSWERS: *1 Kathleen Turner, 2 Dixon, 3 Beatrix Potter, 4 Mosque, 5 Adder, 6 Edward I, 7 Opportunity Knocks, 8 Salman Rushdie, 9 Mark Twain, 10 Jeremy Irons, 11 The Clangers, 12 12 Tyrrhenian Sea, 13 Ardent Productions, 14 Edwin Moses, 15 New York, 16 St Vincent de Paul, 17 Gloria Swanson, 18 John Keats, 19 Norwegian, 20 Twelfth Night.*

General Knowledge

Your rating:
- 0-5 Join a library
- 6-10 Keep at it
- 11-15 Join a quiz team
- 16-20 Join Mensa

1. Which vehicle derives its name from the U.S. Army's General Purpose vehicle or GP?
2. Margaret Dumont was the long-suffering stooge to which comedy team?
3. In the Old Testament, who received the Ten Commandments?
4. Which Spanish actor played the father of the *Spy Kids* in the 2001 film?
5. Of which Irish rock group are Bono and The Edge members?
6. Which condiment takes its name from the French for 'sour wine'?
7. Who was the father of the Cartwright family in the TV series *Bonanza*?
8. Of which European country is Franjo Tudjman president?
9. Who became president of Sinn Fein in 1983?
10. Which rock 'n' roll singer had a hit with *Be-Bop-a-Lula*?
11. Who wrote *Zen and the Art of Motorcycle Maintenance*?
12. Which English critic wrote the five volume work *Modern Painters*?
13. What was the stage name of Harold Jenkins, who had a hit with *It's Only Make Believe* in 1958?
14. Which football team won the 2000/01 first division championship?
15. From which Rossini opera does the *Lone Ranger* TV theme music come?
16. Which Australian city is named after the queen consort of William IV?
17. What profession did the character played by Jack Nicholson have in *Terms of Endearment*?
18. By what name was the only English pope, Nicholas Breakspear, known?
19. Which New Zealand-born actress played Irene in the BBC series *The Forsyte Saga*?
20. Who was the sixth president of the United States?

ANSWERS: *1 Jeep, 2 The Marx Brothers, 3 Moses, 4 Antonio Banderas, 5 U2, 6 Vinegar, 7 Ben, 8 Croatia, 9 Gerry Adams, 10 Gene Vincent, 11 Robert M Pirsig, 12 John Ruskin, 13 Conway Twitty, 14 Fulham, 15 William Tell, 16 Adelaide, 17 Astronaut, 18 Adrian IV, 19 Nyree Dawn Porter, 20 John Quincy Adams.*

General Knowledge

Your rating: ● **0-5** Join a library ● **6-10** Keep at it ● **11-15** Join a quiz team ● **16-20** Join Mensa

1. Who was the first murder victim in the Bible?
2. In which film did the song *Moon River* appear?
3. What was the name of the *Lone Ranger*'s Indian companion?
4. Which British boxer lost his world heavyweight title to Hasim Rahman in 2001?
5. What is the capital of Uruguay?
6. Which British novelist wrote *Brideshead Revisited* and *A Handful of Dust*?
7. For what did Sophia Loren spend time in jail?
8. In which comedy series did Graham Norton play a priest?
9. Which character in Greek mythology opened a box which contained all the evils of life?
10. What name is given to the decree that makes a divorce final?
11. What was the real surname of author Nevil Shute?
12. Which African country was formerly known as Dahomey?
13. In which Sheridan play does the character Mrs Malaprop appear?
14. Which German driver achieved his first Formula 1 victory in the 2001 San Marino Grand Prix?
15. What is the largest of the United Arab Emirates?
16. Which Austrian-born composer is credited with the invention of 12-tone music?
17. Who presented the TV series *Civilisation*?
18. Dagestan is an autonomous republic of which country?
19. Which actress received an Oscar nomination for her performance in the title role of the film *Carmen Jones*?
20. What is the largest lake in the British Isles?

ANSWERS: *1 Abel, 2 Breakfast at Tiffanys, 3 Tonto, 4 Lennox Lewis, 5 Montevideo, 6 Evelyn Waugh, 7 Income tax evasion, 8 Father Ted, 9 Pandora, 10 Decree absolute, 11 Norway, 12 Benin, 13 The Rivals, 14 Ralf Schumacher, 15 Abu Dhabi, 16 Arnold Schoenberg, 17 Kenneth Clark, 18 Russia, 19 Dorothy Dandridge, 20 Lough Neagh.*

Entertainment

Your rating:
- **0-5** Buy a TV
- **6-10** Keep at it
- **11-15** Join a quiz team
- **16-20** Enter a quiz show

1. Which actor appeared as Dithers the gardener to Ronnie Barker's Lord Rustless in the sitcom *Hark at Barker*?
2. Which song provided U.K. number one hits for both Tab Hunter in 1957 and Donny Osmond in 1973?
3. Which 1989 baseball movie featured Tom Berenger and Charlie Sheen as team-mates?
4. In which Channel 4 series did *Goodness, Gracious Me* star Sanjeev Bhaskar search for the truth about the *Kama Sutra*?
5. Which Irish singer had a 2001 U.K. top five hit with *Always Come Back to Your Love*?
6. Which 2000 film featured Denzel Washington as an American football coach?
7. Which former *Coronation Street* actress appeared in ITV's *Heartbeat* as farm owner Peggy Barton?
8. Which song, originally a hit for the Four Pennies in 1965, reached the U.K. top five when Elvis Presley released it in 1972?
9. Who wrote and directed the 1991 thriller *The People Under the Stairs*?
10. In *EastEnders*, which Slater sister was revealed to be the real mother of her 'sister' Zoe in 2001?
11. In which year did Free have a U.K. hit for the second time with *All Right Now*?
12. What type of animals were the title characters of the 2000 film *The Adventures of Rocky and Bullwinkle*?
13. What was the British title of the manic gameshow *Jeux Sans Frontieres*?
14. Which Spice Girl hit the U.K. top five in 2001 with *Feels So Good*?
15. In which 1975 film did Michael Caine and Glenda Jackson star as husband and wife?
16. Which *Emmerdale* character married mysterious hosiery salesman Bob in 2001?
17. With whom did Ricky Martin collaborate on the 2001 U.K. top five single *Nobody Wants to be Lonely*?
18. Which actress took on the role of FBI agent Clarice Starling in the 2001 film sequel *Hannibal*?
19. What was the title of the 2001 hit single by Shaggy featuring Rikrok, which knocked Atomic Kitten off the U.K. number one spot?
20. Which actor played Detective Chief Inspector Jim Taggart in the TV drama series *Taggart* until his death in 1994?

ANSWERS: *1 David Jason, 2 Young Love, 3 Major League, 4 Position Impossible, 5 Samantha Mumba, 6 Remember the Titans, 7 Jean Alexander, 8 Until it's Time for You to Go, 9 Wes Craven, 10 Kat, 11 1991, 12 A moose & a flying squirrel, 13 It's a Knockout, 14 Melanie B, 15 The Romantic Englishwoman, 16 Viv Windsor, 17 Christina Aguilera, 18 Julianne Moore, 19 It Wasn't Me, 20 Mark McManus.*

General Knowledge

Your rating: ● 0-5 Join a library ● 6-10 Keep at it ● 11-15 Join a quiz team ● 16-20 Join Mensa

1. Which suffragette founded the Women's Social and Political Union?
2. What feature did silent film comic Ben Turpin have insured?
3. Who wrote *Charlie and the Chocolate Factory*?
4. Which unit of land measurement is equal to 4840 square yards?
5. What nationality is El Mouaziz, winner of the men's race in the 2001 London Marathon?
6. Which giant planet is between Saturn and Neptune?
7. The TV programme *Death of a Princess* caused a diplomatic rift between Britain and which country?
8. To which genus of plants does the daffodil belong?
9. Which common wild flower has the Latin name *Bellis perennis*?
10. Who plays Mark Darcy in the film *Bridget Jones's Diary*?
11. Who wrote *Anne of Green Gables*?
12. Which pianist and conductor was married to the cellist Jacqueline Du Pre?
13. What was the name of the Queen's favourite corgi, who had to be put down in 2001?
14. Which singer-songwriter recorded the albums *This Year's Model* and *Punch the Clock*?
15. In which Asian country is the city of Da Nang?
16. Which English historian claimed that 'absolute power corrupts absolutely'?
17. Which Evelyn Waugh novel is a satire on the American way of death?
18. Which Italian conductor died during a performance of *Aida* in Berlin in 2001?
19. Who wrote the novel *Absolute Beginners*?
20. Which British dramatist wrote *Equus* and *Amadeus*?

ANSWERS: *1 Emmeline Pankhurst, 2 His squint, 3 Roald Dahl, 4 Acre, 5 Moroccan, 6 Uranus, 7 Saudi Arabia, 8 Narcissus, 9 Daisy, 10 Colin Firth, 11 L M Montgomery, 12 Daniel Barenboim, 13 Kelpie, 14 Elvis Costello, 15 Vietnam, 16 Lord Acton, 17 The Loved One, 18 Giuseppe Sinopoli, 19 Colin MacInnes, 20 Peter Shaffer.*

General Knowledge

Your rating: • 0-5 Join a library • 6-10 Keep at it • 11-15 Join a quiz team • 16-20 Join Mensa

1. Which English king was killed at the Battle of Bosworth Field?
2. How many stories are there in the Decameron?
3. By what name was American comedian Louis Francis Cristillo known?
4. Which seven-a-side ball game is played in a swimming pool?
5. What nationality is Derartu Tulu, winner of the women's race in the 2001 London Marathon?
6. In which film did the famous skirt-blowing scene featuring Marilyn Monroe appear?
7. Who won an Oscar for his performance in the film *My Left Foot*?
8. What is the highest mountain in the Western Hemisphere?
9. After which Scottish engineer is the SI unit of power named?
10. Of which African country is Dakar the capital?
11. What was the name of *The Addams Family* butler?
12. Which word was originally an abbreviation of the German word Fliegerabwehrkanone?
13. In Greek mythology, who was the father of Icarus?
14. Which German football team knocked Manchester United out of the 2000/01 Champions League?
15. What sort of creature is an accentor?
16. Which Welsh poet wrote *A Small Desperation* and *Funland*?
17. What is the name of the local paper in *EastEnders*?
18. High Willhays is the highest point of which upland region of England?
19. Which theoretical temperature corresponds to -273.15 degrees on the Celsius scale?
20. Which Nigerian novelist wrote *Things Fall Apart*?

ANSWERS: *1 Richard III, 2 100, 3 Lou Costello, 4 Water polo, 5 Ethiopian, 6 The Seven Year Itch, 7 Daniel Day-Lewis, 8 Mount Aconcagua, 9 James Watt, 10 Senegal, 11 Lurch, 12 Flak, 13 Daedalus, 14 Bayern Munich, 15 A bird, 16 Dannie Abse, 17 Walford Gazette, 18 Dartmoor, 19 Absolute zero, 20 Chinua Achebe.*

General Knowledge

Your rating:
- **0-5 Join a library**
- **6-10 Keep at it**
- **11-15 Join a quiz team**
- **16-20 Join Mensa**

1. Which word meaning 'rebirth' describes the period in European history that began in the 14th century?
2. In which game show did Bernie the Bolt load the crossbow?
3. What was the nickname of U.S. crime boss Charles Luciano?
4. Which Australian city is the state capital of Victoria?
5. Murray Harkin is the former business partner of which member of the Royal Family?
6. Which member of the Monty Python team played the title role in *The Life of Brian*?
7. In which film did Ronald Reagan appear with Nancy?
8. By what name were the Parliamentarian opponents of the Cavaliers known in the English Civil War?
9. What is the name of Barney Rubble's wife in *The Flintstones*?
10. Which former Beatle was arrested for possessing marijuana in Japan in 1980?
11. Which Roman Catholic organisation takes its name from the Latin for 'God's work'?
12. In medicine, what does the abbreviation ECG stand for?
13. Who created the oriental villain Fu Manchu?
14. *Bamboozled* is a film by which controversial American director?
15. Which prime minister led the republic of Ireland into the Common Market?
16. What is the singular of graffiti?
17. Who won a Best Supporting Actor Oscar for *From Here to Eternity*?
18. What name was given to the part of Anglo-Saxon England controlled by the Vikings?
19. Which Dutch striker joined Manchester United in a record £19 million transfer deal in 2001?
20. Who wrote the novel *Daniel Deronda*?

ANSWERS: *1 Renaissance, 2 The Golden Shot, 3 Lucky, 4 Melbourne, 5 The Countess of Wessex, 6 Graham Chapman, 7 Hellcats of the Navy, 8 Roundheads, 9 Betty, 10 Paul McCartney, 11 Opus Dei, 12 Electrocardiogram, 13 Sax Rohmer, 14 Spike Lee, 15 Jack Lynch, 16 Graffito, 17 Frank Sinatra, 18 Danelaw, 19 Ruud Van Nistelrooy, 20 George Eliot.*

Entertainment

Your rating: ● 0-5 Buy a TV ● 6-10 Keep at it ● 11-15 Join a quiz team ● 16-20 Enter a quiz show

1. Which late British actor starred in the title role of the 1973 film *Hitler - The Last Ten Days*?
2. Who presented the BBC 1 Comic Relief quiz show *1000 to One* in 2001?
3. Which anarchic punk band had a U.K. top five hit in 1977 with *God Save the Queen*?
4. What type of animal is the Emperor turned into in the 2000 Disney movie *The Emperor's New Groove*?
5. Which BBC 2 series followed horticulturalists Gordon Taylor and Guy Cooper on their travels around Britain?
6. Which Motown group had a 1969 U.K. top ten hit with *Get Ready*?
7. Which star of 1985's *The Jewel of the Nile* also produced the film?
8. In *Coronation Street*, which of Ken Barlow's children was killed in a car accident in 2001?
9. Which boy band's U.K. number one hits in the Nineties included *Pray* and *Sure*?
10. Which English actor played villainous wizard Profian in the 2000 film *Dungeons and Dragons*?
11. What was the name of the cook in the Nineties sitcom *You Rang M'Lord*?
12. Which British band entered the U.K. top ten with two different singles in the same week in 2001?
13. Which British author wrote the book upon which the 1984 film *The Little Drummer Girl* was based?
14. Which *Brookside* character married Fred, the Brazilian lover of her friend Lance, in 2001?
15. Which controversial rap star appeared at the 2001 Brit Awards with a mask and chainsaw?
16. Which daring ITV series was presented by Davina McCall?
17. Which vocalist had a 2001 U.K. top five hit with *I'm Like a Bird*?
18. In which BBC 1 series did Alice Evans play Diane, an air stewardess leading two lives?
19. Which sport featured in the 2000 film *The Legend of Bagger Vance*?
20. Which Eighties TV series starred Wendy Craig as Barbara Gray?

ANSWERS: *1 Alec Guinness, 2 Dale Winton, 3 Sex Pistols, 4 A llama, 5 The Curious Gardeners, 6 The Temptations, 7 Michael Douglas, 8 Susan, 9 Take That, 10 Jeremy Irons, 11 Mrs Lipton, 12 Manic Street Preachers, 13 John le Carre, 14 Bev, 15 Eminem, 16 Don't Try This At Home, 17 Nelly Furtado, 18 Best of Both Worlds, 19 Golf, 20 Nanny.*

General Knowledge

Your rating: ● 0-5 Join a library ● 6-10 Keep at it ● 11-15 Join a quiz team ● 16-20 Join Mensa

1. Which Italian dictator was known as *Il Duce*?
2. Which Mel Brooks film featured the song *Springtime For Hitler*?
3. Of which rock group was Francis Rossi lead singer?
4. Which football team clinched the 2000/01 Premiership title with five games still to play?
5. What name is given to the offspring of a male donkey and a female horse?
6. Which heavyweight boxer lost his world titles to James 'Buster' Douglas in 1990?
7. The title of the Ernest Hemingway novel *For Whom the Bell Tolls* is taken from the work of which poet?
8. Who created the fictional diarist *Adrian Mole*?
9. Which king of England was known as 'the Lionheart'?
10. What name is given to someone who makes calculations on which insurance premiums are based?
11. Which Finnish runner won the 5,000m and 10,000m at the 1972 and 1976 Olympics?
12. Who was the second president of the United States?
13. For which film did Elizabeth Taylor receive an Oscar?
14. Who wrote *Goblin Market and Other Poems*?
15. Which English king was known as Harefoot?
16. On which river does the German city of Ulm stand?
17. Which TV series is set on Craggy Island?
18. Of which American city was Richard Daley mayor from 1955 to 1976?
19. Which Algerian-born author wrote *The Outsider*?
20. In what year was the Glorious Revolution in English history?

ANSWERS: *1 Benito Mussolini, 2 The Producers, 3 Status Quo, 4 Manchester United, 5 Mule, 6 Mike Tyson, 7 John Donne, 8 Sue Townsend, 9 Richard I, 10 Actuary, 11 Lasse Viren, 12 John Adams, 13 Butterfield 8, 14 Christina Rossetti, 15 Harold I, 16 Danube, 17 Father Ted, 18 Chicago, 19 Albert Camus, 20 1688.*

General Knowledge

Your rating:
- 0-5 Join a library
- 6-10 Keep at it
- 11-15 Join a quiz team
- 16-20 Join Mensa

1. In which American city were the 1984 summer Olympics held?
2. Which film first made a star of juvenile actor Macaulay Culkin?
3. Who was the first man in the Bible?
4. What name is given to scurf that forms on the scalp and comes off in flakes?
5. In which musical did Denise Van Outen make her West End debut in 2001?
6. Which parallel of latitude divides North and South Korea?
7. How many digits are there in an ISBN?
8. What does the abbreviation Ltd stand for?
9. Which temperature scale is named after the inventor of the mercury thermometer?
10. What was the name of Scrooge's late business partner in Dickens's *A Christmas Carol*?
11. Which art movement took its name from a childish French word for hobby-horse?
12. Which member of the *Have I Got News for You* team also presented the chat show *Room 101*?
13. Which hunter in Greek mythology was changed into a stag by Artemis and killed by his own hounds?
14. Who won her fifth London Marathon wheelchair race in 2001?
15. Which Palestinian terrorist leader has a name which means 'Father of Struggles'?
16. What musical term indicates that a work is to be sung without accompaniment?
17. Who wrote *The Grapes of Wrath*?
18. Which French composer is best known for his *Requiem* of 1887?
19. What the largest New World member of the cat family?
20. Which famous keeper of Leicester Gaol weighed over 52 stone when he died in 1809?

ANSWERS: *1 Los Angeles, 2 Home Alone, 3 Adam, 4 Dandruff, 5 Chicago, 6 38th parallel, 7 Ten, 8 Limited, 9 Fahrenheit, 10 Jacob Marley, 11 Dada, 12 Paul Merton, 13 Actaeon, 14 Tanni Grey-Thompson, 15 Abu Nidal, 16 A cappella, 17 John Steinbeck, 18 Gabriel Fauré, 19 Jaguar, 20 Daniel Lambert.*

General Knowledge

Your rating:
- 0-5 Join a library
- 6-10 Keep at it
- 11-15 Join a quiz team
- 16-20 Join Mensa

1. Who played Rhett Butler in the film *Gone With the Wind*?
2. Who wrote the novel *Mr Midshipman Easy*?
3. Which adjective refers to the reign of James I?
4. Which shrub is also called furze or whin?
5. Which London street is synonymous with the British diamond trade?
6. For which film did Sir John Mills win an Oscar?
7. Where did the children's TV characters *The Clangers* live?
8. What sort of celestial body is also called a minor planet?
9. Which 2001 film starred Julia Roberts and Brad Pitt?
10. What was Emily Brontë's only novel?
11. What was the name of the white calf that survived two attempts to cull it during the 2001 foot-and-mouth epidemic?
12. Which American-born British sculptor created *The Rock Drill* and *St Michael and the Devil*?
13. What name was given to the tax levied in Anglo-Saxon Britain to buy off Viking invaders?
14. Who wrote the book on which the film *Hannibal* was based?
15. What is the largest and most luminous type of star?
16. Which lake in Israel is also called the Sea of Galilee?
17. What sort of bird is a gadwall?
18. The film *A Man For All Seasons* was set during the reign of which monarch?
19. Which rare-earth metal has the symbol La?
20. How many wickets did Courtney Walsh take in his Test career?

ANSWERS: *1 Clark Gable, 2 Frederick Marryat, 3 Jacobean, 4 Gorse, 5 Hatton Garden, 6 Ryan's Daughter, 7 A small blue planet, 8 Asteroid, 9 The Mexican, 10 Wuthering Heights, 11 Phoenix, 12 Sir Jacob Epstein, 13 Danegeld, 14 Thomas Harris, 15 Supergiant, 16 Lake Tiberias, 17 A duck, 18 Henry VIII, 19 Lanthanum, 20 519.*

Entertainment

Your rating: ● **0-5** Buy a TV ● **6-10** Keep at it ● **11-15** Join a quiz team ● **16-20** Enter a quiz show

1. Which popular Channel 4 U.S. teen drama series featured the characters Jen and Joey?
2. Which song provided U.K. top five hits for Emile Ford and the Checkmates in 1959 and Shakin' Stevens in 1987?
3. Which actor played Porter, a career-criminal, in the 1999 film *Payback*?
4. Which young *Coronation Street* character discovered that she was unexpectedly pregnant in 1999?
5. What was the title of Blur's sixth album, released in 1999?
6. Who was the host of the original version of the quiz show *Take Your Pick*?
7. Who starred as an architect who has an affair with a housewife played by Kim Novak in the 1960 film *Strangers When We Meet*?
8. Which *EastEnders* character was forced to resume her battle with breast cancer in 1999?
9. Which Swedish duo released their first new material for four years in 1999, an album entitled *Have a Nice Day*?
10. Which British director was portrayed by Sir Ian McKellen in the film *Gods and Monsters*?
11. Which gameshow was revived on ITV by comedian Julian Clary in 1999?
12. What was the title of the second album of instrumental pop by Mogwai?
13. Whicha women's prison was the subject of the BBC 1 documentary series *Jailbirds*?
14. Which song reached number eight in the U.K. charts for both Matt Monro in 1965 and the Beatles in 1976?
15. Which 1999 Tony Kaye film starred Edward Norton as a young neo-Nazi?
16. Who was the lady racing driver's evil rival in the Hanna-Barbera cartoon *The Perils of Penelope Pitstop*?
17. Which duo were *On A Ragga Tip* in the U.K. top ten in 1992?
18. Which 1999 documentary series, narrated by John Nettles, investigated the impact of natural disasters on the animal and plant kingdoms?
19. Which 1954 film starring Grace Kelly and Stewart Granger was set in the emerald-mining regions of South America?
20. Which comedian appeared as sadistic P.E. teacher Doug 'Dynamo' Digby in ITV's comedy series *The Grimleys*?

ANSWERS: *1 Dawson's Creek, 2 What Do You Want to Make Those Eyes at Me For, 3 Mel Gibson, 4 Leanne Tilsley, 5 Thirteen, 6 Michael Miles, 7 Kirk Douglas, 8 Peggy Mitchell, 9 Roxette, 10 James Whale, 11 Mr & Mrs, 12 Come On Die Young, 13 New Hall Prison, 14 Yesterday, 15 American History X, 16 The Hooded Claw, 17 SL2, 18 Violent Planet, 19 Green Fire, 20 Brian Conley.*

General Knowledge

Your rating: • 0-5 Join a library • 6-10 Keep at it • 11-15 Join a quiz team • 16-20 Join Mensa

1. Which Pall Mall palace was the principal London residence of the monarch from 1697 to 1837?
2. Which Christian sect established its headquarters at Salt Lake City, Utah in 1847?
3. On which day of the year does Martinmas fall?
4. In which year did Elvis Presley die?
5. What is the lowest female singing voice?
6. In which year was America's Declaration of Independence?
7. Which clergyman and poet wrote the satire *A Tale of a Tub*?
8. Of which U.S. state is Richmond the capital?
9. What sort of creature is a warbler?
10. Of which African country is Kampala the capital?
11. Which British statesman was known as the Great Commoner?
12. Which Russian novelist wrote *A Sportsman's Sketches* and *Fathers and Sons*?
13. Who was the Roman god of fire?
14. To which country do the Chatham Islands belong?
15. Which British physician developed the first effective vaccine against smallpox?
16. What is the capital of the Sultanate of Oman?
17. Which Scottish explorer wrote *Travels in the Interior Districts of Africa*?
18. What is the popular name for the British Merchant Navy's Red Ensign?
19. Which British dramatist wrote *French without Tears*?
20. What sort of creature is a viscacha?

ANSWERS: *1 St James's Palace, 2 Mormons, 3 11th of November, 4 1977, 5 Contralto, 6 1776, 7 Jonathan Swift, 8 Virginia, 9 A bird, 10 Uganda, 11 Pitt the Elder, 12 Ivan Turgenev, 13 Vulcan, 14 New Zealand, 15 Edward Jenner, 16 Muscat, 17 Mungo Park, 18 Red Duster, 19 Sir Terence Rattigan, 20 A rodent.*

General Knowledge

Your rating: ● 0-5 Join a library ● 6-10 Keep at it ● 11-15 Join a quiz team ● 16-20 Join Mensa

1. In which U.S. state can the city of Pittsburgh be found?
2. Which organisation was founded by the Geneva Convention of 1864 to provide care for the casualties of war?
3. Which British actor appeared in *Major Barbara* and *Beat the Devil*?
4. At which racecourse is the St Leger run?
5. Who was king of Great Britain and Northern Ireland from 1936 to 1952?
6. Which unit, equal to one tenth of a bel, is often used to express a sound intensity?
7. How many events are involved in a decathlon?
8. Which 'new' Buckinghamshire town is the headquarters of the Open University?
9. Of which country is Stockholm the capital?
10. Which Shakespearian actor was the father of Vanessa Redgrave?
11. To what did Basutoland change its name in 1966?
12. Which English dramatist and poet wrote *Volpone* and *The Alchemist*?
13. Of which country was Richard Seddon prime minister from 1893 to 1906?
14. Who defeated his nephew, the Duke of Monmouth, at the Battle of Sedgemoor?
15. Which vegetable comes from the plant *Brassica napus napobrassica*?
16. Which British actress played the title role in the first production of Shaw's *St Joan*?
17. Which Hertfordshire town was built in 1903 as England's first garden city?
18. What is the heaviest alkali metal?
19. Which Bristol-based film-maker won his third Oscar for the film *A Close Shave*?
20. How many letters are in the Hebrew alphabet?

***ANSWERS:** 1 Pennsylvania, 2 The International Red Cross, 3 Robert Morley, 4 Doncaster, 5 George VI, 6 Decibel, 7 Ten, 8 Milton Keynes, 9 Sweden, 10 Sir Michael Redgrave, 11 Kingdom of Lesotho, 12 Ben Jonson, 13 New Zealand, 14 James II of England and Ireland, 15 Swede, 16 Dame Sybil Thorndike, 17 Letchworth, 18 Francium, 19 Nick Park, 20 Twenty-two.*

General Knowledge

Your rating: ● **0-5** **Join a library** ● **6-10** **Keep at it** ● **11-15** **Join a quiz team** ● **16-20** **Join Mensa**

1. Which French novelist wrote *Strait is the Gate* and *The Immoralist*?
2. On which temperature scale is the temperature of boiling water 212 degrees?
3. Which British motor-racing driver became world champion in 1976?
4. Which Japanese word was used to describe the deliberate crashing of an aircraft by its pilot?
5. What is the official currency of France?
6. Of what was the Vulgate a Latin translation of?
7. Which alcoholic drink takes its name from the Spanish city of Jerez de la Frontera?
8 Who is the patron saint of Wales?
9. Which war was precipitated by the assassination of Archduke Francis Ferdinand in Sarajevo?
10. How many hurdles must be jumped to complete a 110 metre hurdling race?
11. Which British Pre-Raphaelite painted *The Light of the World*?
12. In Greek mythology, who was the father of the Titans?
13. Which U.S. novelist wrote *The House of the Seven Gables*?
14. Which actress won the Oscar for Best Adapted Screenplay at the 1996 Academy Awards?
15. What is the capital of the U.S. state of Wyoming?
16. What sort of creature is a nilgai?
17. Which British physicist discovered the electron?
18. In Hindu mythology, who was the goddess of death and destruction?
19. Which Danish chronicler wrote *Gesta Danorum*?
20. What is the highest peak in England?

ANSWERS: *1 André Gide, 2 Fahrenheit, 3 James Hunt, 4 Kamikaze, 5 The franc, 6 The Bible, 7 Sherry, 8 St David, 9 World War I, 10 Ten, 11 William Holman Hunt, 12 Uranus, 13 Nathaniel Hawthorne, 14 Emma Thompson, 15 Cheyenne, 16 An antelope, 17 Sir Joseph Thomson, 18 Kali, 19 Saxo Grammaticus, 20 Scafell Pike.*

Sports

Your rating:
- **0-5 Wooden spoon**
- **6-10 Bronze medal**
- **11-15 Silver medal**
- **16-20 Gold medal**

1. Which Russian swimmer retained his 100m freestyle title at the world championships in 1998, less than 15 months after being stabbed in Moscow?
2. By what score did New Zealand lose to South Africa in the final of the 1995 rugby union World Cup?
3. Which football team won the 1997/98 Scottish Premiership, ending Rangers' hopes of winning ten titles in a row?
4. Which English snooker player won his last Masters title in 1981?
5. Which three events did Emil Zatopek win at the 1952 Olympic Games?
6. Against which country did Mark Wright score the winning goal for England in the 1990 World Cup?
7. Which team won Rugby Union's Premiership in 1998 by one point from Saracens?
8. Which British Formula 1 driver won his first Grand Prix in 1985?
9. Against which British side did rugby union's Jeff Wilson make his New Zealand debut in 1993?
10. For which county cricket team did Jack Hobbs make 598 appearances?
11. Whom did Joe Fagan succeed as manager of Liverpool football club?
12. Which British golfer won the U.S. Women's Open in 1987?
13. In which year did Carl Lewis win the same four Olympic gold medals as Jesse Owens did in 1936?
14. For which team did Ray Clemence keep goal in the 1987 F.A. Cup final?
15. What is heavyweight boxer Evander Holyfield's nickname?
16. How often does golf's Ryder Cup competition now take place?
17. In 1990, which tennis player became the youngest-ever US Open men's champion?
18. Which nation won the America's Cup in 1995?
19. In which year was the F.A. Cup competition first held?
20. Which nation's basketball team were nicknamed 'The Dream Team' at the 1992 Olympic Games?

ANSWERS: *1 Alexander Popov, 2 15-12, 3 Celtic, 4 Alex Higgins, 5 5,000m, 10,000m & marathon, 6 Egypt, 7 Newcastle, 8 Nigel Mansell, 9 Scotland, 10 Surrey, 11 Bob Paisley, 12 Laura Davies, 13 1984, 14 Tottenham Hotspur, 15 The Real Deal, 16 Every two years, 17 Pete Sampras, 18 New Zealand, 19 1871, 20 The U.S.'s.*

General Knowledge

Your rating:
- 0-5 Join a library
- 6-10 Keep at it
- 11-15 Join a quiz team
- 16-20 Join Mensa

1. In which English county can the town of Maidenhead be found?
2. What is the largest living creature?
3. What is the capital of Belgium?
4. Which two elements are present in all hydrocarbons?
5. Which U.S. national holiday is celebrated on the fourth Thursday in November?
6. Which British writer created the character Noddy?
7. 'No' is a form of theatre from which country?
8. What is the highest mountain in Wales?
9. Which U.S. novelist and journalist wrote *The Naked and the Dead*?
10. The island of Oahu is part of which U.S. state?
11. Which German city was the birthplace of Mendelssohn and Brahms?
12. Which French poet wrote *La Chute d'un ange*?
13. Which Republican president was defeated by F. D. Roosevelt in the 1932 election?
14. What sort of creature is a hamadryas?
15. Which sedative drug caused some 500 deformed babies to be born in the U.K. between 1959 and 1962?
16. In which country can the Coromandel Coast be found?
17. Which grandson of Genghis Khan founded the Yuan dynasty?
18. Which British poet wrote *Idylls of the King*?
19. Which South American people worshipped Tezcatlipoca?
20. In which year did Susan Brown become the first woman to participate in the Boat Race?

ANSWERS: *1 Berkshire, 2 The blue whale, 3 Brussels, 4 Carbon and hydrogen, 5 Thanksgiving Day, 6 Enid Blyton, 7 Japan, 8 Snowdon, 9 Norman Mailer, 10 Hawaii, 11 Hamburg, 12 Alphonse de Lamartine, 13 Herbert Hoover, 14 A monkey, 15 Thalidomide, 16 India, 17 Kublai Khan, 18 Tennyson, 19 Aztecs, 20 1981.*

General Knowledge

Your rating: ● 0-5 Join a library ● 6-10 Keep at it ● 11-15 Join a quiz team ● 16-20 Join Mensa

1. Which athletic event was formerly known as the hop, step, and jump?
2. Of which African country is Accra the capital?
3. With which sort of music is Enrico Caruso usually associated?
4. Which U.S. president delivered the Gettysburg Address in 1863?
5. Which Russian novelist wrote *The Gulag Archipelago*?
6. Which city became the capital of Yugoslavia after World War I?
7. In which English county can Plymouth and Torquay be found?
8. Which Scottish scientist and inventor patented the telephone in 1876?
9. Followers of which religion worship the gods Brahma, Vishnu and Shiva?
10. What was the name of the Nazi secret police, formed in 1933 under Goering?
11. By what name are the elements fluorine, chlorine, bromine, iodine and astatine collectively known?
12. Which U.S. novelist wrote *The Age of Innocence*?
13. Which metallic element is represented by the symbol Tl?
14. What is the capital of Fiji?
15. Which French philosopher published Snell's law in 1638 without crediting it to Snell?
16. What sort of creature is a whippoorwill?
17. Which two identical U.S. spacecraft went into orbit around Mars in 1976?
18. Which Dutch artist painted *The Laughing Cavalier*?
19. Which city is known as 'The Fruit Bowl of New Zealand'?
20. Which German poet wrote *The Ship of Fools*?

ANSWERS: *1 The triple-jump, 2 Ghana, 3 Opera, 4 Abraham Lincoln, 5 Aleksandr Solzhenitsyn, 6 Belgrade, 7 Devon, 8 Alexander Graham Bell, 9 Hinduism, 10 Gestapo, 11 Halogens, 12 Edith Wharton, 13 Thallium, 14 Suva, 15 Descartes, 16 A bird, 17 The Viking probes, 18 Frans Hals, 19 Hastings, 20 Sebastian Brant.*

General Knowledge

Your rating:
- 0-5 Join a library
- 6-10 Keep at it
- 11-15 Join a quiz team
- 16-20 Join Mensa

1. In which country is the port of Casablanca?
2. Brass is an alloy of which two metals?
3. Which oriental art of paper folding developed into a traditional Japanese craft?
4. Who did Hitler marry shortly before committing suicide in 1945?
5. Salt Lake City is the capital of which U.S. state?
6. Which U.S. composer wrote the musicals *The Gay Divorcee* and *Anything Goes*?
7. Near which town can Anne Hathaway's cottage still be seen?
8. Who does the Duchy of Cornwall belong to?
9. Which German composer wrote the oratorio *Carmina Burana*?
10. What sort of creature is a whippet?
11. Which British composer wrote the choral work *Rio Grande*?
12. The word for which male singing voice comes from the Latin for 'to hold'?
13. Which U.S. poet wrote the Pulitzer Prize-winning *Pictures from Brueghel*?
14. Of which U.S. state is Providence the capital?
15. Who became prime minister of Portugal in 1932, and ruled until suffering a stroke in 1968?
16. What is the capital of Haiti?
17. With which country did Germany and Austria-Hungary sign the Triple Alliance of 1882?
18. Which former U.S. Senator headed the inquiry into decommissioning weapons in Ulster?
19. Which British novelist wrote *The Thirty-Nine Steps*?
20. Which Christian festival is celebrated on the second Thursday after Whit Sunday?

ANSWERS: *1 Morocco, 2 Copper and zinc, 3 Origami, 4 Eva Braun, 5 Utah, 6 Cole Porter, 7 Stratford-on-Avon, 8 The Prince of Wales, 9 Carl Orff, 10 A dog, 11 Constant Lambert, 12 Tenor, 13 William Williams, 14 Rhode Island, 15 Antonio Salazar, 16 Port-au-Prince, 17 Italy, 18 George Mitchell, 19 John Buchan, 20 The Feast of Corpus Christi.*

Entertainment

Your rating: ● **0-5** **Buy a TV** ● **6-10** **Keep at it** ● **11-15** **Join a quiz team** ● **16-20** **Enter a quiz show**

1. Which snooker-based game show was presented by Jim Davidson?
2. Which 1969 film about a small army unit detailed to blow up an enemy fuel dump starred Michael Caine as an inexperienced captain?
3. Which BBC 2 sci-fi sitcom embarked upon an eighth series in 1999?
4. Which song provided a U.K. hit for both Shirley Bassey and Sonny and Cher in the Sixties?
5. Which British actress played a Catholic peace campaigner in Belfast in the early Seventies in the 1999 film *Titanic Town*?
6. Which actress played Mrs Bott in the Seventies TV series adaptation of the *Just William* stories?
7. Which band, fronted by Crispian Mills, released an album entitled *Peasants, Pigs and Astronauts* in 1999?
8. Which actress played the *Magnificent Doll* in the 1946 film?
9. Which romantic Scots location was the setting for the BBC 1 documentary series *Love Town*?
10. Which American teenager had a 1999 U.K. number one hit with her debut single *Baby One More Time*?
11. What was the title of the musical game show series presented by Michael Barrymore on ITV?
12. Which American chat show hostess starred as escaped southern slave Sethe in the film adaptation of Toni Morrison's *Beloved*?
13. Which veteran soul and blues singer released an album entitled *Back on Top* in 1999?
14. Which 1977 Martin Scorsese film starred Liza Minnelli and Robert De Niro as a band singer and a saxophonist who get married?
15. Which actress played a woman searching for the murderer of her daughter in ITV's 1999 thriller *Forgotten*?
16. Which Seventies TV series starred Margaret Lockwood as a lady barrister?
17. Which party classic was a U.K. top ten hit for the U.S. group the Gap Band in 1980?
18. Which classic Alfred Hitchcock film about a Canadian on holiday in London who becomes embroiled in espionage was re-released in 1999 to celebrate the centenary of his birth?
19. Which actor recently starred as Alan in the BBC 2 drama series *Births, Marriages and Deaths*?
20. What was the title of the 1974 U.K. number one hit for Paper Lace?

ANSWERS: *1 Big Break, 2 Play Dirty, 3 Red Dwarf, 4 What Now My Love, 5 Julie Walters, 6 Diana Dors, 7 Kula Shaker, 8 Ginger Rogers, 9 Gretna Green, 10 Britney Spears, 11 Michael Barrymore's My Kind of Music, 12 Oprah Winfrey, 13 Van Morrison, 14 New York New York, 15 Amanda Burton, 16 Justice, 17 Oops Up Side Your Head, 18 The Thirty-Nine Steps, 19 Ray Winstone, 20 Billy Don't Be A Hero.*

General Knowledge

Your rating: ● 0-5 Join a library ● 6-10 Keep at it ● 11-15 Join a quiz team ● 16-20 Join Mensa

1. What is the name of the body that governs solicitors in England and Wales?
2. Of which country did Robert Hawke become prime minister in 1983?
3. Which voting system is sometimes known by the initials PR?
4. Which state of the USA was formerly known as the Sandwich Islands?
5. Togo can be found in which continent?
6. What sort of creature is a puffin?
7. The Treaty of Versailles was signed the year after which war ended?
8. Of which group of islands is Funchal the capital?
9. In Greek legend, what sort of creature was Medusa?
10. In which state of the USA is the city of Detroit?
11. Which modified form of the Indian board game pachisi was patented in the 19th century?
12. Which Scottish mathematician invented logarithms?
13. Which *Hi-De-Hi* star died in 1996 at the age of 45?
14. Which Italian film director made *Shoeshine* and *Bicycle Thieves*?
15. What sort of creature is a margay?
16. Against which country did Bolivia and Peru fight the War of the Pacific?
17. What is the capital of Suriname?
18. Who was the Indian founder of Sikhism?
19. Which French revolutionary wrote the *Histoire des Brissotins*?
20. What was the first permanent English settlement in America?

ANSWERS: *1 The Law Society, 2 Australia, 3 Proportional representation, 4 Hawaii, 5 Africa, 6 A bird, 7 World War I, 8 Madeira Islands, 9 A gorgon, 10 Michigan, 11 Ludo, 12 John Napier, 13 Simon Cadell, 14 Vittorio De Sica, 15 A wild cat, 16 Chile, 17 Paramaribo, 18 Nanak, 19 Camille Desmoulins, 20 Jamestown.*

General Knowledge

Your rating: ● 0-5 Join a library ● 6-10 Keep at it ● 11-15 Join a quiz team ● 16-20 Join Mensa

1. Which word is used to describe thick-skinned animals such as the elephant or rhinoceros?
2. Of which country was Eamon De Valera president from 1959 to 1973?
3. Which river flows northwest through Paris to the English Channel?
4. In Greek legend, which city was captured by using a hollow wooden horse?
5. In which county is the resort of Lyme Regis?
6. Which German Nazi became head of the SS in 1929?
7. Of which South American country is Caracas the capital?
8. Which U.S. outlaw was killed by fellow gang member Robert Ford in 1892 for a $10,000 reward?
9. Which 250 mile long footpath extends between Edale in Derbyshire and Kirk Yetholm?
10. In which English county can Windsor Castle be found?
11. Which U.S. actress starred in the films *Grand Hotel* and *Mildred Pierce*?
12. Which British poet collaborated with Coleridge on Lyrical Ballads?
13. Which type of acid gets its name from the Latin word for ant?
14. Which German-born British astronomer discovered Uranus?
15. After which Italian navigator is America named?
16. What was the first land battle of the Hundred Years' War?
17. What is a galvanometer used to measure?
18. In which Scottish market town can Sueno's Stone be found?
19. Who was Archduchess of Austria from 1740 to 1780?
20. What sort of creature is a pompano?

ANSWERS: *1 Pachyderm, 2 Republic of Ireland, 3 The Seine, 4 Troy, 5 Dorset, 6 Heinrich Himmler, 7 Venezuela, 8 Jesse James, 9 The Pennine Way, 10 Berkshire, 11 Joan Crawford, 12 William Wordsworth, 13 Formic acid, 14 Sir William Herschel, 15 Amerigo Vespucci, 16 The Battle of Crécy, 17 Electric current, 18 Forres, 19 Maria Theresa, 20 A fish.*

General Knowledge

Your rating:
- 0-5 Join a library
- 6-10 Keep at it
- 11-15 Join a quiz team
- 16-20 Join Mensa

1. The Gorbals is a district of which Scottish city?
2. What is the Friday before Easter known as?
3. In horseracing, which unit of length is equal to 220 yards?
4. What is the most widely spoken language of India?
5. Which animals are also called hogs or swine?
6. Which ocean reaches its maximum depth in the Marianas Trench?
7. In which county is Margate?
8. After which king of Macedon was Egypt's chief port named?
9. Which Italian fascist led the March on Rome of 1922?
10. What sort of creature is a sturgeon?
11. Who wrote *The Forsyte Saga* novel series?
12. What is the capital of Martinique?
13. Who was president of France from 1969 to 1974?
14. What sort of creature is a capercaillie?
15. The Colossus of Rhodes was a statue of which god?
16. Which unit of measurement is equivalent to an explosion of 1000 tons of TNT?
17. Which Czech film director made *One Flew over the Cuckoo's Nest*?
18. Which British admiral was nicknamed Old Grog?
19. Which U.S. tennis player became the first to win all four major men's singles titles in one year, in 1938?
20. In which country can the town of Timbuktu be found?

ANSWERS: *1 Glasgow, 2 Good Friday, 3 Furlong, 4 Hindi, 5 Pigs, 6 The Pacific Ocean, 7 Kent, 8 Alexander the Great (Alexandria), 9 Mussolini, 10 A fish, 11 John Galsworthy, 12 Fort-de-France, 13 Georges Pompidou, 14 A bird, 15 Helios, 16 Kiloton, 17 Milos Forman, 18 Edward Vernon, 19 Don Budge, 20 Mali*

Entertainment

Your rating: ● **0-5 Buy a TV** ● **6-10 Keep at it** ● **11-15 Join a quiz team** ● **16-20 Enter a quiz show**

1. Which 1999 Channel 4 series explored alleged UFO sightings?
2. Which star of TV's *ER* appeared in the 1999 film *Don't Go Breaking My Heart*?
3. What was the name of the third-year medical student, played by Kellie Martin, who joined the staff of Channel 4's *ER* in 1999?
4. Who wrote and starred in the 1972 film *Play It Again Sam*?
5. Which U.S. vocalist had U.K. top ten hits with *Right Here Waiting* and *Hazard*?
6. Which 1999 film by Neil LaBute starred Jason Patric, Ben Stiller and Nastassja Kinski?
7. What was the title of the Sixties farcical comedy series set in an East End tailoring business?
8. What was the title of the series of compilation albums celebrating the 40th anniversary of Island Records, which featured tracks from Bob Marley and Aswad?
9. Which 1952 film starring Robert Mitchum and Jane Russell was set in a Portuguese colony south of Hong Kong?
10. Which 1999 Channel 4 comedy series charted the rise of a fictional boy band?
11. Which Canadian group had a 1999 U.K. top five hit with *One Week*?
12. What was the name of Alan Titchmarsh's gardening colleague in BBC's *Ground Force*, who became equally famous for her absent underwear?
13. Which award-winning actress played a Heathrow cleaner in the 1999 film *This Year's Love*?
14. Which comedy series about a young widow and her relationships starred Nanette Newman and Paul Eddington?
15. Which former punk singer makes up half of the duo The Creatures, who released their third album, *Anima Animus*, in 1999?
16. Which 1978 thriller starred Faye Dunaway as a fashion photographer and Tommy Lee Jones as a police lieutenant?
17. What was the title of the 1999 BBC 1 series which followed trainee RSPCA inspectors over their six month training period?
18. What was the title of the single released by Kevin Keegan, which got to number 31 in the U.K. charts in 1979?
19. Which actor played the saintly G in the 1999 film *Holy Man*?
20. Which presenter hosted proceedings as two teams of mock politicians attempted to win audience votes in the BBC 2 show *If I Ruled the World*?

ANSWERS: 1 *Riddle of the Skies*, 2 Anthony Edwards, 3 Lucy Knight, 4 Woody Allen, 5 Richard Marx, 6 *Your Friends and Neighbors*, 7 *Never Mind the Quality, Feel the Width*, 8 *Reggae Roots*, 9 *Macao*, 10 *Boyz Unlimited*, 11 Barenaked Ladies, 12 Charlie Dimmock, 13 Kathy Burke, 14 *Let There Be Love*, 15 Siouxsie Sioux, 16 *Eyes of Laura Mars*, 17 *Animal Police*, 18 *Head Over Heels in Love*, 19 Eddie Murphy, 20 Clive Anderson.

General Knowledge

Your rating: • 0-5 Join a library • 6-10 Keep at it • 11-15 Join a quiz team • 16-20 Join Mensa

1. Which U.S. president was presumed to have been killed by Lee Harvey Oswald?
2. Which compulsory U.K. insurance scheme provides funds for the N.H.S. and social security benefits?
3. In which county can the Peak District be found?
4. Which British author wrote *The Jungle Books*?
5. Which Kentucky military base is the site of the U.S. Depository, which contains U.S. gold reserves?
6. What sort of creature is a beagle?
7. In Italy, which currency unit is equal to 100 centesimi?
8. How is the clavicle better known?
9. Of which continent is Cape Horn the most southerly point?
10. Who emerged as supreme dictator of the Soviet Union in the 1920s and remained in power until his death in 1953?
11. What is the capital of Puerto Rico?
12. Which Australian tennis player was men's singles champion at Wimbledon in 1967, 1970 and 1971?
13. Which French motor racing driver won the World Championship in 1985 and 1986?
14. Which British novelist wrote *The Prisoner of Zenda*?
15. In Greek mythology, which son of King Priam was in love with Cressida?
16. Madame de Pompadour was the mistress of which French king?
17. Which prime minister took South Africa out of the Commonwealth in 1960?
18. Of which Canadian province is Fredericton the capital?
19. Which Italian electrical engineer invented transatlantic communication by radio?
20. What was the nickname of the British pirate Edward Teach?

ANSWERS: *1 John F. Kennedy, 2 National Insurance, 3 Derbyshire, 4 Rudyard Kipling, 5 Fort Knox, 6 A dog, 7 Lira, 8 The collarbone, 9 South America, 10 Stalin, 11 San Juan, 12 John Newcombe, 13 Alain Prost, 14 Anthony Hope, 15 Troilus, 16 Louis XV, 17 Hendrik Verwoerd, 18 New Brunswick, 19 Marconi, 20 Blackbeard.*

General Knowledge

Your rating: ● 0-5 Join a library ● 6-10 Keep at it ● 11-15 Join a quiz team ● 16-20 Join Mensa

1. Which town's baroque palace was the residence of the French kings from 1678 to 1769?
2. The firms of Bechstein, Steinway and Bösendorfer are famous for making what sort of musical instrument?
3. In which county can the Isle of Thanet be found?
4. What has been the name of Britain's royal family since 1917?
5. *Women in Love* and *Gothic* were directed by which controversial British film maker?
6. The name of which type of school means 'children's garden' in German?
7. How was French cabaret and music-hall singer Edith Giovanna Gassion better known?
8. What are incisors, canines and molars examples of?
9. The kimono is the traditional costume of which country?
10. In which parliamentary house can the woolsack be found?
11. Who was chairman of the Conservative Party from 1985 to 1987?
12. What is the second largest state of the USA?
13. Which British dramatist wrote *Bedroom Farce* and *Relatively Speaking*?
14. What sort of creature is a motmot?
15. Which British novelist wrote *Henry Esmond*?
16. What sort of creature is a pointer?
17. Which French sculptor made his name with female nudes such as *Mediterranean* and *Night*?
18. In which country was Pablo Picasso born?
19. Which metal can be made pure by the puddling process?
20. With which sport is Billie Jean King associated?

ANSWERS: *1 Versailles, 2 Piano, 3 Kent, 4 Windsor, 5 Ken Russell, 6 Kindergarten, 7 Edith Piaf, 8 Teeth, 9 Japan, 10 The House of Lords, 11 Norman Tebbit, 12 Texas, 13 Alan Ayckbourn, 14 A bird, 15 William Makepeace Thackeray, 16 A dog, 17 Aristide Maillol, 18 Spain, 19 Iron, 20 Tennis.*

General Knowledge

Your rating: ● **0-5** Join a library ● **6-10** Keep at it ● **11-15** Join a quiz team ● **16-20** Join Mensa

1. Which U.S. president introduced legislation known as the New Deal in the 1930s?
2. What is the largest lake in England?
3. Which ancient Chinese game is usually played by 4 people using 2 dice and 136 tiles?
4. Which Spanish artist painted the *Rokeby Venus*?
5. Which US author wrote *The Murders in the Rue Morgue*?
6. Which French mime artist developed the white-faced character Bip?
7. In which country can Ayers Rock be found?
8. In what year did the Communist revolution that overthrew the Russian monarchy take place?
9. What do the initials LED stand for?
10. Is colour-blindness more common in men or women?
11. Who directed the 1969 film *Midnight Cowboy*?
12. The split of which pop group in 1996 caused The Samaritans to set up a hotline?
13. Which Jewish philosopher and physician wrote *The Guide of the Perplexed*?
14. Which branch of geophysics is concerned with the study of earthquakes?
15. Who was the president of West Germany from 1974 to 1979?
16. What do the initials OAU stand for?
17. Onto which planet did the Vega probe drop a helium balloon and land module in 1985?
18. Of which former Soviet republic is Vilnius the capital?
19. Who was the first governor general of India?
20. What sort of creature is a kudu?

ANSWERS: *1 F. D. Roosevelt, 2 Windermere, 3 Mahjong, 4 Velázquez, 5 Edgar Allan Poe, 6 Marcel Marceau, 7 Australia, 8 1917, 9 Light-emitting diode, 10 Men, 11 John Schlesinger, 12 Take That, 13 Moses Maimonides, 14 Seismology, 15 Walter Scheel, 16 Organisation of African Unity, 17 Venus, 18 Lithuania, 19 Warren Hastings, 20 An antelope.*

Entertainment

Your rating: ● 0-5 Buy a TV ● 6-10 Keep at it ● 11-15 Join a quiz team ● 16-20 Enter a quiz show

1. Which 1999 BBC 2 documentary series focussed on the underhand practices of housing professionals?
2. In which 1999 film did Judi Dench play Elizabeth I, a role which won her an Oscar for Best Supporting Actress?
3. What was the title of the 1999 ITV documentary series which followed the round-the-clock work of a group of doctors dealing with emergency situations?
4. Which 1991 film starred John Malkovich and Andie MacDowell as a couple holed up in a London hotel?
5. Which song provided a U.K. top ten hit in 1964 for the Kinks and in 1988 for the Stranglers?
6. Which actor was the guy in the 1999 film *Two Girls and a Guy*?
7. Which Seventies TV series starring Malcolm McDowell and Christopher Cazenove was set in the officers' mess in the days of the Raj?
8. Which dancehall reggae star of the early Nineties released an album featuring collaborations with Maxi Priest and KRS-One in 1999?
9. Which actor played commander of King Company Lt. Joe Clemons in the 1959 film set during the Korean War, *Pork Chop Hill*?
10. Which *London's Burning* character faced personal tragedy in 1999 when his wife suffered a miscarriage?
11. Which Anglo-Indian pop band released their second album, *Bangali Bantam Youth Experience*, in 1999?
12. Which ITV adventure game show was presented by Paul Hendy, Davina McCall and Kate Thornton?
13. In which 1999 film set in the Seventies did Kate Winslet star as a young single mother who takes her two daughters on a spiritual journey to Morocco?
14. Which U.S. singer and actress released her debut album, *Kiss the Sky*, in 1999, featuring her producer and mentor Will Smith?
15. What was the name of the character played by ex-*EastEnder* Michael French in BBC 1's *Holby City*?
16. Which actress played a ruthless Arizona rancher in the 1957 film *Forty Guns*?
17. Which children's programme featured Zippy, George, Bungle and Jeffrey?
18. What was the title of Marvin Rainwater's 1958 U.K. number one hit?
19. What was the name of the intrepid ant hero of the Disney animation, *A Bug's Life*?
20. Which *Hollyoaks* character roared out of the series on his motorbike in 1999 after the breakdown of his marriage to Ruth?

ANSWERS: *1 Raising the Roof, 2 Shakespeare in Love, 3 Trauma Team, 4 The Object of Beauty, 5 All Day and All of the Night, 6 Robert Downey Jnr, 7 The Regiment, 8 Shabba Ranks, 9 Gregory Peck, 10 Sicknote, 11 Black Star Liner, 12 Don't Try This at Home, 13 Hideous Kinky, 14 Tatyana Ali, 15 Nick Jordan, 16 Barbara Stanwyck, 17 Rainbow, 18 Whole Lotta Woman, 19 Flik, 20 Kurt Benson.*

General Knowledge

Your rating: ● 0-5 Join a library ● 6-10 Keep at it ● 11-15 Join a quiz team ● 16-20 Join Mensa

1. Which Australian tennis player became Wimbledon singles champion in 1987?
2. What is the boiling point of water in degrees Celsius?
3. Of which country did Charles Haughey become prime minister in 1979, 1982 and 1987?
4. The island of Corsica is part of which European country?
5. In which English county can Salisbury and Stonehenge be found?
6. Which Spanish tenor starred in film versions of *La Traviata* in 1983 and *Otello* in 1986?
7. With which sport is FIFA associated?
8. In which historic church can Poets' Corner and the Coronation Chair be found?
9. In Greek legend, the centaur was a mixture of a human and which other creature?
10. Which king of England was defeated at the Battle of Hastings?
11. In which European country is the port of Pula?
12. Which British novelist wrote *Tarka the Otter*?
13. What is the London residence of the Archbishop of Canterbury?
14. Who won the Super Bowl in 1996?
15. Which rare Chinese deer was named after a French missionary?
16. What is the largest inland sea in the world?
17. Pablo Casals revolutionised the style and technique of playing which instrument?
18. What is the administrative centre of Fife Region?
19. Which Scottish educationalist wrote *Talking of Summerhill*?
20. Who became king of Morocco in 1961?

ANSWERS: *1 Pat Cash, 2 100 degrees, 3 Republic of Ireland, 4 France, 5 Wiltshire, 6 Placido Domingo, 7 Football, 8 Westminster Abbey, 9 A horse, 10 Harold II, 11 Croatia, 12 Henry Williamson, 13 Lambeth Palace, 14 The Dallas Cowboys, 15 Père David's deer, 16 The Caspian Sea, 17 The cello, 18 Glenrothes, 19 A. S. Neill, 20 Hassan II*

General Knowledge

Your rating: ● 0-5 Join a library ● 6-10 Keep at it ● 11-15 Join a quiz team ● 16-20 Join Mensa

1. In which river can Victoria Falls be found?
2. Who was the first Hanoverian King of Great Britain and Ireland?
3. In Greek legend, who was goddess of epic poetry and the chief of the nine Muses?
4. What is a koto?
5. Which island group is known as Islas Malvinas in Argentina?
6. How is a German shepherd dog otherwise known?
7. What was the nickname of King Richard I of England?
8. Which zodiac sign means Water Bearer in Latin?
9. Which constellation takes its name from the Latin for 'scales'?
10. Which specialised agency of the United Nations is known by the initials IMF?
11. What is the capital of Niger?
12. Which country was ruled by Casimir the Great from 1333 to 1370?
13. Which country was formerly known as British Honduras?
14. Which French dramatist wrote *Andromaque* and *Britannicus*?
15. On what date is Martinmas?
16. What sort of creature is a Percheron?
17. How was U.S. actor William Claude Dukenfield better known?
18. What is the capital and chief port of Mozambique?
19. What sort of creature is a lammergeier?
20. Which U.S. short-story author wrote *Cabbages and Kings*?

***ANSWERS:** 1 Zambezi, 2 George I, 3 Calliope, 4 A Japanese stringed instrument, 5 The Falkland Islands, 6 Alsatian, 7 'The Lionheart', 8 Aquarius, 9 Libra, 10 International Monetary Fund, 11 Niamey, 12 Poland, 13 Belize, 14 Racine, 15 November 11, 16 A horse, 17 W. C. Fields, 18 Maputo, 19 A bird, 20 O. Henry.*

General Knowledge

Your rating: ● 0-5 Join a library ● 6-10 Keep at it ● 11-15 Join a quiz team ● 16-20 Join Mensa

1. Which ancient kingdom was ruled by the pharaohs?
2. How is the contagious disease rubella commonly known?
3. *The Whitsun Weddings* and *High Windows* are volumes written by which British poet?
4. In which English county is the resort of Falmouth?
5. During which war was the Imperial War Museum founded?
6. What nationality was chemist and Nobel Prize founder Alfred Nobel?
7. Of which country is Bucharest the capital?
8. With which instrument is Australian musician John Williams associated?
9. In which U.S. city can the Lincoln Memorial and the Pentagon be found?
10. Which Argentinian footballer captained the team that won the 1986 World Cup?
11. Which Greek dramatist wrote *Ajax* and *Antigone*?
12. Who was the last Carolingian king of France?
13. What is the capital of Liberia?
14. What is the fourth book of the Old Testament?
15. What sort of creature is a flathead?
16. In which country was conductor Sir Georg Solti born?
17. What is the capital of Albania?
18. Which herb is sometimes called vegetable oyster or oyster plant?
19. Which British novelist wrote *A Glastonbury Romance*?
20. Numismatics is a term for the collecting and studying of which objects?

ANSWERS: *1 Egypt, 2 German measles, 3 Philip Larkin, 4 Cornwall, 5 The First World War, 6 Swedish, 7 Romania, 8 Guitar, 9 Washington DC, 10 Diego Maradona, 11 Sophocles, 12 Louis (V) le Fainéant, 13 Monrovia, 14 Numbers, 15 A fish, 16 Hungary, 17 Tirana, 18 Salsify, 19 John Cowper Powys, 20 Coins and medals.*

Entertainment

Your rating:
- **0-5 Buy a TV**
- **6-10 Keep at it**
- **11-15 Join a quiz team**
- **16-20 Enter a quiz show**

1. What was the title of Marmalade's 1968 U.K. number one hit?
2. Which 1999 film featuring Mike Myers told the story of the rise and fall of Manhattan's glitziest disco of the Seventies?
3. Which actor played Gulf veteran Andy McNab in the 1999 BBC 1 dramatisation of McNab's book, *Bravo Two Zero*?
4. Which German female singer had a 1982 U.K. number one hit with *A Little Peace*?
5. Which 1985 film starred John Travolta and Jamie Lee Curtis as a journalist and an aerobics instructor respectively?
6. What was the title of the 1999 ITV crime drama series which followed the activities of a police squad monitoring London's sex trade?
7. What was the title of the 1986 U.K. top ten hit for Stan Ridgway?
8. Which actor played Death in the film *Meet Joe Black*, a remake of 1934's *Death Takes A Holiday*?
9. Of which group of anarchic TV comedians was Graeme Garden a member?
10. Which short-lived Los Angeles band, whose lead singer was Maria McKee, released a retrospective album entitled *This World is Not My Home* in 1999?
11. Which 1989 film starred Richard Pryor as a blind man and Gene Wilder as a deaf man?
12. Which ex-*Drop the Dead Donkey* actress played Dr Joanna Graham in ITV's *Peak Practice*?
13. Which boy band released an album of disco and soul covers in 1999 entitled *There It Is*?
14. Which TV presenter hosted two home improvement shows in 1999 - *Better Homes* on ITV and *Dream House* on BBC 1?
15. Which actress played cellist Jacqueline du Pre in the biographical film, *Hilary and Jackie*?
16. Which all-male band released their self-titled debut album in 1999, featuring their U.K. hit *Say It Once*?
17. In which Channel 4 dating gameshow were the dates picked on the basis of their culinary talents?
18. Who directed the 1987 film *Lethal Weapon*?
19. Which Fifties half-hour crime series introduced Superintendent Lockhart, played by Raymond Francis?

ANSWERS: *1 Ob-La-Di Ob-La-Da, 2 54, 3 Sean Bean, 4 Nicole, 5 Perfect, 6 The Vice, 7 Camouflage, 8 Brad Pitt, 9 The Goodies, 10 Lone Justice, 11 See No Evil, Hear No Evil, 12 Haydn Gwynne, 13 911, 14 Carol Vorderman, 15 Emily Watson, 16 Ultra, 17 Dishes, 18 Richard Donner, 19 Murder Bag, 20 Practical Magic.*

General Knowledge

Your rating: ● 0-5 Join a library ● 6-10 Keep at it ● 11-15 Join a quiz team ● 16-20 Join Mensa

1. Jawaharlal Nehru was the first prime minister of which country?
2. In which cathedral was Horatio Nelson buried?
3. Which French novelist wrote *Remembrance of Things Past*?
4. Which organisation do the initials VSO stand for?
5. Who became prime minister when Harold Wilson resigned in 1976?
6. Riga is the capital of which former Soviet Republic?
7. Of which Canadian province is Toronto the capital?
8. In the card game pontoon, the objective is to score how much?
9. In which country can the River Dordogne be found?
10. Which composer wrote the overture *Fingal's Cave*?
11. Who studied at the London School of Economics before joining the Rolling Stones?
12. What is the capital of Oman?
13. Haematite is the principal ore of which metal?
14. Which British dramatist wrote *Thark* and *The Bed before Yesterday*?
15. Sir Sidney Holland was prime minister of which country from 1949 to 1957?
16. In Roman mythology, who was the goddess of the dawn?
17. Who was the last Stuart monarch?
18. Which Scottish novelist wrote *Waverley*?
19. Which South African surgeon performed the first successful heart transplant operation?
20. Which Englishman invented the spinning jenny, which he named after his daughter?

***ANSWERS:** 1 India, 2 St Paul's, 3 Marcel Proust, 4 Voluntary Services Overseas, 5 James Callaghan, 6 Latvia, 7 Ontario, 8 21, 9 France, 10 Felix Mendelssohn, 11 Mick Jagger, 12 Muscat, 13 Iron, 14 Ben Travers, 15 New Zealand, 16 Aurora, 17 Queen Anne, 18 Sir Walter Scott, 19 Christiaan Barnard, 20 James Hargreaves.*

General Knowledge

Your rating:
- **0-5 Join a library**
- **6-10 Keep at it**
- **11-15 Join a quiz team**
- **16-20 Join Mensa**

1. Which party did the Labour Party replace as the official opposition in 1922?
2. How many lines are in a sonnet?
3. What is the name of the British governing body that regulates and controls horse-racing, both on the flat and over jumps?
4. The Arabian Sea is a section of which ocean?
5. Which organ of the body is affected by cirrhosis?
6. Which British novelist wrote *Sense and Sensibility*?
7. Which Russian dancer joined the Royal Ballet in 1962, where he frequently partnered Margot Fonteyn?
8. Which order of Roman Catholic monks was founded in 1098 at Cîteaux, France?
9. Which number system uses only two digits - 1 and 0?
10. What do the initials NATO stand for?
11. Who married both Louis VII of France and Henry II of England?
12. Who wrote the lyrics for the musicals *West Side Story* and *A Little Night Music*?
13. In which country can Mount Aconcagua be found?
14. What sort of creature is a Camberwell beauty?
15. Who wrote *The Autobiography of Alice B. Toklas*?
16. Which radioactive metal is represented by the symbol Ac?
17. Which French surrealist wrote the novel *Nadja*?
18. Snowdonia is part of which mountain system?
19. Which French novelist wrote *Le Rouge et le Noir*?
20. Which Roman emperor created the Praetorian Guard in 27 BC?

ANSWERS: *1 Liberal Party, 2 Fourteen, 3 The Jockey Club, 4 Indian Ocean, 5 The liver, 6 Jane Austen, 7 Rudolf Nureyev, 8 Cistercians, 9 The binary system, 10 North Atlantic Treaty Organisation, 11 Eleanor of Aquitaine, 12 Stephen Sondheim, 13 Argentina, 14 A butterfly, 15 Gertrude Stein, 16 Actinium, 17 André Breton, 18 The Cambrian Mountains, 19 Stendhal, 20 Augustus.*

General Knowledge

Your rating:
- **0-5 Join a library**
- **6-10 Keep at it**
- **11-15 Join a quiz team**
- **16-20 Join Mensa**

1. Who was the first president of the USA?
2. Which market town is the administrative centre for Dorset?
3. What was a Sopwith Camel?
4. Which advisory organisation is sometimes known by the initials CAB?
5. How many balls are used in a game of English billiards?
6. Which colourless liquid is found in all living matter?
7. Which prehistoric mound in Wiltshire is the largest man-made hill in Europe?
8. What sort of creature is a basenji?
9. What is the capital of Sudan?
10. Which British satirical poet wrote the mock romance *Hudibras*?
11. In which Devon town was William of Orange proclaimed king in 1688?
12. Which Mongol dynasty ruled China after overthrowing the Song dynasty?
13. What is the longest river in New Zealand?
14. Who was prime minister of the Soviet Union from 1964 to 1980?
15. What sort of creature is a hoopoe?
16. Which British novelist wrote *Mrs Dalloway*?
17. Rothesay is the chief town of which Scottish island?
18. Who was general secretary of the TUC from 1973 to 1984?
19. Which metal is represented by the symbol Pd?
20. Salem is the capital of which U.S. state?

***ANSWERS:** 1 George Washington, 2 Dorchester, 3 An aeroplane, 4 Citizens' Advice Bureau, 5 Three, 6 Water, 7 Silbury Hill, 8 A dog, 9 Khartoum, 10 Samuel Butler, 11 Newton Abbot, 12 Yuan, 13 Waikato River, 14 Aleksei Kosygin, 15 A bird, 16 Virginia Woolf, 17 Bute, 18 Len Murray, 19 Palladium, 20 Oregon.*

Entertainment

Your rating: ● **0-5** **Buy a TV** ● **6-10** **Keep at it** ● **11-15** **Join a quiz team** ● **16-20** **Enter a quiz show**

1. Which rock band's fifth album was entitled *By Your Side*?
2. Which actress played Daisy Clover in the 1965 film *Inside Daisy Clover*?
3. Which late comedian was profiled in a 1999 BBC 1 documentary entitled *Bring Me Sunshine*?
4. What was the title of Tab Hunter's 1957 U.K. number one hit?
5. Which actress played the mother of Jane Horrocks' *Little Voice* in the 1999 film?
6. Which 1999 ITV Ruth Rendell mystery drama starred Serena Evans and Jane Hazlegrove as mismatched flatmates?
7. Who had a U.K. top ten hit with *Itsy Bitsy Teeny Weeny Yellow Polka Dot Bikini* in 1960?
8. Who was *The Nanny* in the 1965 film?
9. Which BBC 1 sitcom culminated in a three-part mini series during Christmas 1998?
10. What was the title of Helen Reddy's 1975 U.K. top five hit?
11. Which 1999 political thriller set in New York starred Denzel Washington, Annette Bening and Bruce Willis?
12. Which comedian hosted *The Golden Shot*, *Celebrity Squares* and *Family Fortunes* on TV?
13. Which 1999 soundtrack album featured two new Stevie Nicks recordings produced by Sheryl Crow?
14. Who played *The Singing Nun* in the 1966 film?
15. Which *EastEnder* gave birth to her son Liam on Christmas Day?
16. Which Sixties sex symbol released *The Dance Album* in 1999, a collection of dance mixes of some of his old hits?
17. Which actor played the title role in the 1999 BBC 2 adaptation of Henry James' novel, *The American*?
18. Which American singer-songwriter released her 12th album since 1990 in 1999, entitled *Up Up Up Up Up Up*?
19. Which actor played *Doctor Dolittle* in the 1967 film?
20. What was the title of the Seventies black TV comedy about a south London family, starring Max Wall?

ANSWERS: 1 The Black Crowes', 2 Natalie Wood, 3 Eric Morecambe, 4 Young Love, 5 Brenda Blethyn, 6 You Can't Be Too Careful, 7 Brian Hyland, 8 Bette Davis, 9 Men Behaving Badly, 10 Angie Baby, 11 The Siege, 12 Bob Monkhouse, 13 Practical Magic, 14 Debbie Reynolds, 15 Bianca Butcher, 16 Engelbert Humperdinck, 17 Matthew Modine, 18 Ani DiFranco, 19 Rex Harrison, 20 Born and Bred.

General Knowledge

Your rating: ● 0-5 Join a library ● 6-10 Keep at it ● 11-15 Join a quiz team ● 16-20 Join Mensa

1. What is the capital of Tunisia?
2. Which British racing motorcyclist won the 500 cc world championship in 1976?
3. What is the name for the legislature of the USA, which comprises the Senate and the House of Representatives?
4. Who succeeded Jeremy Thorpe as leader of the Liberal Party in 1976?
5. In which English county is St Albans?
6. What is a thermometer used to measure?
7. Who was the Greek goddess of love?
8. In which country did the Boer Wars take place?
9. What is a ketch?
10. Which cathedral city in NE England has an 11th-century castle which is now part of its university?
11. Which former Yugoslav republic is known as Crna Gora in Serbo-Croat?
12. Which English dramatist wrote *The White Devil* and *The Duchess of Malfi*?
13. What is the largest Fijian island?
14. Which author won the Whitbread novel award for *The Moor's Last Sigh*?
15. Which French aviator was the first to fly the English Channel in a monoplane?
16. Wolfram is an alternative name for which metal?
17. Steel is an alloy based on which metal?
18. In which country can the Apennines mountain range be found?
19. Which actress starred in *Barbarella* and *Klute*?
20. What is the official language of Brazil?

ANSWERS: *1 Tunis, 2 Barry Sheene, 3 Congress, 4 David Steel, 5 Hertfordshire, 6 Temperature, 7 Aphrodite, 8 South Africa, 9 A sailing vessel, 10 Durham, 11 Montenegro, 12 John Webster, 13 Viti Levu, 14 Salman Rushdie, 15 Louis Blériot, 16 Tungsten, 17 Iron, 18 Italy, 19 Jane Fonda, 20 Portuguese.*

General Knowledge

Your rating:
- 0-5 Join a library
- 6-10 Keep at it
- 11-15 Join a quiz team
- 16-20 Join Mensa

1. In which country is the port of Zeebrugge?
2. What sort of creature is a St Bernard?
3. With which sport is Arnold Palmer associated?
4. Which British actor starred in *The Damned* and *Death in Venice*?
5. What are maracas?
6. Honolulu is the capital of which U.S. state?
7. What do the initials CBI stand for?
8. What sort of creature is a yellowhammer?
9. Which classic children's tale was written by Antoine de Saint-Exupéry in 1943?
10. Which country did Zola Budd represent in the 1984 Olympics?
11. In which Spanish city can the Prado art gallery be found?
12. Which London Royal residence was completely redesigned by Nash for George IV?
13. Which French composer wrote the ballets *Coppélia* and *Sylvia*?
14. How many gallons are there to a British bushel?
15. What sort of creature is a boomslang?
16. Which African city has the Arabic name El Qahira?
17. Which U.S. actress starred in *Duel in the Sun* and *The Night of the Hunter*?
18. According to legend, which Italian demonstrated a scientific theory by dropping weights from the Leaning Tower of Pisa?
19. In which city can the Bodleian Library be found?
20. Which shrub of the genus *Ilex* is used for Christmas decorations?

ANSWERS: *1 Belgium, 2 A dog, 3 Golf, 4 Dirk Bogarde, 5 Percussion instruments, 6 Hawaii, 7 Confederation of British Industry, 8 A bird, 9 The Little Prince, 10 Great Britain, 11 Madrid, 12 Buckingham Palace, 13 Leo Delibes, 14 Eight, 15 A snake, 16 Cairo, 17 Lillian Gish, 18 Galileo Galilei, 19 Oxford, 20 Holly.*

General Knowledge

Your rating: ● 0-5 Join a library ● 6-10 Keep at it ● 11-15 Join a quiz team ● 16-20 Join Mensa

1. What is the capital of Scotland?
2. In which county is the New Forest?
3. Who was the Roman god of war?
4. Which black U.S. athlete won four gold medals at the Berlin Olympics in 1936?
5. What is the Welsh name for Wales?
6. What do the initials YWCA stand for?
7. Who was the Greek god of the sea and earthquakes?
8. Zagreb is the capital of which former Yugoslav republic?
9. *La Marseillaise* is the national anthem of which country?
10. What sort of creature is bream?
11. Which English dramatist and poet wrote *Tamburlaine the Great*?
12. What is a celesta?
13. How many players are there in a kabaddi team?
14. Which jazz pianist composed *Off Minor* and *Blue Monk*?
15. Which country did Russia, Denmark and Poland fight against in the Great Northern War (1700-21)?
16. Which island separates North Uist and South Uist, in the Outer Hebrides?
17. In ancient Greece, what was an amphora?
18. Of which Canadian province is Winnipeg the capital?
19. Which French novelist wrote *La Cousine Bette*?
20. Who was the first Hapsburg Holy Roman Emperor?

ANSWERS: *1 Edinburgh, 2 Hampshire, 3 Mars, 4 Jesse Owens, 5 Cymru, 6 Young Women's Christian Association, 7 Poseidon, 8 Croatia, 9 France, 10 A fish, 11 Christopher Marlowe, 12 A keyboard instrument, 13 Seven, 14 Thelonious Monk, 15 Sweden, 16 Benbecula, 17 A vase, 18 Manitoba, 19 Honore de Balzac, 20 Rudolph I.*

Entertainment

Your rating: ● 0-5 Buy a TV ● 6-10 Keep at it ● 11-15 Join a quiz team ● 16-20 Enter a quiz show

1. In which country was the TV nature series *Wild Relations* shot?
2. Who starred as the artist in the 1997 film *Surviving Picasso*?
3. Which cheerful cockney comedian was the first host of *Sunday Night at the London Palladium*?
4. Who had a U.K. top ten hit single in 1976 with *Devil Woman*?
5. Who directed the 1973 film *Mean Streets*?
6. Which Australian rock band released an album entitled *Elegantly Wasted* in 1997?
7. In which city was the 1997 Sylvester Stallone action film *Daylight* set?
8. Which cult TV series began each episode with the following sentence:- “There is a fifth dimension beyond that which is known to men”?
9. Who had a U.K. top ten hit single in 1986 with *Dancing On The Ceiling*?
10. Which rock singer starred in the title role of the 1980 film *McVicar*?
11. Which star of *The Charmer* played shady businessman Richard in the psychological TV thriller *Element of Doubt*?
12. Which band released an album entitled *Le Roi Est Mort, Vive Le Roi!* in 1997?
13. Which daytime gameshow has had Danny Baker, Shane Ritchie and Bob Mills as its hosts?
14. The 1988 film *Hellbound* was a sequel to which horror film?
15. Who had a Christmas U.K. number one hit single in 1978 with *Mary’s Boy Child*?
16. Who starred as Canadian Mountie Benton Fraser in BBC’s *Due South*?
17. Who starred as twin brothers in the 1997 film *Steal Big, Steal Little*?
18. Who was the original host of ITV’s *Catchphrase*?
19. Who starred as the art-gallery owner who falls for two sisters in the 1997 film *Two Much*?
20. Which *Are You Being Served* character was played on TV by Frank Thornton?

ANSWERS: *1 Australia, 2 Sir Anthony Hopkins, 3 Tommy Trinder, 4 Cliff Richard, 5 Martin Scorsese, 6 INXS, 7 New York City, 8 The Twilight Zone, 9 Lionel Richie, 10 Roger Daltrey, 11 Nigel Havers, 12 Enigma, 13 Win, Lose or Draw, 14 Hellraiser, 15 Boney M, 16 Paul Gross, 17 Andy Garcia, 18 Roy Walker, 19 Antonio Banderas, 20 Captain Peacock.*

General Knowledge

Your rating: ● **0-5** **Join a library** ● **6-10** **Keep at it**
● **11-15** **Join a quiz team** ● **16-20** **Join Mensa**

1. Which Sir Walter Scott novel gives a romanticised account of the life of Scottish outlaw Robert Macgregor?
2. Who was poet laureate from 1972 to 1984?
3. The manufacture, sale and transportation of which products were banned during the USA's Prohibition of 1919 to 1933?
4. What sort of creature is a skate?
5. In which Dutch city can the Rijksmuseum art gallery be found?
6. Since World War II, which building has been the venue for the Proms?
7. Which 14-ton bell in the clock tower of the Palace of Westminster is named after Sir Benjamin Hall?
8. Which entertainer won an Oscar for his role in the film *From Here to Eternity*?
9. In April 1912, which luxury passenger ship struck an iceberg and sank near Newfoundland on its maiden voyage?
10. What are Basic, FORTRAN, COBOL and Pascal examples of?
11. Which British novelist wrote *Love on the Dole*?
12. What is the largest Greek island in the Dodecanese group?
13. Which French composer wrote the operas *Faust* and *Romeo and Juliet*?
14. What was the title of Gary Barlow's first solo single?
15. What sort of creature is a dik-dik?
16. Who was the first English cricketer to be knighted?
17. Which French short-story writer and novelist wrote *Une Vie* and *Bel-Ami*?
18. Who became Empress of Russia after the death of her husband Peter III?
19. What is the capital of Kuwait?
20. Who was the Italian director of the film *Last Tango in Paris*?

ANSWERS: *1 Rob Roy, 2 Sir John Betjeman, 3 Alcoholic drinks, 4 A fish, 5 Amsterdam, 6 The Royal Albert Hall, 7 Big Ben, 8 Frank Sinatra, 9 The Titanic, 10 Computer programming languages, 11 Walter Greenwood, 12 Rhodes, 13 Charles Gounod, 14 Forever Love, 15 An antelope, 16 Jack Hobbs, 17 Guy de Maupassant, 18 Catherine the Great, 19 Kuwait, 20 Bernardo Bertolucci.*

General Knowledge

Your rating: ● **0-5 Join a library** ● **6-10 Keep at it** ● **11-15 Join a quiz team** ● **16-20 Join Mensa**

1. In which country was the guillotine introduced as a method of capital punishment in 1792?
2. How many strings are on a cello?
3. Which Italian artist is famous for his celebrated Sistine Chapel ceiling in the Vatican?
4. According to the Old Testament, on which mountain did Moses receive the tablets of the law from Jehovah?
5. Of which country is Wellington the capital?
6. Which word describes the process in animals by which a larva changes into an adult?
7. Which Italian composer wrote *William Tell*?
8. Of which Californian city is Beverly Hills a suburb?
9. How is somnambulism more commonly known?
10. Which Prussian statesman was known as the Iron Chancellor?
11. In which year did the U.K. join the EEC?
12. The Sargasso Sea is a section of which ocean?
13. What is the only town on Guernsey?
14. On which date is the Christian feast of All Saints' Day observed in the West?
15. Of which mineral is amethyst a variety?
16. Which Japanese city was the site of the 1972 winter Olympics?
17. Who wrote the music for the musicals *Annie Get Your Gun* and *Mr President*?
18. Which transition metal is represented by the symbol Zr?
19. Which British novelist wrote *Decline and Fall* and *Brideshead Revisited*?
20. What is the smallest state in the USA?

ANSWERS: *1 France, 2 Four, 3 Michelangelo, 4 Mount Sinai, 5 New Zealand, 6 Metamorphosis, 7 Gioacchino Rossini, 8 Los Angeles, 9 Sleepwalking, 10 Otto von Bismarck, 11 1973, 12 The Atlantic, 13 St Peter Port, 14 November the first, 15 Quartz, 16 Sapporo, 17 Irving Berlin, 18 Zirconium, 19 Evelyn Waugh, 20 Rhode Island.*

General Knowledge

Your rating:
- **0-5 Join a library**
- **6-10 Keep at it**
- **11-15 Join a quiz team**
- **16-20 Join Mensa**

1. Who was president of Yugoslavia from 1953 to 1980?
2. At which university did Prince Charles study?
3. In which state of the USA is the city of Miami situated?
4. Which metallic element is represented by the symbol Ag?
5. Which river flows west from Stockport to the Irish Sea, via Liverpool and Birkenhead?
6. What sort of creature is a Sealyham?
7. In which English county is Guildford situated?
8. What is the skeleton of the head known as?
9. Which New York building was the tallest in the world from 1932 until the World Trade Centre was completed in the 1970s?
10. How is the explosive trinitrotoluene commonly known?
11. Which Conservative politician was prime minister from 1963 to 1964?
12. Which U.S. comedian was born Benjamin Kubelsky?
13. Which is the only nation to have competed in every summer and winter Olympic Games since the modern tournament began?
14. What sort of creature is a gourami?
15. Which Nobel prize-winning French novelist wrote *Thérèse Desqueyroux*?
16. What is the capital and chief port of Tasmania?
17. Which 18th century British artist is famous for his paintings and engravings of *A Rake's Progress*?
18. By what name was the disease Sydenham's chorea formerly known?
19. How many horns does the Indian rhinoceros have?
20. Which Anglo-Saxon epic poem features the marauding monster Grendel?

ANSWERS: *1 Marshal Tito, 2 Cambridge, 3 Florida, 4 Silver, 5 River Mersey, 6 A dog, 7 Surrey, 8 The skull, 9 The Empire State Building, 10 TNT, 11 Alec Douglas-Home, 12 Jack Benny, 13 Great Britain, 14 A fish, 15 François Mauriac, 16 Hobart, 17 William Hogarth, 18 St Vitus's Dance, 19 One, 20 Beowulf.*

Sports

Your rating: ● 0-5 Wooden spoon ● 6-10 Bronze medal ● 11-15 Silver medal ● 16-20 Gold medal

1. Who won the women's singles title at the 2000 Wimbledon tennis championships?
2. Which bowler took a wicket with his first-ever delivery in an Ashes Test in 1993?
3. Jose Napoles and John H Stracey are former champions from which sport?
4. From which club did Liverpool sign Stan Collymore for £8.5m in 1995?
5. At which course is the Derby held?
6. In 2000, who became the youngest man ever to win all four of golf's major championships?
7. Which West Indian scored a century in the final of the 1975 cricket World Cup?
8. Which team won the cricket County Championship from 1952 to 1958?
9. In which position did Briton Fatima Whitbread finish in the 1984 Olympic Games javelin event?
10. Which football team plays at Highbury?
11. Which country denied England's rugby union team a Six Nations Championship grand slam in 2000?
12. What is the maximum number of clubs a player is allowed to carry on a round of golf?
13. What nationality was legendary motor racing driver Juan Manuel Fangio?
14. What did Stephen Roche become the first Irishman to win in 1987?
15. Of which sports chat-show was John Inverdale the host?
16. Which country beat Italy in the final to win football's Euro 2000?
17. Who was the first British golfer to win the U.S. Masters?
18. What is the highest score possible with three darts?
19. Who is the only player to skipper two British Lions Tours?
20. At which course did Europe famously win the Ryder Cup in 1985?

***ANSWERS:** 1 Venus Williams, 2 Shane Warne, 3 Boxing, 4 Notts Forest, 5 Epsom, 6 Tiger Woods, 7 Clive Lloyd, 8 Surrey, 9 3rd, 10 Arsenal, 11 Scotland, 12 14, 13 Argentinian, 14 Tour de France, 15 On Side, 16 France, 17 Sandy Lyle, 18 180, 19 Martin Johnson, 20 The Belfry.*

General Knowledge

Your rating: ● 0-5 Join a library ● 6-10 Keep at it ● 11-15 Join a quiz team ● 16-20 Join Mensa

1. Which British novelist wrote *Mansfield Park* and *Northanger Abbey*?
2. Who starred in the title role of the 1922 film *Robin Hood*?
3. In which London church is Poets' Corner?
4. David Starkey has won a W H Smith Book Award for his biography of which British monarch?
5. Which unit of weight for precious stones is equal to 0.20 grams?
6. Of which African country is Gaborone the capital?
7. What was the name of the policeman in the cartoon *Top Cat*?
8. Whose sons were the traditional ancestors of the 12 tribes of Israel?
9. What was the name of the boy in A A Milne's *Winnie-the-Pooh* stories?
10. Who played the title role in the BBC series *I, Claudius*?
11. In which city are the V I Warshawski novels by Sara Paretsky set?
12. Which German composer wrote the opera *Der Rosenkavalier*?
13. Who replaced Sir Iain Vallance as chairman of British Telecom?
14. Which founder of the Pre-Raphaelite Brotherhood painted *Beata Beatrix* and *The Blessed Damozel*?
15. In which country is the port of Jaffna?
16. Which Irish political leader was known as the Liberator?
17. Which ex-Blue Peter presenter is the daughter of Gloria Hunniford?
18. Which Colombian novelist won the 1982 Nobel Prize for Literature?
19. What was the name of the official bodyguard of Roman emperors created by Augustus?
20. Which archangel announced the birth of John the Baptist to Zechariah?

ANSWERS: *1 Jane Austen, 2 Douglas Fairbanks, 3 Westminster Abbey, 4 Elizabeth I, 5 Carat, 6 Botswana, 7 Officer Dibble, 8 Jacob, 9 Christopher Robin, 10 Derek Jacobi, 11 Chicago, 12 Richard Strauss, 13 Sir Christopher Bland, 14 Dante Gabriel Rossetti, 15 Sri Lanka, 16 Daniel O'Connell, 17 Caron Keating, 18 Gabriel Garcia Marquez, 19 Praetorian Guard, 20 Gabriel.*

General Knowledge

Your rating: ● **0-5 Join a library** ● **6-10 Keep at it** ● **11-15 Join a quiz team** ● **16-20 Join Mensa**

1. Which British crown colony reverted to Chinese rule in 1997?
2. On which island was the detective series *Bergerac* set?
3. Which popular travel author won a W H Smith Book Award for his book *Down Under*?
4. What is the capital of Indonesia?
5. Who directed the films *Manhattan* and *Radio Days*?
6. What shade of red is named after a battle in the struggle for Italian independence?
7. Who wrote the novel *Emil and the Detectives*?
8. What name is given to a wind of between 7 and 10 on the Beaufort scale?
9. Which English king succeeded Queen Victoria?
10. What sort of condition is commonly treated with antihistamines?
11. Who wrote *The Four Feathers*?
12. Which American economist wrote *The Affluent Society*?
13. After which poet was the Russian town Detskoe Selo renamed in 1937?
14. Which American statesman and renowned orator claimed ‘There is always room at the top’?
15. What name was given to supporters of the exiled Stuart king James II?
16. Which English poet wrote the sonnet collection *Delia*?
17. Which pop star appeared in the 1976 film *The Man Who Fell to Earth*?
18. What is the common name for pyrite or iron pyrites?
19. Which English Cavalier poet wrote *To Althea, from Prison*?
20. What name is given to the permanent freezing of the ground in areas bordering on ice sheets?

ANSWERS: *1 Hong Kong, 2 Jersey, 3 Bill Bryson, 4 Jakarta, 5 Woody Allen, 6 Magenta, 7 Erich Kastner, 8 Gale, 9 Edward VII, 10 Allergy, 11 A E W Mason, 12 John Kenneth Galbraith, 13 Aleksandr Pushkin, 14 Daniel Webster, 15 Jacobites, 16 Samuel Daniel, 17 David Bowie, 18 Fool's gold, 19 Richard Lovelace, 20 Permafrost.*

General Knowledge

Your rating:
- **0-5 Join a library**
- **6-10 Keep at it**
- **11-15 Join a quiz team**
- **16-20 Join Mensa**

1. In which game is a flat stone bounced across the surface of water?
2. Which Australian author won the Nobel Prize for literature in 1973?
3. Who was represented in Greek mythology as wearing winged sandals?
4. As what did the Englishman Thomas Sheraton make his name?
5. What was the middle name of the rock singer and songwriter Jim Morrison?
6. Who wrote *A Darkness More Than Night*?
7. A tetragram is any word of how many letters?
8. Which actor plays Jamie Mitchell in *EastEnders*?
9. Who was the first Plantagenet king of England?
10. Who wrote The Satanist?
11. What is the name of the captain in *The Caine Mutiny* by Herman Wouk?
12. Who links *The Bed-Sit Girl* and *The Rag Trade*?
13. Who was the founder of the Mormon Church?
14. Who appeared on television as Nicodemus and Lord Marchmain?
15. Who was the subject of the novel *Lust for Life* by Irving Stone?
16. What was the nationality of the character played by Ralph Fiennes in *The English Patient*?
17. Where in England is Greenham Common?
18. What is a klipspringer?
19. Who played *The Last Action Hero*?
20. Which member of the Monty Python team wrote *The Saga of Erik the Viking*?

ANSWERS: *1 Ducks and drakes, 2 Patrick White, 3 Hermes, 4 Furniture maker, 5 Douglas, 6 Michael Connelly, 7 4, 8 Jack Ryder, 9 Henry II, 10 Dennis Wheatley, 11 Queeg, 12 Sheila Hancock, 13 Joseph Smith, 14 Laurence Olivier, 15 Vincent van Gogh, 16 Hungarian, 17 Berkshire, 18 Antelope, 19 Arnold Schwarzenegger, 20 Terry Jones.*

Entertainment

Your rating: ● 0-5 Buy a TV ● 6-10 Keep at it ● 11-15 Join a quiz team ● 16-20 Enter a quiz show

1. How old was reggae legend Bob Marley when he died?
2. What was the name of Mel Gibson's character in the *Lethal Weapon* movies?
3. Which British band looking to build on U.S. success had a 2001 hit in the U.K. with *Back Here*?
4. Whose *Amazing World of Animals* appeared on BBC 1?
5. Which US vocalist had a U.K. number one hit in 1963 with *Devil in Disguise*?
6. Which 2001 film set in Europe in the sixties featured Cameron Diaz and Christopher Eccleston?
7. Which BBC 1 drama series starred Stephen Tompkinson and Nick Berry as undercover cops?
8. Which country artist hit the U.K. number one spot with *Coward of the County* in 1980?
9. Which actor played mob boss Lucky Luciano in the 1991 film *Mobsters*?
10. Which interviewer famous for his *Weird Weekends Met Paul and Debbie* in a BBC 2 documentary?
11. Which British female vocalist claimed *I Only Want to Be With You* in the U.K. top five in 1963?
12. Which actor played author William Forrester in the 2000 film *Finding Forrester*?
13. What was the name of Paul Nicholas' character in the eighties series *Just Good Friends*?
14. With which band is John Frusciante, who released a solo album in 2001 entitled *To Record Only Water For Ten Days*, also a guitarist with?
15. Who wrote, directed, produced and starred in the 1990 film *Mo' Better Blues*?
16. Which Channel 4 comedy series was co-written by, and starred, Jessica Stevenson, aka Cheryl in *The Royle Family*?
17. Which band, the product of the ITV series *Popstars*, hit the U.K. number one spot with their debut single *Pure and Simple*?
18. Which comedian and writer presided over *The British Academy Film Awards* in 2001?
19. Which 2000 film starred Russell Crowe as Terry Thorne, a professional negotiator?
20. Which BBC 2 comedy series featured two *Royle Family* stars and two former *Hollyoaks* stars?

ANSWERS: *1 36, 2 Martin Riggs, 3 BBMak, 4 Rolf's (Rolf Harris), 5 Elvis Presley, 6 The Invisible Circus, 7 In Deep, 8 Kenny Rogers, 9 Christian Slater, 10 Louis Theroux, 11 Dusty Springfield, 12 Sean Connery, 13 Vince Pinner, 14 The Red Hot Chili Peppers, 15 Spike Lee, 16 Spaced, 17 Hear'Say, 18 Stephen Fry, 19 Proof of Life, 20 Two Pints of Lager (and a Packet of Crisps).*

General Knowledge

Your rating: ● 0-5 Join a library ● 6-10 Keep at it ● 11-15 Join a quiz team ● 16-20 Join Mensa

1. Which child star sued Graham Greene for libel?
2. The novel *Wide Sargasso Sea* by Jean Rhys is a prequel to which classic novel?
3. Who had a U.K. number one hit in 1996 with *Spaceman*?
4. On television, who was smarter than the average bear?
5. In which war did the battle of Leyte Gulf take place?
6. Which horror film star was born William Pratt?
7. What is the most sacred river to Hindus?
8. What is a male bee called?
9. Of which novel is Lorelei Lee the central character?
10. In which continent are the Appalachian Mountains?
11. Who was the first wife of Henry VIII?
12. Who played Fred in the 1994 film *The Flintstones*?
13. What type of animal is a pointer?
14. Who created the detective Sam Spade?
15. What is another name for the aurora borealis?
16. Which member of the Ingalls family was the narrator of *Little House on the Prairie*?
17. In which American state is Silicon Valley?
18. Which rock star was born Reginald Dwight?
19. When did Tony Blair become leader of the Labour Party?
20. Which classic film was based on the play *Everybody Goes To Ricks*?

ANSWERS: *1 Shirley Temple, 2 Jane Eyre, 3 Babylon Zoo, 4 Yogi, 5 World War II, 6 Boris Karloff, 7 Ganges, 8 Drone, 9 Gentlemen Prefer Blondes, 10 North America, 11 Catherine of Aragon, 12 John Goodman, 13 Dog, 14 Dashiell Hammett, 15 Northern lights, 16 Laura, 17 California, 18 Elton John, 19 1994, 20 Casablanca.*

General Knowledge

Your rating: ● 0-5 Join a library ● 6-10 Keep at it ● 11-15 Join a quiz team ● 16-20 Join Mensa

1. Who directed the 1991 film *The Commitments*?
2. Who wrote *Finnegans Wake*?
3. A griffin has the body of which animal?
4. What is the highest ranking officer in the British army?
5. Which pop star appeared in the 1992 film *Freejack*?
6. In which city was *Van Der Valk* set?
7. Where would a Scotsman wear a glengarry?
8. Who wrote *The Guns of Navarone*?
9. How many films did Katherine Hepburn make with Spencer Tracy?
10. What is the chemical symbol for iron?
11. Which Bond film title was taken from a seventeenth century Japanese poem?
12. Which university broadcasts through the night on BBC2?
13. What nationality was Sigrid Undset who won the Nobel Prize for literature in 1928?
14. What is the capital of the Bahamas?
15. What was the name of the Charlie Chaplin role in most of his films?
16. What was the name of the car in *The Love Bug*?
17. The gestation period of an elephant lasts approximately how many days?
18. What pen name does J K Rowling use as the author of *Fantastic Beasts and Where to Find Them*?
19. Children's TV favourite *Pingu* was created in which country?
20. In which year was the X certificate introduced?

ANSWERS: *1 Alan Parker, 2 James Joyce, 3 Lion, 4 Field marshal, 5 Mick Jagger, 6 Amsterdam, 7 Head, 8 Alistair Maclean, 9 9, 10 Fe, 11 You Only Live Twice, 12 Open University, 13 Norwegian, 14 Nassau, 15 Little Tramp, 16 Herbie, 17 624, 18 Newt Scamander, 19 Norway, 20 1950.*

General Knowledge

Your rating: ● 0-5 Join a library ● 6-10 Keep at it ● 11-15 Join a quiz team ● 16-20 Join Mensa

1. What sort of animal is Snowball in *Animal Farm* by George Orwell?
2. *Take My Breath Away* was the 1986 Oscar-winning song from which film?
3. What was the maiden name of former prime minister Margaret Thatcher?
4. In which government ministry was *Yes Minister* set?
5. Mount Logan is the highest peak in which country?
6. Which novel by E M Forster was published 57 years after it was written?
7. Wolfram is another name for which element?
8. Who provided the voice for Rocky the Rooster in the film *Chicken Run*?
9. What type of creature is a roach?
10. Which Irish group provided music for the 1980s TV series *Robin of Sherwood*?
11. Where was *The Jewel in the Crown* set?
12. Who took over the role of *The Saint* from Roger Moore?
13. How many minutes are there in a day?
14. Who wrote the autobiographies *Present Indicative* and *Future Indefinite*?
15. What is the twelfth sign of the zodiac?
16. Which American city is nicknamed the Windy City?
17. What does a fletcher make?
18. How many inches make up a yard?
19. How many pints make up a gallon?
20. *Jigsaw* was the first book by which prolific novelist?

ANSWERS: *1 A pig, 2 Top Gun, 3 Roberts, 4 Administrative Affairs, 5 Canada, 6 Maurice, 7 Tungsten, 8 Mel Gibson, 9 Fish, 10 Clannad, 11 India, 12 Ian Ogilvy, 13 1440, 14 Noel Coward, 15 Pisces, 16 Chicago, 17 Arrows, 18 36, 19 8, 20 Barbara Cartland.*

Entertainment

Your rating: ● 0-5 Buy a TV ● 6-10 Keep at it ● 11-15 Join a quiz team ● 16-20 Enter a quiz show

1. Who played Welsh Sergeant Major B.L. Williams in the TV sitcom *It Ain't Half Hot Mum*?
2. Which Billy Joel song was taken to the U.K. number one spot by Westlife in aid of Comic Relief 2001?
3. Which 1986 film featured Richard Gere as Eddie Jillette, an undercover cop?
4. Which duo presented *The Brit Awards 2001*, shown on ITV?
5. What was the first name of Sigourney Weaver's character Ripley in the Alien series of films?
6. Which former member of Queen had a U.K. top five hit with *Too Much Love Will Kill You* in 1992?
7. Which Australian actress played a single mother with powers of extra-sensory perception in the 2000 film *The Gift*?
8. Which actor played Dr John Carter in Channel 4's *ER*?
9. Whose first solo U.K. hit was 1988's *Suedehead*?
10. Which Hollywood actor starred in both 1988's *Red Heat* and 1985's *Red Sonja*?
11. Which actress followed in her late father's footsteps by starring in the BBC 1 series *Ballykissangel*?
12. Which British group had U.K. number one hits in the Seventies with *Tiger Feet* and *Oh Boy*?
13. Which 2000 Oscar-nominated film starred Juliette Binoche as the owner of a chocolate shop?
14. Which member of the Monkees played Ena Sharples' grandson Colin Lomax in *Coronation Street* in 1961?
15. Who had a U.K. top ten hit with the dance track I Wanna Be U in 2001?
16. Which two actors teamed up to star in films including *Silver Streak*, *Stir Crazy* and *Another You*?
17. Which young yachtswoman was the subject of a 2001 BBC 1 documentary following her progress in the Vendee Globe round-the-world race?
18. Which Welsh band had a 2001 U.K. top five hit with *Mr Writer*?
19. Which ITV soap opera returned to our screens in 2001 after a thirteen year break?
20. Which actor played a serial killer being pursued by James Spader's FBI agent in the 2000 film *The Watcher*?

ANSWERS: *1 Windsor Davies, 2 Uptown Girl, 3 No Mercy, 4 Ant & Dec, 5 Ellen, 6 Brian May, 7 Cate Blanchett, 8 Noah Wyle, 9 Morrissey's, 10 Arnold Schwarzenegger, 11 Susannah Doyle, 12 Mud, 13 Chocolat, 14 Davy Jones, 15 Chocolate Puma, 16 Richard Pryor & Gene Wilder, 17 Ellen MacArthur (Sailing Through Hell), 18 Stereophonics, 19 Crossroads, 20 Keanu Reeves.*

General Knowledge

Your rating:
- 0-5 Join a library
- 6-10 Keep at it
- 11-15 Join a quiz team
- 16-20 Join Mensa

1. The title of the ecological documentary Koyaanisqatsi comes from the Hopi for what?
2. A rickshaw would typically be used in parts of which continent?
3. Who wrote the novel *Manhattan Transfer*?
4. Roberto Duran and Thomas Hearns are legends from which sport?
5. In which year was British entrepreneur Richard Branson born?
6. Who was the original scream queen?
7. Which American author has written novels under the pseudonym Richard Bachman?
8. After working together on which film did Michael Douglas and Catherine Zeta Jones get married?
9. Which character in the Harry Potter stories is the author of *Magical Me*?
10. What is the sixth letter of the Greek alphabet?
11. Where was *Gilligans Island*?
12. Dabs is a slang name for what?
13. Who directed the 1993 film *Schindlers List*?
14. Who is the subject of the novel *Rookwood* by Harrison Ainsworth?
15. Which is the first book of the Old Testament?
16. How many people make up an octet?
17. What is the largest city in Australia?
18. What was the name of the road where Mr Benn lived?
19. Who wrote the novel *Stuart Little*?
20. Who was the first Hanoverian king of Great Britain and Ireland?

ANSWERS: *1 Crazy life, 2 Asia, 3 John Dos Passos, 4 Boxing, 5 1950, 6 Fay Wray, 7 Stephen King, 8 Traffic, 9 Gilderoy Lockhart, 10 Zeta, 11 South Pacific, 12 Fingerprints, 13 Steven Spielberg, 14 Dick Turpin, 15 Genesis, 16 Eight, 17 Sydney, 18 Festive Road, 19 E B White, 20 George I.*

General Knowledge

Your rating:
- 0-5 Join a library
- 6-10 Keep at it
- 11-15 Join a quiz team
- 16-20 Join Mensa

1. Who wrote the TV series *Only Fools And Horses*?
2. Pulque is a light alcoholic drink from which country?
3. Who wrote *The Catcher in the Rye*?
4. Which Bond film was the last to use a title written by Ian Fleming?
5. What is the chemical symbol for zinc?
6. What was the first name of the poet A. E. Housman?
7. What was the name of the band in *Tutti Frutti*?
8. Which sport is central to the 1996 film *Space Jam*?
9. What is the name of the series of novels that includes *The Last of the Mohicans*?
10. How many feet does a biped have?
11. Who wrote the novel *Oranges Are Not the Only Fruit*?
12. What was the first name of Mr Smart in *Get Smart*?
13. Which composer is associated with the film *The Sting*?
14. Which film told the story of Billy Hayes and his stay in a Turkish jail?
15. Which house does Harry Potter belong to in the novels by J. K. Rowling?
16. Which Morgan Freeman film is a remake of the 1981 film *Garde A Vue*?
17. Who sang the theme song for *The Adventures of Champion*?
18. Which feminist author wrote *The Second Sex*?
19. Which Charlie's Angel played Mrs King in *The Scarecrow and Mrs King*?
20. What is the first novel of the Alexandria Quartet by Lawrence Durrell?

ANSWERS: *1 John Sullivan, 2 Mexico, 3 J D Salinger, 4 The Living Daylights, 5 Zn, 6 Alfred, 7 The Majestics, 8 Basketball, 9 The Leatherstocking Tales, 10 Two, 11 Jeanette Winterson, 12 Maxwell, 13 Scott Joplin, 14 Midnight Express, 15 Gryffindor, 16 Under Suspicion, 17 Frankie Laine, 18 Simone de Beauvoir, 19 Kate Jackson, 20 Justine.*

General Knowledge

Your rating: • 0-5 Join a library • 6-10 Keep at it • 11-15 Join a quiz team • 16-20 Join Mensa

1. Which bejewelled item was the target of the thieves in *Topkapi*?
2. In which novel by Charles Dickens does Captain Cuttle appear?
3. Which film star was born Julia Turner?
4. What name does Trigger insist on calling Rodney in *Only Fools and Horses*?
5. Who wrote the Goosebumps series of novels for children?
6. Who was the Roman god of the sea?
7. What is the middle name of the former Tory leader William Hague?
8. How old was the hero of Billy Elliot?
9. Which comedian lived in East Cheam?
10. Who was the hero of the first story by Beatrix Potter?
11. Which state is the biggest producer of oil and gas in the USA?
12. Which Star Trek film has the subtitle *The Voyage Home*?
13. Paul Keating was prime minister of which country from 1991-96?
14. Which Channel 5 game show featured a hidden saboteur?
15. Richard Hadlee and Dennis Lillee are former players of which sport?
16. What type of instrument is a xylophone?
17. In which country was *Treasure of the Sierra Madre* set?
18. The bacterial disease glanders can be passed on to humans from which animal?
19. What was the first novel by Martin Amis?
20. For which series did ex-*Mission Impossible* stars Martin Landau and Barbara Bain team up again?

ANSWERS: *1 A dagger, 2 Dombey and Son, 3 Lana Turner, 4 Dave, 5 R L Stine, 6 Neptune, 7 Jefferson, 8 11, 9 Tony Hancock, 10 Peter Rabbit, 11 Texas, 12 IV, 13 Australia, 14 The Mole, 15 Cricket, 16 Percussion, 17 Mexico, 18 Horse, 19 The Rachel Papers, 20 Space 1999.*

Entertainment

Your rating: ● 0-5 Buy a TV ● 6-10 Keep at it ● 11-15 Join a quiz team ● 16-20 Enter a quiz show

1. Which of Catherine Cookson's most popular heroines was brought to life in a 1999 ITV period drama?
2. Which rock group had top ten hits in the Seventies with *Seven Seas of Rhye*, *You're My Best Friend* and *Don't Stop Me Now*?
3. Which actress starred as Linda, Tom's flatmate in the BBC 2 comedy series *Gimme Gimme Gimme*?
4. What was the title of the Small Faces' 1966 number one hit?
5. Which actor played American sharp-shooter Quigley in the 1990 film *Quigley Down Under*?
6. What was the title of BBC 1's medical drama spin-off from *Casualty*?
7. Which song provided a number one hit for Nilsson in 1972 and Mariah Carey in 1994?
8. Which actor played the one-time liberal U.S. senator *Bulworth* in the 1999 film of the same name?
9. Which actor played Mr Spock in the U.S. TV series *Star Trek*?
10. What nationality are the dance music production team Cassxius, who released an album entitled *1999*?
11. Which 1981 film about 17th-century Japanese political intrigue starred Richard Chamberlain as a shipwrecked Englishman?
12. Which 1999 BBC 2 drama starred Timothy Spall and Lindsay Duncan as Oswald Bates and Marilyn Truman, photographic librarians?
13. Which British band released an album in 1999 entitled *Revolt*?
14. Which ex-*EastEnder* played chief holiday rep Nicki Matthews in BBC 1's drama series *Sunburn*?
15. Which actress played the *Stepmom* in the 1999 film of the same name?
16. Which male vocalist had U.K. top ten hits in 1989 with *Love Train* and *Americanos*?
17. Which *Emmerdale* character left the soap in 1999 after attacking Chris Tate?
18. Which actress played Guinevere in the 1953 film *Knights of the Round Table*?
19. What was the title of Pop Will Eat Itself's 1993 U.K. top ten hit?
20. Which long-running sixties TV series about an oil company was originally entitled *Mogul*?

ANSWERS: *1 Tilly Trotter, 2 Queen, 3 Kathy Burke, 4 All or Nothing, 5 Tom Selleck, 6 Holby City, 7 Without You, 8 Warren Beatty, 9 Leonard Nimoy, 10 French, 11 Shogun, 12 Shooting the Past, 13 3 Colours Red, 14 Michelle Collins, 15 Julia Roberts, 16 Holly Johnson, 17 Kim Marchant, 18 Ava Gardner, 19 Get the Girl! Kill the Baddies!, 20 The Troubleshooters.*

General Knowledge

Your rating: ● 0-5 Join a library ● 6-10 Keep at it ● 11-15 Join a quiz team ● 16-20 Join Mensa

1. In which European country can the city of Gerona be found?
2. By what acronym is radio detection and ranging commonly known?
3. Which Argentinian motor-racing driver won 24 Grand Prix races and was world champion a record five times?
4. Which U.S. actress made several films with Spencer Tracy and also starred in *The Lion in Winter*?
5. Which organ is inflamed when one suffers from hepatitis?
6. Which country was known as Persia until 1935?
7. What is the hardest known mineral?
8. Which Scottish city is the administrative centre of Lothian Region?
9. Which Old Testament figure was the father of Ham, Shem and Japheth?
10. To the nearest mile, how long is a marathon race?
11. What does the acronym OPEC stand for?
12. In what sort of building would one be likely to see the Dewey Decimal Classification System in action?
13. What sort of creature is a noctule?
14. Which British prime minister was assassinated in 1812 by mad and bankrupt broker, John Bellingham?
15. Which U.S. novelist wrote *Cat's Cradle* and *Breakfast of Champions*?
16. What is the capital and main port of Sri Lanka?
17. Which island group was formerly known as the East Indies?
18. Which U.S. dramatist wrote *Who's Afraid of Virginia Woolf*?
19. A statue of a naked youth in the French Embassy in New York is believed to be a lost work of which artist?
20. What is the official language of Sri Lanka?

ANSWERS: *1 Spain, 2 Radar, 3 Juan Manuel Fangio, 4 Katharine Hepburn, 5 The liver, 6 Iran, 7 Diamond, 8 Edinburgh, 9 Noah, 10 26 miles, 11 Organization of Petroleum Exporting Countries, 12 A library, 13 A bat, 14 Spencer Perceval, 15 Kurt Vonnegut, 16 Colombo, 17 Malay Archipelago, 18 Edward Albee, 19 Michelangelo, 20 Sinhala.*

General Knowledge

Your rating:
- 0-5 Join a library
- 6-10 Keep at it
- 11-15 Join a quiz team
- 16-20 Join Mensa

1. What is sodium chloride commonly called?
2. Which Empire came to an end in 1919 to be replaced by the Weimar Republic?
3. To which group of musical instruments do the triangle, cymbals and glockenspiel belong?
4. Of which country is Kuala Lumpur the capital?
5. The young of which fish are known as parr?
6. In Arthurian legend, which magic sword does Arthur succeed in drawing from a stone?
7. Which U.S. composer wrote *Rhapsody in Blue*?
8. Of which political party was Shirley Williams a co-founder in 1981?
9. Which Austrian city is known as Wien in German?
10. The Diary of which English writer describes the Restoration, the Plague, and the Fire of London?
11. Which Italian theologian was known as Doctor Angelicus?
12. Which Labour MP was criticised for sending her son to a selective school 11 miles away from her Peckham constituency?
13. What is the capital of the state of North Dakota?
14. Who was the first Astronomer Royal?
15. What sort of creature is a colobus?
16. Which British novelist wrote *East Lynne*?
17. Which Sanskrit term signifies "truth" in Buddhism and "caste duty" in Hinduism?
18. Which British poet wrote *The Rape of the Lock*?
19. Cory Aquino became president of which country in 1986?
20. What was the original venue for the London Promenade concerts?

ANSWERS: *1 Table salt, 2 The German Empire, 3 Percussion instruments, 4 Malaysia, 5 Salmon, 6 Excalibur, 7 George Gershwin, 8 Social Democratic Party, 9 Vienna, 10 Samuel Pepys, 11 St Thomas Aquinas, 12 Harriet Harman, 13 Bismarck, 14 John Flamsteed, 15 A monkey, 16 Mrs Henry Wood, 17 Dharma, 18 Alexander Pope, 19 The Philippines, 20 The Queen's Hall.*

General Knowledge

Your rating:
- **0-5 Join a library**
- **6-10 Keep at it**
- **11-15 Join a quiz team**
- **16-20 Join Mensa**

1. What is a manometer used to measure?
2. What is the capital of the state of North Carolina?
3. Which actress separated from her husband, rock singer Jim Kerr in 1996 ?
4. Which English philosopher wrote the *Essay concerning Human Understanding*?
5. Which French composer wrote *Castor et Pollux*?
6. What is the highest mountain in Australia?
7. What is the capital of New York State?
8. What sort of creature is an albacore?
9. How is acetylsalicylic acid commonly known?
10. Which British novelist wrote *The Jewel in the Crown*?
11. Which Scandinavian country is known as Suomi in its native language?
12. Which nonresidential university was established in 1969 to provide correspondence courses and TV programmes?
13. Of which state of the USA is Denver the capital?
14. At which racecourse is the One Thousand Guineas race run?
15. What does the CB stand for in CB radio?
16. Which French novelist wrote *Madame Bovary*?
17. Which country withdrew from the Commonwealth in 1949?
18. How is the jazz musician Arthur Arshawsky better known?
19. Annapolis is the capital of which U.S. state?
20. What sort of creature is a nematode?

ANSWERS: *1 Pressure differences, 2 Raleigh, 3 Patsy Kensit, 4 John Locke, 5 Rameau, 6 Mount Kosciusko, 7 Albany, 8 A fish, 9 Aspirin, 10 Paul Scott, 11 Finland, 12 The Open University, 13 Colorado, 14 Newmarket, 15 Citizens' Band, 16 Gustave Flaubert, 17 Republic of Ireland, 18 Artie Shaw, 19 Maryland, 20 A worm.*

Entertainment

Your rating: ● **0-5** Buy a TV ● **6-10** Keep at it ● **11-15** Join a quiz team ● **16-20** Enter a quiz show

1. What was the title of the 1999 BBC 1 real-life documentary series that focused on the lives of a group of people living in an area of west London?
2. Which male singer had a number one hit in 1968 with *I Pretend*?
3. Which co-creator of TV's *Seinfeld* directed the film *Sour Grapes*?
4. What was the title of Vic Reeves and Bob Mortimer's 1999 BBC 2 sketch show?
5. What was the title of the Platters' 1959 number one hit?
6. Which actor played doctor Ben Stone in the 1991 film *Doc Hollywood*?
7. Which comic actor travelled to Africa to film the 1999 BBC 1 documentary *Born to be Wild - Chimpanzee Challenge*?
8. Which U.S. group had top ten hits in the seventies with *You Make Me Feel Brand New*, *Funky Weekend* and *16 Bars*?
9. In which European city was the 1999 film *Dobermann* set?
10. What was the name of the organisation that Captain Scarlet worked for in the Gerry Anderson puppet series *Captain Scarlet and the Mysterons*?
11. Which British vocalist recorded *Beside You*, the theme tune to the 1999 film *What Dreams May Come*?
12. Which 1963 film starring Doris Day and James Garner was a remake of 1940's *My Favorite Wife*, starring Cary Grant and Irene Dunne?
13. Who is the presenter of the ITV general knowledge quiz show *Who Wants to be a Millionaire*?
14. Which Eighties star released a hits compilation entitled *The Collection* in 1999, featuring his work with his original band, the Commotions?
15. Which BBC correspondent presented the 1999 BBC 2 series *Irish Journeys*?
16. Which *Friends* star played school teacher Lucia in the film *The Opposite of Sex*?
17. Which boy band had a 1999 number one hit with *A Little Bit More*, originally a hit in 1976 for Dr Hook?
18. In which 1999 ITV drama did Thora Hird and Pete Postlethwaite star as an elderly woman and her son learning to cope with her failing health?
19. Which 1969 film starred Burt Lancaster and Deborah Kerr as skydivers?
20. Which 1978 TV drama starring Kenneth More imagined the plight of a TV writer trying to tell the truth in Britain 30 years after the Nazis won World War II?

ANSWERS: *1 Paddington Green, 2 Des O'Connor, 3 Larry David, 4 Bang Bang It's Reeves and Mortimer, 5 Smoke Gets In Your Eyes, 6 Michael J. Fox, 7 Nicholas Lyndhurst, 8 Stylistics, 9 Paris, 10 Spectrum, 11 Mick Hucknall, 12 Move Over, Darling, 13 Chris Tarrant, 14 Lloyd Cole, 15 Fergal Keane, 16 Lisa Kudrow, 17 911, 18 Lost For Words, 19 The Gypsy Moths, 20 An Englishman's Castle.*

General Knowledge

Your rating: ● 0-5 Join a library ● 6-10 Keep at it ● 11-15 Join a quiz team ● 16-20 Join Mensa

1. Which British doctor and philanthropist founded the first of his famous homes for destitute children in 1867?
2. Which poet wrote *Paradise Lost*?
3. In which county can Royal Tunbridge Wells be found?
4. Whom did Henry VIII marry in January 1540 and divorce in July 1540?
5. What sort of creature is an asp?
6. What is an ammeter used to measure?
7. Austin is the capital of which U.S. state?
8. Which Irish dramatist wrote *Arms and the Man*?
9. In which organ can the pineal gland be found?
10. What nationality was the long-distance runner Emil Zátopek?
11. Which city became capital of the newly-independent Czechoslovakia in 1918?
12. How is a tunny otherwise known?
13. Which U.S. actor starred in *Casablanca* and *The Big Sleep*?
14. Which New Zealand writer created the character Roderick Alleyn of Scotland Yard?
15. Of which political party was Jo Grimond leader from 1956 to 1967?
16. Which French acrobat walked across a tightrope suspended over Niagara Falls in 1859?
17. In which state did the battle of Little Bighorn take place?
18. Galena is the principal ore of which metal?
19. Which former French president died in 1996, aged 79?
20. Which Hungarian-born British novelist wrote *The Scarlet Pimpernel*?

ANSWERS: *1 Thomas Barnardo, 2 Milton, 3 Kent, 4 Anne of Cleves, 5 A snake, 6 Electric current, 7 Texas, 8 George Bernard Shaw, 9 The brain, 10 Czech, 11 Prague, 12 Tuna, 13 Humphrey Bogart, 14 Dame Ngaio Marsh, 15 The Liberal Party, 16 Charles Blondin, 17 Montana, 18 Lead, 19 Francois Mitterrand, 20 Baroness Orczy.*

General Knowledge

Your rating: ● 0-5 Join a library ● 6-10 Keep at it ● 11-15 Join a quiz team ● 16-20 Join Mensa

1. How many rings can be seen on the Olympic flag?
2. The centre of the U.S. film industry, Hollywood, is a suburb of which city?
3. Which British novelist wrote *The Rachel Papers*?
4. What was the surname of the brothers who made the first successful hot-air balloon flight in 1783?
5. Which city was formerly known as Constantinople?
6. Which Chinese healing system involves inserting needles into selected points in the body?
7. The island of Tasmania is part of which country?
8. Which Italian directed film versions of *The Taming of the Shrew* and *Romeo and Juliet*?
9. In which country is Patna?
10. Which Danish author wrote the classic fairy tale *The Ugly Duckling*?
11. Honshu is the largest island of which country?
12. Which 1962 Ken Kesey novel was made into a successful film by Milos Forman?
13. Which order of mammals complete their development in a pouch after they are born?
14. Which religious community was founded in New York in 1966 by Swami Prabhupada?
15. What was the surname of the German brothers Jakob and Wilhelm who were famous for collecting folk tales?
16. At which Scottish resort was the Royal and Ancient Golf Club founded in 1754?
17. Which monastic order is officially known as the Cistercians of the Strict Observance?
18. Which Spanish novelist wrote *The Four Horsemen of the Apocalypse*?
19. What sort of creature is a Waler?
20. Which great circle goes around the earth at a latitude of zero degrees?

ANSWERS: *1 Five, 2 Los Angeles, 3 Martin Amis, 4 Montgolfier, 5 Istanbul, 6 Acupuncture, 7 Australia, 8 Franco Zeffirelli, 9 India, 10 Hans Christian Andersen, 11 Japan, 12 One Flew Over the Cuckoo's Nest, 13 Marsupials, 14 Hare Krishna movement, 15 Grimm, 16 St Andrews, 17 Trappists, 18 Blasco Ibanez, 19 A horse, 20 The equator.*

General Knowledge

Your rating:
- 0-5 Join a library
- 6-10 Keep at it
- 11-15 Join a quiz team
- 16-20 Join Mensa

1. The Great Lakes can be found along the border between which two countries?
2. Who was granted the title Princess Royal in 1987?
3. What is the capital of Italy?
4. Which British novelist wrote *The Mayor of Casterbridge*?
5. What is a barometer used to measure?
6. Which country in SE Europe was ruled by King Zog from 1928 to 1946?
7. In which Irish village can a famous stone be found which is kissed in order to receive the gift of smooth talk?
8. Which British poet wrote *Songs of Innocence* and *Songs of Experience*?
9. How many players are in a cricket team?
10. Are protons positively or negatively charged?
11. How is the time taken by the earth to complete one revolution around the sun commonly known?
12. Who directed the films *Mouchette* and *Lancelot du lac*?
13. Which British composer wrote the opera *The Olympians*?
14. Which English university city is famous for its Backs?
15. What sort of creature is a bleak?
16. Which adjective describes elements with a higher atomic number than uranium?
17. The Entente Cordiale of 1904 was an agreement between which two countries?
18. Rosh Hashana is the New Year festival for followers of which religion?
19. What is the second largest city of Japan?
20. Who resigned as secretary of state in opposition to President Carter's attempt to rescue the U.S. hostages in Tehran?

ANSWERS: *1 USA and Canada, 2 Princess Anne, 3 Rome, 4 Thomas Hardy, 5 Atmospheric pressure, 6 Albania, 7 Blarney, 8 William Blake, 9 Eleven, 10 Positively, 11 A year, 12 Robert Bresson, 13 Sir Arthur Bliss, 14 Cambridge, 15 A fish, 16 Transuranic, 17 Britain and France, 18 Judaism, 19 Yokohama, 20 Cyrus Vance.*

Entertainment

Your rating:
- **0-5 Buy a TV**
- **6-10 Keep at it**
- **11-15 Join a quiz team**
- **16-20 Enter a quiz show**

1. In which seventies TV series did Ronald Eyre travel around the world finding out what people's religions meant to them in modern life?
2. Which veteran skiffle artist collaborated with Van Morrison on his first new album in 20 years, *Muleskinner Blues*?
3. Who hosted the 1998 *British Comedy Awards*?
4. Which film starred Sharon Stone as the mother of a hunchback boy and Gillian Anderson as a biker's moll?
5. Which Brooklyn rapper's third album was entitled *Hard Knock Life*, the title track of which provided him with a top five hit?
6. What was the name of Ron Dixon's ex, who returned to *Brookside* two years after setting his house alight?
7. Who directed the 1985 film *Pee-wee's Big Adventure*?
8. Which actor played Alf Garnett in *Till Death Us Do Part*?
9. Which male vocalist had a number one hit with *Running Bear* in 1960?
10. In which 1968 film did Jim Brown and Gene Hackman star as leaders of a convict revolt in Arizona State Prison?
11. Which duo had a top ten hit with *Everybody Gonfi-Gon* in 1994?
12. What was the subtitle of the *Star Trek* movie in which the Enterprise rescues a New Age space colony?
13. Which satirical revue show featured the talents of Mel Smith, Rowan Atkinson, Pamela Stephenson and Griff Rhys-Jones?
14. Where were Typically Tropical with their 1975 number one hit?
15. In which 1983 Paul Brickman film did Tom Cruise and Rebecca DeMornay star?
16. What was the title of the ITV period drama based on a Catherine Cookson novel about racial tension in World War I Britain?
17. Which 1999 soundtrack album featured classics such as *Big Spender*, *Goldfinger* and *It's Not Unusual*?
18. Which famous animation studios were responsible for the BBC 2 claymation series *Rex the Runt*?
19. In Gus Van Sant's 1999 version of Alfred Hitchcock's *Psycho*, which actress played Janet Leigh's role of Marion Crane?
20. Which actor played the title role in TV's *Bergerac*?

ANSWERS: *1 The Long Search, 2 Lonnie Donegan, 3 Jonathan Ross, 4 The Mighty, 5 Jay-Z's, 6 Bev McLoughlin, 7 Tim Burton, 8 Warren Mitchell, 9 Johnny Preston, 10 Riot, 11 Two Cowboys, 12 Insurrection, 13 Not the Nine O'Clock News, 14 Barbados, 15 Risky Business, 16 Colour Blind, 17 Little Voice, 18 Aardman, 19 Anne Heche, 20 John Nettles.*

General Knowledge

Your rating: ● 0-5 Join a library ● 6-10 Keep at it ● 11-15 Join a quiz team ● 16-20 Join Mensa

1. Who was president of the Soviet Union from 1977-82?
2. In which city is New Scotland Yard?
3. In which principality is the resort of Monte Carlo?
4. Which religion, founded in the 15th century by the Guru Nanak, is followed by some nine million Indians?
5. What is the largest city in Switzerland?
6. Which explosive plastic solid consists of 75% nitroglycerine and 25% kieselguhr?
7. In which sport might one find a gully and a silly mid on?
8. In which country was the Klondike gold rush?
9. Which Egyptian canal connects the Mediterranean Sea and the Red Sea?
10. With what sort of music is Ronnie Scott associated?
11. Which British novelist wrote the autobiographical *New Grub Street*?
12. What is the second largest city in Argentina?
13. Which English monarch married Elizabeth Woodville in 1464?
14. What name was adopted by the Sadler's Wells Opera Company in 1974?
15. How many spires does Lichfield Cathedral possess?
16. What sort of creature is a quetzal?
17. Which Norwegian politician was the first secretary general of the UN?
18. Which Scottish city was the scene of the assassination of James I?
19. Which British novelist wrote *Love in a Cold Climate*?
20. How many books are there in the New Testament?

ANSWERS: *1 Leonid Brezhnev, 2 London, 3 Monaco, 4 Sikhism, 5 Zürich, 6 Dynamite, 7 Cricket, 8 Canada, 9 Suez Canal, 10 Jazz, 11 George Gissing, 12 Rosario, 13 Edward IV, 14 English National Opera, 15 Three, 16 A bird, 17 Trygve Lie, 18 Perth, 19 Nancy Mitford, 20 27.*

General Knowledge

Your rating: ● 0-5 Join a library ● 6-10 Keep at it ● 11-15 Join a quiz team ● 16-20 Join Mensa

1. Times Square and the Rockefeller Center can be found in which U.S. city?
2. Which U.S. novelist wrote *Of Mice and Men*?
3. In which country is the tourist resort of Montego Bay?
4. Of which country did Kurt Waldheim become president in 1986?
5. Which bird of prey can be tawny or snowy?
6. Which tax was introduced in 1973 to replace purchase tax?
7. Which British admiral commanded the Bounty until the famous mutiny?
8. Which government department, founded in 1653, is responsible with the Bank of England for the management of the economy?
9. Which abundant element is represented by the symbol Si?
10. Which singer/songwriter released *The Times They Are A-changin'* in 1964?
11. Which monarch's last words are said to have been "Let not poor Nellie starve"?
12. In which country can Barkly Tableland be found?
13. Who claimed that Guy Snowden had offered him a bribe to pull out of the race to run the National Lottery?
14. Alabaster is a translucent form of which mineral?
15. Which British fascist married Diana Mitford in 1936?
16. Which French-born actress starred in the Hollywood films *Three-Cornered Moon* and *Midnight*?
17. Entebbe was the administrative centre of which country until 1958?
18. Which family dominated the city of Florence from 1530 to 1737?
19. Which British novelist wrote *Precious Bane*?
20. What is the highest peak in the Rocky Mountains?

ANSWERS: *1 New York City, 2 John Steinbeck, 3 Jamaica, 4 Austria, 5 The owl, 6 VAT, 7 William Bligh, 8 The Treasury, 9 Silicon, 10 Bob Dylan, 11 Charles II, 12 Australia, 13 Richard Branson, 14 Gypsum, 15 Oswald Mosley, 16 Claudette Colbert, 17 Uganda, 18 Medici, 19 Mary Webb, 20 Mount Elbert.*

General Knowledge

Your rating: ● 0-5 Join a library ● 6-10 Keep at it ● 11-15 Join a quiz team ● 16-20 Join Mensa

1. Which Czech author wrote the novels *The Trial* and *The Castle*?
2. Which colourless, odourless gas is represented by the symbol N?
3. Which German composer wrote the opera *Parsifal*?
4. What is the capital of Japan?
5. What sort of creature is a marlin?
6. Which Roman general abandoned his wife Octavia to live with Cleopatra in Egypt?
7. In which county is the town of Basildon?
8. Which British tennis player won the women's singles title at Wimbledon in 1977?
9. How was jazz musician William Basie better known?
10. Which admiral led Britain to victory in the Battle of Trafalgar?
11. Which Australian novelist wrote *Schindler's Ark*?
12. Which South Wales town was formed by the amalgamation of Aberavon and Margam in 1921?
13. Which Scandinavian monarch founded the Oldenburg ruling dynasty of Denmark?
14. Which male singing voice is lower than tenor but higher than bass?
15. Who directed the films *Accident* and *The Servant*?
16. Which 'Hero of New Orleans' became president of the USA in 1829?
17. In Greek mythology, which daughter of Zeus and Demeter was abducted by Hades?
18. Which metal is represented by the symbol Ba?
19. What is the capital of the U.S. state of New Mexico?
20. Which Austrian-born composer wrote the symphonic poem *Pelleas und Melisande*?

ANSWERS: *1 Franz Kafka, 2 Nitrogen, 3 Richard Wagner, 4 Tokyo, 5 A fish, 6 Mark Antony, 7 Essex, 8 Virginia Wade, 9 Count Basie, 10 Nelson, 11 Thomas Keneally, 12 Port Talbot, 13 Christian I, 14 Baritone, 15 Joseph Losey, 16 Andrew Jackson, 17 Persephone, 18 Barium, 19 Santa Fe, 20 Arnold Schoenberg.*

Entertainment

Your rating: ● **0-5** **Buy a TV** ● **6-10** **Keep at it** ● **11-15** **Join a quiz team** ● **16-20** **Enter a quiz show**

1. Which U.S. TV series featured David Chokachi as Cody Madison?
2. Who had a U.K. hit in 1982 with *John Wayne is Big Leggy*?
3. Which *Soldier, Soldier* character was played in the TV drama series by Holly Aird?
4. Who played weather girl Suzanne Stone in the 1995 film *To Die For*?
5. Which TV funnyman was reinstalled as Rector of Dundee University in 1995?
6. *Almost Naked* was the title of a 1995 album by which 48-year-old singer?
7. Film versions of which Shakespeare play have been directed by Orson Welles in 1948, and Roman Polanski in 1972?
8. Which *Coronation Street* character was played by Jean Alexander?
9. Who had a U.K. top ten hit in 1970 with *Instant Karma*?
10. Which 1995 apocalyptic thriller starred Gene Hackman and Denzel Washington?
11. Which 'Fifth Beatle' was set to earn millions after featuring on eight tracks of 1995's *The Beatles Anthology*?
12. Which 1972 boat-disaster film starred Gene Hackman and Ernest Borgnine?
13. Which political TV drama series shared its name with a Pink Floyd album?
14. Which Irish female vocal group had a top ten hit in 1979 with *I'm in the Mood for Dancing*?
15. Who starred as a jewel thief in the 1995 film *French Kiss*?
16. Which former *Blue Peter* presenter could later be seen on *Disney Club*?
17. Who released a 1995 album called *Songs From Heathcliff*?
18. Who played Geraldine Granger in the sitcom *The Vicar of Dibley*?
19. Which 1995 gem of a film was penned by *Basic Instinct* writer Joe Esterhasz?
20. Which popular romantic drama series and its sequel starred Robson Green and Francesca Annis?

ANSWERS: *1 New Baywatch, 2 Haysi Fantayzee, 3 Nancy, 4 Nicole Kidman, 5 Stephen Fry, 6 Kiki Dee, 7 Macbeth, 8 Hilda Ogden, 9 John Lennon, 10 Crimson Tide, 11 Pete Best, 12 The Poseidon Adventure, 13 The Final Cut, 14 The Nolans, 15 Kevin Kline, 16 Yvette Fielding, 17 Cliff Richard, 18 Dawn French, 19 Jade, 20 Reckless.*

General Knowledge

Your rating: ● 0-5 Join a library ● 6-10 Keep at it ● 11-15 Join a quiz team ● 16-20 Join Mensa

1. Which comedian does Jim Carrey play in Milos Forman's film *Man on the Moon*?
2. What was the name of the plane that dropped the bomb on Hiroshima?
3. Which European country is known as Sverige in its native language?
4. Which poker hand consists of cards all in the same suit, irrespective of denomination?
5. Which prime minister introduced the three-day week?
6. Who became President of France in 1995?
7. Which Isle of Wight resort is the headquarters of the Royal Yacht Squadron?
8. Which football team's only F.A. Cup win was in 1988?
9. Which religion received its name at the 1529 Diet of Spires?
10. To which film was *Fierce Creatures* the sequel?
11. Which U.S. separatist movement was founded in 1966 by Huey Newton and Bobby Seale?
12. From which disease did tenor Jose Carreras recover to resume his career in 1988?
13. Which martial art's most popular form is called 'beautiful springtime'?
14. Which British athlete became a grandad at the age of 35?
15. The Augrabies Falls can be found in which country?
16. Which American TV show did Groucho Marx present?
17. What were the Tatars called due to the wealth they gained by plunder?
18. Which song from the 1966 film *A Man Could Get Killed* won a Golden Globe award?
19. Who wrote a series of books featuring the Walkers and the Blacketts?
20. Of which country is the Chelif the principal river?

ANSWERS: *1 Andy Kaufman, 2 Enola Gay, 3 Sweden, 4 A flush, 5 Edward Heath, 6 Jacques Chirac, 7 Cowes, 8 Wimbledon, 9 Protestantism, 10 A Fish Called Wanda, 11 Black Panther Party, 12 Leukemia, 13 Kung fu, 14 Linford Christie, 15 South Africa, 16 You Bet Your Life, 17 Golden Horde, 18 Strangers in the Night, 19 Arthur Ransome, 20 Algeria.*

General Knowledge

Your rating: ● **0-5** Join a library ● **6-10** Keep at it ● **11-15** Join a quiz team ● **16-20** Join Mensa

1. What did British inventor Trevor Bayliss develop in order to tackle communication problems in the Third World?
2. Which Italian astronomer upset the 17th century establishment by claiming that the Earth moved round the Sun?
3. The name of which chocolate-covered cream cake means 'lightning' in French?
4. Which Manchester United footballer married Spice Girl Victoria Adams in 1999?
5. Which clay used in pottery and medicine is also known as china clay?
6. What is a frog-bit?
7. Who was manager of England's football team from 1982-1990?
8. What sort of fruit is an orange pippin?
9. Which Royal couple became the Earl and Countess of Wessex in 1999?
10. At which pole would you find penguins?
11. The disease pellagra is caused by deficiency of which acid in the diet?
12. What is inflamed in a case of phlebitis?
13. Which Scottish economist wrote *An Enquiry into the Nature and Causes of the Wealth of Nations*?
14. Who won the men's singles title at the 1998 French Open tennis championship?
15. Which German poet and playwright wrote *Torquato Tasso* and *Faust*?
16. What is the most extensive glacier in Europe?
17. What is a score of three under par in golf called?
18. What nationality was Hubert Cecil Booth, inventor of the vacuum cleaner?
19. Who performed the first human heart transplant in 1967?
20. Who briefly played professional football at Scunthorpe United, before becoming an England international cricketer?

ANSWERS: *1 The clockwork radio, 2 Galileo Galilei, 3 Eclair, 4 David Beckham, 5 Kaolin, 6 A water plant, 7 Bobby Robson, 8 Apple, 9 Prince Edward & Sophie Rhys-Jones, 10 The south pole, 11 Nicotinic acid, 12 A vein, 13 Adam Smith, 14 Carlos Moyà, 15 Johann Wolfgang von Goethe, 16 Aletsch glacier, 17 An albatross, 18 British, 19 Christiaan Barnard, 20 Ian Botham.*

General Knowledge

Your rating:
- 0-5 Join a library
- 6-10 Keep at it
- 11-15 Join a quiz team
- 16-20 Join Mensa

1. Which common eye condition is also called strabismus?
2. What is the largest draught horse in the world, descended from the English warhorse?
3. In which century did America's Declaration of Independence take place?
4. Of which Asian country is Hanoi the capital?
5. Which Scottish chemist and inventor had a waterproof garment named after him?
6. What does the abbreviation GMT stand for?
7. What is the world's fastest mammal?
8. Against which country did England fight the Battle of Agincourt?
9. What are the two most important ingredients of a Bloody Mary?
10. Which defensive structure in eastern Asia, built around 210 B.C., stretches from the Jiayuguan Pass to Shanhaiguan on the Yellow Sea?
11. Which carbohydrate found in fruit is an essential ingredient for the gelling of jam?
12. What is the third book of the Old Testament?
13. Which well-preserved Inca town in Peru was discovered in 1911?
14. Who designed the beige suits worn by England's 1998 World Cup squad?
15. Which Hampshire town is the chief garrison town and army training centre in the U.K.?
16. Who wrote the *St Louis Blues*?
17. Which popular cricket commentator died in January 1994?
18. Which British poet wrote the epic work *Don Juan*?
19. The young of a rabbit can be known as a kitten - true or false?
20. How are the vegetables "neeps and tatties" otherwise known?

ANSWERS: *1 Squint, 2 Shire horse, 3 The 18th century, 4 Vietnam, 5 Charles Macintosh, 6 Greenwich Mean Time, 7 Cheetah, 8 France, 9 Vodka and tomato juice, 10 The Great Wall of China, 11 Pectin, 12 Leviticus, 13 Machu Picchu, 14 Paul Smith, 15 Aldershot, 16 W C Handy, 17 Brian Johnston, 18 Lord Byron, 19 True, 20 Turnips and potatoes.*

Sports

Your rating: ● **0-5** **Wooden spoon** ● **6-10** **Bronze medal** ● **11-15** **Silver medal** ● **16-20** **Gold medal**

1. What was the score by which the England rugby union team suffered their record defeat against Australia in June 1998?
2. Which nation won the 1938 football World Cup?
3. Which rugby union club play their home matches at Welford Road?
4. Which Olympic title did Marie-Jose Perec successfully defend in 1996?
5. In which year did Damon Hill win the Formula 1 World Motor Racing Championship?
6. Where were the 16th Commonwealth Games held in 1998?
7. Which English club did Nayim famously score against for Real Zaragoza in the 1995 Cup Winners' Cup final?
8. Who beat Perrie Mans in 1978 to win a sixth World Snooker Championship?
9. In which sport might one find a gridiron?
10. What is the name of Blackburn Rovers' stadium?
11. Which British boxer beat Tom Johnson to win the IBF featherweight title in February 1997?
12. Which British athlete won gold in the women's javelin at the 1990 Commonwealth Games?
13. Who won the men's singles title at the 1998 French Open tennis championship?
14. In which year did Nick Faldo win the British Open for the second time?
15. Who replaced Alec Stewart as England's cricket captain in 1999?
16. Which English football team beat Roma to win the 1984 European Cup final?
17. How many Olympic speed skating gold medals did Eric Heiden win in 1980?
18. How many times did David Sole captain Scotland's rugby union side between 1989 and 1992?
19. Which club did Terry Venables manage to European Cup success in 1986?
20. In which year did sprinter Florence Griffith Joyner win three Olympic gold medals?

ANSWERS: *1 76-0, 2 Italy, 3 Leicester, 4 400m, 5 1996, 6 Kuala Lumpur, Malaysia, 7 Arsenal, 8 Ray Reardon, 9 American football, 10 Ewood Park, 11 Prince Naseem Hamed, 12 Tessa Sanderson, 13 Carlos Moyá, 14 1990, 15 Nasser Hussain, 16 Liverpool, 17 Five, 18 25, 19 Barcelona, 20 1988.*

General Knowledge

Your rating:
- 0-5 Join a library
- 6-10 Keep at it
- 11-15 Join a quiz team
- 16-20 Join Mensa

1. What nationality was the poet and dramatist W. B. Yeats?
2. In which European country is the resort of Locarno?
3. Who presented more budgets than any other chancellor in British history?
4. In which U.S. national park can the geyser known as Old Faithful be found?
5. Which Imperial unit of length was redefined in 1963 as 0.9144 metre?
6. What sort of creature is a chow-chow?
7. Kiev is the capital of which former Soviet republic?
8. What is an ugli?
9. How is the Oxford Committee for Famine Relief better known?
10. Where is the Sistine Chapel?
11. Which Nazi politician was ambassador to the U.K. from 1936 to 1938?
12. Which spacecraft sent a probe into Jupiter's atmosphere in 1995?
13. Who co-wrote with Jean Cocteau the ballet *Le Boeuf sur le toit*?
14. Which Essex town was known as Camulodunum to the Romans?
15. What sort of creature is a lory?
16. What is the capital of Trinidad and Tobago?
17. Which Polish composer of French descent lived with the novelist George Sand from 1838 to 1847?
18. What is the longest river in the Republic of Ireland?
19. How is polymethyl methacrylate better known?
20. Which association of insurance underwriters was named after a 17th-century London coffee house?

ANSWERS: *1 Irish, 2 Switzerland, 3 Denis Healey, 4 Yellowstone National Park, 5 Yard, 6 A dog, 7 Ukraine, 8 A fruit, 9 OXFAM, 10 The Vatican, Rome, 11 Joachim von Ribbentrop, 12 Galileo, 13 Darius Milhaud, 14 Colchester, 15 A parrot, 16 Port-of-Spain, 17 Chopin, 18 The River Shannon, 19 Perspex, 20 Lloyd's.*

General Knowledge

Your rating:
- 0-5 Join a library
- 6-10 Keep at it
- 11-15 Join a quiz team
- 16-20 Join Mensa

1. What is measured in amperes?
2. What is the highest mountain in the French Alps?
3. Which socialist became president of France in 1981?
4. The career of newspaper proprietor William Randolph Hearst inspired which Orson Welles film?
5. Which German composer wrote the Brandenburg Concertos?
6. In which country can the Yangtse river be found?
7. In which country was the Rum Rebellion of 1808?
8. Who wrote the play *Twelfth Night*?
9. Which New Testament martyr has his feast day on Boxing Day?
10. Which city has been the capital of India since 1912?
11. Which British dramatist wrote *Epsom Wells* and *The Virtuoso*?
12. Who directed *Some Like It Hot*?
13. Who became NATO Secretary General in 1995?
14. What is the Scottish site of the world's first experimental fast-breeder reactor?
15. What was the Pharos of Alexandria?
16. Who was Queen of England for less than two weeks in 1553?
17. Who was prime minister of India from 1977 to 1979?
18. What sort of creature is a dourocouli?
19. Which British novelist wrote *Whisky Galore*?
20. Which Hungarian monarch granted the Golden Bull of 1222?

ANSWERS: *1 Electric current, 2 Mont Blanc, 3 François Mitterrand, 4 Citizen Kane, 5 Johann Sebastian Bach, 6 China, 7 Australia, 8 William Shakespeare, 9 St Stephen, 10 New Delhi, 11 Thomas Shadwell, 12 Billy Wilder, 13 Javier Solana, 14 Dounreay, 15 A lighthouse, 16 Lady Jane Grey, 17 Morarji Desai, 18 A monkey, 19 Sir Compton Mackenzie, 20 Andrew II.*

General Knowledge

Your rating: ● 0-5 Join a library ● 6-10 Keep at it ● 11-15 Join a quiz team ● 16-20 Join Mensa

1. In which Yorkshire city did the Jorvik Viking Centre open in 1984?
2. In which state of the USA is Yale University?
3. In traditional Chinese cosmology, which principle contrasts with and complements Yin?
4. Wilfred Owen is famous for his poems written during which war?
5. What sort of creature is a linnet?
6. In backgammon, how many pieces does each player begin the game with?
7. What gifts did the Magi bring?
8. What nationality was surrealist painter René Magritte?
9. Which county is often referred to as the Garden of England?
10. If a lion has a mane, is it male or female?
11. At which battle did Robert Clive defeat the Nawab of Bengal?
12. Which market town in SE England is the seat of the Dukes of Norfolk?
13. According to Greek legend, where was the Minotaur kept?
14. Which 1938 agreement was described by Chamberlain as achieving "peace in our time"?
15. What is the capital of the Philippines?
16. Who was Australia's first prime minister?
17. Which Indian novelist wrote *The Man-Eater of Malgudi*?
18. Which German town was the home and burial place of Richard Wagner?
19. What relation was Napoleon III to Napoleon I?
20. Which British artist painted the *Blue Boy* and *Harvest Wagon*?

ANSWERS: *1 York, 2 Connecticut, 3 Yang, 4 World War I, 5 A bird, 6 Fifteen, 7 Gold, frankincense and myrrh, 8 Belgian, 9 Kent, 10 Male, 11 Battle of Plassey, 12 Arundel, 13 The Labyrinth in Crete, 14 Munich Agreement, 15 Manila, 16 Sir Edmund Barton, 17 R. K. Narayan, 18 Bayreuth, 19 Nephew, 20 Thomas Gainsborough.*

Entertainment

Your rating: ● **0-5** **Buy a TV** ● **6-10** **Keep at it** ● **11-15** **Join a quiz team** ● **16-20** **Enter a quiz show**

1. Which co-creator of TV's *Seinfeld* directed the 1998 film *Sour Grapes*?
2. What do Anthea Turner, Caron Keating and Sarah Greene have in common?
3. Who played *Superman*'s father in the 1978 film?
4. Which character in the Australian soap *Neighbours* was played by Eliza Szonert?
5. Which folk star released an album in 1995 called *Sand in Your Shoes*?
6. Which 1995 film starred Alicia Silverstone as Beverly Hills rich kid Cher Horowitz?
7. Madonna, Bono and Neneh Cherry paid tribute to which soul legend on the 1995 album *Inner City Blues*?
8. Which British actor starred as a San Francisco child psychiatrist in the 1995 film *Nine Months*?
9. Who had a U.K. top twenty hit in 1981 with *Once in a Lifetime*?
10. Which Hollywood heart-throb starred in and produced the 1987 film *Ishtar*?
11. *Axis Mutatis* was a 1995 album by which band?
12. Which Channel 4 money programme was presented by Shami Ahmed, founder of the Joe Bloggs clothing range?
13. Who had a U.K. top ten hit in 1980 with *One Day I'll Fly Away*?
14. Which 1995 film starring Christopher Lambert got its title from a violent computer game?
15. *Different Class* was a 1995 album from which Sheffield band?
16. Which late actor played the young Indiana Jones in the 1989 film *Indiana Jones and the Last Crusade*?
17. Who originally presented Channel 4's *The Real Holiday Show*?
18. *Raoul and the Kings of Spain* was a 1995 album by which British band?
19. Which soap opera celebrated its 35th birthday in 1995 by being featured on TV's *The South Bank Show*?
20. Who played Irene in the 1929 film *The Kiss*?

ANSWERS: 1 Larry David, 2 They've all presented Blue Peter, 3 Marlon Brando, 4 Danni Stark, 5 Ralph McTell, 6 Clueless, 7 Marvin Gaye, 8 Hugh Grant, 9 Talking Heads, 10 Warren Beatty, 11 The Shamen, 12 Dosh, 13 Randy Crawford, 14 Mortal Kombat, 15 Pulp, 16 River Phoenix, 17 Gaby Roslin, 18 Tears For Fears, 19 Coronation Street, 20 Greta Garbo.

General Knowledge

Your rating: ● 0-5 Join a library ● 6-10 Keep at it ● 11-15 Join a quiz team ● 16-20 Join Mensa

1. Which Canadian sprinter was stripped of his Olympic gold medal in 1988 for taking anabolic steroids?
2. What is an angle of between 0 and 90 degrees called?
3. Which Formula 1 racing circuit is situated near Towcester, Northamptonshire?
4. How many holes are there in a Tenpin bowling ball?
5. Which British actor starred in *Who Framed Roger Rabbit* and *Mona Lisa*?
6. What was the stage name of Thomas Terry Hoar-Stevens?
7. Which all-girl group had their second Number One hit single with *Say You'll Be There*?
8. Who played lawyer Archie Leach in *A Fish called Wanda*?
9. Laudanum is an alcoholic solution of which drug?
10. Which German composer wrote the *Mass in D Missa Solemnis*?
11. What did bricklayer Joseph Aspdin create and patent in 1824?
12. Which American baseball player was nicknamed The Georgia Peach?
13. To which Archbishop of Canterbury was Terry Waite religious adviser?
14. What is the name of Woody Allen's character in *Annie Hall*?
15. Which country's parliament is called the States General?
16. In which country is Lake Saimaa?
17. Which Bohemian-born general commanded the imperial forces in the Thirty Years' War?
18. For which vitamin is cyanocobalamin the chemical name?
19. Which U.S. golfer won the British Open in 1995?
20. How many months were there in the French Revolutionary Calendar?

ANSWERS: *1 Ben Johnson, 2 Acute, 3 Silverstone, 4 Three, 5 Bob Hoskins, 6 Terry-Thomas, 7 The Spice Girls, 8 John Cleese, 9 Opium, 10 Ludwig van Beethoven, 11 Portland cement, 12 Ty Cobb, 13 Robert Runcie, 14 Alvy Singer, 15 The Netherlands, 16 Finland, 17 Albrecht von Wallenstein, 18 B12, 19 John Daly, 20 Thirteen.*

General Knowledge

Your rating:
- **0-5 Join a library**
- **6-10 Keep at it**
- **11-15 Join a quiz team**
- **16-20 Join Mensa**

1. Which Pakistan cricketer married Jemima Goldsmith in 1995?
2. Which member of the Beatles was married to Yoko Ono?
3. How many pieces does a player have at the start of a game of chess?
4. Which radio and TV star lost his fight against AIDS in April 1995?
5. On which continent would you find the rare dwarf crocodile?
6. Which football team is nicknamed The Owls?
7. Female followers of which religion take the last name Kaur?
8. In which sport did Denmark's team win the World Championships 1983-88?
9. Which George Michael album was Album of the Year at the 1988 Grammies?
10. For which football team did Ian Botham play?
11. Which word for a social upstart comes from the French for 'arrived'?
12. Whose *A Modest Proposal* of 1729 suggested that children of the poor should be eaten?
13. In geology, for what is the darcy a unit?
14. Of which country did Carlo Azeglio Ciampi become president in 1999?
15. What part of the body is abnormally curved in scoliosis?
16. Which Labour baroness was responsible for founding the Open University?
17. Of which metal is cinnabar the only important ore?
18. At which racecourse is the Queen Elizabeth Stakes run?
19. Annual jumping competitions for which amphibians are held in Calaveras, California?
20. What is the maximum length of a baseball bat?

ANSWERS: *1 Imran Khan, 2 John Lennon, 3 Sixteen, 4 Kenny Everett, 5 Africa, 6 Sheffield Wednesday, 7 Sikhism, 8 Speedway, 9 Faith, 10 Scunthorpe United, 11 Parvenu, 12 Jonathan Swift, 13 Permeability, 14 Italy, 15 The spine, 16 Jennie Lee, 17 Mercury, 18 Ascot, 19 Bullfrogs, 20 107 centimetres.*

General Knowledge

Your rating:
- 0-5 Join a library
- 6-10 Keep at it
- 11-15 Join a quiz team
- 16-20 Join Mensa

1. Which U.S. president immortalised the phrase 'if you can't stand the heat, get out of the kitchen'?
2. What do the initials H.R.T. stand for?
3. Which TV personality was born Caterina Irene Elena Maria Imperiali del Principi di Francavilla?
4. What do the initials D.P.P. stand for?
5. Which Islamic fundamentalist group controls most of Afghanistan?
6. Who recorded the albums *Blue* and *Court and Spark*?
7. Which sport is played by Columbus Crew, Dallas Burn and Chicago Fire?
8. What does a.s.a.p. stand for?
9. Which style of riding breeches is named after an Indian city?
10. By what name are the reflective studs used for marking traffic lanes invented by Percy Shaw known?
11. Which 1982 film is based on the true story of Charles Horman's disappearance in Chile?
12. From which country does golfer Se Ri Pak come?
13. Which public school was founded by Kurt Halin in 1935?
14. Which singer won Record of the Year for *Kiss From a Rose* at the 1995 Grammies?
15. What is the trade name of the heat-resistant plastic P.T.F.E.?
16. Which vegetable is commonly known as rutabaga in North America?
17. How many Federal Reserve Districts are there in the USA?
18. Who wrote the science-fiction novel *Neuromancer* in 1984?
19. What was the world's first public railway?
20. Of which country was Boris Trajkovski elected president in 1999?

ANSWERS: *1 Harry S Truman, 2 Hormone replacement therapy, 3 Katie Boyle, 4 Director of Public Prosecutions, 5 The Taliban, 6 Joni Mitchell, 7 Soccer, 8 As soon as possible, 9 Jodhpurs, 10 Cat's-eyes, 11 Missing, 12 South Korea, 13 Gordonstoun, 14 Seal, 15 Teflon, 16 Swede, 17 Twelve, 18 William Gibson, 19 Stockton and Darlington Railway, 20 Former Yugoslav Republic of Macedonia.*

Entertainment

Your rating: ● **0-5 Buy a TV** ● **6-10 Keep at it** ● **11-15 Join a quiz team** ● **16-20 Enter a quiz show**

1. The 1994 film *A Simple Twist of Fate* featured which *Roxanne* star?
2. Children's TV presenters Billy and Johnny were creations of which TV comedy duo?
3. Which U.S. vocalist released an album entitled *Daydream* in 1995?
4. Which James Bond film starred Steven Berkoff as Russian General Orlov?
5. Which *Absolutely Fabulous* actress played Lydia Bennet in the popular BBC adaptation of Jane Austen's *Pride and Prejudice*?
6. Peter Gabriel, Sting and Elton John interpreted the songs of which sombre folk singer on the 1995 album *Tower of Song*?
7. Who played Diana Trent in the TV sitcom *Waiting for God*?
8. Which 1995 film starred Sandra Bullock as a computer nerd?
9. Which *Soldier, Soldier* character was played in the TV drama series by Sophie Heathcote?
10. Which U.S. chat show presenter starred as Divine's daughter in the 1988 John Waters film *Hairspray*?
11. Les Patterson was a comic creation of which Australian entertainer?
12. Which former Miami Sound Machine frontperson released an album in 1995 entitled *Abriendo Puertas*?
13. Who starred as *The Swimmer* in the 1968 film of the same name?
14. Who played Julie Diadoni in the TV drama *Jake's Progress*?
15. Which group had a U.K top ten hit in 1974 with *Seven Seas of Rhye*?
16. Which country was the main setting for the 1995 film *Cold Fever*?
17. *All You Can Eat* was a 1995 album release by which alternative country star?
18. Who wrote and directed the 1967 film *What's Up, Tiger Lily?*?
19. What was the title of Simply Red's 1995 album release?
20. Who starred as *Zorba the Greek* in the 1964 film?

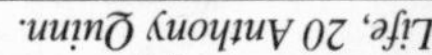

ANSWERS: *1 Steve Martin, 2 Hale and Pace, 3 Mariah Carey, 4 Octopussy, 5 Julia Sawalha, 6 Leonard Cohen, 7 Stephanie Cole, 8 The Net, 9 Tara Jenkins, 10 Ricki Lake, 11 Barry Humphries, 12 Gloria Estefan, 13 Burt Lancaster, 14 Julie Walters, 15 Queen, 16 Iceland, 17 k. d. lang, 18 Woody Allen, 19 Life, 20 Anthony Quinn.*

General Knowledge

Your rating:
- **0-5 Join a library**
- **6-10 Keep at it**
- **11-15 Join a quiz team**
- **16-20 Join Mensa**

1. Which singer played Billie Holiday in the film *Lady Sings the Blues?*
2. What name is given to the belief that violence, including war, is unjustifiable under any circumstances?
3. Which British award for bravery was instituted in 1940, and named after the king at the time?
4. Who was elected Mayor of London in 2000?
5. Which bird has carrion and hooded varieties?
6. What is the chief language of Brazil?
7. Which new-wave rock group was formed in 1975 by singer David Byrne?
8. Of which former Soviet republic is Riga the capital?
9. Which animal has Persian, Siamese and Abyssinian breeds?
10. In Greek mythology, who was the ferryman who carried the souls of the dead?
11. Which ethnic Albanian group is known by the letters K.L.A.?
12. What were the first names of U.S. poet e. e. cummings?
13. For which 1945 film did Angela Lansbury win a Golden Globe award?
14. Which American comedienne and actress was born Caryn Johnson?
15. What is the oldest writing system of which records survive?
16. Which Austrian monk discovered the fundamental principles of genetics?
17. Of which country was Jamil Mahuad elected president in 1998?
18. Which ice hockey team won their first Stanley Cup in 1999?
19. Of which fruit is the cayenne a smoother-skinned variety?
20. Which study of selective breeding is named after the Greek for 'well-born'?

ANSWERS: *1 Diana Ross, 2 Pacifism, 3 The George Cross, 4 Ken Livingstone, 5 Crow, 6 Portuguese, 7 Talking Heads, 8 Latvia, 9 Cat, 10 Charon, 11 Kosovo Liberation Army, 12 Edward Estlin, 13 The Picture of Dorian Gray, 14 Whoopi Goldberg, 15 Cuneiform, 16 Gregor Mendel, 17 Ecuador, 18 Dallas Stars, 19 Pineapple, 20 Eugenics.*

General Knowledge

Your rating: ● 0-5 Join a library ● 6-10 Keep at it ● 11-15 Join a quiz team ● 16-20 Join Mensa

1. Which heavenly beings get their name from the Greek for messengers?
2. In Scottish law, which verdict other than not guilty can accompany an acquittal?
3. Which Manchester United player was named the 2000 Footballer of the Year and P.F.A. Player of the Year?
4. What name is given to creatures such as crabs, shrimps and woodlice?
5. Who recorded the albums *Innervisions* and *Talking Book*?
6. Which Pokémon evolves into Raichu?
7. Which human bone extends from the shoulder to the elbow?
8. Of which French Mediterranean island is Ajaccio the capital?
9. What sort of creature is a pug?
10. In which country was a Scottish court established in 2000 to try the suspects of the Lockerbie bombing?
11. Who scored England's winning drop goal to knock Australia out of the 1995 Rugby World Cup?
12. Which comedian played Hecky Brown in the film *The Front*?
13. What is the largest island in the Netherlands Antilles?
14. Who is the director of the 2000 epic film *Gladiator*?
15. In which continent are pottos found?
16. Which British novelist wrote *The Needle's Eye* and *The Radiant Way*?
17. For which film did George Burns win a Best Supporting Actor Oscar in 1975?
18. Which king married Princess Charlotte Sophia of Mecklenburg-Strelitz?
19. Of what is limnology the study?
20. Who were the top selling British all-girl group of the 1980s?

ANSWERS: *1 Angels, 2 Not proven, 3 Roy Keane, 4 Crustaceans, 5 Stevie Wonder, 6 Pikachu, 7 Cubit, 8 Corsica, 9 A dog, 10 The Netherlands, 11 Rob Andrew, 12 Zero Mostel, 13 Curaçao, 14 Ridley Scott, 15 Africa, 16 Margaret Drabble, 17 The Sunshine Boys, 18 George III, 19 Lakes, 20 Bananarama.*

General Knowledge

Your rating: ● 0-5 Join a library ● 6-10 Keep at it ● 11-15 Join a quiz team ● 16-20 Join Mensa

1. Which Walt Disney film featured animations fitted to pieces of classical music?
2. What is the traditional London address of the Chancellor of the Exchequer?
3. Which comedian has been made Worshipful Master of one of Britain's top Masonic lodges?
4. For which county did Geoffrey Boycott play cricket?
5. Which 1973 film is based on the life of French prisoner Henri Charriere?
6. With whose comic operas is Richard D'Oyly Carte associated?
7. Which diamond is named after the Persian for 'mountain of light'?
8. What was the language of ancient Rome?
9. Which part of the body is inflamed in a case of gingivitis?
10. Of which country did Fidel Castro become prime minister in 1959?
11. Which radical 1960s movement was founded by Abbie Hoffman and Jerry Rubin?
12. Which resinous substance is used by South American Indians as arrow poison?
13. What name is given to the French-speaking inhabitants of Louisiana?
14. Which P&O cruise ship broke down 18 hours into its maiden voyage in 2000?
15. On which game was Ely Culbertson an authority?
16. Which novelist wrote *The Death of the Heart* and *The Heat of the Day*?
17. On which islands was Lord Wilson of Rievaulx buried?
18. Which British actor provided the voice of Scar in Disney's *The Lion King*?
19. With which crime was Townsend Thoresen Ltd the first to be charged in Britain?
20. For which film did Peter Ustinov win a Best Supporting Actor Oscar in 1964?

ANSWERS: *1 Fantasia, 2 No 11 Downing Street, 3 Jim Davidson, 4 Yorkshire, 5 Papillon, 6 Gilbert and Sullivan, 7 Koh-I-noor, 8 Latin, 9 The gums, 10 Cuba, 11 The Youth Party International, or Yippies, 12 Curare, 13 Cajuns, 14 The Aurora, 15 Bridge, 16 Elizabeth Bowen, 17 Isles of Scilly, 18 Jeremy Irons, 19 Corporate manslaughter, 20 Topkapi.*

Entertainment

Your rating: ● **0-5 Buy a TV** ● **6-10 Keep at it** ● **11-15 Join a quiz team** ● **16-20 Enter a quiz show**

1. Who directed and starred in the 1995 film *The Bridges of Madison County*?
2. Which former *Newsround* newsreader co-presented *999 - Lifesavers* with Michael Buerk?
3. *World* was a 1995 album by which Peter Cunnah-fronted pop band?
4. Which *Only Fools and Horses* character was played on TV by Buster Merryfield?
5. In which city was the rock band Chicago formed?
6. Which *This is Your Life* host also presented the TV series *Strange But True*?
7. Which 1995 film starred Hugh O'Conor as Neasden poisoner Graham Young?
8. Who sang lead vocals on the version of *Come Together* found on the War Child charity album *Help*?
9. Who played Johnny in the 1985 film *My Beautiful Laundrette*?
10. Which long-running BBC children's programme is co-presented by Katy Hill?
11. Sonya Aurora Madan is lead singer with which band?
12. In which English county was the 1995 surfing movie *Blue Juice* set?
13. Which *Coronation Street* character is played by Elizabeth Bradley?
14. Which British pianist, comedian and actor starred in the 1984 film farce *Micki + Maude*?
15. Which *EastEnders* character was played by Caroline Paterson?
16. Which 1980s pop star was causing a 'commotion' with his 1995 album, *Lovestory*?
17. What was the title of the 1995 film from *Boyz N the Hood* writer/director John Singleton?
18. Who provided the voice for the baby in the series *How to Be a Little S*d*?
19. Who had a U.K. top ten hit in 1980 with *My Perfect Cousin*?
20. Who played Nina in the 1990 film *Truly, Madly, Deeply*?

ANSWERS: *1 Clint Eastwood, 2 Juliet Morris, 3 D:REAM, 4 Uncle Albert, 5 Chicago, 6 Michael Aspel, 7 The Young Poisoner's Handbook, 8 Paul Weller, 9 Daniel Day Lewis, 10 Blue Peter, 11 Echobelly, 12 Cornwall, 13 Maud Grimes, 14 Dudley Moore, 15 Ruth Fowler, 16 Lloyd Cole, 17 Higher Learning, 18 Rik Mayall, 19 The Undertones, 20 Juliet Stevenson.*

General Knowledge

Your rating: ● 0-5 Join a library ● 6-10 Keep at it ● 11-15 Join a quiz team ● 16-20 Join Mensa

1. Which liquid has the chemical formula H2O?
2 What is Bedloe's Island in New York harbour also known as?
3. In which century did U.S. sculptor Hiram Powers live?
4. Which British singer and songwriter won an Oscar for Best Original Song in 2000?
5. What do the letters D.C. stand for in Washington, D.C.?
6. Which Scottish missionary and explorer was joined by Sir Henry Morton Stanley while trying to find the source of the Nile?
7. What are the organs of locomotion and balance in fishes?
8. Which American novelist created the detective Philip Marlowe?
9. In golf what is a number one wood called?
10. In which European country is the River Marne?
11. Which British landscape artist painted *Rain, Steam and Speed*?
12. What name is given to radioactive particles deposited from the atmosphere after a nuclear explosion?
13. In horticulture, what name is given to the propagation method in which part of one plant is transferred to another?
14. What name is given to the official liturgical plainchant of the Roman Catholic Church codified under the papacy of Gregory I?
15. The commercial centre of which city in Illinois is called 'The Loop'?
16. How many Formula 1 Grands Prix did Jackie Stewart win?
17. What was the name of the street in *Little Shop Of Horrors*?
18. Of which British island is Tristan da Cunha a dependency?
19. Who wrote the thriller novel *Drink with the Devil*?
20. Which U.S. film actress was the highest paid in 1935?

ANSWERS: *1 Water, 2 Liberty Island, 3 19th, 4 Phil Collins, 5 District of Columbia, 6 David Livingstone, 7 Fins, 8 Raymond Chandler, 9 Driver, 10 France, 11 J.M.W. Turner, 12 Fallout, 13 Grafting, 14 Gregorian Chant, 15 Chicago, 16 27, 17 Skid Row, 18 St Helena, 19 Jack Higgins, 20 Mae West.*

General Knowledge

Your rating: ● 0-5 Join a library ● 6-10 Keep at it ● 11-15 Join a quiz team ● 16-20 Join Mensa

1. What is the name of the enclosed space in a law court where the accused sits?
2. Of which country was Bob Hawke prime minister?
3. Which English author wrote the novel *Adam Bede*?
4. What name was given to the practice of sending convicted criminals to the colonies as a punishment?
5. Which minister is responsible for presenting budgets?
6. With what sort of music are Woody Guthrie and Joan Baez associated?
7. Which hit American TV series did Michael Crichton, author of *Jurassic Park*, write?
8. Which leading flat jockey was imprisoned for tax evasion in 1987?
9. What is France's principal seaport?
10. Which country did Britain fight in the Opium War of 1839-42?
11. Which large aquatic bird has a pouch underneath its long bill in which it stores fish?
12. What is the highest adult male singing voice, also known as countertenor?
13. Which perennial plant is also known as a belladonna lily?
14. Which Spanish team knocked Manchester United out of the Champions' League in April 2000?
15. Who provided the voice for Buzz Lightyear in both *Toy Story* and its sequel?
16. Which British politician co-founded the Anti-Corn Law League with John Bright?
17. The author of the Booker Prize-winning novel *The Sea, the Sea* died in 1999. Who was she?
18. On which river is the Indian city of Agra?
19. Which flower is also called fleur-de-lys
20. How much was Steve McQueen paid, in dollars, for the film *Bullitt*?

ANSWERS: 1 Dock, 2 Australia, 3 George Eliot, 4 Transportation, 5 Chancellor of the Exchequer, 6 Folk, 7 E.R., 8 Lester Piggott, 9 Marseilles, 10 China, 11 Puffin, 12 Alto, 13 Amaryllis, 14 Real Madrid, 15 Tim Allen, 16 Richard Cobden, 17 Dame Iris Murdoch, 18 Jumna, 19 Iris, 20 $1m.

General Knowledge

Your rating: ● 0-5 Join a library ● 6-10 Keep at it ● 11-15 Join a quiz team ● 16-20 Join Mensa

1. Which voluntary organisation was set up in 1934 to help people with drink problems?
2. Who is the creator of *Star Wars*?
3. Which British author wrote *The History of Mr Polly*?
4. By what abbreviation is polyvinyl chloride better known?
5. Which river enters the Irish Sea via Liverpool and Birkenhead?
6. What term for excellent cookery is derived from a blue ribbon worn by members of a French order of knighthood?
7. Which American actress made her West End debut as Mrs Robinson in *The Graduate*?
8. Of which British city was Joseph Chamberlain mayor?
9. What was the name of Stephen Tompkinson's character in Channel 4's *Drop the Dead Donkey*?
10. Which fruit is obtained from the plant *Ribes nigrum*?
11. Which English physicist wrote *A Brief History of Time*?
12. Of which ocean is the Coral Sea a section?
13. Which Turkish team knocked Leeds United out of the UEFA Cup in April 2000?
14. Who wrote the controversial novel *American Psycho*?
15. How many people constitute a triumvirate?
16. Which soap star made her film debut in *The Delinquents*?
17. On which gulf is the Italian seaport of Amalfi?
18. Behind what type of shop were the Manhattan headquarters of the spy organisation in TV's *The Man From UNCLE*?
19. What is eisell?
20. Whose novels include *Jack Maggs* and *Illywhacker*?

***ANSWERS:** 1 Alcoholics Anonymous, 2 George Lucas, 3 H G Wells, 4 PVC, 5 River Mersey, 6 Cordon Bleu, 7 Kathleen Turner, 8 Birmingham, 9 Damien Day, 10 Blackcurrant, 11 Stephen Hawking, 12 The Pacific, 13 Galatasaray, 14 Bret Easton Ellis, 15 Three, 16 Kylie Minogue, 17 Gulf of Salerno, 18 Del Floria's tailor shop, 19 Wormwood wine, 20 Peter Carey.*

Entertainment

Your rating: ● 0-5 Buy a TV ● 6-10 Keep at it
● 11-15 Join a quiz team ● 16-20 Enter a quiz show

1. Which comedy series set in a solicitor's office starred Imelda Staunton and Patrick Barlow?
2. *Southpaw Grammar* was a 1995 album by which former Smiths member?
3. Which 1992 Joel Hershman comedy starred Sean Young and Diane Ladd?
4. Which comedian played timeshare salesman Simon Treat in the TV series *One for the Road*?
5. *The Great Escape* was a 1995 album release by which British band?
6. Who played the title role in the 1989 film *Uncle Buck*?
7. Which U.S. comedy series starred Burt Reynolds as a retired American footballer?
8. Keenan Ivory Wayans wrote, directed and starred in which 1994 comedy film about a falsely disgraced cop?
9. Tony Slattery broke the head off a £1,000 antique figurine during the 1990s relaunch of which TV quiz show?
10. Which punk band released an album in 1995 entitled *Soapy Water & Mr Marmalade*?
11. Which 1987 Coen brothers' film starred Nicolas Cage and Holly Hunter as a couple who steal a baby?
12. Which rigorous mental and physical game show was formerly presented by Gordon Burns and Penny Smith?
13. Which jazz band had a U.K. top ten hit in 1961 with *Take Five*?
14. Which actor played Joey Tribbiani in the U.S. sitcom *Friends*?
15. Who directed and starred in the 1995 film *Braveheart*?
16. Which Beach Boy released a 1995 album called *I Just Wasn't Made For These Times*?
17. Which actress starred in the title role of the 1992 film *Orlando*?
18. Which 'middle-class' soap opera was axed by the BBC in 1995 after only 24 episodes?
19. Which former Teardrop Explodes star released an album called *20 Mothers* in 1995?
20. Which interviewer could be seen *Face to Face* on TV?

ANSWERS: *1 Is It Legal, 2 Morrissey, 3 Hold Me, Thrill Me, Kiss Me, 4 Alan Davies, 5 Blur, 6 John Candy, 7 Evening Shade , 8 A Low Down Dirty Shame, 9 Going for a Song, 10 Sham 69, 11 Raising Arizona, 12 The Krypton Factor, 13 Dave Brubeck Quartet, 14 Matt LeBlanc, 15 Mel Gibson, 16 Brian Wilson, 17 Tilda Swinton, 18 Castles, 19 Julian Cope, 20 Jeremy Isaacs.*

General Knowledge

Your rating: ● 0-5 Join a library ● 6-10 Keep at it ● 11-15 Join a quiz team ● 16-20 Join Mensa

1. What is mazuma a slang word for?
2. Which ex-*EastEnder* went on to star as a telephone exchange operator and in *Lucy Sullivan is Getting Married*?
3. Which charity is represented by the initials N.S.P.C.C.?
4. What colour is the dye cochineal?
5. Which French town associated with Saint Bernadette is an important pilgrimage centre for Roman Catholics?
6. What name is given to the fruit of the blackthorn, used to flavour a type of gin?
7. Of which salad plant are cos and iceberg varieties?
8. Which fictional diarist is played by Texan actress Renee Zellwegger in a film adaptation?
9. In what year will Britain stage the I.A.A.F. World Athletics Championships?
10. Which inland sea is bordered by Bulgaria, Romania, Turkey and parts of the former Soviet Union?
11. Of which element is tritium a radioactive isotope?
12. Who won an Oscar in 1982 for *Sophie's Choice*?
13. Which musical instrument was invented by John Philip Sousa?
14. What is the capital of Azerbaijan?
15. Which Dutch footballer's proposed record-breaking transfer to Manchester United fell through after a medical?
16. According to the book of Daniel in the Bible, at whose feast did the guests see the Writing on the Wall?
17. Which instrument used in aircraft measures height above sea level?
18. In which county of the Republic of Ireland is the Twelve Pins mountain range?
19. Which Spanish Cubist painter's father was an art teacher?
20. Whose thriller books include *Executive Orders*?

ANSWERS: *1 Money, 2 Letitia Dean, 3 National Society for the Prevention of Cruelty to Children, 4 Red, 5 Lourdes, 6 Sloe, 7 Lettuce, 8 Bridget Jones, 9 2005, 10 Black Sea, 11 Hydrogen, 12 Meryl Streep, 13 The sousaphone, 14 Baku, 15 Ruud van Nistelrooy, 16 Belshazzar, 17 Altimeter, 18 Galway, 19 Picasso, 20 Tom Clancy.*

General Knowledge

Your rating: ● 0-5 Join a library ● 6-10 Keep at it ● 11-15 Join a quiz team ● 16-20 Join Mensa

1. By what name was British ballerina Margaret Hookham better known?
2. Where was the 1940 Olympic Games first scheduled to be held before war meant that they had to be cancelled?
3. Which fictional detective lives in St Mary Meads?
4. In the Old Testament, who was the father of Isaac?
5. Which English poet and critic wrote *Kubla Khan*?
6. With which alcoholic drink is the town of Cognac associated?
7. What name is given to the form of calcium sulphate used to make casts for broken limbs?
8. Which actress plays the title role in the film *Erin Brockovich*?
9. By what name is nacre popularly known?
10. Which British driver was stripped of his second place in the 2000 Brazilian Grand Prix?
11. What is the S.I. unit of frequency?
12. What is the real name of the singer nicknamed Sporty Spice?
13. How many piano concertos did Beethoven compose?
14. In Arthurian legend, which knight of the Round Table was the son of King Lot?
15. What name is given to the fossilised resin of coniferous trees used for jewellery and ornaments?
16. The Pevensey Levels is a marshy area of which English county?
17. Which country won the third place play-offs in the 1999 Rugby World Cup?
18. What in nautical slang is burgoo?
19. Who played David Bliss in the 1960 sitcom *A Life of Bliss*?
20. In which year did sculptor Henry Moore die?

ANSWERS: *1 Dame Margot Fonteyn, 2 London, 3 Miss Marple, 4 Abraham, 5 Samuel Taylor Coleridge, 6 Brandy, 7 Plaster of Paris, 8 Julia Roberts, 9 Mother-of-pearl, 10 David Coulthard, 11 Hertz, 12 Melanie Chisholm, 13 Five, 14 Gawain, 15 Amber, 16 East Sussex, 17 New Zealand, 18 Porridge, 19 George Cole, 20 1986.*

General Knowledge

Your rating: ● **0-5** Join a library ● **6-10** Keep at it
● **11-15** Join a quiz team ● **16-20** Join Mensa

1. What is the island in the Bristol Channel about 20km northwest of Hartland Point?
2. Which U.S. author wrote *The Naked and The Dead*?
3. How many events are there in the modern pentathlon?
4. Which film picked up five Oscars in 2000, including Best Picture?
5. To which European country does the adjective Hellenic relate?
6. Which widely cultivated cereal grass is grown in paddy fields?
7. Which famous Italian actress starred in the films *Two Women* and *The Millionairess*?
8. The ‘cod wars’ were a series of disputes between Britain and which country?
9. Which precious metal has the symbol Pt?
10. The song *New York, New York* comes from which film?
11. Which British novelist wrote *The Way of All Flesh*?
12. Which wedding anniversary is crystal?
13. Who directed the 1985 film *After Hours*?
14. Which son of Poseidon and Amphitrite is usually depicted blowing a shell?
15. What, in Russia, is a droshky?
16. Which British driver won the 2000 Formula 1 British Grand Prix?
17. What was the name of Robert De Niro’s character in *Taxi Driver*?
18. Who wrote the 1958 play *Chicken Soup with Barley*?
19. What name is given to the flight of Chinese communists to Yan’an, led by Mao Tse-tung?
20. Which intellectual circle included Virginia Woolf, John Maynard Keynes and Lytton Strachey?

ANSWERS: *1 Lundy Island, 2 Norman Mailer, 3 Five, 4 American Beauty, 5 Greece, 6 Rice, 7 Sophia Loren, 8 Iceland, 9 Platinum, 10 On The Town, 11 Samuel Butler, 12 Twentieth, 13 Martin Scorsese, 14 Triton, 15 A four-wheeled horse-drawn carriage, 16 David Coulthard, 17 Travis, 18 Arnold Wesker , 19 The Long March, 20 Bloomsbury group.*

Entertainment

Your rating: ● **0-5** **Buy a TV** ● **6-10** **Keep at it** ● **11-15** **Join a quiz team** ● **16-20** **Enter a quiz show**

1. With whom did guitarist Bill Frisell release a 1995 album called *Deep Dead Blue*?
2. Who played crooked ex-cop Keaton in the 1995 film *The Usual Suspects*?
3. Which Irish boy band released a 1995 album entitled *Said and Done*?
4. Which 1994 film starred Nikita Mikhalkov as a retired Russian colonel?
5. Which newsreader claimed in 1995 that she welcomed "being the first woman to read the news with grey hair"?
6. With which country superstar did George Jones release a 1995 album entitled *One*?
7. Who hosted the quiz show *That's News to Me!*?
8. Which 1995 Michael Winterbottom film starred Saskia Reeves and Amanda Plummer?
9. Which actor starred as *Magnum PI* in the U.S. drama series?
10. *Ring Them Bells* was the title of a 1995 album by which folk singer?
11. Who played the title role in the 1974 film adaptation of *The Great Gatsby*?
12. Who played Charlie Burrows in the sitcom *The Upper Hand*?
13. What was Kate Bush's debut U.K. single?
14. What sort of creature was Willy in the 1995 film *Free Willy 2: The Adventure Home*?
15. Big Audio Dynamite frontman Mick Jones was a founder member of which successful punk band?
16. Which 1995 Peter Segal film starred Rob Lowe and Bo Derek?
17. Which U.S. talk show host spent more than £75,000 on her sick cocker spaniel, Solomon in 1995?
18. With whom did Barbra Streisand sing the 1978 U.K. number one hit *You Don't Bring Me Flowers*?
19. Which TV chef was involved in an advertising campaign for Tate & Lyle sugar?
20. Which 'Godfather of Funk' released an album entitled *The Music of Red Shoe Diaries* in 1995?

ANSWERS: *1 Elvis Costello, 2 Gabriel Byrne, 3 Boyzone, 4 Burnt by the Sun, 5 Anna Ford, 6 Tammy Wynette, 7 Tom O'Connor, 8 Butterfly Kiss, 9 Tom Selleck, 10 Joan Baez, 11 Robert Redford, 12 Joe McGann, 13 Wuthering Heights, 14 A whale, 15 The Clash, 16 Tommy Boy, 17 Oprah Winfrey, 18 Neil Diamond, 19 Gary Rhodes, 20 George Clinton.*

General Knowledge

Your rating: ● 0-5 Join a library ● 6-10 Keep at it ● 11-15 Join a quiz team ● 16-20 Join Mensa

1. For which drink is the Indian town of Darjeeling famous?
2. Who directed the films *Annie Hall* and *Broadway Danny Rose*?
3. Which country is called Österreich in German?
4. What colour is the semi-precious stone lapis lazuli?
5. Which word meaning 'rebirth' describes the period in European cultural history that began in the 14th century?
6. What name is given to tropical birds of the order Psittaciformes?
7. Which breed of sheepdog has bearded and border varieties?
8. In which country is the Grande Dixence Dam?
9. What in law is a felo de se?
10. Who wrote the crime novel *Road Rage*?
11. In the English judicial hierarchy, which judge is second to the Lord Chancellor?
12. Which horse won the 2000 Grand National at Aintree?
13. What name was given to the followers of the Greek moral philosopher Diogenes of Sinope?
14. Which Greek god was also known as Bacchus?
15. In which African country is the Nubian Desert?
16. What name was given to those raised to the papacy in opposition to a lawfully elected pope?
17. Who was described by Frank Muir as 'the thinking man's crumpet'?
18. Which Irish monk founded the monastery at Lindisfarne?
19. Which strait lies between the Persian Gulf and the Gulf of Oman?
20. Which British poet wrote *The Dunciad*?

***ANSWERS:** 1 Tea, 2 Woody Allen, 3 Austria, 4 Blue, 5 Renaissance, 6 Parrot, 7 Collie, 8 Switzerland, 9 Suicide, 10 Ruth Rendell, 11 Lord Chief Justice, 12 Papillon, 13 Cynics, 14 Dionysus, 15 Sudan, 16 Antipopes, 17 Joan Bakewell, 18 St Aidan, 19 Strait of Hormuz, 20 Alexander Pope.*

General Knowledge

Your rating: ● **0-5** Join a library ● **6-10** Keep at it ● **11-15** Join a quiz team ● **16-20** Join Mensa

1. What word meaning ‘belonging to a village’ has come to mean a heathen?
2. On which British island is the seaport of Ramsey?
3. Which common wild plant gets its name from the French for lion’s tooth?
4. What name is given to the mixture of boiled linseed oil and whiting used for fastening glass in windows?
5. In which country did George Papadopoulos seize power in 1967?
6. What sort of celestial body is also called a minor planet?
7. Which infectious disease is caused by the bacterium Bacillus anthracis?
8. In what year was the Easter Rising in Dublin?
9. What name is used to describe drugs such as penicillin and tetracycline?
10. Which inlet of the Irish Sea is at the western end of the border between England and Scotland?
11. What object does the camera follow in the title sequence of the film *Forrest Gump*?
12. From which country did the United States make the Louisiana Purchase?
13. Which Roman Catholic organisation takes its name from the Latin for ‘God’s work’?
14. Who was sacked as manager of Sheffield Wednesday in March 2000?
15. Which French novelist wrote *Gigi* and the ‘Claudine’ series of novels?
16. Which country was ruled by Shah Jahan from 1628 to 1658?
17. What name is given to the curve obtained by suspending a string or cable from two points?
18. Which U.S. inventor discovered the vulcanisation process?
19. Vladimir and Estragon are tramps in which play?
20. Which British general was besieged for ten months in Khartoum?

ANSWERS: *1 Pagan, 2 Isle of Man, 3 Dandelion, 4 Putty, 5 Greece, 6 Asteroid, 7 Anthrax, 8 1916, 9 Antibiotics, 10 Solway Firth, 11 A feather, 12 France, 13 Opus Dei, 14 Danny Wilson, 15 Colette, 16 India, 17 Catenary, 18 Charles Goodyear, 19 Waiting for Godot, 20 Charles Gordon.*

General Knowledge

Your rating:
- 0-5 Join a library
- 6-10 Keep at it
- 11-15 Join a quiz team
- 16-20 Join Mensa

1. Which comedian has played *Mr. Bean* on TV and film?
2. What name is given to the week preceding Easter Sunday?
3. Which veteran singer picked up his first Brit award when he was voted Best British Male Solo Artist at the 2000 awards?
4. What was the pen name of British novelist Eric Blair?
5. Which Scottish port has a ferry service to Larne in Northern Ireland?
6. Which unit of weight for precious stones is equal to 0.20 grams?
7. Camembert cheese is named after a village in which country?
8. What was Helen Zahavi's controversial 1991 novel called?
9. According to legend, at whom did Peeping Tom peep?
10. Which Italian island in the Tyrrhenian Sea is noted for its active volcano?
11. Who won a Best Actor Oscar for his performance in *American Beauty*?
12. Which British charity was founded in 1895 to preserve land and buildings of historic interest or beauty?
13. What was the name of the ancient Egyptian bull god?
14. Which is the largest island of the Inner Hebrides in Scotland?
15. Which English king succeeded Henry III?
16. What sort of plant is a lady's slipper?
17. In which sea is the submerged sandbank Dogger Bank?
18. According to Jewish tradition, who was Adam's first wife?
19. In which Thomas Hardy novel does Eustacia Vye appear?
20. Which pope was born Rodrigo Borgia?

ANSWERS: *1 Rowan Atkinson, 2 Holy Week, 3 Tom Jones, 4 George Orwell, 5 Stranraer, 6 Carat, 7 France, 8 Dirty Weekend, 9 Lady Godiva, 10 Stromboli, 11 Kevin Spacey, 12 The National Trust, 13 Apis, 14 Skye, 15 Edward I, 16 An orchid, 17 North Sea, 18 Lilith, 19 The Return of the Native, 20 Alexander VI.*

Entertainment

Your rating: ● 0-5 Buy a TV ● 6-10 Keep at it ● 11-15 Join a quiz team ● 16-20 Enter a quiz show

1. What type of creature was Brian in the children's TV show *The Magic Roundabout*?
2. The male members of which squeaky-clean British pop band were cautioned by the police in 2001 for being in possession of cannabis?
3. Which actor said, "I have played three presidents, three saints and two geniuses. If that doesn't create an ego problem, nothing does."?
4. Which comic actor explored the intricacies of *The Human Face* on BBC 1?
5. Which Sixties band's members were Steve Marriott, Ronnie Lane, Kenny Jones and Ian McLagen?
6. Which 2000 BBC-financed film was set in a London salsa club and featured Jane Horrocks?
7. Which cause was the week-long 2001 *Celebrity Big Brother* in aid of?
8. Which British band had a 1966 U.K. number one hit with *Paint It, Black*?
9. Which director won Oscar nominations for his films *Rebecca*, *Lifeboat* and *Spellbound*?
10. Which *Coronation Street* character was stalked by Linda Baldwin's brother, Ryan Sykes in 2001?
11. What was the title of the Shamen's 1992 U.K. number one hit?
12. Which 2000 mock-documentary film was set in the world of dog-fancying?
13. Which children's programme of the '60s and '70s aimed to cater for both hearing and non-hearing viewers and featured the talents of Tony Hart?
14. Which British male singer hit the U.K. top ten in 2001 with *Rendezvous*?
15. Which American composer won Oscars for his work on 1961's *Breakfast at Tiffany's* and 1982's *Victor/Victoria*?
16. Which former docu-soap star hosted the BBC 1 talent show *Star for a Night*?
17. Which actress played evil Elektra King in the 1999 Bond film *The World is Not Enough*?
18. Which BBC 1 series followed a group of recruits at the Metropolitan Police Service's training school?
19. Which Welsh rock band released an album entitled *Know Your Enemy* in 2001?
20. Which veteran TV actor appeared in ITV's *Peak Practice* as Dr Alex Redman's dad?

ANSWERS: *1 A snail, 2 S Club 7, 3 Charlton Heston, 4 John Cleese, 5 Small Faces, 6 Born Romantic, 7 Comic Relief, 8 Rolling Stones, 9 Sir Alfred Hitchcock, 10 Emma Watts, 11 Ebeneezer Goode, 12 Best in Show, 13 Vision On, 14 Craig David, 15 Henry Mancini, 16 Jane McDonald, 17 Sophie Marceau, 18 Raw Blues, 19 Manic Street Preachers, 20 Frank Windsor.*

General Knowledge

Your rating:
- 0-5 Join a library
- 6-10 Keep at it
- 11-15 Join a quiz team
- 16-20 Join Mensa

1. Who wrote *Swallows and Amazons*?
2. Who directed the 1941 film *Citizen Kane*?
3. Who was the first Tudor king of England?
4. What is the capital of Wales?
5. Who wrote *All Quiet on the Western Front*?
6. The adjective vernal describes which season?
7. Which British novelist wrote *Fame is the Spur*?
8. What is seismology the study of?
9. What is the title of the autobiography of Martin Kemp?
10. What type of game is Old Maid?
11. Who wrote *The Wind in the Willows*?
12. What does the word moribund mean?
13. What was the surname of the *Little Women* in the book by Louisa M Alcott?
14. Who plays the part of Phil Mitchell in *EastEnders*?
15. Which novel by Charles Kingsley is set in the 16th century?
16. What is the first name of Gulliver in the book by Jonathan Swift?
17. What is the technical name for the human thighbone?
18. The sweetheart of Yogi Bear in the cartoon was called what?
19. In which country is Yellowstone National Park?
20. Soap opera *Knots Landing* was a spin-off from which other soap?

ANSWERS: *1 Arthur Ransome, 2 Orson Welles, 3 Henry VII, 4 Cardiff, 5 Erich Maria Remarque, 6 Spring, 7 Howard Spring, 8 Earthquakes, 9 True, 10 Card, 11 Kenneth Grahame, 12 Near death, 13 March, 14 Steve McFadden, 15 Westward Ho, 16 Lemue, 17 Femur, 18 Cindy Bear, 19 USA, 20 Dallas.*

General Knowledge

Your rating: ● 0-5 Join a library ● 6-10 Keep at it ● 11-15 Join a quiz team ● 16-20 Join Mensa

1. Which actress had the original name Mary Cathleen Collins?
2. Who wrote the novel *The Newcomes*?
3. What is the standard monetary unit of Spain?
4. Who devised the TV series *Thunderbirds*?
5. Who created the detective Adam Dalgliesh?
6. In which country was the 1979 film *My Brilliant Career* set?
7. Who is the manager of the bar that Homer frequents in *The Simpsons*?
8. What is Charley in the nonfiction book *Travels With Charley* by John Steinbeck?
9. Which Bond movie did *Crouching Tiger Hidden Dragon* actress Michelle Yeoh star in?
10. In *Dr Who* what did TARDIS stand for?
11. What is the first sign of the zodiac?
12. What is the surname of Rabbit in books by John Updike?
13. *Game for a Laugh* was based on which American TV show?
14. The plot of which film was relocated to Asia for the 1982 remake *Far East*?
15. What country did the cricketer Sunil Gavaskar play for?
16. Who wrote the autobiography *My Left Foot*?
17. What is the name of the village featured in TV drama *Peak Practice*?
18. What is the capital of Indonesia?
19. Which veteran actor played the *Dad* of Ted Danson in the 1989 film?
20. Jean Valjean is the hero of which novel?

ANSWERS: *1 Bo Derek, 2 William Makepeace Thackeray, 3 Peseta, 4 Gerry Anderson, 5 P D James, 6 Australia, 7 Moe, 8 A dog, 9 Tomorrow Never Dies, 10 Time And Relative Dimensions In Space, 11 Aries, 12 Angstrom, 13 People Are Funny, 14 Casablanca, 15 India, 16 Christy Brown, 17 Cardale, 18 Jakarta, 19 Jack Lemmon, 20 Les Miserables.*

General Knowledge

Your rating: ● **0-5** Join a library ● **6-10** Keep at it ● **11-15** Join a quiz team ● **16-20** Join Mensa

1. Which *Tomorrow's World* presenter previously appeared on *Multi-Coloured Swap Shop*?
2. The Thomas Hardy novel title *Far From the Madding Crowd* is a quotation from which poet?
3. Which *Last of the Summer Wine* actor provided voices for animated film *The Wrong Trousers*?
4. The film *O Brother Where Art Thou* contains references to which classical text?
5. Which well-known actress is quoted as saying "I am a woman who is unfaithful to a million men"?
6. Who had a U.K. number one hit in 1999 with *Praise You*?
7. *God Knows* is a fictional autobiography by Joseph Heller of which Biblical character?
8. Comedy series *Peter Kay's Phoenix Nights* was set where?
9. The Australian adventure *The Man From Snowy River* was inspired by a poem by whom?
10. Who wrote the novel *Elmer Gantry*?
11. What is the chemical symbol for tungsten?
12. Which then chancellor of the exchequer introduced old age pensions in 1908?
13. Which gangland movie was based on Shakespeare's *Macbeth*?
14. Who wrote the novel *Castle Rackrent*?
15. What was the job of the Nicolas Cage character Ronny Cammareri in *Moonstruck*?
16. Who directed the 1973 film *The Exorcist*?
17. What nationality was the composer Edward Elgar?
18. What was *The Beast* in the 1988 film?
19. Cicely Fairfield took the name Rebecca West from a play by which dramatist?
20. How many sides does a nonagon have?

ANSWERS: *1 Maggie Philbin, 2 Thomas Gray, 3 Peter Sallis, 4 The Odyssey, 5 Greta Garbo, 6 Fatboy Slim, 7 King David, 8 A nightclub, 9 Banjo Paterson, 10 Sinclair Lewis, 11 W, 12 David Lloyd George, 13 Men of Respect, 14 Maria Edgeworth, 15 Baker, 16 William Friedkin, 17 English, 18 A tank, 19 Henrik Ibsen, 20 9.*

Entertainment

Your rating: ● **0-5** **Buy a TV** ● **6-10** **Keep at it** ● **11-15** **Join a quiz team** ● **16-20** **Enter a quiz show**

1. Which 2001 film, set during the siege of Stalingrad, starred British actors Jude Law, Rachel Weisz and Joseph Fiennes?
2. What sort of animal was ‘Rag’ in the 1950s children’s series *Rag, Tag and Bobtail*?
3. Who had a UK top five single with *Butterfly* in 2001?
4. Which late British actor once said, “I have a face that’s a cross between two pounds of halibut and an explosion in an old-clothes closet.”?
5. Which TV presenting duo had a 1994 U.K. top ten hit with *Let’s Get Ready to Rhumble* under the guise of PJ & Duncan?
6. Who stars in, and also produced, the 2000 film *Miss Congeniality*?
7. Who emerged as the winner of Comic Relief’s 2001 *Celebrity Big Brother*?
8. With whom did Cliff Richard duet on the 1986 UK top five hit *All I Ask of You*?
9. Which British actress played the title role in the 1986 film *Lady Jane*?
10. Which *EastEnders* hardman was shot in 2001?
11. Which blue cartoon stars had a 1996 U.K. top five hit with *I’ve Got a Little Puppy*?
12. Which 2000 film, set during the Cuban missile crisis in 1962, featured Kevin Costner as presidential advisor Kenny O’Donnell?
13. Who originally made up the *Rainbow* musical trio in the children’s series along with Rod and Jane?
14. Which Parisian duo have released an album entitled *Discovery* in 2001, featuring their hit *One More Time*?
15. In which 1968 film did Peter O’Toole play Henry II opposite Katharine Hepburn as Eleanor of Aquitaine?
16. Who was the presenter of the 2001 Channel 5 endurance game show *Touch the Truck*?
17. Which legendary actress is quoted as saying, “I never said I want to be alone. I only said I want to be let alone.”?
18. Who presented *Planet for the Apes*, a three-part BBC 2 documentary about primates?
19. What was the title of the 2001 debut album by manufactured group Hear’Say?
20. What was the name of the institution in the ITV drama series *Bad Girls*?

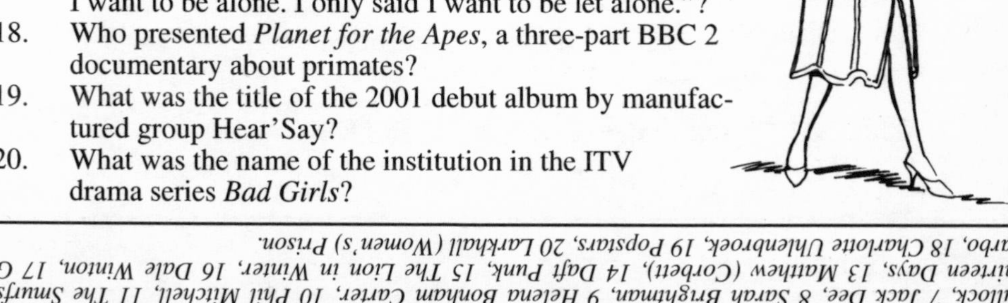

ANSWERS: 1 *Enemy at the Gates*, 2 *A hedgehog*, 3 *Crazy Town*, 4 *David Niven*, 5 *Ant & Dec*, 6 *Sandra Bullock*, 7 *Jack Dee*, 8 *Sarah Brightman*, 9 *Helena Bonham Carter*, 10 *Phil Mitchell*, 11 *The Smurfs*, 12 *Thirteen Days*, 13 *Matthew (Corbett)*, 14 *Daft Punk*, 15 *The Lion in Winter*, 16 *Dale Winton*, 17 *Greta Garbo*, 18 *Charlotte Uhlenbroek*, 19 *Popstars*, 20 *Larkhall (Women's) Prison*.

General Knowledge

Your rating:
- 0-5 Join a library
- 6-10 Keep at it
- 11-15 Join a quiz team
- 16-20 Join Mensa

1. How many novels did Emily Bronte write?
2. Who was the first American astronaut in space?
3. How many months do not have 31 days?
4. The adjective leonine refers to which animal?
5. Who wrote *The Remains of the Day*?
6. What is the nontechnical name for the sternum?
7. Who wrote *The Railway Children*?
8. Which star of *Sex and the City* hails from Britain?
9. In *North By Northwest* director Alfred Hitchcock made a cameo appearance as what?
10. Who took over from Terry Wogan as the presenter of *Blankety Blank*?
11. What is another term for lockjaw?
12. Where is *The French Lieutenant's Woman* set?
13. The town of Glastonbury is in which English county?
14. In which country is *The Good Earth* by Pearl S Buck set?
15. In which country is the Tiber river?
16. What is the name of the family featured in the John Ford film *The Grapes of Wrath*?
17. Cumulus is a type of what?
18. Which horror film features the character Pinhead?
19. What is the name of the newspaper in the novel *Scoop* by Evelyn Waugh?
20. Which comedian played alongside Judi Dench in the film *Mrs Brown*?

ANSWERS: *1 One, 2 Alan Shepard, 3 Five, 4 Lion, 5 Kazuo Ishiguro, 6 Breastbone, 7 Edith Nesbit, 8 Kim Cattrall, 9 A bus passenger, 10 Les Dawson, 11 Tetanus, 12 Dorset, 13 Somerset, 14 China, 15 Italy, 16 Joad, 17 Cloud, 18 Hellraiser, 19 The Beast, 20 Billy Connolly.*

General Knowledge

Your rating:
- **0-5 Join a library**
- **6-10 Keep at it**
- **11-15 Join a quiz team**
- **16-20 Join Mensa**

1. In which ocean does *The Hunt For Red October* take place?
2. In which century did the Gunpowder Plot take place?
3. Which novelist had the forename Huffam?
4. What was the name of the inept British agent in the comedy series *'Allo 'Allo!*?
5. A howdah is a seat used for riding on the back of which animal?
6. What does the Russian word glasnost translate as?
7. Who wrote *The House of Mirth*?
8. Where are the headquarters of the World Health Organisation?
9. Who won the Nobel peace prize in 1906 for mediating in the Russo-Japanese war?
10. The Appian Way is a Roman road in which country?
11. What is the name of the summer camp featured in the Friday the 13th movies?
12. How many white stars are on the national flag of the United States of America?
13. In which year did the Gulf War take place?
14. Where was the soap opera *Eldorado* set?
15. Fitch is another name for which animal?
16. What is the name of the the captain in the novel *Moby-Dick*?
17. What word means the faculty of making fortunate discoveries accidentally?
18. In which country is Transylvania?
19. Which space shuttle exploded in 1986?
20. How many Pink Panther films did Peter Sellers appear in?

ANSWERS: *1 The Atlantic, 2 17th, 3 Charles Dickens, 4 Officer Crabtree, 5 Elephant, 6 Openness, 7 Edith Wharton, 8 Geneva, 9 Theodore Roosevelt, 10 Italy, 11 Camp Crystal Lake, 12 50, 13 1991, 14 Spain (Los Barcos), 15 Polecat, 16 Ahab, 17 Serendipity, 18 Romania, 19 Challenger, 20 6.*

General Knowledge

Your rating: ● 0-5 Join a library ● 6-10 Keep at it ● 11-15 Join a quiz team ● 16-20 Join Mensa

1. Who connects *The Royle Family* and *Brookside*?
2. Who was poet laureate from 1984-98?
3. Who created Detective Inspector Roderick Alleyn?
4. What is a flycatcher?
5. The Blue Ridge Mountains form part of which mountain system?
6. Which TV gameshow was set on an oil rig?
7. Which author used the pen name Robert Markham?
8. Anglia is a Latin name for which country?
9. Who directed the film *Bamboozled*?
10. Which *Cracker* star also played a Bond movie baddie?
11. Who said "Any girl can look glamorous: all you have to do is stand still and look stupid"?
12. What is the name of the omnipotent head of state in *1984* by George Orwell?
13. What is the Red Planet better known as?
14. What is infectious mononucleosis more commonly known as?
15. Which American novelist wrote *The Virginian*?
16. Which zodiac sign is represented by the Archer?
17. From which country does Valpolicella wine originate?
18. Who wrote *Swallows and Amazons*?
19. Noel Sullivan is a member of which pop group?
20. Who wrote the books which were adapted for the TV series *Jeeves and Wooster*?

ANSWERS: *1 Sue Johnston, 2 Ted Hughes, 3 Dame Ngaio Marsh, 4 Bird, 5 Appalachians, 6 Fort Boyard, 7 Kingsley Amis, 8 England, 9 Spike Lee, 10 Robbie Coltrane, 11 Hedy Lamarr, 12 Big Brother, 13 Mars, 14 Glandular fever, 15 Owen Wister, 16 Sagittarius, 17 Italy, 18 Arthur Ransome, 19 HearSay, 20 PG Wodehouse.*

Entertainment

Your rating: ● **0-5 Buy a TV** ● **6-10 Keep at it** ● **11-15 Join a quiz team** ● **16-20 Enter a quiz show**

1. Which 2001 film featured Robert De Niro as a New York cop and Kelsey Grammer as a TV presenter?
2. Which US sitcom, based on a 1968 film, starred Tony Randall and Jack Klugman as incompatible friends?
3. Which Spice Girl hit the U.K. number one spot in 2001 with her solo single *What Took You So Long?*?
4. Which BBC 2 series about the police force starred Katy Cavanagh as Mel?
5. Which Irish band's first U.K. top ten single was 1983's *New Years Day*?
6. Which actress received a Best Actress Oscar nomination for her performance in the 2000 film *You Can Count on Me*?
7. Which actress appeared in the 2001 ITV drama *The Hunt* as adulteress Sarah Campbell?
8. In which year did the Village People have a U.K. number one hit with *Y.M.C.A.*?
9. Which former *Coronation Street* actress played the hero Billy Casper's mother in the 1969 Ken Loach film *Kes*?
10. Which character, played by Tony Adams, returned as a wine supplier to *Crossroads* in 2001?
11. Which US female vocalist had a U.K. top five hit in 1982 with *Heartbreaker*?
12. Which 2000 Barry Levinson film featured Billy Connolly as a serial killer?
13. Which fictitious village was the setting for TV's *Noel's House Party*?
14. Which group, a front for Blur's Damon Albarn, released a self-titled album in 2001, featuring their top five hit, *Clint Eastwood*?
15. Which 1950s rock 'n' roller was immortalised by Lou Diamond Phillips in the 1987 movie *La Bamba*?
16. Which *Emmerdale* character stood trial for the murder and attempted murder of his wife and her lover in 2001?
17. Which member of the Jackson family hit the U.K. top five with the single *All For You* in 2001?
18. Which 2001 BBC 1 drama featured Keith Barron as Superintendent Beausoleil and David Suchet as Inspector Borne?
19. Which 2001 film followed a girl from inner-city Chicago in her quest to study ballet at the Juilliard in New York?
20. What was the first album to be recorded on Richard Branson's Virgin label?

ANSWERS: *1 Fifteen Minutes, 2 The Odd Couple, 3 Emma Bunton, 4 The Cops, 5 U2's, 6 Laura Linney, 7 Amanda Holden, 8 1978, 9 Lynne Perrie, 10 Adam Chance, 11 Dionne Warwick, 12 An Everlasting Piece, 13 Crinkley Bottom, 14 Gorillaz, 15 Ritchie Valens, 16 Jack Sugden, 17 Janet, 18 NCS: Manhunt, 19 Save the Last Dance, 20 Mike Oldfield's Tubular Bells.*

General Knowledge

Your rating:
- **0-5** Join a library
- **6-10** Keep at it
- **11-15** Join a quiz team
- **16-20** Join Mensa

1. Which *Neighbours* role was originally played by Kylie Flinker?
2. Who wrote *The Ipcress File*?
3. How many megabytes are there in a gigabyte?
4. Where is the holy city of Medina?
5. What was the title of the first TV agony column?
6. Which film was advertised with the publicity line "Not every gift is a blessing"?
7. Who wrote *Cautionary Tales*?
8. What part of the body is the carpus?
9. Whose notable films have included *Starting Over* and *Best Friends*?
10. Which actress connects *Beverly Hills 90210* and supernatural series *Charmed*?
11. Chinese gooseberry is another name for what?
12. Which children's characters were *In Paris* for a film?
13. In which British city was TV series *GBH* set?
14. Who is the most-capped Scotland footballer?
15. What was the capital of India from 1833-1912?
16. Who wrote *A Town Like Alice*?
17. Which of the Marx Brothers was born first?
18. What was the nickname of Jack Killian in *Midnight Caller*?
19. A henbit is a type of what?
20. Who created *Sanders of the River*?

ANSWERS: *1 Lucy Robinson, 2 Len Deighton, 3 1024, 4 Saudi Arabia, 5 Is This Your Problem, 6 The Sixth Sense, 7 Hilaire Belloc, 8 Wrist, 9 Burt Reynolds, 10 Shannen Doherty, 11 Kiwi fruit, 12 Rugrats, 13 Liverpool, 14 Kenny Dalglish, 15 Calcutta, 16 Nevil Shute, 17 Chico, 18 Nighthawk, 19 Plant, 20 Edgar Wallace.*

General Knowledge

Your rating:
- **0-5 Join a library**
- **6-10 Keep at it**
- **11-15 Join a quiz team**
- **16-20 Join Mensa**

1. Julian and Gregorian are types of what?
2. Who directed the 1965 film *Cat Ballou*?
3. Gerlachovka is the highest peak in which mountain system?
4. Carriage dog was a former name for which breed of dog?
5. In which city was John F Kennedy assassinated?
6. What is the meaning of the Russian word perestroika?
7. The politicians Jack Straw and Robin Cook were both born in which year?
8. Who was the Roman god of boundaries?
9. Where would a croupier work?
10. What is another name for the North Star?
11. QANTAS is the national airline of which country?
12. What nationality are the Manic Street Preachers?
13. The adjective lupine describes which animal?
14. In which century was Sir Isaac Newton born?
15. What in communications is a code word for the letter q?
16. Who was the first Englishman to sail around the world?
17. What does the word cachinnate mean?
18. Where are the headquarters of the United Nations?
19. Where are the islets of Langerhans situated?
20. What links the Mediterranean with the Atlantic?

ANSWERS: *1 Calendar, 2 Elliot Silverstein, 3 Carpathians, 4 Dalmatian, 5 Dallas, 6 Reconstruction, 7 1946, 8 Terminus, 9 Casino, 10 Polaris, 11 Australia, 12 Welsh, 13 Wolf, 14 17th, 15 Quebec, 16 Francis Drake, 17 Laugh loudly, 18 New York, 19 Pancreas, 20 Strait of Gibraltar.*

General Knowledge

Your rating:
- 0-5 Join a library
- 6-10 Keep at it
- 11-15 Join a quiz team
- 16-20 Join Mensa

1. Who holds the record of most *Jackanory* appearances with 111?
2. The Sierra Madre is the main mountain system of which country?
3. Which novelist wrote *Heart of Darkness*?
4. The tiger snake is native to which country?
5. What was Russian Anna Pavlova best known as?
6. What is decompression sickness also called?
7. What was founded by William Booth?
8. What type of creature is a rudd?
9. Winston Smith is the main character from which book?
10. What is the capital of Spain?
11. What nationality was the explorer Mungo Park?
12. Hibernia was the Roman name for which country?
13. What is a clavichord?
14. Is a meerkat diurnal or nocturnal?
15. Who painted *The Last Supper*?
16. Who was Chancellor of the Exchequer from 1993-97?
17. Who connects the television series *The Good Life* and *Monarch of the Glen*?
18. What is the standard monetary unit of Bulgaria?
19. How many pounds make up a stone?
20. Which English town is at the head of the Orwell estuary?

ANSWERS: *1 Bernard Cribbins, 2 Mexico, 3 Joseph Conrad, 4 Australia, 5 Ballerina, 6 The bends, 7 Salvation Army, 8 Fish, 9 1984, 10 Madrid, 11 Scottish, 12 Ireland, 13 Musical instrument, 14 Diurnal, 15 Leonardo da Vinci, 16 Kenneth Clarke, 17 Richard Briers, 18 Lev, 19 14, 20 Ipswich.*

Sports

Your rating: ● **0-5 Wooden spoon** ● **6-10 Bronze medal** ● **11-15 Silver medal** ● **16-20 Gold medal**

1. How many of an ice hockey team's players are on the pitch at any one time?
2. Which team sold Roy Keane to Manchester United in 1993?
3. In which year did the Republic of Ireland qualify for the European Championship finals for the first time?
4. For which nation did rugby union player Grant Fox score 128 penalty goals between 1985 and 1993?
5. Which Argentinian player was sent off against Holland at the 1998 World Cup?
6. Which golfer was nicknamed 'Slammin' Sam'?
7. Which American football team was coached by George Halas for more than 40 years?
8. Who scored Scotland's only goal in the Euro 96 championships?
9. Which country did Lennox Lewis represent at the 1988 Olympic Games?
10. Which tennis player won his third consecutive U.S. Open title in 1987?
11. Which jockey rode Benny the Dip to victory at the 1997 Derby?
12. Which British motor racing driver won the 1962 German Grand Prix?
13. On the last day of the 1999/2000 season, Bradford City's Premiership survival was secured by victory against which team?
14. Which county cricket team won the 1998 Benson & Hedges Cup?
15. In snooker, how many points is the green ball worth?
16. Which British male athlete won gold for the 5000m at the 1994 Commonwealth Games?
17. What did legendary cricketer W. G. Grace's initials stand for?
18. Which nation caused an upset by knocking out Ukraine in the Euro 2000 qualification play-offs?
19. Why was Fred Lorz disqualified from the marathon at the 1904 Olympic games?
20. Which South African golfer won the U.S. Open for the second time in 1997?

ANSWERS: *1 Six, 2 Nottingham Forest, 3 1988, 4 New Zealand, 5 Ariel Ortega, 6 Sam Snead, 7 Chicago Bears, 8 Ally McCoist, 9 Canada, 10 Ivan Lendl, 11 Willie Ryan, 12 Graham Hill, 13 Liverpool, 14 Essex, 15 Three, 16 Rob Denmark, 17 William Gilbert, 18 Slovenia, 19 He got a lift for part of the race, 20 Ernie Els.*

General Knowledge

Your rating: • **0-5** Join a library • **6-10** Keep at it • **11-15** Join a quiz team • **16-20** Join Mensa

1. On whose novel is the 1996 film *The Chamber* based?
2. Which football team became the first to be valued at over £1billion?
3. By what name is the insect *Mantis religiosa* better known?
4. Which French film director was the son of a famous impressionist painter?
5. What name is given to the amount a borrower is charged for a loan, usually expressed as a percentage?
6. Which chess piece can move in any direction, but only one square at a time?
7. Which abbreviated inscription often appears in paintings of the crucifixion?
8. What was the main river of Hades, over which the souls of the dead were ferried by Charon?
9. Which university won the first Boat Race of the new millennium?
10. On which U.S. river is the Hoover Dam?
11. What is the part of the body called the lumbus also known as?
12. Which British novelist won the Booker Prize for his last novel, *Staying On*?
13. Which ancient city was the first capital of a united Egypt?
14. Who was named Greatest Cricketer of the 20th Century in a poll for Wisden?
15. In which country is the port of Agadir?
16. Which Greek word is used to describe the first five books of the Old Testament?
17. Who starred in *The Rag Trade* and *Just a Minute*?
18. Of which internet company is Martha Lane Fox a co-founder?
19. 'The Early Married Life of the Morels' is the opening chapter in which novel?
20. Which musical term indicates that a work is to be sung without accompaniment?

ANSWERS: *1 John Grisham, 2 Manchester United, 3 Praying mantis, 4 Jean Renoir, 5 Interest, 6 The king, 7 INRI, 8 Styx, 9 Oxford, 10 Colorado, 11 Loin, 12 Paul Scott, 13 Memphis, 14 Sir Donald Bradman, 15 Morocco, 16 Pentateuch, 17 Peter Jones, 18 Lastminute.com, 19 Sons and Lovers, by D.H. Lawrence, 20 A cappella*

General Knowledge

Your rating:
- 0-5 Join a library
- 6-10 Keep at it
- 11-15 Join a quiz team
- 16-20 Join Mensa

1. Who directed the 1997 film *Amistad*?
2. Which London street is synonymous with bespoke tailoring?
3. Who was named as Britain's favourite author in a poll to mark World Book Day?
4. What sort of creature is a marmoset?
5. Which American actor starred in *High Noon* and *The Virginian*?
6. What sort of condition is commonly treated with antihistamines?
7. According to the Bible, what was Judas Iscariot's reward for betraying Jesus?
8. What nickname was given to Sir Robert Peel when Chief Secretary for Ireland between 1812-1818?
9. Which Italian Fascist leader was known as Il Duce?
10. What is the capital of Panama?
11. Which Paris street on the Left Bank of the River Seine is home to the French Foreign Office?
12. Who was principal conductor of the Hallé Orchestra until his death in 1970?
13. Which U.S. statesman succeeded to the presidency on the death of Warren Harding?
14. In which African country is the seaport of Dar-es-Salaam?
15. Who lost to Stuart Bingham in the first round of the 2000 snooker world championship at the Crucible?
16. For what sort of tube is C.R.T. an abbreviation?
17. Which resin, also known as colophony, is applied to the hairs of violin bows?
18. What was the stage name of Canadian-born actress Gladys Mary Smith?
19. Which former MP wrote the novel *She's Leaving Home*?
20. In which country did the merino sheep originate?

ANSWERS: *1 Steven Spielberg, 2 Savile Row, 3 Roald Dahl, 4 A monkey, 5 Gary Cooper, 6 Allergy, 7 Thirty pieces of silver, 8 Orange Peel, 9 Benito Mussolini, 10 Panama City, 11 Quai d'Orsay, 12 Sir John Barbirolli, 13 Calvin Coolidge, 14 Tanzania, 15 Stephen Hendry, 16 Cathode-ray tube, 17 Rosin, 18 Mary Pickford, 19 Edwina Currie, 20 Spain.*

General Knowledge

Your rating: ● **0-5** Join a library ● **6-10** Keep at it ● **11-15** Join a quiz team ● **16-20** Join Mensa

1. Who played Alfie in a 1966 film?
2. What is the name of the five-sided building that houses the headquarters of the U.S. armed forces?
3. Which British novelist wrote *Mansfield Park* and *Northanger Abbey*?
4. How many fences are there in the Grand National?
5. What name is given to animals such as crocodiles, turtles, lizards and snakes?
6. In which Italian city is there a shroud said to bear impressions of Jesus's body?
7. Which northern comedian was born James Whittaker?
8. In what part of the body is the cochlea found?
9. Which TV cook postponed a third *How to Cook* book and series to devote more time to Norwich City F.C.?
10. What is the name of the load line on a ship's hull introduced in 1876?
11. Which French impressionist painter was Fragonard's granddaughter and Manet's sister-in-law?
12. Which Hollywood superstar received the prestigious Irving Thalberg award at the Oscars in 2000?
13. What type of garment is a Jacky Howe?
14. To which genus of plants does the black-eyed Susan belong?
15. Which major river flows through China, Laos, Cambodia and Vietnam to the South China Sea?
16. What sort of creature is a lacewing?
17. Which celestial object is also known as a quasi-stellar object or Q.S.O.?
18. Which British dramatist wrote *Five-Finger Exercise* and *The Royal Hunt of the Sun*?
19. From which country did artist Kurt Schwitters flee to England from the Nazis in 1940?
20. Which Roman statesman wrote the first history of Rome?

ANSWERS: *1 Michael Caine, 2 The Pentagon, 3 Jane Austen, 4 Thirty, 5 Reptiles, 6 Turin, 7 Jim Bowen, 8 The ear, 9 Delia Smith, 10 Plimsoll line, 11 Berthe Morisot, 12 Warren Beatty, 13 A sleeveless shirt, 14 Rudbeckia, 15 Mekong, 16 An insect, 17 Quasar, 18 Peter Shaffer, 19 Norway, 20 Cato the Elder.*

Entertainment

Your rating: ● **0-5 Buy a TV** ● **6-10 Keep at it** ● **11-15 Join a quiz team** ● **16-20 Enter a quiz show**

1. What was the first James Bond film?
2. Which soap celebrated its 2000th episode in 1995 with an extended show?
3. Which 53-year-old founding member of the Grateful Dead died in 1995?
4. Which quintessential English actor played Ralph Gorse in the 1980s TV series *The Charmer*?
5. Which singer was backed by the Dakotas?
6. Who produced, co-wrote, directed and starred in the 1981 film *Reds*?
7. Who had a U.K. hit in 1978 with *Ole Ola (Muhler Brasileira)*, featuring the Scottish World Cup Football Squad?
8. What was the name of *Tintin*'s dog in the cartoon series?
9. Which comic-book hero of Gaul could be seen in a 1994 cartoon film set in America?
10. In which country was the 1980s drama series *Tenko* set?
11. *It's Great When You're Straight ... Yeh* was the debut album from which band?
12. Which British actor played the villainous Simon in the 1995 film *Die Hard With A Vengeance*?
13. What was the home of King Alpha and Queen Bet in a children's TV series?
14. Which German band had a U.K. number one in 1981 with *Computer Love/The Model*?
15. Which Milcho Manchevski film about a war photographer won the Golden Lion Award at Venice in 1994?
16. With whom did Dick Clement write the comedy series *The Likely Lads*?
17. *Hot House* was a 1995 album release from which honorary Grateful Dead pianist?
18. Who played Mariner in the 1995 film *Waterworld*?
19. With which sex symbol did Peter Sellers record the 1960 top ten hit *Goodness Gracious Me*?
20. Which Gerry Anderson puppet series was set in Marineville?

***ANSWERS:** 1 Dr No, 2 Emmerdale, 3 Jerry Garcia, 4 Nigel Havers, 5 Billy J Kramer, 6 Warren Beatty, 7 Rod Stewart, 8 Snowy, 9 Asterix (Asterix Conquers America), 10 Malaysia, 11 Black Grape, 12 Jeremy Irons, 13 Alphabet Castle, 14 Kraftwerk, 15 Before the Rain, 16 Ian La Frenais, 17 Bruce Hornsby, 18 Kevin Costner, 19 Sophia Loren, 20 Stingray.*

General Knowledge

Your rating:
- 0-5 Join a library
- 6-10 Keep at it
- 11-15 Join a quiz team
- 16-20 Join Mensa

1. Which country did the Queen visit in March 2000?
2. What name is given to the Thursday before Good Friday?
3. Which French singer is associated with the song *Je ne regrette rien*?
4. What name is given to the scientific study of celestial bodies and the universe?
5. Which metropolitan county was formed in 1974 from parts of Staffordshire, Warwickshire and Worcestershire?
6. Who is the author of the thriller novel *10lb Penalty*?
7. During the making of which film did Bela Lugosi die?
8. What is the largest county of the Republic of Ireland?
9. Which pressure group is represented by the letters CND?
10. By what name were the Parliamentarian opponents of the Cavaliers known in the English Civil War?
11. Which Hungarian statesman was executed for leading the revolutionary government of 1956?
12. What is a Blindman's Lantern?
13. How many sacraments are there in the Roman Catholic Church?
14. Which British philosopher wrote *On Liberty and Principles of Political Economy*?
15. What nationality was the operatic tenor Jussi Björling?
16. Who was the skipper of Team Philips, the giant catamaran that broke up off the Isles of Scilly?
17. Which musical instrument is the alto member of the oboe family?
18. Of which two vitamins is cod-liver oil a rich source?
19. The town of Wagga Wagga is in which Australian state?
20. Which Shakespeare play is partly based on Thomas Lodge's pastoral romance *Rosalynde*?

ANSWERS: *1 Australia, 2 Maundy Thursday, 3 Edith Piaf, 4 Astronomy, 5 West Midlands, 6 Dick Francis, 7 Plan 9 from Outer Space, 8 Cork, 9 Campaign for Nuclear Disarmament, 10 Roundheads, 11 Imre Nagy, 12 A walking stick, 13 Seven, 14 John Stuart Mill, 15 Swedish, 16 Pete Goss, 17 Cor anglais, 18 A and D, 19 New South Wales, 20 As You Like It.*

General Knowledge

Your rating: ● 0-5 Join a library ● 6-10 Keep at it ● 11-15 Join a quiz team ● 16-20 Join Mensa

1. Which Swedish tennis player won the Wimbledon men's singles title five times in succession?
2. Who played Fitz in the TV series *Cracker*?
3. What is the fourth book of the Old Testament?
4. Who had a Number One in 2000 with a cover version of Don McLean's *American Pie*?
5. In which country is the port of Haifa?
6. What name is commonly used for members of the Unification Church founded by the Reverend Sun Myung Moon?
7. Which choreographer and film director was famous for large-scale dance sequences in films such as the Gold Diggers series in the 1930s?
8. With what genre of novels are Owen Wister and Zane Grey associated?
9. Which German city was the venue for the trials of Nazi war criminals after World War II?
10. Of which country is ukiyoe a school of painting?
11. In Greek mythology, which daughter of Hyperion was the goddess of the moon?
12. Which 17th-century composer died as a result of striking his foot while conducting?
13. The Segovia River forms the boundary between which two Central American countries?
14. For which gemstones is the Australian mining town of Coober Pedy famous?
15. Which British author created the detective Albert Campion?
16. In what year was the Princess Royal born?
17. Which sports car manufacturer designed the Volkswagen car which became known as the Beetle?
18. Which American artist's works include 1960's *People in the Sun*?
19. Who wrote *Gimpel the Fool* and *Old Love*?
20. Which rare-earth metal has the symbol La?

ANSWERS: *1 Bjorn Borg, 2 Robbie Coltrane, 3 Numbers, 4 Madonna, 5 Israel, 6 Moonies, 7 Busby Berkeley, 8 Westerns, 9 Nuremberg, 10 Japan, 11 Selene, 12 Jean-Baptiste Lully, 13 Nicaragua and Honduras, 14 Opals, 15 Margery Allingham, 16 1950, 17 Ferdinand Porsche, 18 Edward Hopper, 19 Isaac Bashevis Singer, 20 Lanthanum.*

General Knowledge

Your rating:
- 0-5 Join a library
- 6-10 Keep at it
- 11-15 Join a quiz team
- 16-20 Join Mensa

1. How many members are there in the pop group Steps?
2. What name is given to exercises, often performed to music, designed to improve the performance of the heart and lungs?
3. Which famous writing partners were the subject of Mike Leigh's Oscar-nominated film *Topsy-Turvy*?
4. In mathematics, what name is given to the likelihood that something will occur?
5. Which foodstuff is named after the French word for 'crescent'?
6. Who was the youngest prime minister in British history?
7. Which European peninsula is shared between Denmark and Germany?
8. What type of star explodes and increases in brightness by a million times or more?
9. In which county is Milton Keynes?
10. What sort of creature is a cassowary?
11. Which Egyptian hermit is considered the founder of Christian monasticism?
12. Who played *Maverick* in a 1994 film?
13. Of what is the sensitivity or speed usually quoted as an A.S.A. rating?
14. Which country did New Zealand beat in their successful defence of the America's Cup in 2000?
15. On which river is the Portuguese city of Lisbon?
16. Which spice is also known as pimento?
17. What was the stage name of American jazz singer Eleanora Gough McKay?
18. Which British author wrote the novel *Memoirs of a Midget*?
19. What name was given to the former annual one-penny tax on English householders for the support of the pope?
20. Which Spike Jonze film stars John Cusack and Cameron Diaz?

ANSWERS: *1 Five, 2 Aerobics, 3 Gilbert and Sullivan, 4 Probability, 5 Croissant, 6 William Pitt the Younger, 7 Jutland, 8 Supernova, 9 Buckinghamshire, 10 A flightless bird, 11 St Anthony, 12 Mel Gibson, 13 Photographic film, 14 Italy, 15 Tagus, 16 Allspice, 17 Billie Holiday, 18 Walter de la Mare, 19 Peter's pence, 20 Being John Malkovich.*

Entertainment

Your rating: ● **0-5 Buy a TV** ● **6-10 Keep at it** ● **11-15 Join a quiz team** ● **16-20 Enter a quiz show**

1. Who played the title role in the 1995 film *Judge Dredd*?
2. Who played Margaret Meldrew in the sitcom *One Foot in the Grave*?
3. Who had a U.K. top ten hit in 1982 with *Senses Working Overtime*?
4. Which children's TV favourites could be seen on the big screen in 1995 doing battle with Ivan Ooze?
5. Which record producer co-presented the TV show *The Hit Man and Her*?
6. Who had a U.K. number one in 1973 with *Blockbuster*?
7. Who played Jimmy Porter in the 1959 film version of *Look Back in Anger*?
8. Which vintage Thames sitcom starred Sid James as Sid Abbott?
9. Which 1995 Kevin Costner film was rumoured to have cost £133m, making it the most expensive movie yet made at that time?
10. Which sci-fi series featured the characters Ensign Ro, Keiko and Guinan?
11. How were Hula and Malik, who had a U.K. number one in 1995 with *Boom Boom Boom*, better known?
12. Who are the two regular team captains on TV's *Have I Got News For You*?
13. Who played Alfie in the 1994 film *A Man of No Importance*?
14. Which TV presenter did tycoon Donald Trump once describe as "sleazy, unattractive, obnoxious and boring"?
15. Which Wigan band released an album in 1995 entitled *A Northern Soul*?
16. Who was the second actor to play Jack Sugden in the TV soap *Emmerdale*?
17. Jazzy B was the driving force behind which dance outfit?
18. Who played Dave Briggs in the comedy series *The Detectives*?
19. Whose 1987 debut album was called *Introducing the Hard Line According To...*?
20. Stretch, Fatso and Stinkie were uncles of which friendly cartoon ghost?

ANSWERS: *1 Sylvester Stallone, 2 Annette Crosbie, 3 XTC, 4 Mighty Morphin Power Rangers, 5 Pete Waterman, 6 Sweet, 7 Richard Burton, 8 Bless This House, 9 Waterworld, 10 Star Trek: The Next Generation, 11 The Outhere Brothers, 12 Paul Merton and Ian Hislop, 13 Albert Finney, 14 Selina Scott, 15 The Verve, 16 Clive Hornby, 17 Soul II Soul, 18 Robert Powell, 19 Terence Trent D'Arby, 20 Casper.*

General Knowledge

Your rating:
- 0-5 Join a library
- 6-10 Keep at it
- 11-15 Join a quiz team
- 16-20 Join Mensa

1. What name is given to the carved and painted poles erected by Native American tribes?
2. In which London church are Poets' Corner and the Coronation Chair?
3. What are Nova Scotia, New Brunswick and Prince Edward Island collectively known as?
4. Which English football legend died in February 2000 at the age of 85?
5. Who directed the 1969 film *Easy Rider*?
6. Which Scottish city is famous for its International Festival which began in 1947?
7. Which colonist did the American Indian Pocahontas supposedly save from being killed?
8. Which Russian author wrote the novel *Anna Karenina*?
9. In which constellation are the stars Castor and Pollux?
10. By what name was composer Israel Baline known?
11. Which dye can be obtained from the shrub anil?
12. Which Greek philosopher was the pupil of Socrates and the teacher of Aristotle?
13. Of which Caribbean state is Santo Domingo the capital?
14. Which British golfer beat Tiger Woods to win the 2000 Andersen Consulting Matchplay Championship?
15. What in Russia is a kazachok?
16. Which Hollywood actor has visited Britain as a United Nations Messenger of Peace?
17. Of which Irish county is Mullingar the county town?
18. Which 1922 novel by D.H. Lawrence features a flautist as the central character?
19. Which extract from cows' stomachs is used in making cheese and junket?
20. Which American producer made the films *Gone with the Wind*, *Rebecca* and *A Farewell to Arms*?

ANSWERS: *1 Totem poles, 2 Westminster Abbey, 3 The Maritime Provinces, 4 Sir Stanley Matthews, 5 Dennis Hopper, 6 Edinburgh, 7 Captain John Smith, 8 Leo Tolstoy, 9 Gemini, 10 Irving Berlin, 11 Indigo, 12 Plato, 13 The Dominican Republic, 14 Darren Clarke, 15 A dance, 16 Michael Douglas, 17 Westmeath, 18 Aaron's Rod, 19 Rennet, 20 David O Selznick.*

General Knowledge

Your rating:
- 0-5 Join a library
- 6-10 Keep at it
- 11-15 Join a quiz team
- 16-20 Join Mensa

1. What name is given to a divine being supposedly assigned by God to every individual?
2. Who wrote *Middlemarch* and *The Mill on the Floss*?
3. What are Pontefract cakes made of?
4. From which country did the hijacked plane that landed at Stansted in February 2000 come?
5. In which U.S. state is the Sequoia National Park?
6. Which property of the surface of a liquid makes it behave as though it has an elastic skin?
7. Who stood as official Labour candidate for the first London mayoral election?
8. What creatures live in an apiary?
9. Which Greek letter gives its name to an accumulation of sediment at the mouth of a river?
10. Larkspur is another name for plants of which genus?
11. What is the name of Hank's wife in the cartoon series *King of the Hill*?
12. Which nonmetallic element has the symbol P?
13. What is the second largest city in Colombia?
14. Which Scottish group won the Best British Album and Best British Group awards at the Brits 2000?
15. What sort of creature is a plains-wanderer?
16. Which Roman empress and saint reputedly found the cross used for the crucifixion?
17. Which market forces control the market price in a free economy?
18. In which French city was Joan of Arc burned at the stake?
19. Whose sculptures included 1929's *Reclining Woman*?
20. Which English king was deposed by Richard III?

ANSWERS: *1 Guardian angel, 2 George Eliot, 3 Liquorice, 4 Afghanistan, 5 California, 6 Surface tension, 7 Frank Dobson, 8 Bees, 9 Delta, 10 Delphinium, 11 Peggy, 12 Phosphorus, 13 Medellin, 14 Travis, 15 A bird, 16 St Helena, 17 Supply and demand, 18 Rouen, 19 Alberto Giacometti, 20 Edward V.*

General Knowledge

Your rating: ● 0-5 Join a library ● 6-10 Keep at it ● 11-15 Join a quiz team ● 16-20 Join Mensa

1. How many millimetres are there in a kilometre?
2. Which Asian island is the third largest in the world?
3. What is Patricia Routledge's character name in *Keeping Up Appearances*?
4. Which Irish novelist and poet wrote the short story collection *Dubliners*?
5. What name was given to festivals at which knights competed against each other in medieval Europe?
6. Which Oscar-winning actor plays a prison guard in the film *The Green Mile*?
7. Which shrub is also called furze or whin?
8. Of which African country is Colonel Gaddafi (de facto) head of state?
9. Which member of the Beyond the Fringe revue is a medical doctor?
10. Kaph is the 11th letter in which alphabet?
11. What does I.V.F. stand for?
12. Which Czech composer wrote the opera *Jenufa*?
13. Who was Hitler's personal secretary who was sentenced to death in absentia at Nuremberg?
14. Which horse won its third successive Champion Hurdle at Cheltenham in 2000?
15. What is the name of the peninsula at the head of the Red Sea?
16. What sort of creature is a grunt?
17. Which French artist painted *Liberty Leading the People*?
18. According to the New Testament, which Jewish festival was taking place when the condemned robber Barabbas was released instead of Jesus?
19. Who wrote the children's fairy stories *The Happy Prince and other Tales*?
20. In which English county is the town of Skipton?

ANSWERS: *1 One million, 2 Borneo, 3 Hyacinth Bucket, 4 James Joyce, 5 Tournaments, 6 Tom Hanks, 7 Gorse, 8 Libya, 9 Jonathan Miller, 10 Hebrew, 11 In vitro fertilisation, 12 Leos Janacek, 13 Martin Bormann, 14 Istabraq, 15 Sinai Peninsula, 16 A fish, 17 Eugene Delacroix, 18 Passover, 19 Oscar Wilde, 20 North Yorkshire.*

Entertainment

Your rating: ● 0-5 Buy a TV ● 6-10 Keep at it ● 11-15 Join a quiz team ● 16-20 Enter a quiz show

1. Who was the singer of Echo & the Bunnymen?
2. Which British actor played Jack in the 1995 film *Jack & Sarah*?
3. What was the *Gladiator* alias of former Olympic heptathlete Judy Simpson on TV?
4. Which Canadian rocker released an album entitled *Mirrorball* in 1995?
5. Who played King Arthur in the 1995 film *First Knight*?
6. Who had a U.K. number one hit in 1972 with *Long Haired Lover From Liverpool*?
7. Who played the evil Harvey Two-Face in the 1995 film *Batman Forever*?
8. Which children's programme was supposedly broadcast from a hotel run by a cow called Morag?
9. Who wrote the U.K. hit song *Do They Know It's Christmas*?
10. The 1995 film *Congo* was based on a novel by which writer?
11. *Going Straight* was a spin-off from which other comedy series?
12. What do The Crazy World of Arthur Brown, The Pointer Sisters and U2 have in common?
13. Which 1995 David Frankel film starred Sarah Jessica Parker and Mia Farrow?
14. Which duo appeared alongside David Baddiel and Rob Newman on the TV sketch show *The Mary Whitehouse Experience*?
15. Which young band recently released an album called *To The Next Level*?
16. Who played Bob Louis in the TV comedy series *The Detectives*?
17. Who played the title role in Ron Shelton's 1994 baseball movie *Cobb*?
18. Which former *Big Breakfast* presenter married singer Colin Peel in 1995?
19. With which instrument is jazz musician John Coltrane associated?
20. Which stalwart of Channel 4's horse racing coverage is a ticktack expert?

***ANSWERS:** 1 Ian McCulloch, 2 Richard E Grant, 3 Nightshade, 4 Neil Young, 5 Sean Connery, 6 Little Jimmy Osmond, 7 Tommy Lee Jones, 8 Fully Booked, 9 Bob Geldof & Midge Ure, 10 Michael Crichton, 11 Porridge, 12 They've all had hits with songs called Fire, 13 Miami Rhapsody, 14 Steve Punt & Hugh Dennis, 15 MN8, 16 Jasper Carrot, 17 Tommy Lee Jones, 18 Gaby Roslin, 19 Saxophone, 20 John McCririck.*

General Knowledge

Your rating:
- **0-5 Join a library**
- **6-10 Keep at it**
- **11-15 Join a quiz team**
- **16-20 Join Mensa**

1. Florence Nightingale was famous for her work during which war?
2. What name is given to sawn wood used for purposes other than fuel?
3. To which country are giant pandas native?
4. Whose crime novels include *The Seven Dials Mystery*?
5. Which actor and kung fu expert starred in the film *Enter the Dragon*?
6. What was the nationality of Adolphe Sax, inventor of the saxophone?
7. Which American tennis player won the men's singles title at the 2000 Australian Open?
8. From what is the Japanese drink sake made?
9. In what country was the mountaineer Sir Edmund Hillary born?
10. Which gland in the abdomen contains the islets of Langerhans which secrete insulin?
11. On which river is the Belgian seaport of Antwerp?
12. Which North American animal is also known as a grey wolf?
13. Who played *Expresso Bongo* in a 1959 film?
14. Which island group off the west coast of Scotland is also known as the Western Isles?
15. What name is given to a method of painting in which the pigment is mixed with egg yolk or glue?
16. In Greek mythology, who was the son of Odysseus and Penelope?
17. Which Swedish director made the films *The Seventh Seal* and *Wild Strawberries*?
18. Which guitarist equalled Michael Jackson's record by winning eight Grammy awards?
19. What name is shared by cities in India and Pakistan?
20. Which German philosopher wrote *A Contribution to the Critique of Political Economy*?

ANSWERS: *1 The Crimean War, 2 Timber, 3 China, 4 Agatha Christie, 5 Bruce Lee, 6 Belgian, 7 Andre Agassi, 8 Rice, 9 New Zealand, 10 Pancreas, 11 River Scheldt, 12 Timber wolf, 13 Cliff Richard, 14 The Hebrides, 15 Tempera, 16 Telemachus, 17 Ingmar Bergman, 18 Carlos Santana, 19 Hyderabad, 20 Karl Marx.*

General Knowledge

Your rating:
- **0-5 Join a library**
- **6-10 Keep at it**
- **11-15 Join a quiz team**
- **16-20 Join Mensa**

1. Which Italian city is famous for its leaning tower?
2. Which Polish trade union confederation was led by Lech Walesa?
3. What name is given to a dome-shaped dwelling made from blocks of snow?
4. Which sugary liquid attracts insects, birds and bats to flowers for pollination?
5. Who was the father of the apostles John and James?
6. What does S.W.A.L.K. mean on the back of an envelope?
7. What sort of creature is a kelpie?
8. Of which U.S. state is Lincoln the capital?
9. What is the subtitle of the play *Twelfth Night*?
10. Which former England footballer was sacked as coach by Celtic in February 2000?
11. What sort of rock is formed by the metamorphosis of sedimentary limestone?
12. Of which African country is Niamey the capital?
13. What sort of seeds are used to flavour the Scandinavian drink aquavit?
14. Which metallic element has the symbol Tb?
15. What is the real name of comic Harry Hill?
16. Which Spanish conquistador founded the city of Lima in 1535?
17. Where is the composer George Frederick Handel buried?
18. Which Micronesian republic was formerly known as Pleasant Island?
19. What kind of animal is the Empress of Blandings in stories by P.G. Wodehouse?
20. Which 16th-century Italian art movement is associated with Pontormo and Parmigianino?

ANSWERS: *1 Pisa, 2 Solidarity, 3 Igloo, 4 Nectar, 5 Zebedee, 6 Sealed with a loving kiss, 7 A dog, 8 Nebraska, 9 What You Will, 10 John Barnes, 11 Marble, 12 Niger, 13 Caraway seeds, 14 Terbium, 15 Matthew Hall, 16 Francisco Pizarro, 17 Westminster Abbey, 18 Nauru, 19 A pig, 20 Mannerism.*

General Knowledge

Your rating: ● **0-5** **Join a library** ● **6-10** **Keep at it** ● **11-15** **Join a quiz team** ● **16-20** **Join Mensa**

1. From which Italian city does Parmesan cheese come?
2. Which British author wrote the novel *A Dance to the Music of Time*?
3. Lactic refers to which liquid?
4. In which American city were the 1984 Summer Olympics held?
5. Which birthday did the Duke of Edinburgh celebrate in 2001?
6. Which suffragette founded the Women's Social and Political Union?
7. Which British crown colony reverted to Chinese rule in 1997?
8. Who was appointed shadow chancellor in February 2000, two months after winning a by-election?
9. Which character in Greek mythology opened a box which contained all the evils of life?
10. Which naval port in France is the base of the French Atlantic Fleet?
11. 'To begin at the beginning: It is spring, moonless night in the small town, starless and bible-black...' is from which poem?
12. Which popular American golfer won the British Open in 1971 and 1972?
13. What name meaning 'armour' was given to mechanised units of the German army in World War II?
14. In which country does the River Tigris rise?
15. Who was the Conservative prime minister from 1963 to 1964?
16. Which actor played Tom Chance in the sitcom *Chance in a Million*?
17. Which country beat Nigeria on penalties to win the 2000 African Nations Cup?
18. What is the S.I. unit of luminous flux?
19. What name is given to the sterile offspring of a male lion and a female tiger?
20. In which country is Mount Popocatépetl?

ANSWERS: *1 Parma, 2 Anthony Powell, 3 Milk, 4 Los Angeles, 5 His 80th, 6 Emmeline Pankhurst, 7 Hong Kong, 8 Michael Portillo, 9 Pandora, 10 Brest, 11 Under Milk Wood, 12 Lee Trevino, 13 Panzer, 14 Turkey, 15 Sir Alec Douglas-Home, 16 Simon Callow, 17 Cameroon, 18 Lumen, 19 Liger, 20 Mexico.*

Entertainment

Your rating: ● 0-5 Buy a TV ● 6-10 Keep at it ● 11-15 Join a quiz team ● 16-20 Enter a quiz show

1. Which ska group had a U.K. number one in 1981 with *Ghost Town*?
2. Which 1995 Ken Loach film was set during the Spanish Civil War?
3. Who played Del in the TV sitcom *Only Fools and Horses*?
4. Which mod revivalist band released the album *Nuisance* in 1995?
5. Which Australian soap opera was set in Coopers Crossing?
6. Which male vocalist has sung with the Power Station and Vinegar Joe?
7. Which drama series featured the Osprey Explorer team?
8. Which 1995 Sylvester Stallone film also starred Antonio Banderas?
9. Which Irish comedian played Father Noel in the Channel 4 comedy series *Father Ted*?
10. Which 1995 horror movie starred Ben Kingsley as a scientist and Natasha Henstridge as an alien desperate to mate?
11. Who presented the morning quiz show *Housemates*?
12. *The Lone Ranger* was the title of a 1995 album by which Madness star?
13. Which 1995 Disney blockbuster was loosely based on the life of a 17th-century Native American princess?
14. Which actress quit her *Coronation Street* role as barmaid of the Rover's Return after 2,002 shows?
15. Who were The Three Tenors?
16. Who played Tomas in the 1988 film *The Unbearable Lightness of Being*?
17. *Ready, Steady, Cook* presenter Fern Britton is the daughter of which *Robin's Nest* star?
18. In 1979-1980, which Pink Floyd song was number one for five weeks?
19. Which 1995 film set in an Hispanic-American community starred former *NYPD Blue* actor Jimmy Smits?
20. *The Isle of View* was a 1995 album release by which band?

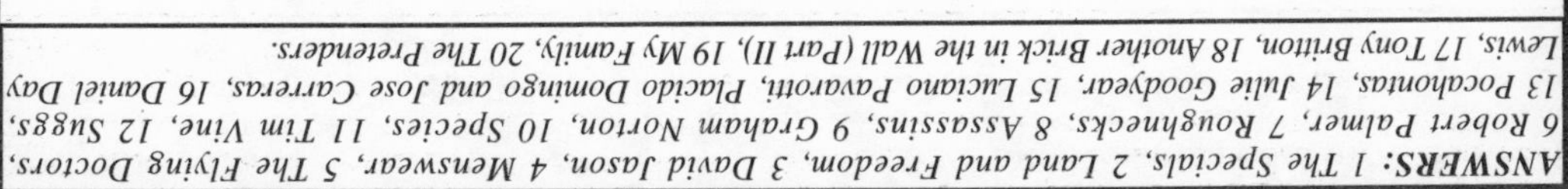

ANSWERS: *1 The Specials, 2 Land and Freedom, 3 David Jason, 4 Menswear, 5 The Flying Doctors, 6 Robert Palmer, 7 Roughnecks, 8 Assassins, 9 Graham Norton, 10 Species, 11 Tim Vine, 12 Suggs, 13 Pocahontas, 14 Julie Goodyear, 15 Luciano Pavarotti, Placido Domingo and Jose Carreras, 16 Daniel Day Lewis, 17 Tony Britton, 18 Another Brick in the Wall (Part II), 19 My Family, 20 The Pretenders.*

General Knowledge

Your rating:
- **0-5 Join a library**
- **6-10 Keep at it**
- **11-15 Join a quiz team**
- **16-20 Join Mensa**

1. Which Paul Simon album was Album of the Year at the 1986 Grammies?
2. Which Scottish golf course contains Hell Bunker and the Valley of Sin?
3. To what did Tamujin, founder of the Mongol empire, change his name?
4. Which Cumbrian nuclear power station was formerly known as Windscale?
5. In the stock market, what is the opposite of a bull?
6. Which football team is nicknamed The Red Devils?
7. To which city does the former village Donnybrook now belong?
8. Who is the lead singer and guitarist of Dire Straits?
9. Which environmental pressure group had its ship *Rainbow Warrior* sunk by French intelligence agents?
10. What are the closest attendants of the Queen called?
11. In what year did digital TV broadcasts begin?
12. At which church was Orlando Gibbons appointed organist in 1623?
13. Which Essex town was founded by Cunobelinus or Cymbeline circa 10 AD?
14. Which American novelist wrote *The Sheltering Sky*?
15. Who directed the films *Dead Poets Society* and *Green Card*?
16. What name is given to a device used to measure liquid flow and wind speed?
17. Which Welsh market town has the highest tides in Britain?
18. The father of which romantic Spanish singer was kidnapped by terrorists in 1983?
19. What is the name for the surgical removal of the spleen?
20. Which warm, dry wind is named after the American Indian for 'snow-eater'?

ANSWERS: *1 Graceland, 2 (The old course at) St Andrews, 3 Ghengis Khan, 4 Sellafield, 5 A bear, 6 Manchester United, 7 Dublin, 8 Mark Knopfler, 9 Greenpeace, 10 Maids of honour, 11 1998, 12 Westminster Abbey, 13 Colchester, 14 Paul Bowles, 15 Peter Weir, 16 Anemometer, 17 Chepstow, 18 Julio Iglesias, 19 Splenectomy, 20 Chinook.*

General Knowledge

Your rating: ● **0-5 Join a library** ● **6-10 Keep at it** ● **11-15 Join a quiz team** ● **16-20 Join Mensa**

1. Who played Jedi master Qui-Gon Jinn in *Star Wars: Episode I - The Phantom Menace*?
2. In which country was Britain's adopted tennis player Greg Rusedski born?
3. What is the connection between the embryo and the placenta called?
4. Which novelist created the character Chief Inspector Wexford?
5. Who is the most famous pupil at Hogwarts School of Witchcraft and Wizardry?
6. Which Paris landmark stands in the Champ de Mars?
7. What is made more regular by defibrillation?
8. How is the speed of 186,281 miles per second otherwise known?
9. What is the common name for facsimile transmission?
10. Which football team is nicknamed The Saints?
11. Who directed the films *Halloween* and *The Thing*?
12. Which Florentine Renaissance artist painted the *Madonna of the Harpies*?
13. In which U.S. state is South Bend, site of the University of Notre Dame?
14. Which Belgian film won the Palme d'Or at the 1999 Cannes Film Festival?
15. Of which country did Atal Bihari Vajpatee become prime minister in 1999?
16. To what is the formula translation computer-programming language abbreviated?
17. Which ancient people's first emperor was Manco Capac?
18. In physics, what does the acronym G.U.T. stand for?
19. Which former U.S. president was Governor of California from 1966 to 1974?
20. In which state of the USA is the Garden of the Gods?

ANSWERS: *1 Liam Neeson, 2 Canada, 3 Umbilical cord, 4 Ruth Rendell, 5 Harry Potter, 6 Eiffel Tower, 7 Heartbeat, 8 The speed of light, 9 Fax, 10 Southampton, 11 John Carpenter, 12 Andrea del Sarto, 13 Indiana, 14 Rosetta, 15 India, 16 Fortran, 17 Incas, 18 Grand Unified Theory, 19 Ronald Reagan, 20 Colorado.*

General Knowledge

Your rating: • 0-5 Join a library • 6-10 Keep at it • 11-15 Join a quiz team • 16-20 Join Mensa

1. What is the first name of Tony and Cherie Blair's fourth child?
2. Which rock star was born Gordon Sumner?
3. Who played English literature professor Dr Frank Bryant in *Educating Rita*?
4. What name is given to pregnancy in animals?
5. Which character did Diana Rigg play in *The Avengers*?
6. Which distinguished British actor won an Oscar for his role in the film *Arthur*?
7. Which birds are affected by the disease psittacosis?
8. Which Welsh snooker player won the 2000 Embassy world championship?
9. For which football club did Bobby Charlton play?
10. Which Hollywood actor played Major Julian Cook in the film *A Bridge Too Far*?
11. Which Fleetwood Mac album was Album of the Year at the 1977 Grammies?
12. Who directed the 1982 film *Diva*?
13. Which diagnostic method is known by the initials MRI?
14. Which British novelist wrote *Wolf Solent* and *A Glastonbury Romance*?
15. Of which constellation is Alpheratz the brightest star?
16. Which former unit of radioactivity has the symbol Ci?
17. In mathematics, which diagram represents the relationships between sets?
18. Which screen cowboy was born Leonard Slye?
19. What colour flowers does the guelder rose have?
20. Which actor won Best Supporting Actor Oscars for *All the President's Men* and *Julia*?

ANSWERS: *1 Leo, 2 Sting, 3 Michael Caine, 4 Gestation, 5 Emma Peel, 6 Sir John Gielgud, 7 Parrots, 8 Mark Williams, 9 Manchester United, 10 Robert Redford, 11 Rumours, 12 Jean-Jacques Beineix, 13 Magnetic resonance imaging, 14 John Cowper Powys, 15 Andromeda, 16 Curie, 17 Venn diagram, 18 Roy Rogers, 19 White, 20 Jason Robards.*

Entertainment

Your rating: ● 0-5 Buy a TV ● 6-10 Keep at it ● 11-15 Join a quiz team ● 16-20 Enter a quiz show

1. Which British actress played the title role in the 1995 film *Carrington*?
2. Who presented the TV show *Mondo Rosso*?
3. *D'eux* was the title of a 1995 album by which Canadian singer?
4. In the 1991 film *What About Bob?*, who played Bob?
5. In the TV drama series *Soldier, Soldier*, which character was played by Shaun Dingwall?
6. Which 1995 western starred Sharon Stone and Gene Hackman?
7. *Something Special* was a 1995 album by which country star?
8. Who played Jamie Diadoni in the TV series *Jake's Progress*?
9. *(What's The Story) Morning Glory* was a 1995 album by which Manchester band?
10. Which 1995 film starred comedian Lee Evans as a mime artist?
11. Which tennis-star-turned-sports-presenter replaced David Coleman as the host of the panel game show *A Question of Sport*?
12. Which Hole singer was given a suspended one-year jail sentence in 1995 for attacking a member of a rival band?
13. Who directed and starred in the 1981 film *Sharky's Machine*?
14. Which *Brookside* character was played on TV by Diane Burke?
15. Who had a U.K. number one hit in 1982 with *Ebony and Ivory*?
16. Which comedian directed, produced and starred in the 1995 film *Forget Paris*?
17. *The X Factor* was the title of a 1995 album release by which heavy metal band?
18. Who directed the 1983 film *Rumble Fish*?
19. Which Sean was the star of the comedy series *Sean's Show*?
20. Which Rolling Stone had a U.K. top twenty hit in 1981 with *(Si Si) Je Suis Un Rock Star*?

ANSWERS: *1 Emma Thompson, 2 Jonathan Ross, 3 Celine Dion, 4 Bill Murray, 5 Lance Corporal Steve Evans, 6 The Quick and the Dead, 7 Dolly Parton, 8 Robert Lindsay, 9 Oasis, 10 Funny Bones, 11 Sue Barker, 12 Courtney Love, 13 Burt Reynolds, 14 Katie Rogers, 15 Paul McCartney with Stevie Wonder, 16 Billy Crystal, 17 Iron Maiden, 18 Francis Coppola, 19 Sean Hughes, 20 Bill Wyman.*

General Knowledge

Your rating:
- 0-5 Join a library
- 6-10 Keep at it
- 11-15 Join a quiz team
- 16-20 Join Mensa

1. In which European country is the region of Dalmatia located?
2. What name is given to a zone of undeveloped land around an urban area to prevent it from spreading?
3. Which 2000 sci-fi film spoof stars Tim Allen, Alan Rickman and Sigourney Weaver?
4. Which Conservative politician resigned in 1963 following the disclosure of his involvement with Christine Keeler?
5. Which veteran actor played Curly in the film *City Slickers*?
6. In which animated TV series do Ash, Misty and Brock appear?
7. Which Indian musical instrument has a pear-shaped body and seven strings?
8. In which country did the Great Proletarian Cultural Revolution begin in 1966?
9. Which Shakespeare comedy features Puck, Oberon and Bottom?
10. What is another name for an eft?
11. Who was disqualified from Wimbledon in 1995 after hitting a ball girl with a ball?
12. Which French composer wrote *Le Marteau sans maître* and *Pli selon pli*?
13. What is the capital of South Australia?
14. Which British racing driver survived a Learjet crash in 2000?
15. Who choreographed the experimental ballets *Suite for Five* and *Antic Meet*?
16. Who was appointed Archbishop of York in 1995?
17. Which basketball team won their first N.B.A. championship in 1999?
18. What does E stand for in the food additives known as E numbers?
19. Which Dutch international joined Arsenal from Inter Milan in 1995?
20. For which film did Marisa Tomei win a Best Supporting Actress Oscar in 1992?

ANSWERS: *1 Croatia, 2 Green belt, 3 Galaxy Quest, 4 John Profumo, 5 Jack Palance, 6 Pokémon, 7 The sitar, 8 China, 9 A Midsummer Night's Dream, 10 A newt, 11 Tim Henman, 12 Pierre Boulez, 13 Adelaide, 14 David Coulthard, 15 Merce Cunningham, 16 Dr David Hope, 17 San Antonio Spurs, 18 European, 19 Dennis Bergkamp, 20 My Cousin Vinny.*

General Knowledge

Your rating: ● **0-5** Join a library ● **6-10** Keep at it ● **11-15** Join a quiz team ● **16-20** Join Mensa

1. Which British travel agent organised his first excursion, a train journey from Leicester to Loughborough, in 1841?
2. In which country is the black swan found?
3. Which Spanish team knocked Chelsea out of the Champions League in 2000?
4. What term was applied to the writers John Osborne, Kingsley Amis, John Braine and John Wain in the 1950s?
5. Which small parrots appear to have great affection for each other?
6. Who created the character *Paddington Bear*?
7. In which English county is the port of Lowestoft?
8. Which football team is nicknamed The Gunners?
9. On which New York island are Broadway, Wall Street and Central Park?
10. Which singer-songwriter played singer Tony Lacey in the film *Annie Hall*?
11. In which U.S. state is the city of Milwaukee?
12. Which port is known in its country's language as Abertawe?
13. Which strong fibre is obtained from the plant abaca, native to the Philippines?
14. Who was the foreign secretary who was injured when he fought Lord Castlereagh in a duel?
15. With which musical instrument was Sir Clifford Curzon associated?
16. Of which country was Vasa the ruling dynasty from 1523 to 1818?
17. Which language is spoken in Lusophone countries?
18. What is the abbreviation for the computer format Motion Picture Experts Group 1, Audio Layer 3?
19. Which country's motto is '*nemo me impune lacessit*'?
20. By what name is the small herb *Nigella damascena* known?

ANSWERS: *1 Thomas Cook, 2 Australia, 3 Barcelona, 4 Angry Young Men, 5 Lovebirds, 6 Michael Bond, 7 Suffolk, 8 Arsenal, 9 Manhattan, 10 Paul Simon, 11 Wisconsin, 12 Swansea, 13 Manila hemp, 14 George Canning, 15 Piano, 16 Sweden, 17 Portuguese, 18 MP3, 19 Scotland, 20 Love-in-a-mist.*

General Knowledge

Your rating: • 0-5 Join a library • 6-10 Keep at it • 11-15 Join a quiz team • 16-20 Join Mensa

1. Who played Melanie in the film *Gone with the Wind*?
2. Which British naval explorer landed at Botany Bay in 1770?
3. What are louse eggs called?
4. Which country's cricket team was captained by Hansie Cronje until his sacking over match-fixing allegations?
5. Which aquatic bird has Canada, barnacle and brent varieties?
6. Which British playwright wrote Pericles and Cymbeline?
7. Which Swiss resort on Lake Geneva hosts an annual television festival which awards a Golden Rose?
8. Who played the infamous Norman Bates in the *Psycho* movies?
9. From which European language is the South African language Afrikaans derived?
10. Which Polish astronomer discovered that the sun was at the centre of the universe?
11. Which waterfall is on the border between Zimbabwe and Zambia?
12. Which comedian plays Kevin in the film *Kevin and Perry Go Large*?
13. To which European country does the island of Lampedusa belong?
14. Which drama series links Amanda Burton with Neil Morrissey?
15. Which Russian writer wrote *The Government Inspector* and *Dead Souls*?
16. The sauce Marchand de Vins is made with red wine and what other main ingredient?
17. In which European country is the publishing centre of Lund?
18. Of what is a nunny bag made?
19. Which football team gained promotion to the Premiership as Nationwide League champions in 2000?
20. Who wrote the novel *Armadillo,* about loss adjustor Lorimer Black?

ANSWERS: *1 Olivia de Havilland, 2 Captain James Cook, 3 Nits, 4 South Africa, 5 Goose, 6 William Shakespeare, 7 Montreux, 8 Anthony Perkins, 9 Dutch, 10 Nicolaus Copernicus, 11 Victoria Falls, 12 Harry Enfield, 13 Italy, 14 Boon, 15 Nikolai Gogol, 16 Shallots, 17 Sweden, 18 Sealskin, 19 Charlton Athletic, 20 William Boyd.*

Entertainment

Your rating: ● **0-5** Buy a TV ● **6-10** Keep at it ● **11-15** Join a quiz team ● **16-20** Enter a quiz show

1. Which comedian made a *World Tour of Scotland* on TV?
2. Who played the title role in the 1995 film *Dolores Claiborne*?
3. Who had a U.K. top twenty hit in 1981 with *There's a Guy Works Down the Chipshop Swears He's Elvis*?
4. Which medical drama series won eight Emmy awards in 1995?
5. Which 14-year-old American schoolgirl released an album entitled *Miss Thang* in 1995?
6. Which 1993 He Ping film was about a rich family of firework manufacturers?
7. Who had a U.K. number one in 1973 with *Tie a Yellow Ribbon Round the Old Oak Tree*?
8. Who played Demetrius in Mira Nair's 1991 film *Mississippi Masala*?
9. Which comedy series won five Emmy awards in 1995?
10. Which Motown legend released an album in 1995 entitled *Take Me Higher*?
11. Which 80-year-old British comedian returned to Pinewood Studios in 1995 after 25 years to make a new film?
12. *Circus* was the title of a 1995 album by which retro rocker?
13. Who played Captain Ahab in John Huston's 1956 film version of *Moby Dick*?
14. Who played Sicknote in the TV drama series *London's Burning*?
15. Which band cancelled most of their UK tour in 1995 due to bass player Paul McGuigan's nervous exhaustion?
16. Which *Brookside* character was played on TV by Sarah White?
17. Which comedy duo hosted the panel game show *Shooting Stars*?
18. Who played Butch in the 1969 film *Butch Cassidy and the Sundance Kid*?
19. Which queen of daytime TV got a black eye in 1995 by "bumping into a mantelpiece"?
20. Who had a U.K. top ten hit in 1982 with *The Bitterest Pill (I Ever Had to Swallow)*?

ANSWERS: *1 Billy Connolly, 2 Kathy Bates, 3 Kirsty MacColl, 4 ER, 5 Monica, 6 Red Firecracker, Green Firecracker, 7 Dawn, 8 Denzel Washington, 9 Frasier, 10 Diana Ross, 11 Norman Wisdom, 12 Lenny Kravitz, 13 Gregory Peck, 14 Richard Walsh, 15 Oasis, 16 Bev McLoughlin, 17 Vic Reeves and Bob Mortimer, 18 Paul Newman, 19 Judy Finnigan, 20 The Jam.*

General Knowledge

Your rating:
- **0-5 Join a library**
- **6-10 Keep at it**
- **11-15 Join a quiz team**
- **16-20 Join Mensa**

1. What is the lowest female singing voice?
2. In which athletics field event is a heavy sphere attached to a chain with a handle thrown?
3. What is the second largest planet?
4. Which British novelist wrote *Ivanhoe*?
5. By what name is the blowfly commonly known?
6. In the acronym SCUBA what does the S stand for?
7. In which country is the winter sports resort of Chamonix?
8. Who played Lord Alfred Douglas in the film *Wilde*?
9. What is the 50th state of the United States of America?
10. Which metallic element has the symbol K?
11. What sort of blood cells are also called leucocytes?
12. Which U.S. tennis player was nicknamed pepper?
13. To which king of Israel is the Old Testament book Proverbs ascribed?
14. Which remedy against unlawful imprisonment is in the form of a writ requiring a detained person to be brought before a court?
15. What relation was William of Orange to Charles I?
16. What sort of substance is gabbro?
17. Which tragic hero of medieval romances fell in love with Isolde or Iseult?
18. What was the name of the pet pig in the U.S. comedy *Green Acres*?
19. On which island of Asia is the seaport of Surabaya?
20. Whose novels include *Going to Meet the Man*?

ANSWERS: *1 Contralto, 2 Hammer, 3 Saturn, 4 Sir Walter Scott, 5 Bluebottle, 6 Self, 7 France, 8 Jude Law, 9 Hawaii, 10 Potassium, 11 White blood cells, 12 Anne Smith, 13 Solomon, 14 Habeas corpus, 15 Grandson, 16 Rock, 17 Tristan, 18 Arnold, 19 Java, 20 James Baldwin.*

General Knowledge

Your rating:
- 0-5 Join a library
- 6-10 Keep at it
- 11-15 Join a quiz team
- 16-20 Join Mensa

1. How many pounds are there in a pony?
2. Which piece of music did Torvill and Dean use for their 1984 Olympic win?
3. Which narcotic is derived from the leaves of the coca plant?
4. Which resort in East Sussex is famous for its Royal Pavilion?
5. What type of music is associated with the Jamaican cult of Rastafarianism?
6. Which football team denied Newcastle United a third successive F.A. Cup Final appearance in 2000?
7. Which black form of carbon is used for fuel, filters and drawing?
8. In Roman Catholicism, what is the name of the state in which souls are purified after death to make them fit for heaven?
9. What is the highest mountain in England?
10. Of which science are quantum mechanics and thermodynamics branches?
11. In which English county is the port and resort of Falmouth?
12. Which Scot authored the controversial novel *How late it was, how late*?
13. Which former world heavyweight boxing champion was known as the Brown Bomber?
14. In what year did the English Civil War end?
15. Which Conservative politician married Jennie Jerome in 1874?
16. In which fictional town does Bart Simpson live?
17. Who, or what, is small-back?
18. Which member of The Grumbleweeds was Wilf 'Gasmask' Grimshaw?
19. Which is the largest city in Alaska?
20. Which British novelist wrote *The Human Factor* and *Monsignor Quixote*?

***ANSWERS:** 1 £25, 2 Ravel's Bolero, 3 Cocaine, 4 Brighton, 5 Reggae, 6 Chelsea, 7 Charcoal, 8 Purgatory, 9 Scafell Pike, 10 Physics, 11 Cornwall, 12 James Kelman, 13 Joe Louis, 14 1651, 15 Randolph Churchill, 16 Springfield, 17 Death, 18 Carl Sutcliffe, 19 Anchorage, 20 Graham Greene.*

General Knowledge

Your rating:
- 0-5 Join a library
- 6-10 Keep at it
- 11-15 Join a quiz team
- 16-20 Join Mensa

1. What is the capital of Italy?
2. In which year did the drama start at Ewing Oil in *Dallas*?
3. Of what form of surgery are skin grafts and facelifts examples?
4. Which condiment is derived from the climbing plant piper nigrum?
5. Which country denied England a Six Nations Championship grand slam in 2000?
6. By what name was American showman William F. Cody better known?
7. Which islands do the French call the Iles Normandes?
8. Which British singer was born Gordon Sumner?
9. In which sport are parallel bars, pommel horse and balance beam used?
10. By what abbreviation is deoxyribonucleic acid usually known?
11. Which Spanish composer wrote *Nights in the Gardens of Spain*?
12. What are the first three numbers of the telephone area code for London?
13. Which struggling football team sacked manager Egil Olsen in April 2000?
14. Who succeeded to the U.S. presidency on the death of Zachary Taylor?
15. Which veins in the neck return blood from the head to the vena cava?
16. In which city was painter Kandinsky born?
17. Which film won the Best Picture Oscar in 1977?
18. What is ugali made with?
19. Which ancient city of Italy, at the mouth of the River Tiber, was once the port of Rome?
20. Who played Catherine of Aragon in the 1970 drama series *The Six Wives of Henry VIII*?

ANSWERS: *1 Rome, 2 1978, 3 Plastic surgery, 4 Pepper, 5 Scotland, 6 Buffalo Bill, 7 Channel Islands, 8 Sting, 9 Gymnastics, 10 DNA, 11 Manuel de Falla, 12 020, 13 Wimbledon, 14 Millard Fillmore, 15 Jugular veins, 16 Moscow, 17 Annie Hall, 18 Cornmeal and water, 19 Ostia, 20 Annette Crosbie.*

Entertainment

Your rating: ● 0-5 Buy a TV ● 6-10 Keep at it ● 11-15 Join a quiz team ● 16-20 Enter a quiz show

1. Which of the original *Breakfast Time* hosts also presented the TV series *Eye Spy*?
2. *Boombastic* was a 1995 album release by which former U.S. Marine and reggae star?
3. The series *Taste of the Sea* was presented by which TV chef?
4. Which 1995 David O. Russell film starred Jeremy Davies and Alberta Watson?
5. Which *Brookside* character was played on TV by Kate Beckett?
6. Which Seventies progressive rock band released a 1995 live double album called *B'BOOM*?
7. Who is Adrian Edmondson's *Absolutely Fabulous* wife?
8. Who is Laura Dern's actress mother?
9. Who had a U.K. top ten hit in 1979 with *Green Onions*?
10. Who wrote and directed the 1973 film *Westworld*?
11. Who was voted entertainment presenter of the year at the 1995 National TV Awards?
12. *Free Like We Want to Be* was a 1995 album release from which late reggae superstar's son?
13. *Speed* star Sandra Bullock played a toll booth attendant in which 1995 film?
14. What does E.M.I. stand for?
15. Which star of *A Passage to India* almost drowned in 1995 after windsurfing without a lifejacket?
16. Which *Coronation Street* star received a 12-month driving ban in 1995 after he was recorded doing 70mph in a 40mph zone?
17. Which vocalist, famous for his hit song *Baker Street*, released an album called *Over My Head* in 1995?
18. Which *Coronation Street* star, who plays Ken Barlow, was in 2000 the only remaining original cast member?
19. Which 1994 film starred Susan Sarandon as a mother of seven young men?
20. Who was voted most popular actress at the 1995 National TV Awards?

ANSWERS: *1 Selina Scott, 2 Shaggy, 3 Rick Stein, 4 Spanking the Monkey, 5 Jenny Swift, 6 King Crimson, 7 Jennifer Saunders, 8 Diane Ladd, 9 Booker T. and the M.G.s, 10 Michael Crichton, 11 Michael Barrymore, 12 Bob Marley's son Ziggy, 13 While You Were Sleeping, 14 Electrical & Musical Industries Ltd, 15 James Fox, 16 Simon Gregson, 17 Gerry Rafferty, 18 William Roache, 19 Safe Passage, 20 Anna Friel.*

General Knowledge

Your rating:
- 0-5 Join a library
- 6-10 Keep at it
- 11-15 Join a quiz team
- 16-20 Join Mensa

1. Who wrote the novel *Jane Eyre*?
2. What was the surname of the Angevin, Lancastrian and Yorkist kings of England?
3. In which country is the Bog of Allen?
4. Who was the Roman goddess of the hearth, whose shrine was attended by six virgins?
5. What is a sackbut?
6. Which highly venomous snake can extend its neck ribs to form a hood?
7. What sort of buns are traditionally eaten on Good Friday?
8. Which son of David and Bathsheba was the third king of Israel?
9. By what acronym is soccer's world governing body known?
10. In which American country is the Mesa del Norte plateau?
11. Which major unit of biological classification of animals can be divided into classes?
12. Who won a Best Actress Oscar for her performance in *Boys Don't Cry*?
13. What sort of creature is a pompano?
14. Which Fijian golfer won the 2000 U.S. Masters?
15. In which year did Fox studios fire Spencer Tracy after a spell in jail?
16. Which duelling French writer and dramatist was famous for his long nose?
17. Who painted 1905's *Women in front of Fireplace*?
18. What is the smallest county in the Republic of Ireland?
19. Which English Romantic poet wrote *The Eve of St Agnes*?
20. Who did Bryan Murray play in the TV comedy *Bread*?

ANSWERS: *1 Charlotte Brontë, 2 Plantagenet, 3 Republic of Ireland, 4 Vesta, 5 A musical instrument, 6 Cobra, 7 Hot cross buns, 8 Solomon, 9 F.I.F.A., 10 Mexico, 11 Phylum, 12 Hilary Swank, 13 A fish, 14 Vijay Singh, 15 1935, 16 Cyrano de Bergerac, 17 André Derain, 18 Louth, 19 John Keats, 20 Shifty.*

General Knowledge

Your rating: ● **0-5** **Join a library** ● **6-10** **Keep at it** ● **11-15** **Join a quiz team** ● **16-20** **Join Mensa**

1. By what name is the plant *Solanum tuberosum*, introduced into England by Sir Walter Raleigh, better known?
2. Whose novels include *Keep the Aspidistra Flying*?
3. Which former Spice Girl had a number one hit with *Bag It Up*?
4. In which European country is Salzburg?
5. What is the fourth planet from the sun?
6. Which British poet wrote *The Whitsun Weddings* and *High Windows*?
7. What name is given to the fibrous skeleton of the fruit of the dishcloth gourd, used as a bath sponge?
8. Which unpopular tax was a direct cause of the Peasants' Revolt of 1381?
9. Who won the men's 1500m at the 1980 and 1984 Olympics?
10. East London is a seaport and holiday resort in which African country?
11. Who composed the score for the 1976 film *Taxi Driver*?
12. Which chemical element has the symbol Mn?
13. What is the plant deadly nightshade also called?
14. Which British director won the Best Director Oscar in 2000 for his first film?
15. What does a speleologist explore and study?
16. Which Ugandan statesman was overthrown by Idi Amin in 1971?
17. Which French patron saint has his feast day on November 11th?
18. What sort of bird is a rosella?
19. Which Portuguese runner smashed his own record in winning the men's race in the 2000 London Marathon?
20. Who narrated the children's TV series *Mr. Benn*?

ANSWERS: *1 Potato, 2 George Orwell, 3 Geri Halliwell, 4 Austria, 5 Mars, 6 Philip Larkin, 7 Loofah, 8 Poll Tax, 9 Sebastian Coe, 10 South Africa, 11 Bernard Herrmann, 12 Manganese, 13 Belladonna, or dwale, 14 Sam Mendes, 15 Caves, 16 Milton Obote, 17 St Martin (Martinmas), 18 A parakeet, 19 Antonio Pinto, 20 Ray Brooks.*

General Knowledge

Your rating:
- **0-5 Join a library**
- **6-10 Keep at it**
- **11-15 Join a quiz team**
- **16-20 Join Mensa**

1. Who directed the 1929 film *Blackmail*?
2. What is the official map-making body of the U.K. called?
3. Of which Australian state is Melbourne the capital?
4. What were the first names of A. A. Milne's son?
5. In the New Testament, what was the occupation of Mary's husband Joseph?
6. Which flower is used as a symbol of remembrance for the dead of the World Wars?
7. Which British author created the detective Father Brown?
8. What is the highest number on a roulette wheel?
9. On which part of the body would you wear a larrigan?
10. Which French city in the Côte d'Or department is famous for its mustard?
11. What was the first jumbo jet?
12. In which African country did the Coptic Church originate?
13. Who killed essayist Charles Lamb's mother?
14. Which American composer wrote the ballets *Billy the Kid* and *Rodeo*?
15. Who created the 1963 sculpture *Boomerang*?
16. To which genus of plants does the sensitive plant belong?
17. Which German director made the films *La Ronde* and *Lola Montes*?
18. Who composed the series of percussive works entitled *Imaginary Landscape*?
19. Who captained the Continental European team to victory in the inaugural golf competition for the trophy that bears his name?
20. In which Sheridan play does Mrs Malaprop appear?

ANSWERS: *1 Alfred Hitchcock, 2 Ordnance Survey, 3 Victoria, 4 Christopher Robin, 5 Carpenter, 6 Poppy, 7 G K Chesterton, 8 36, 9 The foot, 10 Dijon, 11 Boeing 747, 12 Egypt, 13 His sister Mary, 14 Aaron Copland, 15 Matt Rugg, 16 Mimosa, 17 Max Ophuls, 18 John Cage, 19 Severiano Ballesteros, 20 The Rivals.*

Entertainment

Your rating:
- 0-5 Buy a TV
- 6-10 Keep at it
- 11-15 Join a quiz team
- 16-20 Enter a quiz show

1. Which puppet gang introduced a new character, Clifford the Rastafarian, when it returned with a revamped 1990s series?
2. How is off-beat film director and actor Allen Stewart Konigsberg better known?
3. Which chart-topping 1980s band was fronted by Kevin Rowland?
4. Who starred as ranchhand Jett in the 1956 film *Giant*?
5. *Rhoda* was a spin-off from which U.S. sitcom?
6. Who had a U.K. number two hit in 1983 with *China Girl*?
7. Who won a Best Actor Oscar in 1971 for his role as Popeye Doyle in *The French Connection*?
8. Which TV chef boosted the sale of eggs when she presented the series *How To Cook*?
9. In which 1973 film musical did the song *I Don't Know How To Love Him* appear?
10. On which TV show could we hear "the voice of the balls"- Alan Dedicoat?
11. Which Beatle married Linda Eastman?
12. Who played the title role in the U.S. children's TV series *Clarissa Explains It All*?
13. In the 1995 film *Waterworld*, who played Deacon, the villainous leader of the Smokers?
14. From which musical does the song *Send In the Clowns* come?
15. *Take It Like a Man* was the autobiography of which 80s pop megastar?
16. Who played Fletcher Christian in the 1962 film *Mutiny on the Bounty*?
17. *Mork and Mindy* was a spin-off from which comedy series?
18. Who was the lead singer with Soft Cell?
19. On which Shakespeare play was the 1961 film musical *West Side Story* based?
20. What type of animal was the star of the *White Fang* films?

ANSWERS: *1 The Muppets, 2 Woody Allen, 3 Dexy's Midnight Runners, 4 James Dean, 5 The Mary Tyler Moore Show, 6 David Bowie, 7 Gene Hackman, 8 Delia Smith, 9 Jesus Christ Superstar, 10 The National Lottery Live, 11 Paul McCartney, 12 Melissa Joan Hart, 13 Dennis Hopper, 14 A Little Night Music, 15 Boy George, 16 Marlon Brando, 17 Happy Days, 18 Marc Almond, 19 Romeo and Juliet, 20 A half-dog half-wolf.*

General Knowledge

Your rating:
- 0-5 Join a library
- 6-10 Keep at it
- 11-15 Join a quiz team
- 16-20 Join Mensa

1. Who wrote about the adventures of Peter Rabbit?
2. How many hulls does a trimaran have?
3. To which Italian city does the adjective Neapolitan relate?
4. What is the name of the branch of law relating to ships and shipping?
5. Which plant is commonly known as a Michaelmas daisy?
6. What is the name of the group of chalk stacks in the English Channel off the west coast of the Isle of Wight?
7. Which British writer created *Dixon of Dock Green*?
8. What is the highest law court in the United States?
9. Which fungal infection commonly affects the areas between the toes?
10. Of which country was Henry Pu-Yi the last emperor?
11. What name is given to chemical compounds of boron and hydrogen?
12. Which resort in North Wales was designed by Clough Williams-Ellis?
13. Which Hollywood film star played Danny Zuko on Broadway in *Grease*?
14. In which century was Old Moore's Almanac first published?
15. What is the largest and most luminous type of star?
16. Which character in Greek mythology promised to marry any man who could outrun her?
17. What does U.S.M. stand for on the Stock Exchange?
18. Which New York borough is the site of La Guardia and JFK airports?
19. What is geoponics?
20. Which British dramatist wrote *Luther* and *Inadmissible Evidence*?

ANSWERS: *1 Beatrix Potter, 2 Three, 3 Naples, 4 Maritime law, 5 Aster, 6 The Needles, 7 Ted Willis, 8 The Supreme Court, 9 Athlete's foot, 10 China, 11 Boranes, 12 Portmeirion, 13 Richard Gere, 14 17th, 15 Supergiant, 16 Atalanta, 17 Unlisted securities market, 18 Queens, 19 The science of agriculture, 20 John Osborne.*

General Knowledge

Your rating: ● 0-5 Join a library ● 6-10 Keep at it ● 11-15 Join a quiz team ● 16-20 Join Mensa

1. In which German city was a dividing wall built in the 1960s?
2. Which Hollywood heart-throb stars in *The Beach*?
3. Where on your body is the nape?
4. In which country did hussars originate?
5. In Greek mythology, what creatures formed the hair of the Gorgons such as Medusa?
6. Which English king succeeded Queen Victoria?
7. Who directed the 1997 film *Scream 2*?
8. Which French composer wrote the *Symphonie fantastique*?
9. By what name was the diminutive Charles Stratton known when he was exhibited by P. T. Barnum?
10. Which London street is synonymous with the British diamond trade?
11. Who authored the novel *Mary Anne*?
12. Which disease is caused by a deficiency of thiamine in the diet?
13. With which Italian city is a criminal secret society called the Camorra associated?
14. What is the name of the petrol-thickening jelly used in incendiary bombs and flame-throwers?
15. Which English king succeeded Henry VIII?
16. What name is given to the earliest period of the Mesozoic era?
17. Which British artist painted a portrait of Winston Churchill that was destroyed on the instructions of Lady Churchill?
18. The town of Sault Ste. Marie, Canada is connected by bridge to which town in Michigan?
19. What is the lightest metal?
20. Which minister referred to the Army's Household Division as 'chinless wonders' on Irish radio?

ANSWERS: *1 Berlin, 2 Leonardo DiCaprio, 3 The back of the neck, 4 Hungary, 5 Snakes, 6 Edward VII, 7 Wes Craven, 8 Hector Berlioz, 9 General Tom Thumb, 10 Hatton Garden, 11 Daphne du Maurier, 12 Beriberi, 13 Naples, 14 Napalm, 15 Edward VI, 16 Triassic, 17 Graham Sutherland, 18 Sault Ste. Marie, 19 Lithium, 20 Peter Mandelson.*

General Knowledge

Your rating:
- 0-5 Join a library
- 6-10 Keep at it
- 11-15 Join a quiz team
- 16-20 Join Mensa

1. Which prolific U.S. inventor devised the gramophone, which he called a phonograph?
2. On which river does Leicester stand?
3. What name is given to a horse that does not measure more than 1.47m in height?
4. Which woodwind instrument is the smallest member of the flute family?
5. Who was thrown out of the Labour Party for standing as an independent candidate in the London mayoral election?
6. Which comedian's characters include Portuguese singer Tony Ferrino?
7. Which British author wrote a series of novels set in Barsetshire?
8. What colour does litmus turn to indicate acidity?
9. In which country is the town of Delft, famous for its pottery and porcelain?
10. Which Swedish actress starred in *Casablanca* and *Gaslight*?
11. Who painted 1912's *Simultaneous Windows*?
12. Of which radio station was Helen Boaden made controller in 2000?
13. Who formed the Irish political party Fianna Fáil in 1926?
14. Which Italian general was the model for Machiavelli's *The Prince*?
15. What is an I.C.B.M.?
16. In physics, which fundamental constant is represented by the symbol *h*?
17. Who plays the title role in the film *Whatever Happened to Harold Smith*?
18. Which Roman frontier defence work linked the Firths of Forth and Clyde?
19. What is the latest date on which Easter Sunday can fall?
20. Which German composer wrote *Also sprach Zarathustra* and *Ein Heldenleben*?

ANSWERS: *1 Thomas Edison, 2 River Soar, 3 Pony, 4 Piccolo, 5 Ken Livingstone, 6 Steve Coogan, 7 Anthony Trollope, 8 Red, 9 The Netherlands, 10 Ingrid Bergman, 11 Robert Delaunay, 12 Radio 4, 13 Eamon de Valera, 14 Cesare Borgia, 15 An intercontinental ballistic missile, 16 Planck's constant, 17 Tom Courtenay, 18 Antonine Wall, 19 April 25th, 20 Richard Strauss.*

Entertainment

Your rating:
- 0-5 Buy a TV
- 6-10 Keep at it
- 11-15 Join a quiz team
- 16-20 Enter a quiz show

1. Who played the title role in the 1991 film *Johnny Suede*?
2. Which *EastEnders* character celebrated her 18th birthday in 1995?
3. Which 'Killer' released an album called *Young Blood* in 1995?
4. Which 1994 Bertrand Tavernier film took a light-hearted approach to Dumas' *Musketeers*?
5. Which early morning programme featured the segment *Eggs On Legs*?
6. Which band's 1995 album was entitled *No Need to Argue*?
7. Which 1941 classic Disney film featured the song *Pink Elephants on Parade*?
8. Anita, Matthew, Margaret and Paul were members of which soap family?
9. *Forbidden* was the title of a 1995 album by which veteran heavy metal band?
10. Which 1994 Garry Marshall movie starred Dan Aykroyd and Rosie O'Donnell as cops?
11. Who directed the 1990 film *Wild At Heart*?
12. Which sci-fi series featured the android Twiki?
13. Which British singer released a three-CD compilation album called *I Love to Sing* in 1995?
14. Which *Brookside* character was played by Steven Pinder?
15. In which 1998 film did Jennifer Lopez star opposite George Clooney?
16. *The Colbys* was a spin-off from which U.S. soap opera?
17. Which 1994 Australian film based on Chekhov's *Uncle Vanya* starred Greta Scacchi and Sam Neill?
18. Which member of Take That was the first to leave the band?
19. Which artist was played by Kirk Douglas in the 1956 film *Lust For Life*?
20. Which reggae star released an album called *Natural High* in 1995?

ANSWERS: *1 Brad Pitt, 2 Bianca Jackson, 3 Jerry Lee Lewis, 4 D'Artagnan's Daughter, 5 The Big Breakfast, 6 The Cranberries, 7 Dumbo, 8 Castles, 9 Black Sabbath, 10 Exit to Eden, 11 David Lynch, 12 Buck Rogers in the 25th Century, 13 Petula Clark, 14 Max Farnham, 15 Out of Sight, 16 Dynasty, 17 Country Life, 18 Robbie Williams, 19 Vincent Van Gogh, 20 Bitty McLean.*

General Knowledge

Your rating: ● 0-5 Join a library ● 6-10 Keep at it ● 11-15 Join a quiz team ● 16-20 Join Mensa

1. What name is given to an artificial lake in which water is stored?
2. Who starred as Gandhi in a 1982 film?
3. Which member of the Royal Family wore a 'rasta tam' on a visit to Jamaica?
4. Who wrote the *Enigma Variations*?
5. What sort of creature is a marlin?
6. Of which county is Kingston-upon-Thames the administrative centre?
7. What sort of creature is a greylag?
8. For which film did Sir John Mills win an Oscar?
9. What nationality was the runner Paavo Nurmi?
10. In which English county is the holiday resort of Minehead?
11. In radio, what does A.M. stand for?
12. Which Swedish dramatist wrote the play *Easter*?
13. In ancient Rome, what name was given to a plebeian magistrate who defended the interests of the common people?
14. To which British composer was Eric Fenby amanuensis?
15. What vegetable is also known as jibbons?
16. In which 1742 novel by Henry Fielding do Squire Booby and Mrs. Slipshod feature?
17. Which psychological illness causes someone to diet obsessively?
18. What name is given to the southern landmass formed by the splitting of the single world continent over 200 million years ago?
19. Which English Cavalier poet wrote *To Althea, From Prison*?
20. In Greek mythology, which god fell in love with Psyche?

ANSWERS: *1 Reservoir, 2 Ben Kingsley, 3 Prince Charles, 4 Sir Edward Elgar, 5 A fish, 6 Surrey, 7 A goose, 8 Ryan's Daughter, 9 Finnish, 10 Somerset, 11 Amplitude modulation, 12 August Strindberg, 13 Tribune, 14 Frederick Delius, 15 Spring onion, 16 The Adventures of Joseph Andrews, 17 Anorexia nervosa, 18 Gondwanaland, 19 Richard Lovelace, 20 Eros.*

General Knowledge

Your rating:
- 0-5 Join a library
- 6-10 Keep at it
- 11-15 Join a quiz team
- 16-20 Join Mensa

1. Which athletics field event was formerly known as the hop, step and jump?
2. What sort of building might have a keep and bailey?
3. In the Old Testament, which miraculous food sustained the Israelites in the wilderness?
4. What is the name for a male duck?
5. Of which African country is Mbabane the capital?
6. Which English king abdicated in 1936?
7. Who wrote *To Kill a Mockingbird*?
8. Which British award for industry was established in 1965?
9. What shade of red is named after a battle in the struggle for Italian independence?
10. In which film does Tim Allen play an actor pretending to be a spaceship captain?
11. Which soft fruit comes from plants of the genus Fragaria?
12. What is the capital of Western Samoa?
13. Which Russian composer wrote *In the Steppes of Central Asia*?
14. What name is given to the permanent freezing of the ground in areas bordering on ice sheets?
15. Who directed the 1988 film *Earth Girls Are Easy*?
16. Which Egyptian script was found on the Rosetta Stone along with hieroglyphic and Greek?
17. Which North Yorkshire town is associated with a 7th century synod that decided the date of Easter?
18. What is the technical name for weakening of the bones?
19. Which war was ended by the peace of Westphalia?
20. On which river is Louisville, Kentucky?

ANSWERS: *1 Triple jump, 2 Castle, 3 Manna, 4 Drake, 5 Swaziland, 6 Edward VIII, 7 Harper Lee, 8 Queen's Award, 9 Magenta, 10 Galaxy Quest, 11 Strawberry, 12 Apia, 13 Aleksandr Borodin, 14 Permafrost, 15 Julian Temple, 16 Demotic, 17 Whitby, 18 Osteoporosis, 19 Thirty Years' War, 20 Ohio River.*

General Knowledge

Your rating:
- **0-5 Join a library**
- **6-10 Keep at it**
- **11-15 Join a quiz team**
- **16-20 Join Mensa**

1. Which ancient forest is famous for its associations with Robin Hood?
2. What sort of creature is a macaw?
3. Which red hair dye is obtained from the powdered leaves of the shrub *Lawsonia inermis*?
4. Of which ocean is the Sea of Japan a part?
5. What name is given to the Sunday before Easter?
6. Monetarily speaking, how much was a bender?
7. Which member of the rock group Oasis has a daughter called Anaïs?
8. Who succeeded Richard Nixon as U.S. president?
9. Which well-known comet revolves around the sun in a period of about 76 years?
10. Who directed the 1999 film *eXistenZ*?
11. What is the second largest city in Norway?
12. Which British author wrote *The Doors of Perception* and *Heaven and Hell*?
13. What was the code name for the U.S. project to develop an atom bomb?
14. Which genus of plants includes busy lizzie and touch-me-not?
15. In which English county is Chesil Beach?
16. Who wrote *One Hundred Years of Solitude*?
17. Which Kent all-rounder recorded the best-ever English one-day international bowling figures?
18. What name is given to an excess of sugar in the blood?
19. Which river forms most of the boundary between Devon and Cornwall?
20. Which English queen lost Calais to the French?

ANSWERS: *1 Sherwood Forest, 2 A parrot, 3 Henna, 4 Pacific, 5 Palm Sunday, 6 Sixpence, 7 Noel Gallagher, 8 Gerald Ford, 9 Halley's comet, 10 David Cronenberg, 11 Bergen, 12 Aldous Huxley, 13 Manhattan Project, 14 Impatiens, 15 Dorset, 16 Gabriel García Márquez, 17 Mark Ealham, 18 Hyperglycaemia, 19 Tamar, 20 Mary I.*

Sports

Your rating: ● 0-5 Wooden spoon ● 6-10 Bronze medal ● 11-15 Silver medal ● 16-20 Gold medal

1. Who scored the winning goal of the 1980 F.A. Cup final?
2. Which England cricketer scored 333 against India at Lords in 1990?
3. What fabric covers a snooker table?
4. What is the points value of a converted try in rugby league?
5. Which sport was invented by James Naismith in 1891?
6. Which Irish-trained horse won the 2000 Derby?
7. In which position did Tessa Sanderson finish in the 1984 Olympic Games javelin competition?
8. Albert Park motor racing circuit is in which country?
9. Against which country did Marcus Trescothick score his maiden Test century?
10. Who won the football World Cup in 1982?
11. Who lost to Stuart Bingham in the first round of the 2000 snooker world championship at the Crucible?
12. With which sport is Murray Walker connected?
13. In which sport does a hooter sound the end of the game?
14. How many players make up a softball team?
15. In which year did Harbhajan Singh become the first Indian bowler to take a hat-trick in Test cricket?
16. Which Portuguese runner smashed his own record in winning the men's race in the 2000 London Marathon?
17. Shinty is a form of which sport?
18. Which football team plays at Craven Cottage?
19. Which game was invented by Ernest Pitiot?
20. Who was the first bowler in cricket to take 500 Test wickets?

ANSWERS: *1 Trevor Brooking, 2 Graham Gooch, 3 Baize, 4 6, 5 Basketball, 6 Sinndar, 7 1st, 8 Australia, 9 Sri Lanka, 10 Italy, 11 Stephen Hendry, 12 Motor racing, 13 Rugby league, 14 9, 15 2001, 16 Antonio Pinto, 17 Hockey, 18 Fulham, 19 Petanque, 20 Courtney Walsh.*

General Knowledge

Your rating: ● 0-5 Join a library ● 6-10 Keep at it ● 11-15 Join a quiz team ● 16-20 Join Mensa

1. Who was the 42nd president of the United States?
2. Which medical TV series is set in Cardale?
3. What was The Pink Panther?
4. Who was the first male centrefold in Cosmopolitan magazine?
5. What was the first name of A.A. Milne?
6. In which continent is Patagonia?
7. What is another name for a terrapin?
8. What type of creature is a cassowary?
9. Which novel is partly based on the experiences of Alexander Selkirk?
10. What is a young eel called?
11. Who was president of the United States from 1963-69?
12. Whom did Sue Barker succeed as presenter of *A Question of Sport*?
13. How many eggs had to be eaten as a bet in *Cool Hand Luke*?
14. Which poet claimed - "Love is my religion - I could die for that"?
15. From which film does the song *White Christmas* come?
16. What is the capital of Paraguay?
17. What is the chemical symbol for gold?
18. The Crocodile River is another name for which river?
19. What is another name for mother-of-pearl?
20. Which film was based on the Joseph Conrad story *Heart of Darkness*?

ANSWERS: *1 Bill Clinton, 2 Peak Practice, 3 A jewel, 4 Burt Reynolds, 5 Alan, 6 South America, 7 Water tortoise, 8 Bird, 9 Robinson Crusoe, 10 Elver, 11 Lyndon Baines Johnson, 12 David Coleman, 13 50, 14 John Keats, 15 Holiday Inn, 16 Asuncion, 17 Au, 18 Limpopo, 19 Nacre, 20 Apocalypse Now.*

General Knowledge

Your rating:
- 0-5 Join a library
- 6-10 Keep at it
- 11-15 Join a quiz team
- 16-20 Join Mensa

1. The adjective vulpine relates to which animal?
2. In which century was the French writer Voltaire born?
3. What was the name of the boy who befriended *ET* in the film of that name?
4. Which comedy duo had the theme song *Bring Me Sunshine*?
5. What is Low Sunday also known as?
6. Which book is believed to be the first detective story?
7. What is the official language of Brazil?
8. What is the first name of the heroine of the Flaubert novel *Madame Bovary*?
9. What nationality was *Robinson Crusoe* writer Daniel Defoe?
10. What is the occupation of Nicholas Bulstrode in the George Eliot novel *Middlemarch*?
11. What was the name of the daughter of Samantha and Darrin in *Bewitched*?
12. In which country is *To Catch a Thief* set?
13. Which member of *The Dirty Dozen* was also in *The Magificent Seven*?
14. Who wrote the autobiography *The Moon's a Balloon*?
15. What is Roquefort a type of?
16. Which island group is Ibiza in?
17. Which D.H. Lawrence novel concerns several generations of the Brangwen family?
18. Aconcagua is the highest peak in which mountain system?
19. Cyberphobia is the irrational fear of what?
20. Who wrote the story *Where the Wild Things Are*?

ANSWERS: *1 Fox, 2 17th, 3 Elliott, 4 Morecambe and Wise, 5 The first Sunday after Easter, 6 The Murders in the Rue Morgue, 7 Portuguese, 8 Emma, 9 English, 10 Banker, 11 Tabitha, 12 Monaco, 13 Charles Bronson, 14 David Niven, 15 Cheese, 16 Balearics, 17 The Rainbow, 18 Andes, 19 Computers, 20 Maurice Sendak.*

General Knowledge

Your rating:
- **0-5 Join a library**
- **6-10 Keep at it**
- **11-15 Join a quiz team**
- **16-20 Join Mensa**

1. The characters Roderick Random, Peregrine Pickle and Humphry Clinker appear in novels by whom?
2. Who succeeded Jeremy Beadle as presenter of *You've Been Framed*?
3. Which actor was born Alexander Archibald Leach?
4. Which of these birds can fly; kookaburra, ostrich, kiwi or cassowary?
5. Who have Robert Donat, Kenneth More and Robert Powell all played on film?
6. What is a tench?
7. What nationality was the composer Erik Satie?
8. From which series was *The Fenn Street Gang* a spin-off?
9. Which Dickens novel is partly set in the United States?
10. Who directed *Apocalypse Now*?
11. Sid Waddell is most famous for commentating on which sport?
12. When did the *Titanic* sink?
13. Jacqueline Pirie stars as which character in *Coronation Street*?
14. When was U.S. Democrat politician Al Gore born?
15. What is a diadem?
16. The adjective ursine describes which animal?
17. *Crotchet Castle*, *Headlong Hall* and *Gryll Grange* are all titles of novels by which author?
18. From which country does paella originate?
19. What is the capital of Sri Lanka?
20. Which TV series about an oil company became *The Troubleshooters*?

ANSWERS: *1 Tobias Smollett, 2 Lisa Riley, 3 Cary Grant, 4 Kookaburra, 5 Richard Hannay of The Thirty-Nine Steps, 6 Fish, 7 French, 8 Please Sir, 9 Martin Chuzzlewit, 10 Francis Ford Coppola, 11 Darts, 12 1912, 13 Linda Baldwin, 14 1948, 15 Crown, 16 Bear, 17 Thomas Love Peacock, 18 Spain, 19 Colombo, 20 Mogul.*

Entertainment

Your rating: ● 0-5 Buy a TV ● 6-10 Keep at it ● 11-15 Join a quiz team ● 16-20 Enter a quiz show

1. Who played the second *Doctor Who* on TV from 1966 to 1969?
2. Which 2001 U.K. top five hit by Gabrielle featured in the film *Bridget Jones's Diary*?
3. Which Hollywood star once said "Young actors love me. They think if that big slob can make it, there's a chance for us."?
4. Which 2001 three-part ITV series used the histories of three families to depict the course of life in Britain since 1945?
5. How many weeks did Bryan Adams's *(Everything I Do) I Do It For You* spend at the U.K. number one spot in 1991?
6. Who played Carl Brashear, the first black salvage diver in the U.S. Navy, in the 2000 film *Men of Honor*?
7. Whose U.K. top ten hits of the Nineties included collaborations with George Michael, RuPaul and Luciano Pavarotti?
8. Which actress played single mother Dana Barrett in the 1989 film *Ghostbusters II*?
9. Who played voiceover actor Danny in the BBC 2 comedy series *Happiness*?
10. Which British group had a U.K. number one hit with *I Like It* in 1963?
11. In which 2001 Anglo-American film did Alan Rickman and Natasha Richardson play a hairdressing ex-husband and wife?
12. Which *Coronation Street* character was played by Bernard Youens for twenty years until his death in 1984?
13. Which 1962 film was directed and written by Orson Welles from a novel by Franz Kafka?
14. Which popstar had a 2001 U.K. top ten hit with *Let Love Be Your Energy*?
15. Which actor played 1950s filmmaker David Merrill in the 1991 movie *Guilty By Suspicion*?
16. Whose gun was used to shoot *EastEnders*' Phil Mitchell?
17. In 2001, which trio released their first studio album in four years, *This is Where I Came In*?
18. Which BBC 1 documentary series about the life of Jesus was presented by *BBC Breakfast*'s Jeremy Bowen?
19. Which actress and singer played *The Wedding Planner* in the 2001 movie of that name?
20. Which TV chef became the new presenter of BBC 2's *Masterchef 2001*?

ANSWERS: *1 Patrick Troughton, 2 Out of Reach, 3 Robert Mitchum, 4 Time of Our Lives, 5 16, 6 Cuba Gooding Jr, 7 Elton John's, 8 Sigourney Weaver, 9 Paul Whitehouse, 10 Gerry and the Pacemakers, 11 Blow Dry, 12 Stan Ogden, 13 The Trial, 14 Robbie Williams, 15 Robert De Niro, 16 Steve Owen's, 17 The Bee Gees, 18 Son of God, 19 Jennifer Lopez, 20 Gary Rhodes.*

General Knowledge

Your rating:
- 0-5 Join a library
- 6-10 Keep at it
- 11-15 Join a quiz team
- 16-20 Join Mensa

1. What does the Latin phrase *vox populi* mean?
2. In the TV sitcom *Porridge* what was the middle name of Norman Fletcher?
3. Who followed William Taft as U.S. president?
4. Anton Meyer is a character in which TV medical drama?
5. Who was forced to decline the Nobel prize for literature in 1958?
6. Christopher Plummer described working with which actress as like "being hit over the head with a Valentine card"?
7. Which horror film was advertised with the slogan "Make Your Last Breath Count"?
8. In which state was *The High Chaparral* set?
9. Which actor was born Maurice Micklewhite?
10. What is the capital of South Australia?
11. Ganymede is a satellite of which planet?
12. Who played DI Frances O'Neil in the Lynda La Plante drama *Mind Games*?
13. Who are Milo, Bella, Fizz and Jake?
14. Who did Margaret Thatcher replace as leader of the Conservative Party in 1975?
15. Where would a stevedore be employed?
16. Which of the original *Big Brother* contestants was first to be evicted?
17. What nationality was the composer Wolfgang Amadeus Mozart?
18. Who directed *Rosemary's Baby*?
19. Lake Garda is the largest lake in which country?
20. What is Co the chemical symbol for?

ANSWERS: *1 Voice of the people, 2 Stanley, 3 Woodrow Wilson, 4 Holby City, 5 Boris Pasternak, 6 Julie Andrews, 7 Scream, 8 Arizona, 9 Michael Caine, 10 Adelaide, 11 Jupiter, 12 Fiona Shaw, 13 The Tweenies, 14 Edward Heath, 15 Dock, 16 Sada, 17 Austrian, 18 Roman Polanski, 19 Italy, 20 Cobalt.*

General Knowledge

Your rating: ● 0-5 Join a library ● 6-10 Keep at it ● 11-15 Join a quiz team ● 16-20 Join Mensa

1. Who learnt how to play the cello for the 1999 biopic *Hilary and Jackie*?
2. Which British author wrote *Whisky Galore*?
3. How is Sarah Michelle Gellar better known to millions?
4. Which band sang the theme song to *The World is Not Enough*?
5. What does Jack exchange for magic beans in the fairy story *Jack and the Beanstalk*?
6. Which *Star Wars* actor provided the voice of the Joker in the 1993 animated Batman film?
7. How much did Anna Sewell earn for writing *Black Beauty*?
8. What was the preferred style of music of *Inspector Morse*?
9. Who played two roles in *The Great Race*?
10. Which of the following is the shortest river: Volga, Ganges, Amazon or Euphrates?
11. Which animal is the adjective equine used to describe?
12. In which continent are the Atlas Mountains?
13. Who wrote *The Loneliness of the Long Distance Runner*?
14. Who had a U.K. number one hit in 1994 with *Saturday Night*?
15. What is the nontechnical name for the talus?
16. Tamale is a dish native to which country?
17. Who starred as James Bond in the movie *Moonraker*?
18. What is the name of the dog belonging to Dorothy in *The Wizard of Oz*?
19. What is the real name of *The Scarlet Pimpernel*?
20. Who played *The Incredible Shrinking Man*?

ANSWERS: *1 Emily Watson, 2 Sir Compton Mackenzie, 3 Buffy, 4 Garbage, 5 A cow, 6 Mark Hamill, 7 20 pounds, 8 Opera, 9 Jack Lemmon, 10 Ganges, 11 Horse, 12 Africa, 13 Alan Sillitoe, 14 Whigfield, 15 Anklebone, 16 Mexico, 17 Roger Moore, 18 Toto, 19 Sir Percy Blakeney, 20 Grant Williams.*

General Knowledge

Your rating:
- 0-5 Join a library
- 6-10 Keep at it
- 11-15 Join a quiz team
- 16-20 Join Mensa

1. Without what was *Joe 90* just an ordinary boy?
2. By what name are non-wizards known in the Harry Potter books?
3. What do the French call La Manche?
4. Which was the first film to feature Lauren Bacall?
5. In which modern-day country was Doris Lessing born?
6. Who was leader of the Labour Party prior to Neil Kinnock?
7. What is another name for a mangetout?
8. Which Gene Wilder film was a remake of the French film *Pardon Mon Affaire*?
9. Of which work by James Joyce is Leopold Bloom the central character?
10. What is the capital of Venezuela?
11. How many yards make up a mile?
12. Who went *Solo* on TV for 13 episodes in 1981?
13. Which country visited by Gulliver during his travels was populated by giants?
14. Who starred in *An Unseen Enemy* in 1912 and *The Whales of August* in 1987?
15. Who was the first president of the United States?
16. Who had a U.K. number one hit in 1979 with *I Will Survive*?
17. What relation is Frodo to Bilbo Baggins in stories by J.R.R. Tolkien?
18. Which actor connects *Dave* with *A Fish Called Wanda*?
19. George is an informal name for what feature of an aircraft?
20. Who was the youngest member of the Beatles?

ANSWERS: *1 His glasses, 2 Muggles, 3 English Channel, 4 To Have and Have Not, 5 Iran, 6 Michael Foot, 7 Sugar pea, 8 The Woman In Red, 9 Ulysses, 10 Caracas, 11 1760, 12 Felicity Kendal, 13 Brobdingnag, 14 Lillian Gish, 15 George Washington, 16 Gloria Gaynor, 17 Cousin, 18 Kevin Kline, 19 Automatic pilot, 20 George Harrison.*

Entertainment

Your rating:
- 0-5 Buy a TV
- 6-10 Keep at it
- 11-15 Join a quiz team
- 16-20 Enter a quiz show

1. Which long-running U.K. sci fi series was first screened on the day after President Kennedy was assassinated in 1963?
2. Which U.S. girl group hit the U.K. number one spot with *Survivor* in 2001?
3. Which legendary Hollywood actress and dancer's real name was Margarita Carmen Cansino?
4. Which BBC 1 drama series was set in a Manchester factory called Mackintosh Textiles?
5. What was the title of Whitney Houston's debut single in the U.K., which hit the number one spot in 1985?
6. Who wrote and directed the 2000 film *Bamboozled*?
7. Which BBC 2 sitcom, described as *The Simpsons* with real people, centred on a dysfunctional U.S. family?
8. Which British group had a U.K. number one hit in 1977 with *So You Win Again*?
9. Which TV comedian and quizshow presenter appeared in *Brookside* as Katrina's dad Jeff Evans?
10. Which late filmstar and performer was once quoted as saying "If I'm such a legend, why am I so lonely?"?
11. With which rugby-related song did South Africa's Ladysmith Black Mambazo featuring China Black have a U.K. top twenty hit in 1995?
12. Which actor played an advertising executive who pretends to be married to the woman next door in the 1964 film *Good Neighbor Sam*?
13. What was the name of the ship in the children's series *Captain Pugwash*?
14. In which European city was the 2001 *Rugrats* movie set?
15. Which former member of Boyzone hit the U.K. top five in 2001 with *Lovin' Each Day*?
16. Which 1977 film was directed and co-written by Terry Gilliam and starred fellow *Monty Python* member Michael Palin?
17. Which stand-up comedian was the star of the BBC 1 sitcom *So What Now*?
18. Which pop group had a 2001 U.K. number one hit (twice) with *Don't Stop Movin'*?
19. Which actress played the title character in the 2001 film adaptation of *Bridget Jones's Diary*?
20. Of which sitcom was the Seventies series *Don't Drink the Water* a spin-off?

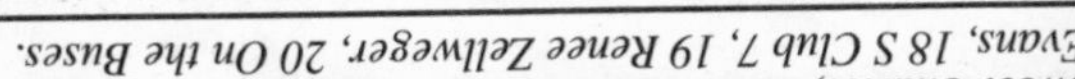

ANSWERS: *1 Doctor Who, 2 Destiny's Child, 3 Rita Hayworth, 4 Clocking Off, 5 Saving All My Love For You, 6 Spike Lee, 7 Malcolm in the Middle, 8 Hot Chocolate, 9 Les Dennis, 10 Judy Garland, 11 Swing Low Sweet Chariot, 12 Jack Lemmon, 13 The Black Pig, 14 Paris, 15 Ronan Keating, 16 Jabberwocky, 17 Lee Evans, 18 S Club 7, 19 Renee Zellweger, 20 On the Buses.*

General Knowledge

Your rating:
- 0-5 Join a library
- 6-10 Keep at it
- 11-15 Join a quiz team
- 16-20 Join Mensa

1. Which writer created *The Saint*?
2. Which actor's real name was Marion Michael Morrison?
3. What is the official language of Mexico?
4. What is the standard monetary unit of Turkey?
5. Who wrote *Bleak House*?
6. A Catherine wheel is a type of what?
7. Des Moines is the capital of which American state?
8. In which continent is the Orinoco river?
9. Who resigned as England football manager in 2000?
10. What type of creature is an eland?
11. A daddy-longlegs is also known as what?
12. From which club did Leeds United sign Rio Ferdinand?
13. Which was the Oscar-winning song from *Mary Poppins*?
14. Who, in 1977, became the 39th president of the United States?
15. What is the capital of Queensland?
16. Who played Jane opposite Johnny Weismuller as Tarzan?
17. Who wrote the poem *Death Be Not Proud*?
18. What would a costermonger sell?
19. Which comedy star was born Arthur S Jefferson?
20. Which team won the F.A. Cup in 1988?

ANSWERS: *1 Leslie Charteris, 2 John Wayne, 3 Spanish, 4 Lira, 5 Charles Dickens, 6 Firework, 7 Iowa, 8 South America, 9 Kevin Keegan, 10 Antelope, 11 Crane fly, 12 West Ham, 13 Chim Chim Cher-ee, 14 Jimmy Carter, 15 Brisbane, 16 Maureen O'Sullivan, 17 John Donne, 18 Fruit and vegetables, 19 Stan Laurel, 20 Wimbledon.*

General Knowledge

Your rating: ● 0-5 Join a library ● 6-10 Keep at it ● 11-15 Join a quiz team ● 16-20 Join Mensa

1. Which team beat Celtic 9-8 on penalties to win the Scottish Cup in 1990?
2. In which film did Arnold Schwarzenegger star as a cyborg?
3. What was the name of The Avengers' controller?
4. On what day did 1st January 2000 fall?
5. What nationality was the composer Anton Dvorak?
6. Who provided the voice for the evil Hades in the Disney movie *Hercules*?
7. Where were *The Killing Fields*?
8. Which detective series is set in Denton?
9. Who had a U.K. number one hit in 1998 with *Never Ever*?
10. Which footballer missed a penalty during the 1988 F.A. Cup final at Wembley?
11. Which adjective is used to describe the lungs?
12. What is the middle name of Margaret Thatcher?
13. Who played Little Big Man in 1970?
14. Which TV series introduced us to Windy Miller?
15. In which American state is the city of Tallahassee?
16. Big Kahuna Burgers and Red Apple Cigarettes are screen trademarks of which director?
17. Who appeared in the pocket of David Owen on *Spitting Image*?
18. How many ounces make up a pound?
19. Which sport is central to the film *Escape to Victory*?
20. Who directed the Tom Hanks film *Cast Away*?

ANSWERS: *1 Aberdeen, 2 The Terminator, 3 Mother, 4 Saturday, 5 Czech, 6 James Woods, 7 Cambodia, 8 A Touch of Frost, 9 All Saints, 10 John Aldridge, 11 Pulmonary, 12 Hilda, 13 Dustin Hoffman, 14 Camberwick Green, 15 Florida, 16 Quentin Tarantino, 17 David Steel, 18 16, 19 Football, 20 Robert Zemeckis.*

General Knowledge

Your rating:
- 0-5 Join a library
- 6-10 Keep at it
- 11-15 Join a quiz team
- 16-20 Join Mensa

1. Which U.S. golfer won the British Open in 1981?
2. Who wrote *A Brief History of Time*?
3. Which was the first film directed by Jodie Foster?
4. How many sides does a heptagon have?
5. Which author introduced the word 'robot' into the modern vocabulary?
6. What is the name of the estate in TV's *Monarch of the Glen*?
7. Which animal featured in the 1969 film *Ring of Bright Water*?
8. What type of creature is a katydid?
9. With what genre of novels is Zane Grey associated?
10. Which was the first Beatles film?
11. Which Channel 4 show shot Zig and Zag to stardom?
12. What is the capital of Norway?
13. In which century did the Crimean War take place?
14. To which novel by David Lodge is *Small World* a sequel?
15. What was the first name of the 19th-century English cookery writer Mrs Beeton?
16. Which literary figure is portrayed by Geoffrey Rush in the film *Quills*?
17. In which television series does the radio station KACL appear?
18. Which novel by Ian Fleming was the first to feature James Bond?
19. Which pop star was born Harry Rodger Webb?
20. Which historical event is described in the Thomas Hardy poem *The Convergence of the Twain*?

ANSWERS: *1 Bill Rogers, 2 Stephen Hawking, 3 Little Man Tate, 4 Seven, 5 Karel Capek, 6 Glenbogle, 7 Otter, 8 Grasshopper, 9 Westerns, 10 A Hard Days Night, 11 The Big Breakfast, 12 Oslo, 13 19th, 14 Changing Places, 15 Isabella, 16 Marquis de Sade, 17 Frasier, 18 Casino Royale, 19 Cliff Richard, 20 Sinking of the Titanic.*